# The Lladró Authorized Reference Guide

## 2003–2004 Edition

## The Lladró Authorized Reference Guide

Published in 2003 by Lladró
Moonachie, NJ 07074

ISBN: 0-9667025-2-2

Third Edition: 2003–2004

*All current pricing shown is 2003 suggested retail.*

Pictured on cover: *Tea in the Garden*, Elite Limited edition of 2,000, 01001759

# Table of Contents

# The History of Lladró

The "miracle" that is Lladró began, as most miracles do, with a dream — the dream of three brothers to create in porcelain. And as with most dreams, that of the Lladró brothers was brought to reality through dedication, ingenuity, cooperation and hard work.

## The Lladró Brothers' Introduction to the World of Art

It all started in Almacera, Spain, where Juan, José and Vicente Lladró were born a mere five kilometers from the city of Valencia. If tradition had prevailed, the Lladró brothers would have devoted their lives to agriculture; but their mother, Rosa, wanted more for her children. It was she who guided them toward an education and occupation in the arts. Perhaps it can be said that the miracle of Lladró really began with this tenacious and persuasive woman. Even as her sons learned cultivation from their father, Juan, they each attended the San Carlos de Valencia School of Arts and Crafts.

In 1951, Juan, José and Vicente built their first kiln, a moruno (moorish) type made of brick. Using rosemary and furze from the nearby mountains as fuel, they achieved the temperatures necessary to fire ceramics. The kiln enabled them to make small flowers for decorative lamps.

## The Founding of the Company

It wasn't long before a great demand for these small pieces developed and the Lladrós found it necessary to increase their labor force. Within two years, the three brothers resigned their factory jobs, and, with a loan of 12 euros from a friend, they founded Lladró Porcelains. This gave them the freedom to investigate new procedures for glazing and firing, and led to the development of their own very special porcelain.

## *From Local Success to International Acclaim*

Soon, a new kiln was built. Still rudimentary, this kiln could produce the temperatures needed to vitrify porcelain. And thus, the first Lladró porcelain was made. By 1965, Lladró was already a phenomenon. An export program was initiated when the first Lladró factory opened, and the market outside Spain blossomed immediately. The 1960s brought Lladró to the attention of a notable collection of celebrities.

Today, Lladró is known, admired and collected around the world. Its international presence encompasses more than 120 countries on five continents. Juan, José and Vicente had dared to dream such a dream. Yet, even they are dazzled by the esteem and popularity accorded them and their porcelains.

## *Looking Toward the Future*

The younger members of the three founding brothers' families take up new responsibilities within the company. The members of the new generation have all grown up in a family that considers porcelain art as a way of life, completing their education by working within the company so that they can gain firsthand knowledge of the creations that bear their names, and become fully integrated in company management circles.

At present, the new generation plays an active role in the sculpture creation process and in many events of a social nature, infusing new life and skills in the tradition founded by their parents. Among other activities, they perform a duty that they think is one of the most gratifying of all, that of representing Lladró at events and meetings attended by the public.

## *Lladró Studios — The City of Porcelain*

Tavernes Blanques, a village near Valencia, is the home to The City of Porcelain, where all Lladró creations are born. Visiting it means discovering step-by-step the entire creation process of porcelain admired by people across the globe.

If you wish to book your visit please call in advance 800 634 9088 (toll free in the USA), +34 96 318 70 01 (Customer Service Department in Spain), or arrange a visit through our website: **www.lladro.com/visit.html**

This guided tour, in Spanish or English, is free and lasts approximately one and a half hours. There are no visits on Friday afternoon, Saturday, Sunday or local holidays.

# Behind the Legend – The Lladró Family

## The Founding Brothers

### Juan Lladró

A connoisseur and collector of fine art, Juan Lladró is a man of many visions and pursuits. He possesses an intense curiosity about nature, people and landscapes that constantly fuels his imagination.

Juan Lladró has been described as possessing an "ever-critical spirit that demands accuracy and elaborate delicacy." And these standards are applied to all of the products made by Lladró today. As an artist, he is constantly on the lookout for new discoveries in line, color and shadow. As an art expert, he is ever-searching for new interpretations of subjects and themes. His inspirations are said to come from the various sights he sees while traveling.

### José Lladró

Over fifty years ago, José Lladró joined his brothers in founding what would become one of the most famous houses of porcelain in the world.

A born organizer, José has been credited with possessing the imagination and foresight necessary to bring to fruition the dreams of a family porcelain dynasty. José devotes his free time to contemplation, partaking in conferences and writing opinion columns in the press. José Lladró makes trips throughout Spain and abroad, during which he meets with collectors and talks to admirers.

### Vicente Lladró

The youngest of the three Lladró brothers, Vicente Lladró pooled his sculpting talents with his older brothers and established what would become the internationally renowned porcelain house that bears their name.

When not in his office, Vicente Lladró is often in various departments of the factory, sharing his ideas and enthusiasm with those who work at Lladró. It has been said that he works with an intense fervor. When he is not contributing his time and expertise to the Lladró enterprise in Valencia, he practices golf, flies light aircraft, and enjoys the company of his friends.

## *The Next Generation*

### *Mamen Lladró*

Mamen Lladró is the daughter of José Lladró. Executive Vice President and a member of the company's Board of Directors, she has received a solid formation in Economic Sciences and Business Studies.

Between 1996 and 2000, Mamen was a professor in the Commercial and Market Researches Area (Enterprises Management department) at the Valencia University. Later on, after being elected Executive Vice President in April 2001, she devoted herself completely to her tasks at the head of the company.

Responsible for the Lladró School of Art, from its creation in 1990, and a member of the Creativity Committee since 1986, Mamen Lladró takes part in the birth of Lladró creations. Given her extensive knowledge of the company, Mamen represents Lladró at international events and enjoys meeting with porcelain art lovers and sharing their interest in Lladró.

### *Rosa Lladró*

Rosa Lladró is the daughter of Juan Lladró, the eldest of the three brothers who founded the porcelain company.

After studying at the *San Carlos* Faculty of Fine Arts of Valencia, Rosa Lladró took a number of courses and programs organized by IESE (Institute of Business Studies) and others.

Her well-proven business and managerial skills are put to good use in her work for the Lladró Administration Board as well as in the Creativity Committee. She is a member of the Administration Board of the Bank of Valencia, President of the Deco-cevider show for ceramics, glass and decoration of the Valencia Fair and Director of the interior design event, Casa Décor Valencia.

Rosa Lladró regularly represents the company in many kinds of social and cultural events. Her own social concerns encouraged her to promote the Fundación Asindown of which she became the first President. She still keeps in close touch with this foundation, which helps Down Syndrome children. Her main passions are fine arts and dance.

### Juan Vicente Lladró

Born in 1962, Juan Vicente Lladró is the son of Vicente Lladró. After finishing his studies in Architecture at the Universidad Politécnica of Valencia, he went on to further his training with an MBA at the same university.

In 1984 he joined Lladró, where he carried out a number of managerial posts in areas of creativity, R&D, market research, and corporate identity. He is currently a member of the company's Administration Board.

Juan Vicente is a regular collaborator with several non-profit organizations. Music, art, reading and computers are his main interests. He is fond of traveling, fascinated by ancient civilizations and eager to get to know other cultures and societies, something which has taken him on journeys all over the world.

### David Lladró

David Lladró is the youngest son of Vicente, one of the founding brothers of Lladró porcelain. He is currently Advisor to the President and member of the company's Administration Board.

After graduating in Business Management and Administration, David joined the Lladró group to carry out an intensive training period in Spain, the United States and the United Kingdom. He has also traveled to many countries in order to get acquainted with different company markets.

Given his extensive knowledge of Lladró, David combines his job with tasks of representing the company at international events. He enjoys meeting with porcelain art lovers and sharing their interest in Lladró. David says he has managed to see one of his dreams come true. "Ever since I was small, I have wanted to help towards the success of this company".

# *Lladró Privilege Society*

A symbol of the affinity Lladró has always wanted to maintain with its best customers, the Lladró Privilege Society is a meeting place for all porcelain lovers. Members of the Lladró Privilege Society can take advantage of exclusive services and cultural and artistic activities worldwide.

They also have exclusive access to the Privilege Collection designed especially for them. Members receive updates about everything new happening in the company through the Lladró Privilege magazine, which has quickly become the principal channel of communication between Lladró and lovers of its work.

Lladró Privilege Society
1 Lladró Drive
Moonachie, NJ 07074-9835

Tel. 800 634 9088 (toll free)
E-mail: **lladroprivilege@us.lladro.com**
**www.lladro.com**

# *The Creation of a Lladró Sculpture*

Lladró porcelain is made following a meticulous process, starting with the design of the original model by sculptors and ending with the firing of the piece at high temperatures in the kiln.

Between the initial sketch and the definitive test by fire, each work passes through several phases. Artisans put the pieces together from dozens of individual fragments, and apply the colors, glazes and varnishes to create the completed sculpture.

One of the key factors in this process lies in achieving the highest artistic and technical quality in each one of the phases.

A sculptor works his clay to give shape to a new model. His hands outline all the details of a sculpture one by one.

Specialists slice the sculptures into sections. These parts will be used for making molds.

Liquid porcelain paste is injected into the molds.

Once the porcelain paste has set, the sections are carefully removed from the molds.

In the assembly department, the piece is reassembled with the help of liquid porcelain, used as an adhesive.

The task of painting requires intense concentration and a steady wrist.

Once painted, some pieces are covered with a coat of varnish to give it a glazed finish.

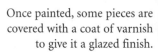

Porcelain flowers — some of the most admired of all Lladró creations — are made petal by petal.

Sculptures are ready for firing in the kilns.

After removal from the kiln, a surprising metamorphosis has occurred: pieces undergo a 15% reduction in size; vitrification has taken place, making the porcelain waterproof; the varnish has become translucent and the true Lladró colors have appeared on the surface of the pieces.

# *Caring for your Lladró Collection*

Well cared-for porcelain sculptures only need detergent washing once or twice a year. Rather, occasional careful dusting of the sculptures as needed provides sufficient ongoing maintenance.

When washing a sculpture, lukewarm water and mild detergent will do the trick. *(Important: You do not want the water to be too hot, as it will soften any adhesives.)* You must be extra careful if your sculptures have tiny flowers or other delicate parts. These are individually attached and should not be immersed for an extended period of time. Line your sink and the surrounding area with towels to protect the sculpture in case it accidentally slips during cleaning. Always let your sculpture air dry.

Many collectors use compressed air (cans are available at any photography store), small, soft bristled paint brushes and feather dusters to get in between flowers and other hard to reach places.

Cleaning matte sculptures, with their textured surfaces, can sometimes be a challenge. If blowing off the dust does not work, you may consider gently wiping the sculpture with a soft, damp cloth.

# Lladró on the Secondary Market

After a Lladró sculpture has retired and is no longer available through Authorized Lladró Retailers, it can only be purchased from a previous owner on what is called the **secondary market.** There are several ways to obtain a sculpture in the secondary market: at auctions, directly from a private owner or through a dealer who acts as a broker or buys and sells retired sculptures. Even though Lladró sculptures are actively sold and traded on the secondary market, Lladró does not have a role in establishing values on retired sculptures. The value placed on a retired item is determined by the agreement made between buyer and seller. From time to time, Lladró reports on secondary market activity by providing auction prices, which are included in this book. To help you determine the secondary market value of retired sculptures, two resources with extensive experience in the secondary market are listed below.

**European Imports & Gifts**
7900 North Milwaukee Avenue
Niles, IL 60714
847-967-5253
800-227-8670

**Janet Gale Hammer's A Retired Collection**
www.aRetiredCollection.com
janet@aRetiredCollection.com
941-387-0102
800-332-8594

# *2003 Introductions*

**Ref. No.:** 6917
**Name:** Nature's Duet
**Height:** 5.25
**Status:** Open issue, active
**Issue Year:** 2003
**2003 Retail Price:** $320

**Ref. No.:** 6931
**Name:** Forestland Encounter
**Height:** 5.5
**Status:** Open issue, active
**Issue Year:** 2003
**2003 Retail Price:** $290

**Ref. No.:** 6920
**Name:** Born in Springtime
**Height:** 7.25
**Status:** Open issue, active
**Issue Year:** 2003
**2003 Retail Price:** $395

**Ref. No.:** 6919
**Name:** Somewhere in the Garden
**Height:** 7.5
**Status:** Open issue, active
**Issue Year:** 2003
**2003 Retail Price:** $395

**Ref. No.:** 6938
**Name:** The Show Begins
**Height:** 8
**Status:** Open issue, active
**Issue Year:** 2003
**2003 Retail Price:** $275

**Ref. No.:** 6915
**Name:** For a Special Someone
**Height:** 8.5
**Status:** Open issue, active
**Issue Year:** 2003
**2003 Retail Price:** $290

**Ref. No.:** 6939
**Name:** Welcome to the Family
**Height:** 8.75
**Status:** Open issue, active
**Issue Year:** 2003
**2003 Retail Price:** $390

**Ref. No.:** 6815
**Name:** A Moment to Remember
**Height:** 9.25
**Status:** Open issue, active
**Issue Year:** 2003
**2003 Retail Price:** $375

**Ref. No.:** 6875
**Name:** Butterfly Wings
**Height:** 9.25
**Status:** Open issue, active
**Issue Year:** 2003
**2003 Retail Price:** $395

**Ref. No.:** 6916
**Name:** Circus Days
**Height:** 9.5
**Status:** Open issue, active
**Issue Year:** 2003
**2003 Retail Price:** $295

**Ref. No.:** 6922
**Name:** The Goat
**Height:** 9.5
**Status:** Open issue, active
**Issue Year:** 2003
**2003 Retail Price:** $270
**Comment:** Base included;
Chinese Zodiac Collection

**Ref. No.:** 6937
**Name:** For a Smile
**Height:** 9.5
**Status:** Open issue, active
**Issue Year:** 2003
**2003 Retail Price:** $350

**Ref. No.:** 6901
**Name:** My Sister, My Friend
**Height:** 10.5
**Status:** Open issue, active
**Issue Year:** 2003
**2003 Retail Price:** $425

**Ref. No.:** 6910
**Name:** As Pretty as a Flower
**Height:** 10.75
**Status:** Open issue, active
**Issue Year:** 2003
**2003 Retail Price:** $990

**Ref. No.:** 6921
**Name:** Treasures of the Earth
**Height:** 13.25
**Status:** Open issue, active
**Issue Year:** 2003
**2003 Retail Price:** $350

**Ref. No.:** 6918
**Name:** A Flower's Whisper
**Height:** 14.75
**Status:** Open issue, active
**Issue Year:** 2003
**2003 Retail Price:** $390

**Ref. No.:** 6912
**Name:** Our Savior (wall art)
**Height:** 18
**Status:** Open issue, active
**Issue Year:** 2003
**2003 Retail Price:** $495

**Ref. No.:** 6952
**Name:** Seagulls in Flight
**Height:** 22
**Status:** Open issue, active
**Issue Year:** 2003
**2003 Retail Price:** $2950
**Comment:** Base included

**The Peaceable Kingdom Collection**

**Ref. No.:** 6925
**Name:** "The Wolf Also Shall
   Dwell with the Lamb"
**Height:** 2.75
**Status:** Open issue, active
**Issue Year:** 2003
**2003 Retail Price:** $175
**Comment:** The Peaceable
   Kingdom Collection

**Ref. No.:** 6926
**Name:** "And the Leopard Shall
   Lie Down with the Kid"
**Height:** 4
**Status:** Open issue, active
**Issue Year:** 2003
**2003 Retail Price:** $225
**Comment:** The Peaceable
   Kingdom Collection

**Ref. No.:** 6927
**Name:** "And the Calf and the
   Young Lion"
**Height:** 4.5
**Status:** Open issue, active
**Issue Year:** 2003
**2003 Retail Price:** $225
**Comment:** The Peaceable
   Kingdom Collection

**Movement Collection**

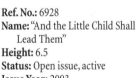

**Ref. No.:** 6928
**Name:** "And the Little Child Shall
   Lead Them"
**Height:** 6.5
**Status:** Open issue, active
**Issue Year:** 2003
**2003 Retail Price:** $275
**Comment:** The Peaceable
   Kingdom Collection

**Ref. No.:** 6954
**Name:** Gallop I
**Height:** 6.75
**Status:** Open issue, active
**Issue Year:** 2003
**2003 Retail Price:** $275
**Comment:** Movement Collection

**Ref. No.:** 6955
**Name:** Gallop II
**Height:** 8
**Status:** Open issue, active
**Issue Year:** 2003
**2003 Retail Price:** $275
**Comment:** Movement Collection

**Ref. No.:** 6956
**Name:** Gallop III
**Height:** 8.5
**Status:** Open issue, active
**Issue Year:** 2003
**2003 Retail Price:** $275
**Comment:** Movement Collection

**Ref. No.:** 6957
**Name:** Gallop IV
**Height:** 8.75
**Status:** Open issue, active
**Issue Year:** 2003
**2003 Retail Price:** $275
**Comment:** Movement Collection

**Ref. No.:** 6958
**Name:** Fight
**Height:** 7.25
**Status:** Open issue, active
**Issue Year:** 2003
**2003 Retail Price:** $250
**Comment:** Movement Collection

**Gres**

**Ref. No.:** 6959
**Name:** Jump
**Height:** 8.5
**Status:** Open issue, active
**Issue Year:** 2003
**2003 Retail Price:** $250
**Comment:** Movement Collection

**Ref. No.:** 6960
**Name:** Flight
**Height:** 10
**Status:** Open issue, active
**Issue Year:** 2003
**2003 Retail Price:** $250
**Comment:** Movement Collection

**Ref. No.:** 2455
**Name:** Dreaming of Peace
**Height:** 7.5
**Status:** Open issue, active
**Issue Year:** 2003
**2003 Retail Price:** $475

**Limited Edition**

**Ref. No.:** 2447
**Name:** A Moment of Tenderness
**Height:** 10.5
**Status:** Open issue, active
**Issue Year:** 2003
**2003 Retail Price:** $375

**Ref. No.:** 2454
**Name:** Thinking of Peace
**Height:** 12.5
**Status:** Open issue, active
**Issue Year:** 2003
**2003 Retail Price:** $400

**Ref. No.:** 1885
**Name:** Spirit of Shambala
**Height:** 11.25
**Status:** Limited Edition, active
**Edition Size:** 1000
**Issue Year:** 2003
**2003 Retail Price:** $1000
**Comment:** Base included

**Ref. No.:** 1882
**Name:** May My Wish Come True
**Height:** 15.25
**Status:** Limited Edition, active
**Edition Size:** 2000
**Issue Year:** 2003
**2003 Retail Price:** $1175
**Comment:** Base included

**Ref. No.:** 1884
**Name:** Breezes of the Heart
**Height:** 15.5
**Status:** Limited Edition, active
**Edition Size:** 1000
**Issue Year:** 2003
**2003 Retail Price:** $1200
**Comment:** Base included

**Ref. No.:** 1869
**Name:** A Vow of Love
**Height:** 20.5
**Status:** Limited Edition, active
**Edition Size:** 1000
**Issue Year:** 2003
**2003 Retail Price:** $2400
**Comment:** Base included

**Ref. No.:** 1888
**Name:** A Grand Adventure
**Height:** 17.25
**Status:** Limited Edition, active
**Edition Size:** 500
**Issue Year:** 2003
**2003 Retail Price:** $35,000
**Comment:** Elite Limited Edition

**2003 Privilege Society**

**2003 Event Piece**

**Ref. No.:** 6828
**Name:** My Little Explorers
**Height:** 10
**Status:** 2003 Open Series, active
**Issue Year:** 2003
**2003 Retail Price:** $695

**Ref. No.:** 7697
**Name:** Magical Unicorn
**Height:** 8.75
**Status:** 2003 Annual Piece, active
**Issue Year:** 2003
**2003 Retail Price:** $325
**Comment:** Third and last
   Sculpture, "Enchanted Forest
   Collection"

**Ref. No.:** 6846
**Name:** Friendly Duet
**Height:** 9.5
**Status:** Open issue, retired
**Issue Year:** 2003
**2003 Retail Price:** $275
**Comment:** Spring 2003 Event
   Piece

**Name:** Travel the World of Lladró
**Height:** 6.75
**Status:** Open issue, active
**Issue Year:** 2003
**2003 Retail Price:** $250
**Comment:** Exclusive for Lladró
 shops — personalized with
 location

**Ref. No.:**  7301 (Valencia)
 7302 (Madrid)
 7303 (Barcelona)
 7304 (Paris)
 7305 (London)
 7306 (Hong Kong)
 7307 (Singapore)
 7308 (Tokyo)
 7309 (Sydney)
 7310 (New York)
 7311 (Beverly Hills)
 7312 (Las Vegas)
 7313 (Tampa)
 7314 (Orlando)
 7315 (St. Louis)

**Ref. No.:** 6961
**Name:** My Guardian Angel
**Height:** 5.5
**Status:** Open edition, active
**Issue Year:** 2003
**2003 Retail Price:** $195

**Ref. No.:** 6944
**Name:** Camel
**Height:** 6
**Status:** Open edition, active
**Issue Year:** 2003
**2003 Retail Price:** $275

**Ref. No.:** 6924
**Name:** Heavenly Stars
**Height:** 7.5
**Status:** Open edition, active
**Issue Year:** 2003
**2003 Retail Price:** $245

**Ref. No.:** 6949
**Name:** Girlfriends
**Height:** 10
**Status:** Open edition, active
**Issue Year:** 2003
**2003 Retail Price:** $495

**Ref. No.:** 6998
**Name:** First Ovation
**Height:** 10.5
**Status:** Open edition, active
**Issue Year:** 2003
**2003 Retail Price:** $425

**Ref. No.:** 6945
**Name:** Giant of the Sea
**Height:** 11.5
**Status:** Open edition, active
**Issue Year:** 2003
**2003 Retail Price:** $775
**Comment:** Base included

**Ref. No.:** 6994
**Name:** Birth of Jesus
**Height:** 12
**Status:** Open edition, active
**Issue Year:** 2003
**2003 Retail Price:** $550

**Ref. No.:** 6953
**Name:** Sea Turtles
**Height:** 14.5
**Status:** Open edition, active
**Issue Year:** 2003
**2003 Retail Price:** $2500
**Comment:** Base included

**Ref. No.:** 6951
**Name:** Sunlit Garden
**Height:** 15.25
**Status:** Open edition, active
**Issue Year:** 2003
**2003 Retail Price:** $495

**Allegory of the Flowers Collection**

**Ref. No.:** 6965
**Name:** Allegory of the Sea
**Height:** 15.5
**Status:** Open edition, active
**Issue Year:** 2003
**2003 Retail Price:** $995

**Ref. No.:** 6946
**Name:** Daisies, Time of Joy
**Height:** 8
**Status:** Open edition, active
**Issue Year:** 2003
**2003 Retail Price:** $195
**Comment:** Allegory of the
Flowers Collection

**Ref. No.:** 6990
**Name:** Bellflower, Symbol of
Gratitude
**Height:** 8
**Status:** Open edition, active
**Issue Year:** 2003
**2003 Retail Price:** $195
**Comment:** Allegory of the
Flowers Collection

**My Family Album Collection**

**Ref. No.:** 6947
**Name:** Violets, Time of
    Innocence
**Height:** 8.5
**Status:** Open edition, active
**Issue Year:** 2003
**2003 Retail Price:** $195
**Comment:** Allegory of the
    Flowers Collection

**Ref. No.:** 6989
**Name:** Lily, Symbol of Purity
**Height:** 8.5
**Status:** Open edition, active
**Issue Year:** 2003
**2003 Retail Price:** $195
**Comment:** Allegory of the
    Flowers Collection

**Ref. No.:** 6987
**Name:** How Sweet!
**Height:** 2.75
**Status:** Open edition, active
**Issue Year:** 2003
**2003 Retail Price:** $175
**Comment:** My Family Album
    Collection

**Ref. No.:** 6976
**Name:** A New Treasure (boy)
**Height:** 3.5
**Status:** Open edition, active
**Issue Year:** 2003
**2003 Retail Price:** $150
**Comment:** My Family Album
    Collection

**Ref. No.:** 6977
**Name:** A New Treasure (girl)
**Height:** 3.5
**Status:** Open edition, active
**Issue Year:** 2003
**2003 Retail Price:** $150
**Comment:** My Family Album
    Collection

**Ref. No.:** 6985
**Name:** My Favorite Companion
**Height:** 4.5
**Status:** Open edition, active
**Issue Year:** 2003
**2003 Retail Price:** $100
**Comment:** My Family Album
    Collection

**Ref. No.:** 6983
**Name:** Growing up Together
**Height:** 4.75
**Status:** Open edition, active
**Issue Year:** 2003
**2003 Retail Price:** $195
**Comment:** My Family Album
    Collection

**Ref. No.:** 6974
**Name:** First Discoveries
**Height:** 6
**Status:** Open edition, active
**Issue Year:** 2003
**2003 Retail Price:** $150
**Comment:** My Family Album
    Collection

**Ref. No.:** 6980
**Name:** Playful Mates
**Height:** 6.5
**Status:** Open edition, active
**Issue Year:** 2003
**2003 Retail Price:** $295
**Comment:** My Family Album
    Collection

**Ref. No.:** 6973
**Name:** My Sweet Princess
**Height:** 7.25
**Status:** Open edition, active
**Issue Year:** 2003
**2003 Retail Price:** $150
**Comment:** My Family Album
    Collection

**Ref. No.:** 6972
**Name:** Caring Father
**Height:** 7.5
**Status:** Open edition, active
**Issue Year:** 2003
**2003 Retail Price:** $225
**Comment:** My Family Album
    Collection

**Ref. No.:** 6979
**Name:** Grandfather's Stories
**Height:** 8
**Status:** Open edition, active
**Issue Year:** 2003
**2003 Retail Price:** $475
**Comment:** My Family Album
    Collection

**Ref. No.:** 6982
**Name:** Treasures of Childhood
**Height:** 8.75
**Status:** Open edition, active
**Issue Year:** 2003
**2003 Retail Price:** $175
**Comment:** My Family Album
Collection

**Ref. No.:** 6986
**Name:** A Circle of Love
**Height:** 10
**Status:** Open edition, active
**Issue Year:** 2003
**2003 Retail Price:** $575
**Comment:** My Family Album
Collection

**Ref. No.:** 6975
**Name:** Wonderful Mother
**Height:** 11.25
**Status:** Open edition, active
**Issue Year:** 2003
**2003 Retail Price:** $250
**Comment:** My Family Album
Collection

**Ref. No.:** 6978
**Name:** Time to Share
**Height:** 12
**Status:** Open edition, active
**Issue Year:** 2003
**2003 Retail Price:** $295
**Comment:** My Family Album
Collection

**Ref. No.:** 6981
**Name:** A Grandmother's Love
**Height:** 12
**Status:** Open edition, active
**Issue Year:** 2003
**2003 Retail Price:** $275
**Comment:** My Family Album
Collection

**Ref. No.:** 6984
**Name:** Window in Springtime
**Height:** 12.75
**Status:** Open edition, active
**Issue Year:** 2003
**2003 Retail Price:** $1100
**Comment:** My Family Album
Collection

## Klimt Collection

## Aura Collection

**Ref. No.:** 6993
**Name:** Fountain of Life
**Height:** 12.5
**Status:** Open edition, active
**Issue Year:** 2003
**2003 Retail Price:** $475
**Comment:** Klimt Collection

**Ref. No.:** 6992
**Name:** Yearning for Happiness
**Height:** 14
**Status:** Open edition, active
**Issue Year:** 2003
**2003 Retail Price:** $475
**Comment:** Klimt Collection

**Ref. No.:** 8005
**Name:** Memory
**Height:** 4.5
**Status:** Open edition, active
**Issue Year:** 2003
**2003 Retail Price:** $475
**Comment:** Aura Collection

**Ref. No.:** 8004
**Name:** Idea
**Height:** 7.5
**Status:** Open edition, active
**Issue Year:** 2003
**2003 Retail Price:** $475
**Comment:** Aura Collection

**Ref. No.:** 8006
**Name:** Destiny
**Height:** 8
**Status:** Open edition, active
**Issue Year:** 2003
**2003 Retail Price:** $475
**Comment:** Aura Collection

**Ref. No.:** 8000
**Name:** Essence
**Height:** 19.5
**Status:** Open edition, active
**Issue Year:** 2003
**2003 Retail Price:** $575
**Comment:** Aura Collection

**Ref. No.:** 8001
**Name:** Infinity
**Height:** 20
**Status:** Open edition, active
**Issue Year:** 2003
**2003 Retail Price:** $575
**Comment:** Aura Collection

**Ref. No.:** 8003
**Name:** Life
**Height:** 20
**Status:** Open edition, active
**Issue Year:** 2003
**2003 Retail Price:** $650
**Comment:** Aura Collection

**Ref. No.:** 8002
**Name:** Guide
**Height:** 22.5
**Status:** Open edition, active
**Issue Year:** 2003
**2003 Retail Price:** $650
**Comment:** Aura Collection

### Holiday & Ornaments

**Ref. No.:** 6728
**Name:** 2003 Christmas Bell
**Height:** 3.25
**Status:** Open edition, active
**Issue Year:** 2003
**2003 Retail Price:** $40
**Comment:** To be retired as of
December 31, 2003

**Ref. No.:** 6729
**Name:** Baby's First Christmas
2003
**Height:** 4
**Status:** Open edition, active
**Issue Year:** 2003
**2003 Retail Price:** $65
**Comment:** To be retired as of
December 31, 2003

**Ref. No.:** 6730
**Name:** Baby's First Christmas
2003 (Black Legacy)
**Height:** 4
**Status:** Open edition, active
**Issue Year:** 2003
**2003 Retail Price:** $65
**Comment:** To be retired as of
December 31, 2003

**Ref. No.:** 6731
**Name:** Our First Christmas 2003
**Height:** 4
**Status:** Open edition, active
**Issue Year:** 2003
**2003 Retail Price:** $65
**Comment:** To be retired as of
December 31, 2003

**Ref. No.:** 6727
**Name:** 2003 Christmas Ball
**Height:** 4.5
**Status:** Open edition, active
**Issue Year:** 2003
**2003 Retail Price:** $55
**Comment:** To be retired as of
December 31, 2003

**Ref. No.:** 6991
**Name:** Celestial Scent
**Height:** 9.25
**Status:** Open edition, active
**Issue Year:** 2003
**2003 Retail Price:** $175
**Comment:** 2003 Treetopper.
To be retired as of
December 31, 2003

### Angel Wishes Collection

**Ref. No.:** 6734
**Name:** A Wish for Romance
**Height:** 4
**Status:** Open edition, active
**Issue Year:** 2003
**2003 Retail Price:** $70
**Comment:** Angel Wishes
Collection — USA/Canada
Exclusive

**Ref. No.:** 6735
**Name:** A wish for a dream
**Height:** 4
**Status:** Open edition, active
**Issue Year:** 2003
**2003 Retail Price:** $70
**Comment:** Angel Wishes
Collection — USA/Canada
Exclusive

**Ref. No.:** 6732
**Name:** A Wish for Harmony
**Height:** 4.5
**Status:** Open edition, active
**Issue Year:** 2003
**2003 Retail Price:** $70
**Comment:** Angel Wishes
Collection — USA/Canada
Exclusive

## Santa's Magical Workshop Collection

**Ref. No.:** 6733
**Name:** A Wish of Hope
**Height:** 4.5
**Status:** Open edition, active
**Issue Year:** 2003
**2003 Retail Price:** $70
**Comment:** Angel Wishes
Collection — USA/Canada
Exclusive

**Ref. No.:** 6894
**Name:** Santa's Sack of Dreams
**Height:** 7.5
**Status:** Open edition, active
**Issue Year:** 2003
**2003 Retail Price:** $250
**Comment:** Santa's Magical
Workshop Collection

**Ref. No.:** 6893
**Name:** Mrs. Santa Claus
**Height:** 10.5
**Status:** Open edition, active
**Issue Year:** 2003
**2003 Retail Price:** $375
**Comment:** Santa's Magical
Workshop Collection

## Gres

**Ref. No.:** 6895
**Name:** It's Almost Time
**Height:** 11.25
**Status:** Open edition, active
**Issue Year:** 2003
**2003 Retail Price:** $450
**Comment:** Santa's Magical
Workshop Collection

**Ref. No.:** 2456
**Name:** Camel
**Height:** 6.5
**Status:** Open edition, active
**Issue Year:** 2003
**2003 Retail Price:** $295

**Ref. No.:** 2458
**Name:** Winds of Springtime
**Height:** 22
**Status:** Open edition, active
**Issue Year:** 2003
**2003 Retail Price:** $1900

**Limited Edition**

**2003 Privilege Society**

**Ref. No.:** 1890
**Name:** Father Christmas —
Spirit of Nature
**Height:** 13.5
**Status:** Limited edition, active
**Edition Size:** 2000
**Issue Year:** 2003
**2003 Retail Price:** $695

**Ref. No.:** 1887
**Name:** A World of Magic
**Height:** 17.25
**Status:** Limited edition, active
**Edition Size:** 1000
**Issue Year:** 2003
**2003 Retail Price:** $2900

**Ref. No.:** 1889
**Name:** Dreams of a Ballerina
**Height:** 22.75
**Status:** Limited edition, active
**Edition Size:** 1000
**Issue Year:** 2003
**2003 Retail Price:** $790
**Comment:** Base included

**2003 Event Piece**

**Ref. No.:** 6941
**Name:** Kittens Gathering
**Height:** 10
**Status:** Open issue, retired
**Issue Year:** 2003
**2003 Retail Price:** $275
**Comment:** Fall 2003 Event Piece

# Lladró Privilege Society

**Ref. No.:** 7694
**Name:** Princess of the Fairies
**Height:** 4.5
**Status:** 2002 Annual Piece, retired
**Issue Year:** 2002
**Issue Price:** $315
**Last Year:** 2003
**Last Retail Price:** $315
**Comment:** Second Sculpture, "Enchanted Forest Collection"

**Ref. No.:** 7690
**Name:** Prince of the Elves
**Height:** 9.25
**Status:** 2001 Annual Piece, retired
**Issue Year:** 2001
**Issue Price:** $295
**Last Year:** 2002
**Last Retail Price:** $315
**Comment:** First Sculpture, "Enchanted Forest Collection"

**Ref. No.:** 6784
**Name:** Puppy Parade
**Height:** 9.5
**Status:** 2001 Open Series, active
**Issue Year:** 2001
**Issue Price:** $660
**2003 Retail Price:** $765

**Ref. No.:** 2444
**Name:** Leda and the Swan
**Height:** 12
**Status:** 2002 Gres Open Series, active
**Issue Year:** 2002
**Issue Price:** $1685
**2003 Retail Price:** $1695

**Ref. No.:** 6854
**Name:** Beauty in Bloom
**Height:** 14.5
**Status:** Matte Limited Edition, active
**Edition Size:** 3000
**Issue Year:** 2002
**Issue Price:** $2275
**2003 Retail Price:** $2395

**Ref. No.:** 7693
**Name:** Thinking of Love
**Height:** 15.25
**Status:** Limited Edition, active
**Edition Size:** 4000
**Issue Year:** 2001
**Issue Price:** $1550
**2003 Retail Price:** $1595

**Ref. No.:** 2422
**Name:** Sincerity
**Height:** 17.25
**Status:** 2001 Gres Open Series,
   retired
**Issue Year:** 2001
**Issue Price:** $550
**Last Year:** 2003
**Last Retail Price:** $595

**Ref. No.:** 3583
**Name:** Garden Breeze
**Height:** 24
**Status:** Gres Limited Edition,
   sold out
**Edition Size:** 1500
**Issue Year:** 2001
**Issue Price:** $1800
**Last Year:** 2003
**Last Retail Price:** $1895

*Lladró Privilege Society*

# Lladró Society

**Ref. No.:** 7685
**Name:** A Friend For Life
**Height:** 2.75
**Status:** Open issue, retired
**Issue Year:** 2000
**Last Year:** 2000
**Comment:** 2000 Lladró Society Renewal Gift

**Ref. No.:** 7657
**Name:** Sailing the Seas
**Height:** 3.5
**Issue Year:** 1997
**Last Year:** 1997
**Last Retail Price:** $35
**Comment:** 1997 Membership Gift

**Ref. No.:** 7658
**Name:** Dolphins At Play
**Height:** 4
**Issue Year:** 1998
**Issue Price:** $35
**Last Year:** 1998
**Last Retail Price:** $21
**Comment:** 1998 Membership Gift

**Ref. No.:** 7672
**Name:** It Wasn't Me!
**Height:** 4
**Status:** Limited edition, sold out
**Issue Year:** 1998
**Issue Price:** $295
**Last Year:** 1999
**Last Retail Price:** $295
**Comment:** 1998 Lladró Society Figurine

**Ref. No.:** 7619
**Name:** All Aboard
**Height:** 5.25
**Status:** Limited edition, sold out
**Issue Year:** 1992
**Issue Price:** $165
**Last Year:** 1993
**Last Retail Price:** $165
**High Auction Price:** $575
**Low Auction Price:** $325

**Ref. No.:** 7677
**Name:** Art Brings Us Together
**Height:** 6
**Status:** Open issue, retired
**Issue Year:** 1999
**Comment:** Membership Gift / 1999 Renewal Gift

**Ref. No.:** 7620
**Name:** Best Friend
**Height:** 6.5
**Status:** Limited edition, sold out
**Issue Year:** 1993
**Issue Price:** $195
**Last Year:** 1994
**Last Retail Price:** $195
**High Auction Price:** $350
**Low Auction Price:** $275

**Ref. No.:** 7607
**Name:** Flower Song
**Height:** 7
**Status:** Limited edition, sold out
**Issue Year:** 1988
**Issue Price:** $175
**Last Year:** 1989
**Last Retail Price:** $175
**High Auction Price:** $900
**Low Auction Price:** $550

**Ref. No.:** 7635
**Name:** Ten and Growing
**Height:** 7.5
**Status:** Limited edition, sold out
**Issue Year:** 1995
**Issue Price:** $395
**Last Year:** 1996
**Last Retail Price:** $395
**Auction Price:** $550
**Comment:** Lladró Society 10th
Anniversary Special

*Lladró Society*

**Ref. No.:** 7609
**Name:** My Buddy
**Height:** 8
**Status:** Limited edition, sold out
**Issue Year:** 1989
**Issue Price:** $145
**Last Year:** 1990
**Last Retail Price:** $145
**High Auction Price:** $1150
**Low Auction Price:** $375

**Ref. No.:** 7603
**Name:** Spring Bouquets
**Height:** 8.25
**Status:** Limited edition, sold out
**Issue Year:** 1987
**Issue Price:** $125
**Last Year:** 1988
**Last Retail Price:** $125
**High Auction Price:** $1250
**Low Auction Price:** $700

**Ref. No.:** 7604
**Name:** School Days
**Height:** 8.25
**Status:** Limited edition, sold out
**Issue Year:** 1988
**Issue Price:** $125
**Last Year:** 1989
**Last Retail Price:** $125
**High Auction Price:** $900
**Low Auction Price:** $550

**Ref. No.:** 7610
**Name:** Can I Play?
**Height:** 8.25
**Status:** Limited edition, sold out
**Issue Year:** 1990
**Issue Price:** $150
**Last Year:** 1991
**Last Retail Price:** $150
**High Auction Price:** $625
**Low Auction Price:** $325

**Ref. No.:** 7602
**Name:** Little Traveller
**Height:** 8.5
**Status:** Limited edition, sold out
**Issue Year:** 1986
**Issue Price:** $95
**Last Year:** 1987
**Last Retail Price:** $95
**High Auction Price:** $2100
**Low Auction Price:** $1000

**Ref. No.:** 7612
**Name:** Picture Perfect
**Height:** 8.5
**Status:** Limited edition, sold out
**Issue Year:** 1991
**Issue Price:** $350
**Last Year:** 1991
**Last Retail Price:** $350
**High Auction Price:** $750
**Low Auction Price:** $450
**Comment:** Lladró Society 5th
    Anniversary Special

**Ref. No.:** 7600
**Name:** Little Pals
**Height:** 8.75
**Status:** Limited edition, sold out
**Issue Year:** 1985
**Issue Price:** $95
**Last Year:** 1986
**Last Retail Price:** $95
**High Auction Price:** $4500
**Low Auction Price:** $2500

**Ref. No.:** 7686
**Name:** Pals Forever
**Height:** 8.75
**Status:** Open issue, retired
**Issue Year:** 2000
**Last Year:** 2000
**Last Retail Price:** $350
**Comment:** 2000 Lladró Society
    Figurine

**Ref. No.:** 7611
**Name:** Summer Stroll
**Height:** 9
**Status:** Limited edition, sold out
**Issue Year:** 1991
**Issue Price:** $195
**Last Year:** 1992
**Last Retail Price:** $195
**High Auction Price:** $600
**Low Auction Price:** $275

**Ref. No.:** 7622
**Name:** Basket of Love
**Height:** 9.5
**Status:** Limited edition, sold out
**Issue Year:** 1994
**Issue Price:** $225
**Last Year:** 1995
**Last Retail Price:** $225
**High Auction Price:** $400
**Low Auction Price:** $350

**Ref. No.:** 7636
**Name:** Afternoon Promenade
**Height:** 9.5
**Status:** Limited edition, sold out
**Issue Year:** 1995
**Issue Price:** $240
**Last Year:** 1996
**Last Retail Price:** $240
**Auction Price:** $350

**Ref. No.:** 7644
**Name:** Innocence In Bloom
**Height:** 9.5
**Status:** Limited edition, sold out
**Issue Year:** 1996
**Issue Price:** $250
**Last Year:** 1997
**Last Retail Price:** $250

**Ref. No.:** 7676
**Name:** A Wish Come True
**Height:** 10
**Status:** Open issue, retired
**Issue Year:** 1999
**Issue Price:** $340
**Last Year:** 2000
**Last Retail Price:** $340

**Ref. No.:** 7642
**Name:** Now and Forever
**Height:** 10.75
**Status:** Limited edition, retired
**Issue Year:** 1995
**Issue Price:** $395
**Last Year:** 2002
**Last Retail Price:** $395
**Comment:** Membership "Ten Year" commemorative figurine

**Ref. No.:** 7650
**Name:** Pocket Full of Wishes
**Height:** 11
**Status:** Limited edition, sold out
**Issue Year:** 1997
**Issue Price:** $360
**Last Year:** 1998
**Last Retail Price:** $360

**Ref. No.:** 1824
**Name:** Heaven and Earth
**Height:** 12
**Status:** Limited edition, sold out
**Edition Size:** 5000
**Issue Year:** 1998
**Issue Price:** $725
**Last Year:** 1998
**Last Retail Price:** $725
**Comment:** 1998 Lladró Society
Limited Edition

**Ref. No.:** 7634
**Name:** Garden of Dreams
**Height:** 12.5
**Status:** Limited edition, sold out
**Edition Size:** 4000
**Issue Year:** 1994
**Issue Price:** $1250
**Last Year:** 1996
**Last Retail Price:** $1250

**Ref. No.:** 6686
**Name:** Mystical Garden
**Height:** 14
**Status:** Limited edition, active
**Edition Size:** 5000
**Issue Year:** 2000
**Last Year:** 2002
**Last Retail Price:** $1100
**Comment:** 2000 Lladró Society
Limited Edition

**Ref. No.:** 7649
**Name:** Where Love Begins
**Height:** 14
**Status:** Limited edition, sold out
**Edition Size:** 4000
**Issue Year:** 1996
**Issue Price:** $895
**Last Year:** 1996
**Last Retail Price:** $895
**Auction Price:** $1450

**Ref. No.:** 7678
**Name:** Scheherazade
**Height:** 14
**Status:** Limited edition, sold out
**Edition Size:** 1000
**Issue Year:** 1999
**Issue Price:** $975
**Last Year:** 1999
**Last Retail Price:** $975
**Comment:** 1st Society Gres
Limited Edition

**Ref. No.:** 5932
**Name:** Jester's Serenade
**Height:** 14.5
**Status:** Limited edition, sold out
**Edition Size :** 3000
**Issue Year:** 1993
**Issue Price:** $1995
**Last Year:** 1994
**Last Retail Price:** $1995

**Ref. No.:** 7679
**Name:** Enchanted Lake
**Height:** 15.75
**Status:** Limited edition, sold out
**Edition Size:** 4000
**Issue Year:** 1999
**Issue Price:** $1225
**Last Year:** 1999
**Last Retail Price:** $1225

**Ref. No.:** 6352
**Name:** Guardian Angel
**Height:** 20
**Status:** Limited edition, sold out
**Edition Size:** 4000
**Issue Year:** 1997
**Issue Price:** $1300
**Last Year:** 1997
**Last Retail Price:** $1300

*Lladró Society*

# *Children*

**Newborns**

 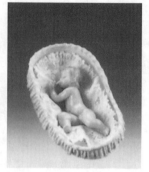 

**Ref. No.:** 5638
**Name:** Bundle of Joy
**Height:** 1.25
**Status:** Open edition, retired
**Issue Year:** 1989
**Issue Price:** $170
**Last Year:** 1991
**Last Retail Price:** $200
**Auction Price:** $575

**Ref. No.:** 5637
**Name:** Bundle of Love
**Height:** 2
**Status:** Open edition, retired
**Issue Year:** 1989
**Issue Price:** $275
**Last Year:** 1991
**Last Retail Price:** $325

**Ref. No.:** 5617
**Name:** Little Joy
**Height:** 2.25
**Status:** Open edition, retired
**Issue Year:** 1989
**Issue Price:** $400
**Last Year:** 1991
**Last Retail Price:** $460

**Ref. No.:** 5805
**Name:** Tumbling
**Height:** 2.25
**Status:** Open edition, retired
**Issue Year:** 1991
**Issue Price:** $130
**Last Year:** 1993
**Last Retail Price:** $140

**Ref. No.:** 5619
**Name:** Ruffles and Lace
**Height:** 2.5
**Status:** Open edition, retired
**Issue Year:** 1989
**Issue Price:** $425
**Last Year:** 1991
**Last Retail Price:** $485
**Auction Price:** $900

**Ref. No.:** 5806
**Name:** Tickling
**Height:** 2.75
**Status:** Open edition, retired
**Issue Year:** 1991
**Issue Price:** $130
**Last Year:** 1993
**Last Retail Price:** $145

**Ref. No.:** 6497
**Name:** Sleepy Time
**Height:** 3
**Status:** Open issue, active
**Issue Year:** 1998
**Issue Price:** $89
**2003 Retail Price:** $95

**Ref. No.:** 216.08
**Name:** Toddler
**Height:** 3.5
**Status:** Very Rare
**Issue Year:** 1956
**Issue Price:** Unknown
**Last Year:** Unknown
**Last Retail Price:** Unknown

**Ref. No.:** 5772
**Name:** Little Dreamers
**Height:** 3.5
**Status:** Open issue, active
**Issue Year:** 1991
**Issue Price:** $230
**2003 Retail Price:** $250

**Ref. No.:** 5804
**Name:** Playing Tag
**Height:** 3.5
**Status:** Open edition, retired
**Issue Year:** 1991
**Issue Price:** $170
**Last Year:** 1993
**Last Retail Price:** $190

**Ref. No.:** 6791
**Name:** Taking a Snoozzze...
**Height:** 3.5
**Status:** Open issue, active
**Issue Year:** 2001
**Issue Price:** $225
**2003 Retail Price:** $225

**Ref. No.:** 6710
**Name:** Comforting Dreams
**Height:** 4
**Status:** Open issue, active
**Issue Year:** 2000
**Issue Price:** $150
**2003 Retail Price:** $150

*Children*

**Ref. No.:** 6790
**Name:** Counting Sheep
**Height:** 4
**Status:** Open issue, active
**Issue Year:** 2001
**Issue Price:** $225
**2003 Retail Price:** $225

**Ref. No.:** 5101
**Name:** Baby on Floor
**Height:** 4.5
**Status:** Open edition, retired
**Issue Year:** 1982
**Issue Price:** $57.50
**Last Year:** 1985
**Last Retail Price:** $57.50
**Auction Price:** $350

**Ref. No.:** 5102
**Name:** Baby with Pacifier
**Height:** 4.5
**Status:** Open edition, retired
**Issue Year:** 1982
**Issue Price:** $57.50
**Last Year:** 1985
**Last Retail Price:** $57.50
**High Auction Price:** $325
**Low Auction Price:** $175

**Ref. No.:** 6831
**Name:** A New Beginning
**Height:** 4.5
**Status:** Open issue, active
**Issue Year:** 2001
**Issue Price:** $150
**2003 Retail Price:** $165
**Comment:** To be retired or sold
out as of December 31, 2003

**Ref. No.:** 5717
**Name:** Rock a' Bye Baby
**Height:** 4.75
**Status:** Open issue, retired
**Issue Year:** 1990
**Issue Price:** $300
**Last Year:** 1999
**Last Retail Price:** $365

**Ref. No.:** 6626
**Name:** Heaven's Gift (Girl)
**Height:** 4.75
**Status:** Open issue, retired
**Issue Year:** 1999
**Issue Price:** $135
**Last Year:** 2001
**Last Retail Price:** $135

**Ref. No.:** 6627
**Name:** Heaven's Gift (Girl—blank card)
**Height:** 4.75
**Status:** Open issue, active
**Issue Year:** 1999
**Issue Price:** $135
**2003 Retail Price:** $135

**Ref. No.:** 7588
**Name:** Heaven's Gift (Girl – 2000 Card)
**Height:** 4.75
**Status:** Open issue, retired
**Issue Year:** 2000
**Issue Price:** $140
**Last Year:** 2000
**Last Retail Price:** $140
**Comment:** Introduced by select dealers in 1999

**Ref. No.:** 7589
**Name:** Heaven's Gift (It's a Girl Card)
**Height:** 4.75
**Status:** Open issue, retired
**Issue Year:** 2000
**Issue Price:** $140
**Last Year:** 2002
**Last Retail Price:** $140

**Ref. No.:** 5099
**Name:** Baby with Pacifier
**Height:** 5
**Status:** Open edition, retired
**Issue Year:** 1982
**Issue Price:** $57.50
**Last Year:** 1985
**Last Retail Price:** $57.50
**High Auction Price:** $300
**Low Auction Price:** $175

**Ref. No.:** 5100
**Name:** Baby with Pacifier, Yawning
**Height:** 5
**Status:** Open edition, retired
**Issue Year:** 1982
**Issue Price:** $57.50
**Last Year:** 1985
**Last Retail Price:** $57.50
**Auction Price:** $275

**Ref. No.:** 5103
**Name:** Baby Holding Bottle
**Height:** 5
**Status:** Open edition, retired
**Issue Year:** 1982
**Issue Price:** $57.50
**Last Year:** 1985
**Last Retail Price:** $57.50

*Children*

**Ref. No.:** 6496
**Name:** A Child's Prayer
**Height:** 5
**Status:** Open issue, active
**Issue Year:** 1998
**Issue Price:** $89
**2003 Retail Price:** $95

**Ref. No.:** 6656
**Name:** Tender Dreams
**Height:** 5.25
**Status: Status:** Open issue, active
**Issue Year:** 2000
**Issue Price:** $150
**2003 Retail Price:** $150
**Comment:** Introduced by select
    dealers in 1999

**Ref. No.:** 6612
**Name:** Heaven's Gift (Boy)
**Height:** 5.5
**Status:** Open issue, retired
**Issue Year:** 1999
**Issue Price:** $135
**Last Year:** 2001
**Last Retail Price:** $135

**Ref. No.:** 6613
**Name:** Heaven's Gift (Boy—
    blank card)
**Height:** 5.5
**Status:** Open issue, active
**Issue Year:** 1999
**Issue Price:** $135
**2003 Retail Price:** $135

**Ref. No.:** 7586
**Name:** Heaven's Gift (Boy –
    2000 Card)
**Height:** 5.5
**Status:** Open issue, retired
**Issue Year:** 2000
**Issue Price:** $140
**Last Year:** 2000
**Last Retail Price:** $140
**Comment:** Introduced by select
    dealers in 1999

**Ref. No.:** 7587
**Name:** Heaven's Gift (It's A Boy
    Card)
**Height:** 5.5
**Status:** Open issue, retired
**Issue Year:** 2000
**Issue Price:** $140
**Last Year:** 2002
**Last Retail Price:** $140

**Ref. No.:** 6127
**Name:** Sweet Dreamers
**Height:** 7
**Status:** Open issue, retired
**Issue Year:** 1994
**Issue Price:** $280
**Last Year:** 2001
**Last Retail Price:** $290

**Ref. No.:** 6479
**Name:** Heavenly Slumber
**Height:** 7
**Status:** Open issue, active
**Issue Year:** 1997
**Issue Price:** $185
**2003 Retail Price:** $225

**Ref. No.:** 6583
**Name:** Heavens' Lullaby
**Height:** 8
**Status:** Open issue, active
**Issue Year:** 1998
**Issue Price:** $185
**2003 Retail Price:** $225

**Ref. No.:** 6228
**Name:** Special Gift
**Height:** 9.75
**Status:** Open issue, retired
**Issue Year:** 1995
**Issue Price:** $265
**Last Year:** 2001
**Last Retail Price:** $265
**Comment:** Blue Blanket

**Ref. No.:** 6382
**Name:** New Arrival
**Height:** 10
**Status:** Open issue, retired
**Issue Year:** 1997
**Issue Price:** $265
**Last Year:** 2001
**Last Retail Price:** $265
**Comment:** Pink Blanket

**Ref. No.:** 6843
**Name:** Sleep Well Sweet Baby
**Height:** 10.75
**Status:** Open issue, active
**Issue Year:** 2002
**2003 Retail Price:** $475

*Children*

## Children with Animals

**Ref. No.:** 5609
**Name:** Playful Friends
**Height:** 3.5
**Status:** Open issue, retired
**Issue Year:** 1989
**Issue Price:** $135
**Last Year:** 1995
**Last Retail Price:** $170

**Ref. No.:** 5988
**Name:** Taking Time
**Height:** 3.5
**Status:** Open issue, retired
**Issue Year:** 1993
**Issue Price:** $190
**Last Year:** 1998
**Last Retail Price:** $175

**Ref. No.:** 1535
**Name:** Sweet Dreams
**Height:** 4
**Status:** Open issue, active
**Issue Year:** 1988
**Issue Price:** $150
**2003 Retail Price:** $250

**Ref. No.:** 5451
**Name:** Study Buddies
**Height:** 4
**Status:** Open issue, active
**Issue Year:** 1988
**Issue Price:** $225
**2003 Retail Price:** $295

**Ref. No.:** 5594
**Name:** Playful Romp
**Height:** 4
**Status:** Open issue, retired
**Issue Year:** 1989
**Issue Price:** $215
**Last Year:** 1996
**Last Retail Price:** $270

**Ref. No.:** 5837
**Name:** Sing With Me
**Height:** 4
**Status:** Open issue, retired
**Issue Year:** 1991
**Issue Price:** $240
**Last Year:** 1997
**Last Retail Price:** $250

**Ref. No.:** 6540
**Name:** Cozy Companions
**Height:** 4
**Status:** Open issue, active
**Issue Year:** 1998
**Issue Price:** $195
**2003 Retail Price:** $225

**Ref. No.:** 6541
**Name:** Bedtime Buddies
**Height:** 4
**Status:** Open issue, active
**Issue Year:** 1998
**Issue Price:** $195
**2003 Retail Price:** $225

**Ref. No.:** 5760
**Name:** Interrupted Nap
**Height:** 4.5
**Status:** Open issue, retired
**Issue Year:** 1991
**Issue Price:** $325
**Last Year:** 1995
**Last Retail Price:** $350

**Ref. No.:** 5456
**Name:** New Playmates
**Height:** 4.75
**Status:** Open issue, active
**Issue Year:** 1988
**Issue Price:** $160
**2003 Retail Price:** $275

**Ref. No.:** 5178
**Name:** Stubborn Donkey
**Height:** 5
**Status:** Open issue, retired
**Issue Year:** 1982
**Issue Price:** $250
**Last Year:** 1993
**Last Retail Price:** $420
**Auction Price:** $500

**Ref. No.:** 5450
**Name:** I Hope She Does
**Height:** 5
**Status:** Open issue, retired
**Issue Year:** 1987
**Issue Price:** $190
**Last Year:** 1997
**Last Retail Price:** $345

Children

**Ref. No.:** 5455
**Name:** Bashful Bather
**Height:** 5
**Status:** Open issue, active
**Issue Year:** 1988
**Issue Price:** $150
**2003 Retail Price:** $195

**Ref. No.:** 6204
**Name:** Grace and Beauty
**Height:** 5.25
**Status:** Open issue, retired
**Issue Year:** 1995
**Issue Price:** $325
**Last Year:** 1998
**Last Retail Price:** $325

**Ref. No.:** 4569
**Name:** Girl with Turkey
**Height:** 5.5
**Status:** Open issue, retired
**Issue Year:** 1969
**Issue Price:** $28.50
**Last Year:** 1981
**Last Retail Price:** $165
**High Auction Price:** $400
**Low Auction Price:** $350

**Ref. No.:** 4858
**Name:** Pleasant Encounter
**Height:** 5.5
**Status:** Open issue, retired
**Issue Year:** 1974
**Issue Price:** $60
**Last Year:** 1981
**Last Retail Price:** $60
**Auction Price:** $450

**Ref. No.:** 5468
**Name:** Who's the Fairest?
**Height:** 5.5
**Status:** Open issue, retired
**Issue Year:** 1988
**Issue Price:** $150
**Last Year:** 2000
**Last Retail Price:** $205

**Ref. No.:** 5595
**Name:** Joy in a Basket
**Height:** 5.5
**Status:** Open issue, retired
**Issue Year:** 1989
**Issue Price:** $215
**Last Year:** 1997
**Last Retail Price:** $270

**Ref. No.:** 5640
**Name:** Cat Nap
**Height:** 5.5
**Status:** Open issue, active
**Issue Year:** 1990
**Issue Price:** $125
**2003 Retail Price:** $165

**Ref. No.:** 5781
**Name:** Not Too Close!
**Height:** 5.5
**Status:** Open issue, retired
**Issue Year:** 1991
**Issue Price:** $365
**Last Year:** 1994
**Last Retail Price:** $395

**Ref. No.:** 5987
**Name:** Talk To Me
**Height:** 5.5
**Status:** Open issue, retired
**Issue Year:** 1993
**Issue Price:** $180
**Last Year:** 1998
**Last Retail Price:** $175

**Ref. No.:** 6693
**Name:** Programming Pals
**Height:** 5.5
**Status:** Open issue, active
**Issue Year:** 2000
**2003 Retail Price:** $295

**Ref. No.:** 6229
**Name:** Contented Companion
**Height:** 5.75
**Status:** Open issue, retired
**Issue Year:** 1995
**Issue Price:** $195
**Last Year:** 2000
**Last Retail Price:** $195

**Ref. No.:** 6318
**Name:** Little Distraction
**Height:** 5.75
**Status:** Open issue, retired
**Issue Year:** 1996
**Issue Price:** $350
**Last Year:** 1999
**Last Retail Price:** $350

*Children*

**Ref. No.:** 7623
**Name:** Little Riders
**Height:** 5.75
**Status:** Limited edition, sold out
**Issue Year:** 1994
**Issue Price:** Unknown
**Last Year:** 1994
**Last Retail Price:** $250
**Auction Price:** $350
**Comment:** Special event

**Ref. No.:** 311.13
**Name:** Boy with Bull
**Height:** 6
**Status:** Very rare
**Issue Year:** 1963
**Issue Price:** Unknown
**Last Year:** Unknown
**Last Retail Price:** Unknown

**Ref. No.:** 5469
**Name:** Lambkins
**Height:** 6
**Status:** Open issue, retired
**Issue Year:** 1988
**Issue Price:** $150
**Last Year:** 1993
**Last Retail Price:** $210

**Ref. No.:** 5475
**Name:** A Lesson Shared
**Height:** 6
**Status:** Open issue, retired
**Issue Year:** 1988
**Issue Price:** $150
**Last Year:** 1997
**Last Retail Price:** $190

**Ref. No.:** 5553
**Name:** Wild Goose Chase
**Height:** 6
**Status:** Open issue, retired
**Issue Year:** 1989
**Issue Price:** $175
**Last Year:** 1997
**Last Retail Price:** $230

**Ref. No.:** 5679
**Name:** In No Hurry
**Height:** 6
**Status:** Open issue, retired
**Issue Year:** 1990
**Issue Price:** $550
**Last Year:** 1994
**Last Retail Price:** $640
**Auction Price:** $750

**Ref. No.:** 5688
**Name:** Dog's Best Friend
**Height:** 6
**Status:** Open issue, active
**Issue Year:** 1990
**Issue Price:** $250
**2003 Retail Price:** $325

**Ref. No.:** 5703
**Name:** Behave!
**Height:** 6
**Status:** Open issue, retired
**Issue Year:** 1990
**Issue Price:** $230
**Last Year:** 1994
**Last Retail Price:** $265

**Ref. No.:** 5706
**Name:** We Can't Play
**Height:** 6
**Status:** Open issue, retired
**Issue Year:** 1990
**Issue Price:** $200
**Last Year:** 1998
**Last Retail Price:** $235

**Ref. No.:** 5736
**Name:** Puppet Show
**Height:** 6
**Status:** Open issue, retired
**Issue Year:** 1991
**Issue Price:** $280
**Last Year:** 1996
**Last Retail Price:** $295

**Ref. No.:** 5784
**Name:** A Cradle of Kittens
**Height:** 6
**Status:** Open issue, retired
**Issue Year:** 1991
**Issue Price:** $360
**Last Year:** 1997
**Last Retail Price:** $385

**Ref. No.:** 5881
**Name:** Mischievous Mouse
**Height:** 6
**Status:** Open issue, retired
**Issue Year:** 1992
**Issue Price:** $285
**Last Year:** 1998
**Last Retail Price:** $295

*Children*

**Ref. No.:** 6025
**Name:** Barnyard See-Saw
**Height:** 6
**Status:** Open issue, retired
**Issue Year:** 1993
**Issue Price:** $500
**Last Year:** 1997
**Last Retail Price:** $500

**Ref. No.:** 6549
**Name:** Naptime Friends
**Height:** 6
**Status:** Open issue, retired
**Issue Year:** 1998
**Issue Price:** $200
**Last Year:** 2001
**Last Retail Price:** $215

**Ref. No.:** 6550
**Name:** Shhh... They're Sleeping
**Height:** 6
**Status:** Open issue, retired
**Issue Year:** 1998
**Issue Price:** $200
**Last Year:** 2001
**Last Retail Price:** $215

**Ref. No.:** 6862
**Name:** An Elegant Touch
**Height:** 6
**Status:** Open issue, active
**Issue Year:** 2002
**Issue Price:** $295
**2003 Retail Price:** $295

**Ref. No.:** 6905
**Name:** Bundle of Dreams
**Height:** 6
**Status:** Open issue, active
**Issue Year:** 2002
**Issue Price:** $320
**2003 Retail Price:** $325

**Ref. No.:** 4730
**Name:** Bird Watcher
**Height:** 6.25
**Status:** Open issue, retired
**Issue Year:** 1970
**Issue Price:** $35
**Last Year:** 1985
**Last Retail Price:** $190
**High Auction Price:** $475
**Low Auction Price:** $275

**Ref. No.:** 5474
**Name:** How You've Grown!
**Height:** 6.25
**Status:** Open issue, retired
**Issue Year:** 1988
**Issue Price:** $180
**Last Year:** 1997
**Last Retail Price:** $270

**Ref. No.:** 6140
**Name:** Springtime Friends
**Height:** 6.25
**Status:** Open issue, retired
**Issue Year:** 1994
**Issue Price:** $485
**Last Year:** 2001
**Last Retail Price:** $485

**Ref. No.:** 6226
**Name:** Snuggle Up
**Height:** 6.25
**Status:** Open issue, retired
**Issue Year:** 1995
**Issue Price:** $170
**Last Year:** 2000
**Last Retail Price:** $170

**Ref. No.:** 7645
**Name:** By My Side
**Height:** 6.25
**Status:** Open issue, retired
**Issue Year:** 1996
**Issue Price:** $250
**Last Year:** 1999
**Last Retail Price:** $250

**Ref. No.:** 1312
**Name:** Little Bo Peep
**Height:** 6.5
**Status:** Open issue, retired
**Issue Year:** 1974
**Issue Price:** $72.50
**Last Year:** 1985
**Last Retail Price:** $195
**Auction Price:** $425

**Ref. No.:** 1312.3
**Name:** Little Bo Peep (White)
**Height:** 6.5
**Status:** Open issue, retired
**Issue Year:** 1984
**Issue Price:** $92.50
**Last Year:** 1985
**Last Retail Price:** $92.50
**Auction Price:** $250

*Children*

**Ref. No.:** 4660
**Name:** Shepherdess with Dove
**Height:** 6.5
**Status:** Open issue, retired
**Issue Year:** 1969
**Issue Price:** $21
**Last Year:** 1993
**Last Retail Price:** $175
**Auction Price:** $300

**Ref. No.:** 4849
**Name:** Feeding the Ducks
**Height:** 6.5
**Status:** Open issue, retired
**Issue Year:** 1973
**Issue Price:** $60
**Last Year:** 1995
**Last Retail Price:** $270

**Ref. No.:** 5074
**Name:** My Hungry Brood
**Height:** 6.5
**Status:** Open issue, retired
**Issue Year:** 1980
**Issue Price:** $295
**Last Year:** 1997
**Last Retail Price:** $415

**Ref. No.:** 5376
**Name:** This One's Mine
**Height:** 6.5
**Status:** Open issue, retired
**Issue Year:** 1986
**Issue Price:** $300
**Last Year:** 1995
**Last Retail Price:** $520

**Ref. No.:** 5401
**Name:** My Best Friend
**Height:** 6.5
**Status:** Open issue, retired
**Issue Year:** 1987
**Issue Price:** $150
**Last Year:** 1998
**Last Retail Price:** $240

**Ref. No.:** 5680
**Name:** Traveling in Style
**Height:** 6.5
**Status:** Open issue, retired
**Issue Year:** 1990
**Issue Price:** $425
**Last Year:** 1994
**Last Retail Price:** $495

**Ref. No.:** 5712
**Name:** Sleepy Kitten
**Height:** 6.5
**Status:** Open issue, retired
**Issue Year:** 1990
**Issue Price:** $110
**Last Year:** 2002
**Last Retail Price:** $130

**Ref. No.:** 5921
**Name:** Take Your Medicine
**Height:** 6.5
**Status:** Open issue, retired
**Issue Year:** 1992
**Issue Price:** $360
**Last Year:** 1998
**Last Retail Price:** $370

**Ref. No.:** 5959
**Name:** It's Your Turn
**Height:** 6.5
**Status:** Open issue, retired
**Issue Year:** 1993
**Issue Price:** $365
**Last Year:** 1996
**Last Retail Price:** $365

**Ref. No.:** 6904
**Name:** Bundle of Surprises
**Height:** 6.5
**Status:** Open issue, active
**Issue Year:** 2002
**Issue Price:** $320
**2003 Retail Price:** $325

**Ref. No.:** 5032
**Name:** Dog and Cat
**Height:** 6.75
**Status:** Open issue, retired
**Issue Year:** 1979
**Issue Price:** $107.50
**Last Year:** 1997
**Last Retail Price:** $220.

**Ref. No.:** 5704
**Name:** Swan Song
**Height:** 6.75
**Status:** Open issue, retired
**Issue Year:** 1990
**Issue Price:** $350
**Last Year:** 1995
**Last Retail Price:** $410

*Children*

**Ref. No.:** 5770
**Name:** Out For a Spin
**Height:** 6.75
**Status:** Open issue, retired
**Issue Year:** 1991
**Issue Price:** $390
**Last Year:** 1994
**Last Retail Price:** $420
**Auction Price:** $400

**Ref. No.:** 6165
**Name:** Pretty Cargo
**Height:** 6.75
**Status:** Open issue, retired
**Issue Year:** 1995
**Issue Price:** $500
**Last Year:** 1998
**Last Retail Price:** $500

**Ref. No.:** 6680
**Name:** Friends Forever
**Height:** 6.75
**Status:** Open issue, retired
**Issue Year:** 1999
**Issue Price:** $210
**Last Year:** 1999
**Last Retail Price:** $210
**Comment:** Lladró Events
    Exclusive Sculpture

**Ref. No.:** 6692
**Name:** Computing Companions
**Height:** 6.75
**Status:** Open issue, active
**Issue Year:** 2000
**Issue Price:** $290
**2003 Retail Price:** $295

**Ref. No.:** 6759
**Name:** What a Surprise!
**Height:** 6.75
**Status:** Open issue, active
**Issue Year:** 2001
**Issue Price:** $160
**2003 Retail Price:** $165

**Ref. No.:** 1011
**Name:** Girl with Pig
**Height:** 7
**Status:** Open issue, retired
**Issue Year:** 1969
**Issue Price:** $13
**Auction Price:** $175
**Last Year:** 2001
**Last Retail Price:** $100

**Ref. No.:** 1334
**Name:** "Chow Time"
**Height:** 7
**Status:** Open issue, retired
**Issue Year:** 1977
**Issue Price:** $135
**Last Year:** 1981
**Last Retail Price:** $175
**High Auction Price:** $700
**Low Auction Price:** $450

**Ref. No.:** 1483
**Name:** Free as a Butterfly
**Height:** 7
**Status:** Open issue, retired
**Issue Year:** 1985
**Issue Price:** $145
**Last Year:** 1988
**Last Retail Price:** $175
**High Auction Price:** $550
**Low Auction Price:** $350

**Ref. No.:** 5503
**Name:** Hurry Now
**Height:** 7
**Status:** Open issue, active
**Issue Year:** 1988
**Issue Price:** $180
**2003 Retail Price:** $275

**Ref. No.:** 5689
**Name:** Can I Help?
**Height:** 7
**Status:** Open issue, retired
**Issue Year:** 1990
**Issue Price:** $250
**Last Year:** 1997
**Last Retail Price:** $335

**Ref. No.:** 5836
**Name:** Sharing Sweets
**Height:** 7
**Status:** Open issue, retired
**Issue Year:** 1991
**Issue Price:** $220
**Last Year:** 1997
**Last Retail Price:** $245

**Ref. No.:** 6201
**Name:** Cuddly Kitten
**Height:** 7
**Status:** Open issue, retired
**Issue Year:** 1995
**Issue Price:** $270
**Last Year:** 1999
**Last Retail Price:** $270

*Children*

**Ref. No.:** 6399
**Name:** Generous Gesture
**Height:** 7
**Status:** Open issue, retired
**Issue Year:** 1997
**Issue Price:** $345
**Last Year:** 2000
**Last Retail Price:** $345

**Ref. No.:** 6446
**Name:** Surrounded by Love
**Height:** 7
**Status:** Open issue, active
**Issue Year:** 1997
**Issue Price:** $315
**2003 Retail Price:** $325

**Ref. No.:** 6635
**Name:** My Pretty Puppy
**Height:** 7.25
**Status:** Open issue, retired
**Issue Year:** 1999
**Issue Price:** $295
**Last Year:** 2002
**Last Retail Price:** $295

**Ref. No.:** 7621
**Name:** Pick of the Litter
**Height:** 7.25
**Status:** Limited edition, sold out
**Issue Year:** 1993
**Issue Price:** $350
**Last Year:** 1993
**Last Retail Price:** $350
**High Auction Price:** $550
**Low Auction Price:** $425
**Comment:** Special event

**Ref. No.:** 1248
**Name:** Sweety
**Height:** 7.5
**Status:** Open issue, retired
**Issue Year:** 1974
**Issue Price:** $100
**Last Year:** 1990
**Last Retail Price:** $350
**High Auction Price:** $775
**Low Auction Price:** $425

**Ref. No.:** 1280
**Name:** Child's Play
**Height:** 7.5
**Status:** Open issue, retired
**Issue Year:** 1974
**Issue Price:** $110
**Last Year:** 1983
**Last Retail Price:** $310
**High Auction Price:** $725
**Low Auction Price:** $650

**Ref. No.:** 4522
**Name:** Boy with Dog
**Height:** 7.5
**Status:** Open issue, retired
**Issue Year:** 1970
**Issue Price:** $25
**Last Year:** 1997
**Last Retail Price:** $180

**Ref. No.:** 4827
**Name:** Caressing a Little Calf
**Height:** 7.5
**Status:** Open issue, retired
**Issue Year:** 1972
**Last Year:** 1981
**Issue Price:** $55
**Last Retail Price:** $105
**Auction Price:** $475

**Ref. No.:** 4971
**Name:** Hunter Puppet
**Height:** 7.5
**Status:** Open issue, retired
**Issue Year:** 1977
**Issue Price:** $95
**Last Year:** 1985
**Last Retail Price:** $112.5
**High Auction Price:** $825
**Low Auction Price:** $700

**Ref. No.:** 5217
**Name:** Spring
**Height:** 7.5
**Status:** Open issue, active
**Issue Year:** 1984
**Issue Price:** $90
**2003 Retail Price:** $225

**Ref. No.:** 5354
**Name:** Ride in the Country
**Height:** 7.5
**Status:** Open issue, retired
**Issue Year:** 1986
**Issue Price:** $225
**Last Year:** 1993
**Last Retail Price:** $415
**Auction Price:** $500

**Ref. No.:** 5465
**Name:** Look At Me!
**Height:** 7.5
**Status:** Open issue, active
**Issue Year:** 1988
**Issue Price:** $375
**2003 Retail Price:** $550

*Children*

**Ref. No.:** 5794
**Name:** Precious Cargo
**Height:** 7.5
**Status:** Open issue, retired
**Issue Year:** 1991
**Issue Price:** $460
**Last Year:** 1994
**Last Retail Price:** $495

**Ref. No.:** 5797
**Name:** Come Out and Play
**Height:** 7.5
**Status:** Open issue, retired
**Issue Year:** 1991
**Issue Price:** $275
**Last Year:** 1994
**Last Retail Price:** $295
**Auction Price:** $450

**Ref. No.:** 5883
**Name:** Loving Mouse
**Height:** 7.5
**Status:** Open issue, retired
**Issue Year:** 1992
**Issue Price:** $285
**Last Year:** 1996
**Last Retail Price:** $295

**Ref. No.:** 6109
**Name:** Meal Time
**Height:** 7.5
**Status:** Open issue, retired
**Issue Year:** 1994
**Issue Price:** $495
**Last Year:** 2000
**Last Retail Price:** $525

**Ref. No.:** 6205
**Name:** Graceful Dance
**Height:** 7.5
**Status:** Open issue, retired
**Issue Year:** 1995
**Issue Price:** $340
**Last Year:** 1998
**Last Retail Price:** $340

**Ref. No.:** 6741
**Name:** Bunny Kisses
**Height:** 7.5
**Status:** Open issue, retired
**Issue Year:** 2001
**Issue Price:** $250
**Last Year:** 2001
**Last Retail Price:** $250
**Comment:** Event Piece 2001

**Ref. No.:** 1180
**Name:** Little Girl with Turkeys
**Height:** 7.75
**Status:** Open issue, retired
**Issue Year:** 1971
**Issue Price:** $55
**Last Year:** 1981
**Last Retail Price:** $150
**High Auction Price:** $475
**Low Auction Price:** $400

**Ref. No.:** 1181
**Name:** Platero and Marcelino
**Height:** 7.75
**Status:** Open issue, retired
**Issue Year:** 1971
**Issue Price:** $40
**Last Year:** 1989
**Last Retail Price:** $240
**High Auction Price:** $600
**Low Auction Price:** $375

**Ref. No.:** 1267
**Name:** Duck Seller
**Height:** 7.75
**Status:** Open issue, retired
**Issue Year:** 1974
**Issue Price:** $55
**Last Year:** 1993
**Last Retail Price:** $260
**Auction Price:** $375

**Ref. No.:** 4867
**Name:** Seesaw
**Height:** 7.75
**Status:** Open issue, retired
**Issue Year:** 1974
**Issue Price:** $80
**Last Year:** 1996
**Last Retail Price:** $350

**Ref. No.:** 4909
**Name:** Girl with Dove
**Height:** 7.75
**Status:** Open issue, retired
**Issue Year:** 1974
**Issue Price:** $70
**Last Year:** 1982
**Last Retail Price:** $137.50
**High Auction Price:** $450
**Low Auction Price:** $400

**Ref. No.:** 4982
**Name:** Naughty Dog
**Height:** 7.75
**Status:** Open issue, retired
**Issue Year:** 1978
**Issue Price:** $130
**Last Year:** 1995
**Last Retail Price:** $250

*Children*

**Ref. No.:** 5220
**Name:** Winter
**Height:** 7.75
**Status:** Open issue, retired
**Issue Year:** 1984
**Issue Price:** $90
**Last Year:** 2001
**Last Retail Price:** $195

**Ref. No.:** 5250
**Name:** Exam Day
**Height:** 7.75
**Status:** Open issue, retired
**Issue Year:** 1984
**Issue Price:** $115
**Last Year:** 1994
**Last Retail Price:** $210

**Ref. No.:** 5466
**Name:** "Chit-Chat"
**Height:** 7.75
**Status:** Open issue, active
**Issue Year:** 1988
**Issue Price:** $150
**2003 Retail Price:** $225

**Ref. No.:** 5645
**Name:** Elizabeth
**Height:** 7.75
**Status:** Open issue, retired
**Issue Year:** 1990
**Issue Price:** $190
**Last Year:** 1998
**Last Retail Price:** $215

**Ref. No.:** 5882
**Name:** Restful Mouse
**Height:** 7.75
**Status:** Open issue, retired
**Issue Year:** 1992
**Issue Price:** $285
**Last Year:** 1996
**Last Retail Price:** $295

**Ref. No.:** 6154
**Name:** African Love
**Height:** 7.75
**Status:** Open issue, retired
**Issue Year:** 1994
**Issue Price:** $225
**Last Year:** 1999
**Last Retail Price:** $235

**Ref. No.:** 5753
**Name:** Hold Her Still
**Height:** 8
**Status:** Open issue, retired
**Issue Year:** 1991
**Issue Price:** $650
**Last Year:** 1993
**Last Retail Price:** $695
**Auction Price:** $750

**Ref. No.:** 6402
**Name:** Little Ballerina
**Height:** 8
**Status:** Open issue, retired
**Issue Year:** 1997
**Issue Price:** $200
**Last Year:** 2001
**Last Retail Price:** $200

**Ref. No.:** 6422
**Name:** My Chubby Kitty
**Height:** 8
**Status:** Open issue, active
**Issue Year:** 1997
**Issue Price:** $135
**Last Year:** 2002
**Last Retail Price:** $145

**Ref. No.:** 6510
**Name:** An Unexpected Gift
**Height:** 8
**Status:** Open issue, retired
**Issue Year:** 1998
**Issue Price:** $260
**Last Year:** 2000
**Last Retail Price:** $265

**Ref. No.:** 6825
**Name:** Hello Little Squirrel!
**Height:** 8
**Status:** Open issue, active
**Issue Year:** 2002
**Issue Price:** $415
**2003 Retail Price:** $425

**Ref. No.:** 6853
**Name:** Little Napmates
**Height:** 8
**Status:** Open issue, active
**Issue Year:** 2002
**Issue Price:** $460
**2003 Retail Price:** $475

Children

**Ref. No.:** 1088
**Name:** Girl with Flowers
**Height:** 8.25
**Status:** Open issue, retired
**Issue Year:** 1969
**Issue Price:** $42.50
**Last Year:** 1989
**Last Retail Price:** $400
**High Auction Price:** $725
**Low Auction Price:** $600

**Ref. No.:** 1187
**Name:** Little Girl with Cat
**Height:** 8.25
**Status:** Open issue, retired
**Issue Year:** 1972
**Issue Price:** $37
**Last Year:** 1989
**Last Retail Price:** $200
**High Auction Price:** $450
**Low Auction Price:** $375

**Ref. No.:** 1246
**Name:** Caress and Rest
**Height:** 8.25
**Status:** Open issue, retired
**Issue Year:** 1972
**Issue Price:** $50
**Last Year:** 1990
**Last Retail Price:** $190
**Auction Price:** $400

**Ref. No.:** 1288
**Name:** Aggressive Duck
**Height:** 8.25
**Status:** Open issue, retired
**Issue Year:** 1974
**Issue Price:** $170
**Last Year:** 1995
**Last Retail Price:** $475

**Ref. No.:** 1533
**Name:** Not So Fast
**Height:** 8.25
**Status:** Open issue, retired
**Issue Year:** 1987
**Issue Price:** $175
**Last Year:** 1996
**Last Retail Price:** $285

**Ref. No.:** 4929
**Name:** Children Reading
**Height:** 8.25
**Status:** Open issue, retired
**Issue Year:** 1974
**Issue Price:** $180
**Last Year:** 1983
**Last Retail Price:** $275

**Ref. No.:** 5232
**Name:** Playful Kittens
**Height:** 8.25
**Status:** Open issue, retired
**Issue Year:** 1984
**Issue Price:** $130
**Last Year:** 2002
**Last Retail Price:** $300

**Ref. No.:** 5358
**Name:** Little Sculptor
**Height:** 8.25
**Status:** Open issue, retired
**Issue Year:** 1986
**Issue Price:** $160
**Last Year:** 1990
**Last Retail Price:** $215
**High Auction Price:** $400
**Low Auction Price:** $300

**Ref. No.:** 5460
**Name:** A Barrow of Fun
**Height:** 8.25
**Status:** Open issue, active
**Issue Year:** 1988
**Issue Price:** $370
**2003 Retail Price:** $675

**Ref. No.:** 5549
**Name:** My New Pet
**Height:** 8.25
**Status:** Open issue, retired
**Issue Year:** 1989
**Issue Price:** $150
**Last Year:** 1998
**Last Retail Price:** $185

**Ref. No.:** 5738
**Name:** Best Foot Forward
**Height:** 8.25
**Status:** Open issue, retired
**Issue Year:** 1991
**Issue Price:** $280
**Last Year:** 1994
**Last Retail Price:** $305

**Ref. No.:** 5739
**Name:** Lap Full of Love
**Height:** 8.25
**Status:** Open issue, retired
**Issue Year:** 1991
**Issue Price:** $275
**Last Year:** 1995
**Last Retail Price:** $295

*Children*

**Ref. No.:** 5743
**Name:** Don't Forget Me!
**Height:** 8.25
**Status:** Open issue, active
**Issue Year:** 1991
**Issue Price:** $150
**2003 Retail Price:** $165

**Ref. No.:** 6102
**Name:** Mother's Helper
**Height:** 8.25
**Status:** Open issue, retired
**Issue Year:** 1994
**Issue Price:** $275
**Last Year:** 1998
**Last Retail Price:** $285

**Ref. No.:** 6134
**Name:** Birthday Party
**Height:** 8.25
**Status:** Open issue, retired
**Issue Year:** 1994
**Issue Price:** $395
**Last Year:** 1998
**Last Retail Price:** $455

**Ref. No.:** 6141
**Name:** Kitty Cart
**Height:** 8.25
**Status:** Open issue, active
**Issue Year:** 1994
**Issue Price:** $750
**2003 Retail Price:** $795

**Ref. No.:** 1010
**Name:** Girl with Lamb
**Height:** 8.5
**Status:** Open issue, retired
**Issue Year:** 1969
**Issue Price:** $26
**Last Year:** 1993
**Last Retail Price:** $180
**High Auction Price:** $375
**Low Auction Price:** $200

**Ref. No.:** 1245
**Name:** The Cart
**Height:** 8.5
**Status:** Open issue, retired
**Issue Year:** 1973
**Issue Price:** $75
**Last Year:** 1981
**Last Retail Price:** $320
**High Auction Price:** $650
**Low Auction Price:** $450

**Ref. No.:** 4852
**Name:** Gardener in Trouble
**Height:** 8.5
**Status:** Open issue, retired
**Issue Year:** 1973
**Issue Price:** $65
**Last Year:** 1981
**Last Retail Price:** $235
**Auction Price:** $400

**Ref. No.:** 4910
**Name:** Girl with Lantern
**Height:** 8.5
**Status:** Open issue, retired
**Issue Year:** 1974
**Issue Price:** $85
**Last Year:** 1990
**Last Retail Price:** $185

**Ref. No.:** 4915
**Name:** Girl with Pigeons
**Height:** 8.5
**Status:** Open issue, retired
**Issue Year:** 1974
**Issue Price:** $110
**Last Year:** 1990
**Last Retail Price:** $215
**Auction Price:** $400

**Ref. No.:** 5364
**Name:** Litter of Fun
**Height:** 8.5
**Status:** Open issue, retired
**Issue Year:** 1986
**Issue Price:** $275
**Last Year:** 2000
**Last Retail Price:** $465

**Ref. No.:** 5379
**Name:** Children's Games
**Height:** 8.5
**Status:** Open issue, retired
**Issue Year:** 1986
**Issue Price:** $325
**Last Year:** 1991
**Last Retail Price:** $480
**High Auction Price:** $650
**Low Auction Price:** $600

**Ref. No.:** 5603
**Name:** Close to My Heart
**Height:** 8.5
**Status:** Open issue, retired
**Issue Year:** 1989
**Issue Price:** $125
**Last Year:** 1997
**Last Retail Price:** $165

*Children*

**Ref. No.:** 5761
**Name:** Out For a Romp
**Height:** 8.5
**Status:** Open issue, retired
**Issue Year:** 1991
**Issue Price:** $375
**Last Year:** 1995
**Last Retail Price:** $410

**Ref. No.:** 5807
**Name:** My Puppies
**Height:** 8.5
**Status:** Open issue, retired
**Issue Year:** 1991
**Issue Price:** $325
**Last Year:** 1993
**Last Retail Price:** $360

**Ref. No.:** 6166
**Name:** Dear Santa
**Height:** 8.5
**Status:** Open issue, retired
**Issue Year:** 1995
**Issue Price:** $260
**Last Year:** 1999
**Last Retail Price:** $260

**Ref. No.:** 6196
**Name:** Seaside Companions
**Height:** 8.5
**Status:** Open issue, retired
**Issue Year:** 1995
**Issue Price:** $230
**Last Year:** 1998
**Last Retail Price:** $230

**Ref. No.:** 6632
**Name:** A Birthday Kiss
**Height:** 8.5
**Status:** Open issue, active
**Issue Year:** 1999
**Issue Price:** $575
**2003 Retail Price:** $595

**Ref. No.:** 6824
**Name:** My Happy Friend
**Height:** 8.5
**Status:** Open issue, active
**Issue Year:** 2002
**Issue Price:** $325
**2003 Retail Price:** $325

**Ref. No.:** 6826
**Name:** You're So Cute!
**Height:** 8.5
**Status:** Open issue, active
**Issue Year:** 2002
**Issue Price:** $330
**2003 Retail Price:** $350

**Ref. No.:** 6169
**Name:** Seesaw Friends
**Height:** 8.75
**Status:** Open issue, retired
**Issue Year:** 1995
**Issue Price:** $795
**Last Year:** 2000
**Last Retail Price:** $795

**Ref. No.:** 6171
**Name:** Magical Moment
**Height:** 8.75
**Status:** Open issue, retired
**Issue Year:** 1995
**Issue Price:** $200
**Last Year:** 1999
**Last Retail Price:** $200

**Ref. No.:** 5737
**Name:** Little Prince
**Height:** 8.75
**Status:** Open issue, retired
**Issue Year:** 1991
**Issue Price:** $295
**Last Year:** 1993
**Last Retail Price:** $315
**Auction Price:** $350

**Ref. No.:** 6197
**Name:** Seaside Serenade
**Height:** 8.75
**Status:** Open issue, retired
**Issue Year:** 1995
**Issue Price:** $275
**Last Year:** 1998
**Last Retail Price:** $275

**Ref. No.:** 6907
**Name:** A Romp in the Garden
**Height:** 8.75
**Status:** Open issue, active
**Issue Year:** 2002
**Issue Price:** $625
**2003 Retail Price:** $625

*Children*

**Ref. No.:** 7618
**Name:** Garden Song
**Height:** 8.75
**Status:** Limited edition, sold out
**Issue Year:** 1992
**Issue Price:** $295
**Last Year:** 1992
**Last Retail Price:** $295
**High Auction Price:** $750
**Low Auction Price:** $400
**Comment:** Special event

**Ref. No.:** 1052
**Name:** Girl with Duck
**Height:** 9
**Status:** Open issue, retired
**Issue Year:** 1969
**Issue Price:** $30
**Last Year:** 1998
**Last Retail Price:** $205

**Ref. No.:** 1103
**Name:** Girl with Hens
**Height:** 9
**Status:** Open issue, retired
**Issue Year:** 1971
**Issue Price:** $50
**Last Year:** 1981
**Last Retail Price:** $160
**High Auction Price:** $425
**Low Auction Price:** $375

**Ref. No.:** 1278
**Name:** Devotion
**Height:** 9
**Status:** Open issue, retired
**Issue Year:** 1974
**Issue Price:** $140
**Last Year:** 1990
**Last Retail Price:** $350
**High Auction Price:** $475
**Low Auction Price:** $400

**Ref. No.:** 4812
**Name:** Little Girl with Goat
**Height:** 9
**Status:** Open issue, retired
**Issue Year:** 1972
**Issue Price:** $50
**Last Year:** 1988
**Last Retail Price:** $250
**High Auction Price:** $600
**Low Auction Price:** $400

**Ref. No.:** 4826
**Name:** Rabbit's Food
**Height:** 9
**Status:** Open issue, retired
**Issue Year:** 1972
**Issue Price:** $40
**Last Year:** 1993
**Last Retail Price:** $185
**High Auction Price:** $325
**Low Auction Price:** $225

**Ref. No.:** 4896
**Name:** Boy with Snails
**Height:** 9
**Status:** Open issue, retired
**Issue Year:** 1974
**Issue Price:** $50
**Last Year:** 1979
**Last Retail Price:** $65
**High Auction Price:** $600
**Low Auction Price:** $400

**Ref. No.:** 5166
**Name:** Sea Fever
**Height:** 9
**Status:** Open issue, retired
**Issue Year:** 1982
**Issue Price:** $130
**Last Year:** 1993
**Last Retail Price:** $255
**High Auction Price:** $375
**Low Auction Price:** $325

**Ref. No.:** 5303
**Name:** Playing with Ducks
**Height:** 9
**Status:** Open issue, retired
**Issue Year:** 1985
**Issue Price:** $310
**Last Year:** 1990
**Last Retail Price:** $425
**High Auction Price:** $900
**Low Auction Price:** $650

**Ref. No.:** 5908
**Name:** Just a Little More
**Height:** 9
**Status:** Open issue, retired
**Issue Year:** 1992
**Issue Price:** $370
**Last Year:** 1997
**Last Retail Price:** $380

**Ref. No.:** 6101
**Name:** Follow Us
**Height:** 9
**Status:** Open issue, retired
**Issue Year:** 1994
**Issue Price:** $198
**Last Year:** 1997
**Last Retail Price:** $215

**Ref. No.:** 6170
**Name:** Under My Spell
**Height:** 9
**Status:** Open issue, retired
**Issue Year:** 1995
**Issue Price:** $195
**Last Year:** 1999
**Last Retail Price:** $200

*Children*

**Ref. No.:** 6093
**Name:** Songbird
**Height:** 9
**Status:** Open issue, retired
**Issue Year:** 1994
**Issue Price:** $395
**Last Year:** 2001
**Last Retail Price:** $400

**Ref. No.:** 6400
**Name:** Daydreams
**Height:** 9
**Status:** Open issue, active
**Issue Year:** 1997
**Issue Price:** $325
**2003 Retail Price:** $325

**Ref. No.:** 6511
**Name:** A Birthday Surprise
**Height:** 9
**Status:** Open issue, retired
**Issue Year:** 1998
**Issue Price:** $230
**Last Year:** 2000
**Last Retail Price:** $230

**Ref. No.:** 5910
**Name:** Making a Wish
**Height:** 9.25
**Status:** Open issue, retired
**Issue Year:** 1992
**Issue Price:** $790
**Last Year:** 1998
**Last Retail Price:** $825

**Ref. No.:** 6577
**Name:** Afternoon Snack
**Height:** 9.25
**Status:** Open issue, retired
**Issue Year:** 2000
**Issue Price:** $335
**Last Year:** 2002
**Last Retail Price:** $340

**Ref. No.:** 1001
**Name:** Shepherdess with Goats
**Height:** 9.5
**Status:** Open issue, retired
**Issue Year:** 1969
**Issue Price:** $67.50
**Last Year:** 1987
**Last Retail Price:** $420
**High Auction Price:** $675
**Low Auction Price:** $400

**Ref. No.:** 1277
**Name:** Feeding Time
**Height:** 9.5
**Status:** Open issue, retired
**Issue Year:** 1974
**Issue Price:** $120
**Last Year:** 1993
**Last Retail Price:** $380
**Auction Price:** $350

**Ref. No.:** 1309
**Name:** Following Her Cats
**Height:** 9.5
**Status:** Open issue, active
**Issue Year:** 1974
**Issue Price:** $120
**2003 Retail Price:** $325

**Ref. No.:** 1460
**Name:** A Boy and His Pony
**Height:** 9.5
**Status:** Open issue, retired
**Issue Year:** 1985
**Issue Price:** $285
**Last Year:** 1988
**Last Retail Price:** $330
**High Auction Price:** $800
**Low Auction Price:** $400

**Ref. No.:** 4756
**Name:** Girl with Goat
**Height:** 9.5
**Status:** Open issue, retired
**Issue Year:** 1971
**Issue Price:** $50
**Last Year:** 1978
**Last Retail Price:** $95
**Auction Price:** $450

**Ref. No.:** 5034
**Name:** Goose Trying to Eat
**Height:** 9.5
**Status:** Open issue, retired
**Issue Year:** 1979
**Issue Price:** $135
**Last Year:** 1996
**Last Retail Price:** $315

**Ref. No.:** 5285
**Name:** Summer on the Farm
**Height:** 9.5
**Status:** Open issue, active
**Issue Year:** 1985
**Issue Price:** $235
**2003 Retail Price:** $475

*Children*

**Ref. No.:** 5416
**Name:** In the Garden
**Height:** 9.5
**Status:** Open issue, retired
**Issue Year:** 1987
**Issue Price:** $200
**Last Year:** 1996
**Last Retail Price:** $350

**Ref. No.:** 6026
**Name:** My Turn
**Height:** 9.5
**Status:** Open issue, retired
**Issue Year:** 1993
**Issue Price:** $515
**Last Year:** 1997
**Last Retail Price:** $515

**Ref. No.:** 6129
**Name:** Little Friends
**Height:** 9.5
**Status:** Open issue, retired
**Issue Year:** 1994
**Issue Price:** $225
**Last Year:** 1998
**Last Retail Price:** $235

**Ref. No.:** 5705
**Name:** The Swan and the
   Princess
**Height:** 9.5
**Status:** Open issue, retired
**Issue Year:** 1990
**Issue Price:** $350
**Last Year:** 1994
**Last Retail Price:** $410
**Auction Price:** $450

**Ref. No.:** 6807
**Name:** Peaceful
**Height:** 9.5
**Status:** Open issue, active
**Issue Year:** 2001
**Issue Price:** $180
**2003 Retail Price:** $195

**Ref. No.:** 1306
**Name:** On the Farm
**Height:** 9.75
**Status:** Open issue, retired
**Issue Year:** 1974
**Issue Price:** $130
**Last Year:** 1990
**Last Retail Price:** $240

**Ref. No.:** 1311
**Name:** Girl with Puppies
**Height:** 9.75
**Status:** Open issue, retired
**Issue Year:** 1974
**Issue Price:** $120
**Last Year:** 1996
**Last Retail Price:** $345

**Ref. No.:** 4755
**Name:** Boy with Dog
**Height:** 9.75
**Status:** Open issue, retired
**Issue Year:** 1971
**Issue Price:** $50
**Last Year:** 1978
**Last Retail Price:** $95
**Auction Price:** $600

**Ref. No.:** 4816
**Name:** Girl with Wheelbarrow
**Height:** 9.75
**Status:** Open issue, retired
**Issue Year:** 1972
**Issue Price:** $50
**Last Year:** 1981
**Last Retail Price:** $130
**High Auction Price:** $425
**Low Auction Price:** $375

*Children*

**Ref. No.:** 4817
**Name:** Little Shepherd with Goat
**Height:** 9.75
**Status:** Open issue, retired
**Issue Year:** 1972
**Issue Price:** $50
**Last Year:** 1981
**Last Retail Price:** $80
**Auction Price:** $475

**Ref. No.:** 4835
**Name:** Girl with Lamb
**Height:** 9.75
**Status:** Open issue, retired
**Issue Year:** 1972
**Issue Price:** $42
**Last Year:** 1991
**Last Retail Price:** $225
**Auction Price:** $350

**Ref. No.:** 5033
**Name:** Avoiding the Goose
**Height:** 9.75
**Status:** Open issue, retired
**Issue Year:** 1979
**Issue Price:** $160
**Last Year:** 1993
**Last Retail Price:** $350

**Ref. No.:** 5202
**Name:** Aracely with Her Pet Duck
**Height:** 9.75
**Status:** Open issue, retired
**Issue Year:** 1984
**Issue Price:** $125
**Last Year:** 1991
**Last Retail Price:** $220
**Auction Price:** $300

**Ref. No.:** 5443
**Name:** Bedtime
**Height:** 9.75
**Status:** Open issue, retired
**Issue Year:** 1987
**Issue Price:** $190
**Last Year:** 1996
**Last Retail Price:** $305

**Ref. No.:** 6512
**Name:** Purr-fect Friends
**Height:** 10
**Status:** Open issue, retired
**Issue Year:** 1998
**Issue Price:** $295
**Last Year:** 1998
**Last Retail Price:** $295
**Comment:** 1998 Special Events
    Figurine

**Ref. No.:** 6817
**Name:** Childhood Dreams
**Height:** 10
**Status:** Open issue, active
**Issue Year:** 2002
**Issue Price:** $775
**2003 Retail Price:** $775

**Ref. No.:** 6852
**Name:** Waiting for Your Letter
**Height:** 10
**Status:** Open issue, active
**Issue Year:** 2002
**Issue Price:** $425
**2003 Retail Price:** $425

**Ref. No.:** 6902
**Name:** My Loyal Friend
**Height:** 10
**Status:** Open issue, active
**Issue Year:** 2002
**Issue Price:** $295
**2003 Retail Price:** $295

**Ref. No.:** 4814
**Name:** Little Girl with Turkey
**Height:** 10.25
**Status:** Open issue, retired
**Issue Year:** 1972
**Issue Price:** $45
**Last Year:** 1981
**Last Retail Price:** $125

**Ref. No.:** 4920
**Name:** Country Lass with Dog
**Height:** 10.25
**Status:** Open issue, retired
**Issue Year:** 1974
**Issue Price:** $165
**Last Year:** 1995
**Last Retail Price:** $495

**Ref. No.:** 5078
**Name:** Teasing the Dog
**Height:** 10.25
**Status:** Open issue, retired
**Issue Year:** 1980
**Issue Price:** $300
**Last Year:** 1985
**Last Retail Price:** $300
**High Auction Price:** $800
**Low Auction Price:** $475

**Ref. No.:** 5201
**Name:** Josefa Feeding Her Duck
**Height:** 10.25
**Status:** Open issue, retired
**Issue Year:** 1984
**Issue Price:** $125
**Last Year:** 1991
**Last Retail Price:** $215
**Auction Price:** $250

**Ref. No.:** 6002
**Name:** Down You Go
**Height:** 10.25
**Status:** Open issue, retired
**Issue Year:** 1993
**Issue Price:** $815
**Last Year:** 1997
**Last Retail Price:** $815

**Ref. No.:** 4911
**Name:** Shepherd
**Height:** 10.25
**Status:** Open issue, retired
**Issue Year:** 1974
**Issue Price:** $175
**Last Year:** 1979
**Last Retail Price:** $220

*Children*

**Ref. No.:** 1276
**Name:** Christmas Seller
**Height:** 10.25
**Status:** Open issue, retired
**Issue Year:** 1974
**Issue Price:** $120
**Last Year:** 1981
**Last Retail Price:** $195
**High Auction Price:** $750
**Low Auction Price:** $675

**Ref. No.:** 4505
**Name:** Girl with Lamb
**Height:** 10.5
**Status:** Open issue, retired
**Issue Year:** 1969
**Issue Price:** $20
**Last Year:** 2001
**Last Retail Price:** $130

**Ref. No.:** 4506
**Name:** Boy with Goat
**Height:** 10.5
**Status:** Open issue, retired
**Issue Year:** 1969
**Issue Price:** $22.50
**Last Year:** 1985
**Last Retail Price:** $112.50
**High Auction Price:** $500
**Low Auction Price:** $250

**Ref. No.:** 4509
**Name:** Boy with Lambs
**Height:** 10.5
**Status:** Open issue, retired
**Issue Year:** 1969
**Issue Price:** $37.50
**Last Year:** 1981
**Last Retail Price:** $165
**High Auction Price:** $400
**Low Auction Price:** $250

**Ref. No.:** 4570
**Name:** Girl with Goat
**Height:** 10.5
**Status:** Open issue, retired
**Issue Year:** 1969
**Issue Price:** $70
**Last Year:** 1978
**Last Retail Price:** $130

**Ref. No.:** 4572
**Name:** Girl with Piglets
**Height:** 10.5
**Status:** Open issue, retired
**Issue Year:** 1969
**Issue Price:** $70
**Last Year:** 1985
**Last Retail Price:** $235
**Auction Price:** $550

**Ref. No.:** 4584
**Name:** Girl with Sheep
**Height:** 10.5
**Status:** Open issue, retired
**Issue Year:** 1969
**Issue Price:** $27
**Last Year:** 1993
**Last Retail Price:** $170
**Auction Price:** $200

**Ref. No.:** 4590
**Name:** Girl with Pitcher
**Height:** 10.5
**Status:** Open issue, retired
**Issue Year:** 1969
**Issue Price:** $47.50
**Last Year:** 1981
**Last Retail Price:** $90
**High Auction Price:** $425
**Low Auction Price:** $400

**Ref. No.:** 4866
**Name:** Girl with Goose and Dog
**Height:** 10.5
**Status:** Open issue, retired
**Issue Year:** 1974
**Issue Price:** $33
**Last Year:** 1993
**Last Retail Price:** $205
**High Auction Price:** $350
**Low Auction Price:** $250

**Ref. No.:** 4926
**Name:** Milk for the Lamb
**Height:** 10.5
**Status:** Open issue, retired
**Issue Year:** 1974
**Issue Price:** $185
**Last Year:** 1980
**Last Retail Price:** $280

**Ref. No.:** 5347
**Name:** Bedtime
**Height:** 10.5
**Status:** Open issue, retired
**Issue Year:** 1986
**Issue Price:** $300
**Last Year:** 1998
**Last Retail Price:** $545

**Ref. No.:** 6903
**Name:** A Warm Welcome
**Height:** 10.5
**Status:** Open issue, active
**Issue Year:** 2002
**Issue Price:** $350
**2003 Retail Price:** $350

*Children*

**Ref. No.:** 1035
**Name:** Girl with Geese
**Height:** 11
**Status:** Open issue, retired
**Issue Year:** 1969
**Issue Price:** $37.50
**Last Year:** 1995
**Last Retail Price:** $180

**Ref. No.:** 4638
**Name:** Honey Peddler
**Height:** 11
**Status:** Open issue, retired
**Issue Year:** 1969
**Issue Price:** $60
**Last Year:** 1978
**Last Retail Price:** $150
**High Auction Price:** $575
**Low Auction Price:** $500

**Ref. No.:** 4813
**Name:** Girl with Calf
**Height:** 11
**Status:** Open issue, retired
**Issue Year:** 1972
**Issue Price:** $50
**Last Year:** 1981
**Last Retail Price:** $135
**Auction Price:** $650

**Ref. No.:** 5037
**Name:** Sleigh Ride
**Height:** 11
**Status:** Open issue, retired
**Issue Year:** 1980
**Issue Price:** $585
**Last Year:** 1996
**Last Retail Price:** $1300

**Ref. No.:** 5346
**Name:** Nature Girl
**Height:** 11
**Status:** Open issue, retired
**Issue Year:** 1986
**Issue Price:** $450
**Last Year:** 1988
**Last Retail Price:** $490
**High Auction Price:** $1000
**Low Auction Price:** $550

**Ref. No.:** 6430
**Name:** Pony Ride
**Height:** 11
**Status:** Open issue, retired
**Issue Year:** 1997
**Issue Price:** $825
**Last Year:** 2000
**Last Retail Price:** $825

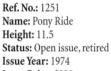

**Ref. No.:** 1251
**Name:** Pony Ride
**Height:** 11.5
**Status:** Open issue, retired
**Issue Year:** 1974
**Issue Price:** $220
**Last Year:** 1979
**Last Retail Price:** $400
**Auction Price:** $700

**Ref. No.:** 1256
**Name:** Caught Napping
**Height:** 11.5
**Status:** Open issue, retired
**Issue Year:** 1974
**Last Year:** 1981

**Ref. No.:** 4601
**Name:** Girl with Swan
**Height:** 11.5
**Status:** Open issue, retired
**Issue Year:** 1969
**Issue Price:** $65
**Last Year:** 1972
**Last Retail Price:** $65

**Ref. No.:** 4758
**Name:** Girl and Sparrow
**Height:** 11.5
**Status:** Open issue, retired
**Issue Year:** 1971
**Issue Price:** $35
**Last Year:** 1979
**Last Retail Price:** $90
**Auction Price:** $600

**Ref. No.:** 4891
**Name:** Looking for Refuge
**Height:** 11.5
**Status:** Open issue, retired
**Issue Year:** 1974
**Issue Price:** $400
**Last Year:** 1979
**Last Retail Price:** $725

**Ref. No.:** 5798
**Name:** Milkmaid
**Height:** 11.5
**Status:** Open issue, retired
**Issue Year:** 1991
**Issue Price:** $450
**Last Year:** 1993
**Last Retail Price:** $495
**High Auction Price:** $550
**Low Auction Price:** $400

*Children*

**Ref. No.:** 4513
**Name:** Girl with Calf
**Height:** 12.25
**Status:** Open issue, retired
**Issue Year:** 1969
**Last Year:** 1978
**Issue Price:** $72.50
**Last Retail Price:** $85
**High Auction Price:** $600
**Low Auction Price:** $525

**Ref. No.:** 4815
**Name:** Girl with Goose
**Height:** 12.25
**Status:** Open issue, retired
**Issue Year:** 1972
**Issue Price:** $65
**Last Year:** 1991
**Last Retail Price:** $295
**High Auction Price:** $400
**Low Auction Price:** $275

**Ref. No.:** 4806
**Name:** Girl with Dog
**Height:** 12.5
**Status:** Open issue, retired
**Issue Year:** 1972
**Issue Price:** $80
**Last Year:** 1981
**Last Retail Price:** $342.5
**High Auction Price:** $600
**Low Auction Price:** $550

**Ref. No.:** 5049
**Name:** At the Pond
**Height:** 12.75
**Status:** Open issue, retired
**Issue Year:** 1980
**Issue Price:** $525
**Last Year:** 1981
**Last Retail Price:** $570

**Ref. No.:** 1091
**Name:** Girl and Gazelle
**Height:** 14.5
**Status:** Open issue, retired
**Issue Year:** 1971
**Issue Price:** $225
**Last Year:** 1975
**Last Retail Price:** $475

**Ref. No.:** 1038
**Name:** Girl with Turkeys
**Height:** 15
**Status:** Very rare
**Issue Year:** 1969
**Issue Price:** $95
**Last Year:** 1978
**Last Retail Price:** Unknown
**High Auction Price:** $550
**Low Auction Price:** $375

**Ref. No.:** 4780
**Name:** Boy with Goat
**Height:** 15
**Status:** Open issue, retired
**Issue Year:** 1971
**Issue Price:** $60
**Last Year:** 1978
**Last Retail Price:** $90
**Auction Price:** $600

**Ref. No.:** 5229
**Name:** Story Time
**Height:** 15
**Status:** Open issue, retired
**Issue Year:** 1984
**Issue Price:** $245
**Last Year:** 1990
**Last Retail Price:** $360
**High Auction Price:** $1450
**Low Auction Price:** $850

**Ref. No.** 5539
**Name:** Puppy Dog Tails
**Height:** 15
**Status:** Open issue, active
**Issue Year:** 1989
**Issue Price:** $1200
**2003 Retail Price:** $1750

## Children with Flowers

**Ref. No.:** 1055
**Name:** Girl with Pheasant
**Height:** 15.75
**Status:** Very rare
**Issue Year:** 1969
**Issue Price:** $105
**Last Year:** 1978
**Last Retail Price:** Unknown

**Ref. No.:** 1505
**Name:** Nature Boy
**Height:** 2.5
**Status:** Open issue, retired
**Issue Year:** 1986
**Issue Price:** $100
**Last Year:** 1991
**Last Retail Price:** $180
**Auction Price:** $375

**Ref. No.:** 1506
**Name:** A New Friend
**Height:** 3.25
**Status:** Open issue, retired
**Issue Year:** 1986
**Issue Price:** $110
**Last Year:** 1991
**Last Retail Price:** $180
**Auction Price:** $325

*Children*

**Ref. No.:** 75.05
**Name:** Girl in the Garden
**Height:** 4.25
**Status:** Very rare
**Issue Year:** 1956
**Issue Price:** Unknown
**Last Year:** Unknown
**Last Retail Price:** Unknown

**Ref. No.:** 1508
**Name:** In The Meadow
**Height:** 4.25
**Status:** Open issue, retired
**Issue Year:** 1986
**Issue Price:** $100
**Last Year:** 1991
**Last Retail Price:** $180
**Auction Price:** $300

**Ref. No.:** 5041
**Name:** Tulips In My Basket
**Height:** 4.25
**Status:** Open issue, retired
**Issue Year:** 1980
**Issue Price:** $160
**Last Year:** 1981
**Last Retail Price:** $175

**Ref. No.:** 1507
**Name:** Boy and His Bunny
**Height:** 4.75
**Status:** Open issue, retired
**Issue Year:** 1986
**Issue Price:** $90
**Last Year:** 1991
**Last Retail Price:** $160
**Auction Price:** $250

**Ref. No.:** 1509
**Name:** Spring Flowers
**Height:** 4.75
**Status:** Open issue, retired
**Issue Year:** 1986
**Issue Price:** $100
**Last Year:** 1991
**Last Retail Price:** $185
**Auction Price:** $275

**Ref. No.:** 5384
**Name:** Petite Pair
**Height:** 4.75
**Status:** Open issue, retired
**Issue Year:** 1986
**Issue Price:** $225
**Last Year:** 1990
**Last Retail Price:** $300
**High Auction Price:** $400
**Low Auction Price:** $375

**Ref. No.:** 5591
**Name:** Garden Treasures
**Height:** 4.75
**Status:** Open issue, retired
**Issue Year:** 1989
**Issue Price:** $185
**Last Year:** 1993
**Last Retail Price:** $230

**Ref. No.:** 5383
**Name:** Petite Maiden
**Height:** 4.75
**Status:** Open issue, retired
**Issue Year:** 1986
**Issue Price:** $110
**Last Year:** 1990
**Last Retail Price:** $150
**High Auction Price:** $350
**Low Auction Price:** $300

**Ref. No.:** 4596
**Name:** Girl with Flower
**Height:** 6
**Status:** Open issue, retired
**Issue Year:** 1969
**Issue Price:** $25
**Last Year:** 1980
**Last Retail Price:** $72.50
**High Auction Price:** $275
**Low Auction Price:** $175

**Ref. No.:** 1287
**Name:** Picking Flowers
**Height:** 6.25
**Status:** Open issue, retired
**Issue Year:** 1974
**Issue Price:** $170
**Last Year:** 1998
**Last Retail Price:** $440

**Ref. No.:** 5071
**Name:** Nostalgia
**Height:** 6.25
**Status:** Open issue, retired
**Issue Year:** 1980
**Issue Price:** $240
**Last Year:** 1993
**Last Retail Price:** $310
**Auction Price:** $350

**Ref. No.:** 5221
**Name:** Sweet Scent
**Height:** 6.25
**Status:** Open issue, active
**Issue Year:** 1984
**Issue Price:** $80
**2003 Retail Price:** $190

*Children*

**Ref. No.:** 5554
**Name:** Pretty and Prim
**Height:** 6.25
**Status:** Open issue, retired
**Issue Year:** 1989
**Issue Price:** $215
**Last Year:** 1998
**Last Retail Price:** $270

**Ref. No.:** 4907
**Name:** Admiration
**Height:** 6.5
**Status:** Open issue, retired
**Issue Year:** 1974
**Issue Price:** $165
**Last Year:** 1985
**Last Retail Price:** $345
**High Auction Price:** $750
**Low Auction Price:** $550

**Ref. No.:** 5173
**Name:** Pondering
**Height:** 6.5
**Status:** Open issue, retired
**Issue Year:** 1982
**Issue Price:** $300
**Last Year:** 1993
**Last Retail Price:** $495
**High Auction Price:** $750
**Low Auction Price:** $475

**Ref. No.:** 5223
**Name:** Spring is Here
**Height:** 6.5
**Status:** Open issue, active
**Issue Year:** 1984
**Issue Price:** $80
**2003 Retail Price:** $190

**Ref. No.:** 5467
**Name:** May Flowers
**Height:** 6.5
**Status:** Open issue, active
**Issue Year:** 1988
**Issue Price:** $160
**2003 Retail Price:** $250

**Ref. No.:** 5548
**Name:** Pretty Posies
**Height:** 6.5
**Status:** Open issue, retired
**Issue Year:** 1989
**Issue Price:** $425
**Last Year:** 1994
**Last Retail Price:** $530

**Ref. No.:** 5699
**Name:** Sitting Pretty
**Height:** 6.5
**Status:** Open issue, retired
**Issue Year:** 1990
**Issue Price:** $300
**Last Year:** 1998
**Last Retail Price:** $340

**Ref. No.:** 5895
**Name:** Bouquet of Blossoms
**Height:** 6.5
**Status:** Open issue, retired
**Issue Year:** 1992
**Issue Price:** $295
**Last Year:** 1997
**Last Retail Price:** $295

**Ref. No.:** 6701
**Name:** Petals Of Hope
**Height:** 6.75
**Status:** Open issue, retired
**Issue Year:** 2000
**Issue Price:** $575
**Last Year:** 2002
**Last Retail Price:** $575
**Comment:** Introduced by select dealers in 1999

**Ref. No.:** 226.09
**Name:** Girl with Flower Basket
**Height:** 7
**Status:** Very rare
**Issue Year:** 1958
**Issue Price:** Unknown
**Last Year:** Unknown
**Last Retail Price:** Unknown

**Ref. No.:** 5222
**Name:** Pretty Pickings
**Height:** 7
**Status:** Open edition, active
**Issue Year:** 1984
**Issue Price:** $80
**2003 Retail Price:** $190

**Ref. No.:** 5073
**Name:** Country Flowers
**Height:** 7.5
**Status:** Open issue, retired
**Issue Year:** 1980
**Issue Price:** $315
**Last Year:** 1985
**Last Retail Price:** $350
**Auction Price:** $800

*Children*

**Ref. No.:** 5537
**Name:** Flowers For Sale
**Height:** 7.5
**Status:** Open issue, retired
**Issue Year:** 1989
**Issue Price:** $1200
**Last Year:** 2000
**Last Retail Price:** $1550

**Ref. No.:** 5543
**Name:** Hello, Flowers
**Height:** 7.5
**Status:** Open issue, retired
**Issue Year:** 1989
**Issue Price:** $385
**Last Year:** 1993
**Last Retail Price:** $485

**Ref. No.:** 5605
**Name:** Floral Treasures
**Height:** 7.5
**Status:** Open edition, active
**Issue Year:** 1989
**Issue Price:** $195
**2003 Retail Price:** $250

**Ref. No.:** 5795
**Name:** Floral Getaway
**Height:** 7.5
**Status:** Open issue, retired
**Issue Year:** 1991
**Issue Price:** $625
**Last Year:** 1993
**Last Retail Price:** $685
**High Auction Price:** $750
**Low Auction Price:** $650

**Ref. No.:** 6822
**Name:** Sweet Fragrance
**Height:** 7.5
**Status:** Open issue, active
**Issue Year:** 2002
**Issue Price:** $195
**2003 Retail Price:** $195

**Ref. No.:** 6876
**Name:** Springtime Fun
**Height:** 7.5
**Status:** Open issue, active
**Issue Year:** 2002
**Issue Price:** $275
**2003 Retail Price:** $275

**Ref. No.:** 5862
**Name:** Fragrant Bouquet
**Height:** 8
**Status:** Open edition, active
**Issue Year:** 1992
**Issue Price:** $350
**2003 Retail Price:** $375

**Ref. No.:** 6869
**Name:** Blossom Time
**Height:** 8
**Status:** Open issue, active
**Issue Year:** 2002
**Issue Price:** $250
**2003 Retail Price:** $250

**Ref. No.:** 1172
**Name:** Girl Gathering Flowers
**Height:** 8.25
**Status:** Open issue, retired
**Issue Year:** 1971
**Issue Price:** $32.50
**Last Year:** 1993
**Last Retail Price:** $295
**High Auction Price:** $350
**Low Auction Price:** $275

**Ref. No.:** 1418
**Name:** Flower Harmony
**Height:** 8.25
**Status:** Open issue, retired
**Issue Year:** 1982
**Issue Price:** $130
**Last Year:** 1995
**Last Retail Price:** $270

**Ref. No.:** 4720
**Name:** Girl with Tulips
**Height:** 8.25
**Status:** Open issue, retired
**Issue Year:** 1970
**Issue Price:** $65
**Last Year:** 1978
**Last Retail Price:** $165
**High Auction Price:** $475
**Low Auction Price:** $400

**Ref. No.:** 4836
**Name:** Rosalinda
**Height:** 8.25
**Status:** Open issue, retired
**Issue Year:** 1973
**Issue Price:** $66
**Last Year:** 1983
**Last Retail Price:** $170
**High Auction Price:** $475
**Low Auction Price:** $200

*Children*

**Ref. No.:** 1284
**Name:** Flowers on the Lap
**Height:** 8.5
**Status:** Open edition, active
**Issue Year:** 1974
**Issue Price:** $200
**2003 Retail Price:** $550

**Ref. No.:** 1285
**Name:** My Goodness
**Height:** 8.5
**Status:** Open issue, retired
**Issue Year:** 1974
**Issue Price:** $190
**Last Year:** 1995
**Last Retail Price:** $415

**Ref. No.:** 1376
**Name:** Watering Flowers
**Height:** 8.5
**Status:** Open issue, retired
**Issue Year:** 1978
**Issue Price:** $400
**Last Year:** 1990
**Last Retail Price:** $675
**High Auction Price:** $1150
**Low Auction Price:** $700

**Ref. No.:** 5028
**Name:** Flowers in Pot
**Height:** 8.5
**Status:** Open issue, retired
**Issue Year:** 1980
**Issue Price:** $325
**Last Year:** 1985
**Last Retail Price:** $460
**High Auction Price:** $650
**Low Auction Price:** $550

**Ref. No.:** 5604
**Name:** Spring Token
**Height:** 8.5
**Status:** Open edition, active
**Issue Year:** 1989
**Issue Price:** $175
**2003 Retail Price:** $250

**Ref. No.:** 5790
**Name:** Carefree
**Height:** 8.75
**Status:** Open edition, active
**Issue Year:** 1991
**Issue Price:** $300
**2003 Retail Price:** $325

**Ref. No.:** 6250
**Name:** Springtime Harvest
**Height:** 8.75
**Status:** Open issue, retired
**Issue Year:** 1996
**Issue Price:** $760
**Last Year:** 2002
**Last Retail Price:** $760

**Ref. No.:** 1283
**Name:** Wheelbarrow with
  Flowers
**Height:** 9
**Status:** Open issue, active
**Issue Year:** 1974
**Issue Price:** $250
**2003 Retail Price:** $785

**Ref. No.:** 1286
**Name:** Flower Harvest
**Height:** 9
**Status:** Open issue, retired
**Issue Year:** 1974
**Issue Price:** $200
**Auction Price:** $525
**Last Year:** 1998
**Last Retail Price:** $495

Children

**Ref. No.:** 4650
**Name:** Girl with Calla Lilies
**Height:** 9
**Status:** Open edition, retired
**Issue Year:** 1969
**Issue Price:** $16.50
**Last Year:** 1998
**Last Retail Price:** $155

**Ref. No.:** 4972
**Name:** Girl with Lilies, Sitting
**Height:** 9
**Status:** Open edition, retired
**Issue Year:** 1977
**Issue Price:** $65
**Last Year:** 1997
**Last Retail Price:** $190

**Ref. No.:** 6414
**Name:** Hello Friend!
**Height:** 9
**Status:** Open issue, retired
**Issue Year:** 1997
**Issue Price:** $235
**Last Year:** 2000
**Last Retail Price:** $235

**Ref. No.:** 6439
**Name:** Caught In The Act
**Height:** 9
**Status:** Open issue, retired
**Issue Year:** 1998
**Issue Price:** $260
**Last Year:** 2000
**Last Retail Price:** $260
**Comment:** 1997 Vanguard Dealer
Exclusive

**Ref. No.:** 6471
**Name:** My Pretty Flowers
**Height:** 9
**Status:** Open issue, active
**Issue Year:** 1997
**Issue Price:** $160
**2003 Retail Price:** $175

**Ref. No.:** 6472
**Name:** Gardening Buddies
**Height:** 9
**Status:** Open issue, active
**Issue Year:** 1997
**Issue Price:** $195
**2003 Retail Price:** $200

**Ref. No.:** 6521
**Name:** Love's Tender Tokens
**Height:** 9
**Status:** Open issue, active
**Issue Year:** 1998
**Issue Price:** $895
**2003 Retail Price:** $950
**Comment:** Introduced by select
dealers in 1997

**Ref. No.:** 6580
**Name:** Garden Dance
**Height:** 9
**Status:** Open issue, retired
**Issue Year:** 1999
**Issue Price:** $250
**Last Year:** 1999
**Last Retail Price:** $250

**Ref. No.:** 6808
**Name:** Enchanting
**Height:** 9.25
**Status:** Open issue, active
**Issue Year:** 2001
**Issue Price:** $165
**2003 Retail Price:** $175

**Ref. No.:** 1354
**Name:** Girl Watering
**Height:** 9.5
**Status:** Open issue, retired
**Issue Year:** 1978
**Issue Price:** $242.50
**Last Year:** 1988
**Last Retail Price:** $575
**Auction Price:** $700

**Ref. No.:** 5894
**Name:** Precious Petals
**Height:** 9.5
**Status:** Open edition, retired
**Issue Year:** 1991
**Issue Price:** $395
**Last Year:** 1996
**Last Issue Price:** $415

**Ref. No.:** 6658
**Name:** Morning Song
**Height:** 9.5
**Status:** Open issue, active
**Issue Year:** 2000
**Issue Price:** $885
**2003 Retail Price:** $895

**Ref. No.:** 6756
**Name:** Bountiful Blossoms
**Height:** 9.5
**Status:** Open issue, active
**Issue Year:** 2001
**Issue Price:** $290
**2003 Retail Price:** $295

**Ref. No.:** 6757
**Name:** First Flowers
**Height:** 9.5
**Status:** Open issue, active
**Issue Year:** 2001
**Issue Price:** $240
**2003 Retail Price:** $250

**Ref. No.:** 6850
**Name:** The Prettiest of All
**Height:** 9.5
**Status:** Open issue, active
**Issue Year:** 2002
**Issue Price:** $745
**2003 Retail Price:** $750

*Children*

**Ref. No.:** 4726
**Name:** Little Gardener
**Height:** 9.75
**Status:** Open issue, retired
**Issue Year:** 1970
**Issue Price:** $40
**Last Year:** 1978
**Last Retail Price:** $110
**High Auction Price:** $450
**Low Auction Price:** $400

**Ref. No.:** 5027
**Name:** Flowers in the Basket
**Height:** 9.75
**Status:** Open edition, active
**Issue Year:** 1979
**Issue Price:** $230
**2003 Retail Price:** $475

**Ref. No.:** 6167
**Name:** Delicate Bundle
**Height:** 10
**Status:** Open edition, retired
**Issue Year:** 1995
**Issue Price:** $275
**Last Year:** 1999
**Last Retail Price:** $275

**Ref. No.:** 6551
**Name:** Pretty Posies
**Height:** 10
**Status:** Open issue, retired
**Issue Year:** 1998
**Issue Price:** $180
**Last Year:** 2001
**Last Retail Price:** $180

**Ref. No.:** 1419
**Name:** A Barrel of Blossoms
**Height:** 10.25
**Status:** Open edition, active
**Issue Year:** 1982
**Issue Price:** $390
**2003 Retail Price:** $675

**Ref. No.:** 5029
**Name:** The Flower Peddler
**Height:** 10.25
**Status:** Open issue, retired
**Issue Year:** 1979
**Issue Price:** $675
**Last Year:** 1985
**Last Retail Price:** $880
**High Auction Price:** $1500
**Low Auction Price:** $950

**Ref. No.:** 5065
**Name:** Ingrid
**Height:** 10.25
**Status:** Open issue, retired
**Issue Year:** 1980
**Issue Price:** $370
**Last Year:** 1990
**Last Retail Price:** $400
**High Auction Price:** $950
**Low Auction Price:** $550

**Ref. No.:** 5298
**Name:** Girl Sitting Under Trellis
**Height:** 10.25
**Status:** Open issue, retired
**Issue Year:** 1985
**Issue Price:** $340
**Last Year:** 1988
**Last Retail Price:** $390
**High Auction Price:** $900
**Low Auction Price:** $600

**Ref. No.:** 5893
**Name:** Friendship In Bloom
**Height:** 10.25
**Status:** Open issue, retired
**Issue Year:** 1992
**Issue Price:** $650
**Last Year:** 1995
**Last Retail Price:** $685

**Ref. No.:** 4757
**Name:** Doncel with Roses
**Height:** 10.5
**Status:** Open issue, retired
**Issue Year:** 1971
**Issue Price:** $35
**Last Year:** 1979
**Last Retail Price:** $90
**High Auction Price:** $600
**Low Auction Price:** $400

**Ref. No.:** 5031
**Name:** Girl with Flowers in Tow
**Height:** 10.5
**Status:** Open issue, retired
**Issue Year:** 1979
**Issue Price:** $785
**Last Year:** 1985
**Last Retail Price:** $1020
**Auction Price:** $1800

**Ref. No.:** 5088
**Name:** Roses For My Mom
**Height:** 10.5
**Status:** Open issue, retired
**Issue Year:** 1980
**Issue Price:** $645
**Last Year:** 1988
**Last Retail Price:** $740

*Children*

**Ref. No.:** 5958
**Name:** Country Ride
**Height:** 10.5
**Status:** Open issue, active
**Issue Year:** 1993
**Issue Price:** $2850
**2003 Retail Price:** $2875

**Ref. No.:** 6647
**Name:** Wild Flowers
**Height:** 10.5
**Status:** Open issue, active
**Issue Year:** 1999
**Issue Price:** $525
**2003 Retail Price:** $525

**Ref. No.:** 1313
**Name:** Exquisite Scent
**Height:** 11
**Status:** Open issue, retired
**Issue Year:** 1974
**Issue Price:** $200
**Last Year:** 1990
**Last Retail Price:** $525
**High Auction Price:** $750
**Low Auction Price:** $550

**Ref. No.:** 1454
**Name:** Flowers of the Season
**Height:** 11
**Status:** Open issue, active
**Issue Year:** 1983
**Issue Price:** $1460
**2003 Retail Price:** $2575

**Ref. No.:** 5030
**Name:** Wild Flower
**Height:** 11
**Status:** Open issue, retired
**Issue Year:** 1979
**Issue Price:** $360
**Last Year:** 1994
**Last Retail Price:** $695

**Ref. No.:** 5284
**Name:** Glorious Spring
**Height:** 11
**Status:** Open issue, active
**Issue Year:** 1985
**Issue Price:** $355
**2003 Retail Price:** $750

**Ref. No.:** 6646
**Name:** Floral Path
**Height:** 11.25
**Status:** Open issue, active
**Issue Year:** 1999
**Issue Price:** $495
**2003 Retail Price:** $495

**Ref. No.:** 1339
**Name:** Girl with Watering Can
**Height:** 11.5
**Status:** Open issue, retired
**Issue Year:** 1977
**Issue Price:** $162.50
**Last Year:** 1988
**Last Retail Price:** $350
**High Auction Price:** $550
**Low Auction Price:** $400

**Ref. No.:** 3508
**Name:** Girl with Geranium
**Height:** 12.5
**Status:** Open issue, retired
**Issue Year:** 1978
**Issue Price:** $230
**Last Year:** 1988
**Last Retail Price:** $250
**Auction Price:** $375

### Children Playing

**Ref. No.:** 5966
**Name:** Flowers Forever
**Height:** 13.5
**Status:** Open issue, active
**Issue Year:** 1993
**Issue Price:** $4150
**2003 Retail Price:** $4250

**Ref. No.:** 5664
**Name:** Giddy Up
**Height:** 4.25
**Status:** Open issue, retired
**Issue Year:** 1990
**Issue Price:** $190
**Last Year:** 1994
**Last Retail Price:** $230

**Ref. No.:** 5827
**Name:** I've Got It!
**Height:** 5
**Status:** Open issue, retired
**Issue Year:** 1991
**Issue Price:** $170
**Last Year:** 1995
**Last Retail Price:** $180

*Children*

**Ref. No.:** 6795
**Name:** My Favourite Place
**Height:** 5.25
**Status:** Open issue, active
**Issue Year:** 2001
**Issue Price:** $265
**2003 Retail Price:** $295

**Ref. No.:** 5665
**Name:** Hang On!
**Height:** 6
**Status:** Open issue, retired
**Issue Year:** 1990
**Issue Price:** $225
**Last Year:** 1995
**Last Retail Price:** $285

**Ref. No.:** 6640
**Name:** Little Explorer
**Height:** 6
**Status:** Open issue, retired
**Issue Year:** 1999
**Issue Price:** $430
**Last Year:** 2000
**Last Retail Price:** $430

**Ref. No.:** 5698
**Name:** Don't Look Down
**Height:** 6.25
**Status:** Open issue, active
**Issue Year:** 1990
**Issue Price:** $330
**2003 Retail Price:** $425

**Ref. No.:** 243.1
**Name:** Jumping the Hoop
**Height:** 6.5
**Status:** Very rare
**Issue Year:** 1958
**Issue Price:** Unknown
**Last Year:** Unknown
**Last Retail Price:** Unknown

**Ref. No.:** 5290
**Name:** Little Leaguer, Catcher
**Height:** 6.5
**Status:** Open issue, retired
**Issue Year:** 1985
**Issue Price:** $150
**Last Year:** 1990
**Last Retail Price:** $215
**High Auction Price:** $600
**Low Auction Price:** $300

**Ref. No.:** 5363
**Name:** Still Life
**Height:** 6.5
**Status:** Open issue, retired
**Issue Year:** 1986
**Issue Price:** $180
**Last Year:** 1997
**Last Retail Price:** $425

**Ref. No.:** 6872
**Name:** Let's Take a Bath!
**Height:** 6.5
**Status:** Open issue, active
**Issue Year:** 2002
**Issue Price:** $215
**2003 Retail Price:** $225

**Ref. No.:** 6185
**Name:** Team Player
**Height:** 6.75
**Status:** Open issue, retired
**Issue Year:** 1994
**Issue Price:** $215
**Last Year:** 1999
**Last Retail Price:** $220

**Ref. No.:** 4970
**Name:** Skier Puppet
**Height:** 7
**Status:** Open issue, retired
**Issue Year:** 1977
**Issue Price:** $85
**Last Year:** 1983
**Last Retail Price:** $112.50
**High Auction Price:** $650
**Low Auction Price:** $500

**Ref. No.:** 6090
**Name:** Baseball Player
**Height:** 7
**Status:** Open issue, retired
**Issue Year:** 1994
**Issue Price:** $295
**Last Year:** 1997
**Last Retail Price:** $310

**Ref. No.:** 6137
**Name:** Baseball Star
**Height:** 7
**Status:** Open issue, retired
**Issue Year:** 1994
**Issue Price:** $295
**Last Year:** 1997
**Last Retail Price:** $295

*Children*

**Ref. No.:** 5291
**Name:** Little Leaguer,
on the Bench
**Height:** 7.5
**Status:** Open issue, retired
**Issue Year:** 1985
**Issue Price:** $150
**Last Year:** 1990
**Last Retail Price:** $215
**High Auction Price:** $625
**Low Auction Price:** $375

**Ref. No.:** 5675
**Name:** Tee Time
**Height:** 7.5
**Status:** Open issue, retired
**Issue Year:** 1990
**Issue Price:** $270
**Last Year:** 1993
**Last Retail Price:** $315

**Ref. No.:** 6107
**Name:** Football Player
**Height:** 7.5
**Status:** Open issue, retired
**Issue Year:** 1994
**Issue Price:** $295
**Last Year:** 1997
**Last Retail Price:** $310

**Ref. No.:** 6108
**Name:** Hockey Player
**Height:** 7.5
**Status:** Open issue, retired
**Issue Year:** 1994
**Issue Price:** $295
**Last Year:** 1998
**Last Retail Price:** $310

**Ref. No.:** 4967
**Name:** Soccer Player Puppet
**Height:** 7.75
**Status:** Open issue, retired
**Issue Year:** 1977
**Issue Price:** $65
**Last Year:** 1985
**Last Retail Price:** $85
**Auction Price:** $525

**Ref. No.:** 5136
**Name:** Billy, the Skier
**Height:** 8.25
**Status:** Open issue, retired
**Issue Year:** 1982
**Issue Price:** $140
**Last Year:** 1983
**Last Retail Price:** $140
**High Auction Price:** $1000
**Low Auction Price:** $850

**Ref. No.:** 5872
**Name:** Olympic Pride
**Height:** 8.25
**Status:** Open issue, retired
**Issue Year:** 1992
**Issue Price:** Unknown
**Last Year:** 1994
**Last Retail Price:** $145

**Ref. No.:** 6563
**Name:** A Day's Work
**Height:** 8
**Status:** Open issue, retired
**Issue Year:** 1999
**Issue Price:** $615
**Last Year:** 2002
**Last Retail Price:** $625

**Ref. No.:** 6564
**Name:** Want A Lift?
**Height:** 8
**Status:** Open issue, retired
**Issue Year:** 1999
**Issue Price:** $515
**Last Year:** 2002
**Last Retail Price:** $525

**Ref. No.:** 6119
**Name:** Aramis, Musketeer
**Height:** 8.25
**Status:** Open issue, retired
**Issue Year:** 1994
**Issue Price:** $275
**Last Year:** 1996
**Last Retail Price:** $295

**Ref. No.:** 7605
**Name:** Starting Forward
**Height:** 8.25
**Status:** Open issue, active
**Issue Year:** 1989
**Issue Price:** $125
**2003 Retail Price:** $195
**Comment:** A Rotary Club
special

**Ref. No.:** 4809
**Name:** Going Fishing
**Height:** 8.5
**Status:** Open issue, retired
**Issue Year:** 1972
**Issue Price:** $30
**Last Year:** 2001
**Last Retail Price:** $160

*Children*

**Ref. No.:** 5135
**Name:** Billy Soccer Player
**Height:** 8.5
**Status:** Open issue, retired
**Issue Year:** 1982
**Issue Price:** $140
**Last Year:** 1983
**Last Retail Price:** $140
**High Auction Price:** $700
**Low Auction Price:** $500

**Ref. No.:** 6110
**Name:** Medieval Maiden
**Height:** 8.5
**Status:** Open issue, retired
**Issue Year:** 1994
**Issue Price:** $150
**Last Year:** 1996
**Last Retail Price:** $165

**Ref. No.:** 6111
**Name:** Medieval Soldier
**Height:** 8.5
**Status:** Open issue, retired
**Issue Year:** 1994
**Issue Price:** $225
**Last Year:** 1996
**Last Retail Price:** $245

**Ref. No.:** 6112
**Name:** Medieval Lord
**Height:** 8.5
**Status:** Open issue, retired
**Issue Year:** 1994
**Issue Price:** $235
**Last Year:** 1996
**Last Retail Price:** $300

**Ref. No.:** 6115
**Name:** Medieval Prince
**Height:** 8.5
**Status:** Open issue, retired
**Issue Year:** 1994
**Issue Price:** $295
**Last Year:** 1996
**Last Retail Price:** $315

**Ref. No.:** 6118
**Name:** Musketeer Portos
**Height:** 8.5
**Status:** Open issue, retired
**Issue Year:** 1994
**Issue Price:** $220
**Last Year:** 1996
**Last Retail Price:** $230

**Ref. No.:** 6198
**Name:** Soccer Practice
**Height:** 8.5
**Status:** Open issue, active
**Issue Year:** 1995
**Issue Price:** $195
**2003 Retail Price:** $195

**Ref. No.:** 7515
**Name:** Special Pride
**Height:** 8.5
**Status:** Open edition, retired
**Issue Year:** 1992
**Issue Price:** $165
**Last Year:** 1996
**Last Retail Price:** $175
**Comment:** Special Olympics

**Ref. No.:** 7522
**Name:** Courage
**Height:** 8.5
**Status:** Open issue, retired
**Issue Year:** 1993
**Issue Price:** $195
**Last Year:** 1996
**Last Retail Price:** $235
**Comment:** Special Olympics

**Ref. No.:** 6091
**Name:** Basketball Player
**Height:** 8.75
**Status:** Open issue, retired
**Issue Year:** 1994
**Issue Price:** $295
**Last Year:** 1997
**Last Retail Price:** $325

**Ref. No.:** 6120
**Name:** Musketeer D'Artagnan
**Height:** 8.75
**Status:** Open issue, retired
**Issue Year:** 1994
**Issue Price:** $245
**Last Year:** 1996
**Last Retail Price:** $285

**Ref. No.:** 6121
**Name:** Musketeer Athos
**Height:** 8.75
**Status:** Open issue, retired
**Issue Year:** 1994
**Issue Price:** $245
**Last Year:** 1996
**Last Retail Price:** $290

*Children*

**Ref. No.:** 6135
**Name:** Football Star
**Height:** 8.75
**Status:** Open issue, retired
**Issue Year:** 1994
**Issue Price:** $295
**Last Year:** 1997
**Last Retail Price:** $295

**Ref. No.:** 4966
**Name:** Tennis Player Puppet
**Height:** 9
**Status:** Open issue, retired
**Issue Year:** 1977
**Issue Price:** $60
**Last Year:** 1985
**Last Retail Price:** $80
**High Auction Price:** $950
**Low Auction Price:** $500

**Ref. No.:** 5134
**Name:** Lilly, Soccer Player
**Height:** 9
**Status:** Open issue, retired
**Issue Year:** 1982
**Issue Price:** $140
**Last Year:** 1983
**Last Retail Price:** $140
**High Auction Price:** $900
**Low Auction Price:** $350

**Ref. No.:** 5828
**Name:** Next At Bat
**Height:** 9
**Status:** Open issue, retired
**Issue Year:** 1991
**Issue Price:** $170
**Last Year:** 1998
**Last Retail Price:** $180

**Ref. No.:** 5871
**Name:** Olympic Champion
**Height:** 9
**Status:** Open issue, retired
**Issue Year:** 1992
**Issue Price:** Unknown
**Last Year:** 1994
**Last Retail Price:** $145

**Ref. No.:** 6113
**Name:** Medieval Lady
**Height:** 9
**Status:** Open issue, retired
**Issue Year:** 1994
**Issue Price:** $225
**Last Year:** 1996
**Last Retail Price:** $225

**Ref. No.:** 6116
**Name:** Medieval Majesty
**Height:** 9
**Status:** Open issue, retired
**Issue Year:** 1994
**Issue Price:** $315
**Last Year:** 1996
**Last Retail Price:** $325

**Ref. No.:** 6136
**Name:** Basketball Star
**Height:** 9
**Status:** Open issue, retired
**Issue Year:** 1994
**Issue Price:** $295
**Last Year:** 1997
**Last Retail Price:** $295

**Ref. No.:** 6114
**Name:** Medieval Princess
**Height:** 9.25
**Status:** Open issue, retired
**Issue Year:** 1994
**Issue Price:** $245
**Last Year:** 1996
**Last Retail Price:** $245

**Ref. No.:** 1255
**Name:** Seesaw
**Height:** 9.5
**Status:** Open issue, retired
**Issue Year:** 1974
**Issue Price:** $110
**Last Year:** 1978
**Last Retail Price:** $550
**High Auction Price:** $850
**Low Auction Price:** $450

**Ref. No.:** 5137
**Name:** Billy, the Baseball Player
**Height:** 9.5
**Status:** Open issue, retired
**Issue Year:** 1982
**Issue Price:** $140
**Last Year:** 1983
**Last Retail Price:** $140
**High Auction Price:** $675
**Low Auction Price:** $500

**Ref. No.:** 5138
**Name:** Billy, the Golfer
**Height:** 9.5
**Status:** Open issue, retired
**Issue Year:** 1982
**Issue Price:** $140
**Last Year:** 1983
**Last Retail Price:** $140
**High Auction Price:** $1050
**Low Auction Price:** $700

*Children*

**Ref. No.:** 5759
**Name:** Presto!
**Height:** 9.5
**Status:** Open issue, retired
**Issue Year:** 1991
**Issue Price:** $275
**Last Year:** 1993
**Last Retail Price:** $295
**Auction Price:** $300

**Ref. No.:** 6855
**Name:** By the Seashore
**Height:** 9.5
**Status:** Open issue, active
**Issue Year:** 2002
**Issue Price:** $290
**2003 Retail Price:** $295

**Ref. No.:** 7514
**Name:** Special Champion
**Height:** 9.5
**Status:** Open issue, retired
**Issue Year:** 1992
**Issue Price:** $165
**Last Year:** 1996
**Last Retail Price:** $175
**Comment:** Special Olympics

**Ref. No.:** 4968
**Name:** Olympic Puppet
**Height:** 9.75
**Status:** Open issue, retired
**Issue Year:** 1977
**Issue Price:** $65
**Last Year:** 1983
**Last Retail Price:** $95
**High Auction Price:** $3800
**Low Auction Price:** $650

**Ref. No.:** 5870
**Name:** Olympic Torch
**Height:** 9.75
**Status:** Open issue, retired
**Issue Year:** 1992
**Issue Price:** Unknown
**Last Year:** 1994
**Last Retail Price:** $145

**Ref. No.:** 6191
**Name:** All American
**Height:** 9.75
**Status:** Open issue, retired
**Issue Year:** 1995
**Issue Price:** $225
**Last Year:** 1998
**Last Retail Price:** $225

**Ref. No.:** 5997
**Name:** One More Try
**Height:** 10
**Status:** Open issue, retired
**Issue Year:** 1993
**Issue Price:** $715
**Last Year:** 1996
**Last Issue Price:** $715

**Ref. No.:** 6552
**Name:** Pretty Pinwheel
**Height:** 10
**Status:** Open issue, retired
**Issue Year:** 1998
**Issue Price:** $145
**Last Year:** 2001
**Last Retail Price:** $150

**Ref. No.:** 7513
**Name:** Special Torch
**Height:** 10
**Status:** Open issue, retired
**Issue Year:** 1992
**Issue Price:** $165
**Last Year:** 1996
**Last Retail Price:** $175
**Comment:** Special Olympics

Children

**Ref. No.:** 4969
**Name:** "Sheriff" Puppet
**Height:** 10.5
**Status:** Open issue, retired
**Issue Year:** 1977
**Issue Price:** $85
**Last Year:** 1985
**Last Retail Price:** $120
**High Auction Price:** $850
**Low Auction Price:** $550

**Ref. No.:** 5067
**Name:** Halloween
**Height:** 10.5
**Status:** Open issue, retired
**Issue Year:** 1980
**Issue Price:** $375
**Last Year:** 1983
**Last Retail Price:** $382.50
**High Auction Price:** $1250
**Low Auction Price:** $875

**Ref. No.:** 6227
**Name:** Trick Or Treat
**Height:** 10.5
**Status:** Open issue, retired
**Issue Year:** 1995
**Issue Price:** $250
**Last Year:** 1997
**Last Retail Price:** $250

**Ref. No.:** 5304
**Name:** Children at Play
**Height:** 11
**Status:** Open issue, retired
**Issue Year:** 1985
**Issue Price:** $220
**Last Year:** 1990
**Last Retail Price:** $300
**High Auction Price:** $550
**Low Auction Price:** $450

**Ref. No.:** 5289
**Name:** Little Leaguer, Exercising
**Height:** 12.25
**Status:** Open issue, retired
**Issue Year:** 1985
**Issue Price:** $150
**Last Year:** 1990
**Last Retail Price:** $215
**High Auction Price:** $475
**Low Auction Price:** $275

**Ref. No.:** 4983
**Name:** Courtier Boy
**Height:** 12.5
**Status:** Open issue, retired
**Issue Year:** 1978
**Issue Price:** $235
**Last Year:** 1979
**Last Retail Price:** $245

Little Professionals

**Ref. No.:** 6350
**Name:** Hunting Butterflies
**Height:** 13
**Status:** Open issue, retired
**Issue Year:** 1997
**Issue Price:** $425
**Last Year:** 2000
**Last Retail Price:** $475

**Ref. No.:** 1366
**Name:** Girls in the Swing
**Height:** 15.5
**Status:** Open issue, retired
**Issue Year:** 1978
**Issue Price:** $825
**Last Year:** 1988
**Last Retail Price:** $1200
**Auction Price:** $1900

**Ref. No.:** 5697
**Name:** Over the Clouds
**Height:** 5
**Status:** Open issue, active
**Issue Year:** 1990
**Issue Price:** $275
**2003 Retail Price:** $325

**Ref. No.:** 5936
**Name:** Little Skipper
**Height:** 5.5
**Status:** Open issue, retired
**Issue Year:** 1993
**Issue Price:** $320
**Last Year:** 1996
**Last Retail Price:** $320

**Ref. No.:** 6087
**Name:** Loving Care
**Height:** 6.5
**Status:** Open issue, retired
**Issue Year:** 1994
**Issue Price:** $250
**Last Year:** 1999
**Last Retail Price:** $270

**Ref. No.:** 6348
**Name:** Little Veterinarian
**Height:** 7
**Status:** Open issue, retired
**Issue Year:** 1997
**Issue Price:** $210
**Last Year:** 1999
**Last Retail Price:** $210

**Ref. No.:** 6234
**Name:** The Great Chef
**Height:** 7.5
**Status:** Open issue, retired
**Issue Year:** 1995
**Issue Price:** $195
**Last Year:** 1998
**Last Retail Price:** $195

**Ref. No.:** 6235
**Name:** Dinner Is Served
**Height:** 7.5
**Status:** Open edition, retired
**Issue Year:** 1995
**Issue Price:** $185
**Last Year:** 1998
**Last Retail Price:** $185

**Ref. No.:** 6307
**Name:** Young Nurse
**Height:** 7.5
**Status:** Open issue, retired
**Issue Year:** 1996
**Issue Price:** $185
**Last Year:** 2001
**Last Retail Price:** $185

Children

**Ref. No.:** 6233
**Name:** Chef's Apprentice
**Height:** 8
**Status:** Open issue, retired
**Issue Year:** 1995
**Issue Price:** $260
**Last Year:** 1998
**Last Retail Price:** $260

**Ref. No.:** 6368
**Name:** Little Artist
**Height:** 8
**Status:** Open issue, retired
**Issue Year:** 1997
**Issue Price:** $175
**Last Year:** 2000
**Last Retail Price:** $175

**Ref. No.:** 4897
**Name:** Mechanic
**Height:** 8.25
**Status:** Open issue, retired
**Issue Year:** 1974
**Issue Price:** $45
**Last Year:** 1985
**Last Retail Price:** $82.50
**High Auction Price:** $375
**Low Auction Price:** $300

**Ref. No.:** 4906
**Name:** Delivery Boy
**Height:** 9
**Status:** Open issue, retired
**Issue Year:** 1974
**Issue Price:** $70
**Last Year:** 1979
**Last Retail Price:** $110
**Auction Price:** $375

**Ref. No.:** 6334
**Name:** Little Fireman
**Height:** 9
**Status:** Open issue, retired
**Issue Year:** 1997
**Issue Price:** $185
**Last Year:** 2000
**Last Retail Price:** $185

**Ref. No.:** 6349
**Name:** Little Maestro
**Height:** 9
**Status:** Open issue, retired
**Issue Year:** 1997
**Issue Price:** $165
**Last Year:** 2000
**Last Retail Price:** $165

**Ref. No.:** 6451
**Name:** Little Pilot
**Height:** 9
**Status:** Open issue, retired
**Issue Year:** 1997
**Issue Price:** $170
**Last Year:** 2002
**Last Retail Price:** $190

**Ref. No.:** 6367
**Name:** Little Policeman
**Height:** 9
**Status:** Open issue, retired
**Issue Year:** 1997
**Issue Price:** $185
**Last Year:** 2000
**Last Retail Price:** $185

**Ref. No.:** 6314
**Name:** Little Sailor Boy
**Height:** 9
**Status:** Open issue, retired
**Issue Price:** $225
**Issue Year:** 1996
**Last Year:** 1999
**Last Retail Price:** $225

**Ref. No.:** 4608
**Name:** Cook in Trouble
**Height:** 9.5
**Status:** Open issue, retired
**Issue Year:** 1969
**Issue Price:** $27.50
**Last Year:** 1985
**Last Retail Price:** $112.5
**High Auction Price:** $850
**Low Auction Price:** $425

**Ref. No.:** 6431
**Name:** Little Lawyer
**Height:** 10
**Status:** Open issue, retired
**Issue Year:** 1997
**Issue Price:** $210
**Last Year:** 1999
**Last Retail Price:** $210

**Ref. No.:** 5055
**Name:** Apprentice Seaman
**Height:** 10.5
**Status:** Open issue, retired
**Issue Year:** 1980
**Issue Price:** $140
**Last Year:** 1985
**Last Retail Price:** $155
**High Auction Price:** $450
**Low Auction Price:** $375

*Children*

**Ref. No.:** 5783
**Name:** Special Delivery
**Height:** 11.25
**Status:** Open issue, retired
**Issue Year:** 1991
**Issue Price:** $525
**Last Year:** 1994
**Last Retail Price:** $550

**Ref. No.:** 1161
**Name:** Little Town Mayor
**Height:** 12.25
**Status:** Very rare
**Issue Year:** 1971
**Issue Price:** $30
**Last Year:** 1973
**Last Retail Price:** Unknown

**Ref. No.:** 1163
**Name:** Soldier with Saber
**Height:** 12.25
**Status:** Open issue, retired
**Issue Year:** 1971
**Issue Price:** $27.50
**Last Year:** 1978
**Last Retail Price:** $55

**Ref. No.:** 1164
**Name:** Soldier with Gun
**Height:** 12.25
**Status:** Open issue, retired
**Issue Year:** 1971
**Issue Price:** $27.50
**Last Year:** 1978
**Last Retail Price:** $55

**Ref. No.:** 1165
**Name:** Soldier with Flag
**Height:** 12.25
**Status:** Open issue, retired
**Issue Year:** 1971
**Issue Price:** $27.50
**Last Year:** 1978
**Last Retail Price:** $55

**Ref. No.:** 1166
**Name:** Soldier with Cornet
**Height:** 12.25
**Status:** Open issue, retired
**Issue Year:** 1971
**Issue Price:** $27.50
**Last Year:** 1978
**Last Retail Price:** $55

**Ref. No.:** 1167
**Name:** Soldier with Drum
**Height:** 12.25
**Status:** Open issue, retired
**Issue Year:** 1971
**Issue Price:** $27.50
**Last Year:** 1978
**Last Retail Price:** $55

**Ref. No.:** 5403
**Name:** The Drummer Boy
**Height:** 12.5
**Status:** Open issue, retired
**Issue Year:** 1987
**Issue Price:** $225
**Last Year:** 1990
**Last Retail Price:** $280
**High Auction Price:** $550
**Low Auction Price:** $350

**Ref. No.:** 5404
**Name:** Cadet Captain
**Height:** 12.5
**Status:** Open issue, retired
**Issue Year:** 1987
**Issue Price:** $175
**Last Year:** 1990
**Last Retail Price:** 215
**High Auction Price:** 450
**Low Auction Price:** $250

*Children*

**Ref. No.:** 5405
**Name:** The Flag Bearer
**Height:** 12.5
**Status:** Open issue, retired
**Issue Year:** 1987
**Issue Price:** $200
**Last Year:** 1990
**Last Retail Price:** $240
**High Auction Price:** $550
**Low Auction Price:** $275

**Ref. No.:** 5406
**Name:** The Bugler
**Height:** 12.5
**Status:** Open issue, retired
**Issue Year:** 1987
**Issue Price:** $175
**Last Year:** 1990
**Last Retail Price:** $215
**High Auction Price:** $475
**Low Auction Price:** $275

**Ref. No:** 5407
**Name:** At Attention
**Height:** 12.5
**Status:** Open issue, retired
**Issue Year:** 1987
**Issue Price:** $175
**Last Year:** 1990
**Last Retail Price:** $215
**High Auction Price:** $450
**Low Auction Price:** $300

## Romantic Children

**Ref. No.:** 5941
**Name:** Riding the Waves
**Height:** 5.5
**Status:** Open issue, retired
**Issue Year:** 1993
**Issue Price:** $405
**Last Year:** 1997
**Last Retail Price:** $405

**Ref. No.:** 1230
**Name:** Friendship
**Height:** 6
**Status:** Open issue, retired
**Issue Year:** 1972
**Issue Price:** $68
**Last Year:** 1991
**Last Retail Price:** $325
**High Auction Price:** $500
**Low Auction Price:** $475

**Ref. No.:** 5072
**Name:** Precocious Courtship
**Height:** 6
**Status:** Open issue, retired
**Issue Year:** 1980
**Issue Price:** $410
**Last Year:** 1990
**Last Retail Price:** $450

**Ref. No.:** 5072.3
**Name:** Courtship (White)
**Height:** 6
**Status:** Open issue, retired
**Issue Year:** 1983
**Issue Price:** $242.50
**Last Year:** 1987
**Last Retail Price:** $275

**Ref. No.:** 5361
**Name:** Try This One
**Height:** 6
**Status:** Open issue, retired
**Issue Year:** 1986
**Issue Price:** $225
**Last Year:** 1997
**Last Retail Price:** $385

**Ref. No.:** 5454
**Name:** For Me?
**Height:** 6
**Status:** Open issue, retired
**Issue Year:** 1988
**Issue Price:** $290
**Last Year:** 1997
**Last Retail Price:** $395

**Ref. No.:** 5779
**Name:** Lover's Paradise
**Height:** 6
**Status:** Open issue, retired
**Issue Year:** 1991
**Issue Price:** $2250
**Last Year:** 1997
**Last Retail Price:** $2450

**Ref. No.:** 5701
**Name:** Just a Little Kiss
**Height:** 6.5
**Status:** Open issue, retired
**Issue Year:** 1990
**Issue Price:** $320
**Last Year:** 1997
**Last Retail Price:** $375

**Ref. No.:** 6144
**Name:** Caribbean Kiss
**Height:** 7.5
**Status:** Open issue, retired
**Issue Year:** 1995
**Issue Price:** $340
**Last Year:** 1999
**Last Retail Price:** $340

**Ref. No.:** 6630
**Name:** A Little Romance
**Height:** 7.5
**Status:** Open issue, active
**Issue Year:** 1999
**Issue Price:** $695
**2003 Retail Price:** $695

**Ref. No.:** 1188
**Name:** Boy Meets Girl
**Height:** 8.5
**Status:** Open issue, retired
**Issue Year:** 1972
**Issue Price:** $60
**Last Year:** 1989
**Last Retail Price:** $270
**High Auction Price:** $550
**Low Auction Price:** $325

**Ref. No.:** 5292
**Name:** Love in Bloom
**Height:** 8.5
**Status:** Open issue, retired
**Issue Year:** 1985
**Issue Price:** $225
**Last Year:** 1998
**Last Retail Price:** $435

*Children*

**Ref. No.:** 5409
**Name:** Courting Time
**Height:** 8.5
**Status:** Open issue, retired
**Issue Year:** 1987
**Issue Price:** $425
**Last Year:** 1990
**Last Retail Price:** $500
**High Auction Price:** $625
**Low Auction Price:** $425

**Ref. No.:** 5442
**Name:** Poetry of Love
**Height:** 8.5
**Status:** Open issue, retired
**Issue Year:** 1987
**Issue Price:** $500
**Last Year:** 1998
**Last Retail Price:** $875

**Ref. No.:** 6906
**Name:** With All My Heart
**Height:** 8.75
**Status:** Open issue, active
**Issue Year:** 2002
**Issue Price:** $415
**2003 Retail Price:** $425

**Ref. No.:** 5453
**Name:** For You
**Height:** 9
**Status:** Open issue, retired
**Issue Year:** 1988
**Issue Price:** $450
**Last Year:** 1998
**Last Retail Price:** $640

**Ref. No.:** 6821
**Name:** A Poem for My Girl
**Height:** 9.25
**Status:** Open issue, active
**Issue Year:** 2002
**Issue Price:** $565
**2003 Retail Price:** $575

**Ref. No.:** 4856
**Name:** Waltz Time
**Height:** 9.5
**Status:** Open issue, retired
**Issue Year:** 1974
**Issue Price:** $65
**Last Year:** 1985
**Last Retail Price:** $270
**High Auction Price:** $650
**Low Auction Price:** $375

**Ref. No.:** 4878
**Name:** Adolescence
**Height:** 9.75
**Status:** Open issue, retired
**Issue Year:** 1974
**Issue Price:** $65
**Last Year:** 1979
**Last Retail Price:** $115

**Ref. No.:** 1127
**Name:** Puppy Love
**Height:** 10.25
**Status:** Open issue, retired
**Issue Year:** 1971
**Issue Price:** $50
**Last Year:** 1996
**Last Retail Price:** $330

**Ref. No.:** 1241
**Name:** Country Flirt
**Height:** 10.5
**Status:** Open issue, retired
**Issue Year:** 1973
**Issue Price:** $110
**Last Year:** 1980
**Last Retail Price:** $150
**Auction Price:** $500

Children

**Ref. No.:** 5382
**Name:** Lovers Serenade
**Height:** 10.5
**Status:** Open issue, retired
**Issue Year:** 1986
**Issue Price:** $350
**Last Year:** 1990
**Last Retail Price:** $500
**High Auction Price:** $850
**Low Auction Price:** $600

**Ref. No.:** 5426
**Name:** One, Two, Three
**Height:** 10.5
**Status:** Open issue, retired
**Issue Year:** 1987
**Issue Price:** $240
**Last Year:** 1995
**Last Retail Price:** $390

**Ref. No.:** 4913
**Name:** Lesson In The Country
**Height:** 11.5
**Status:** Open issue, retired
**Issue Year:** 1974
**Issue Price:** $240
**Last Year:** 1978
**Last Retail Price:** $340

**Brothers and Sisters**

**Ref. No.:** 4760
**Name:** Rest in the Country
**Height:** 11.75
**Status:** Open issue, retired
**Issue Year:** 1971
**Issue Price:** $70
**Last Year:** 1981
**Last Retail Price:** $225

**Ref. No.:** 6395
**Name:** Through the Park
**Height:** 12
**Status:** Open issue, retired
**Issue Year:** 1997
**Issue Price:** $2350
**Last Year:** 2002
**Last Retail Price:** $2350

**Ref. No.:** 5735
**Name:** Big Sister
**Height:** 6.75
**Status:** Open issue, active
**Issue Year:** 1991
**Issue Price:** $650
**2003 Retail Price:** $695

**Ref. No.:** 1534
**Name:** Little Sister
**Height:** 7
**Status:** Open issue, active
**Issue Year:** 1988
**Issue Price:** $180
**2003 Retail Price:** $250

**Ref. No.:** 6674
**Name:** Thank You Santa!
**Height:** 8.5
**Status:** Open issue, active
**Issue Year:** 2000
**Issue Price:** $335
**2003 Retail Price:** $350

**Ref. No.:** 4800
**Name:** Gypsy with Brother
**Height:** 9.5
**Status:** Open issue, retired
**Issue Year:** 1972
**Issue Price:** $36
**Last Year:** 1979
**Last Retail Price:** $105
**Auction Price:** $400

**Ref. No.:** 6681
**Name:** Playing Mom
**Height:** 9.5
**Status:** Open issue, sold out
**Issue Year:** 2000
**Issue Price:** $295
**Last Year:** 2000
**Last Retail Price:** $295
**Comment:** Event Piece 2000

**Ref. No.:** 6794
**Name:** Shh...Let Him Sleep
**Height:** 11.25
**Status:** Open issue, active
**Issue Year:** 2001
**Issue Price:** $585
**2003 Retail Price:** $650

**Ref. No.:** 4930
**Name:** Sisters
**Height:** 11.5
**Status:** Open issue, retired
**Issue Year:** 1974
**Issue Price:** $250
**Last Year:** 1981
**Last Retail Price:** $410

**Ref. No.:** 5878
**Name:** Sister's Pride
**Height:** 11.75
**Status:** Open issue, retired
**Issue Year:** 1992
**Issue Price:** $595
**Last Year:** 1996
**Last Retail Price:** $615

**Ref. No.:** 5013
**Name:** Daughters
**Height:** 12.5
**Status:** Open issue, retired
**Issue Year:** 1978
**Issue Price:** $250
**Last Year:** 1991
**Last Retail Price:** $775
**High Auction Price:** $1250
**Low Auction Price:** $900

**Ref. No.:** 6766
**Name:** A Reading Lesson
**Height:** 12.5
**Status:** Open issue, active
**Issue Year:** 2001
**Issue Price:** $995
**2003 Retail Price:** $995

*Children*

## Other Children

**Ref. No.:** 215.08
**Name:** Sea Shell White
**Height:** 3
**Status:** Very rare
**Issue Year:** 1956
**Issue Price:** Unknown
**Last Year:** Unknown
**Last Retail Price:** Unknown

**Ref. No.:** 89.06
**Name:** Sea Shell
**Height:** 3.25
**Status:** Very rare
**Issue Year:** 1956
**Issue Price:** Unknown
**Last Year:** Unknown
**Last Retail Price:** Unknown

**Ref. No.:** 214.08
**Name:** Little Gypsy
**Height:** 3.25
**Status:** Very rare
**Issue Year:** 1956
**Issue Price:** Unknown
**Last Year:** Unknown
**Last Retail Price:** Unknown

**Ref. No.:** 5589
**Name:** Pretty Pose
**Height:** 3.5
**Status:** Open issue, retired
**Issue Year:** 1989
**Issue Price:** $185
**Last Year:** 1993
**Last Retail Price:** $230

**Ref. No.:** 112.06
**Name:** Girl With Book Open
**Height:** 3.75
**Status:** Very rare
**Issue Year:** 1958
**Issue Price:** Unknown
**Last Year:** Unknown
**Last Retail Price:** Unknown

**Ref. No.:** 114.06
**Name:** Little Lady Sitting
**Height:** 4
**Status:** Very rare
**Issue Year:** 1958
**Issue Price:** Unknown
**Last Year:** Unknown
**Last Retail Price:** Unknown

**Ref. No.:** 4716
**Name:** Little Maurice
**Height:** 4.25
**Status:** Open edition, retired
**Issue Year:** 1970
**Issue Price:** $55
**Last Year:** 1973
**Last Retail Price:** $75
**Auction Price:** $750

**Ref. No.:** 5109
**Name:** Gayle
**Height:** 4.25
**Status:** Open issue, retired
**Issue Year:** 1982
**Issue Price:** $85
**Last Year:** 1985
**Last Retail Price:** $85
**High Auction Price:** $450
**Low Auction Price:** $400

**Ref. No.:** 5108
**Name:** Gelsy
**Height:** 4.75
**Status:** Open issue, retired
**Issue Year:** 1982
**Issue Price:** $85
**Last Year:** 1985
**Last Retail Price:** $85
**High Auction Price:** $400
**Low Auction Price:** $325

**Ref. No.:** 5148
**Name:** "O" is for Olivia
**Height:** 4.75
**Status:** Open issue, retired
**Issue Year:** 1982
**Issue Price:** $100
**Last Year:** 1985
**Last Retail Price:** $110
**High Auction Price:** $600
**Low Auction Price:** $275

**Ref. No.:** 5846
**Name:** All Tuckered Out
**Height:** 4.75
**Status:** Open issue, active
**Issue Year:** 1992
**Issue Price:** $220
**2003 Retail Price:** $275

**Ref. No.:** 6276
**Name:** Iris
**Height:** 4.75
**Status:** Open issue, active
**Issue Year:** 1996
**Issue Price:** $150
**2003 Retail Price:** $150

**Ref. No:** 5399
**Name:** A Time to Rest
**Height:** 4.75
**Status:** Open issue, retired
**Issue Year:** 1987
**Issue Price:** $175
**Last Year:** 1993
**Last Retail Price:** $295
**Auction Price:** $475

**Ref. No.:** 5448
**Name:** Naptime
**Height:** 4.75
**Status:** Open issue, active
**Issue Year:** 1987
**Issue Price:** $135
**2003 Retail Price:** $275

**Ref. No.:** 6764
**Name:** My Debut
**Height:** 4.75
**Status:** Open issue, active
**Issue Year:** 2001
**Issue Price:** $195
**2003 Retail Price:** $195

**Ref. No.:** 6411
**Name:** Bath Time
**Height:** 5
**Status:** Open issue, active
**Issue Year:** 1997
**Issue Price:** $195
**2003 Retail Price:** $195

**Ref. No.:** 6429
**Name:** Ready to Roll
**Height:** 5
**Status:** Open issue, retired
**Issue Year:** 1997
**Issue Price:** $165
**Last Year:** 2001
**Last Retail Price:** $165

**Ref. No.:** 1087
**Name:** Little Green-Grocer
**Height:** 5.5
**Status:** Open issue, retired
**Issue Year:** 1969
**Issue Price:** $40
**Last Year:** 1981
**Last Retail Price:** $135
**High Auction Price:** $325
**Low Auction Price:** $300

**Ref. No.:** 4523
**Name:** Little Girl with Slippers
**Height:** 5.5
**Status:** Open issue, retired
**Issue Year:** 1969
**Issue Price:** $17
**Last Year:** 1993
**Last Retail Price:** $100

**Ref. No.:** 5488
**Name:** Sandcastles
**Height:** 5.5
**Status:** Open issue, retired
**Issue Year:** 1988
**Issue Price:** $160
**Last Year:** 1993
**Last Retail Price:** $220

**Ref. No.:** 5943
**Name:** World of Fantasy
**Height:** 5.5
**Status:** Open issue, retired
**Issue Year:** 1993
**Issue Price:** $295
**Last Year:** 1995
**Last Retail Price:** $295

Children

**Ref. No.:** 228.09
**Name:** Teenage Boy
**Height:** 5.75
**Status:** Very rare
**Issue Year:** 1958
**Issue Price:** Unknown
**Last Year:** Unknown
**Last Retail Price:** Unknown

**Ref. No.:** 227.09
**Name:** Teenage Girl
**Height:** 6
**Status:** Very rare
**Issue Year:** 1958
**Issue Price:** Unknown
**Last Year:** Unknown
**Last Retail Price:** Unknown

**Ref. No.:** 1024
**Name:** Boy with Book
**Height:** 6
**Status:** Open issue, retired
**Issue Year:** 1969
**Issue Price:** $47.50
**Last Year:** 1971
**Last Retail Price:** $47.50

**Ref. No.:** 5410
**Name:** Pilar
**Height:** 6
**Status:** Open issue, retired
**Issue Year:** 1987
**Issue Price:** $200
**Last Year:** 1990
**Last Retail Price:** $250
**High Auction Price:** $400
**Low Auction Price:** $325

**Ref. No.:** 5411
**Name:** Teresa
**Height:** 6
**Status:** Open issue, retired
**Issue Year:** 1987
**Issue Price:** $225
**Last Year:** 1990
**Last Retail Price:** $290
**High Auction Price:** $500
**Low Auction Price:** $350

**Ref. No.:** 5649
**Name:** Nothing To Do
**Height:** 6
**Status:** Open issue, retired
**Issue Year:** 1990
**Issue Price:** $190
**Last Year:** 1997
**Last Retail Price:** $220

**Ref. No.:** 5990
**Name:** Thoughtful Caress
**Height:** 6
**Status:** Open issue, retired
**Issue Year:** 1993
**Issue Price:** $245
**Last Year:** 1996
**Last Retail Price:** $225

**Ref. No.:** 6428
**Name:** My First Step
**Height:** 6
**Status:** Open issue, retired
**Issue Year:** 1997
**Issue Price:** $165
**Last Year:** 2001
**Last Retail Price:** $165

**Ref. No.:** 6763
**Name:** First Performance
**Height:** 6
**Status:** Open issue, active
**Issue Year:** 2001
**Issue Price:** $195
**2003 Retail Price:** $225

**Ref. No.:** 46.03
**Name:** Sitting Girl
**Height:** 6.25
**Status:** Very rare
**Issue Year:** 1957
**Issue Price:** Unknown
**Last Year:** Unknown
**Last Retail Price:** Unknown

**Ref. No.:** 5678
**Name:** I Feel Pretty
**Height:** 6.25
**Status:** Open issue, retired
**Issue Year:** 1990
**Issue Price:** $190
**Last Year:** 1997
**Last Retail Price:** $230

**Ref. No.:** 5782
**Name:** My Chores
**Height:** 6.25
**Status:** Open issue, retired
**Issue Year:** 1991
**Issue Price:** $325
**Last Year:** 1995
**Last Retail Price:** $355

**Ref. No.:** 6299
**Name:** Little Bear
**Height:** 6.5
**Status:** Open issue, retired
**Issue Year:** 1996
**Last Year:** 1999
**Last Retail Price:** $285

**Ref. No.:** 4567
**Name:** Thinking Girl
**Height:** 6.5
**Status:** Open issue, retired
**Issue Year:** 1969
**Issue Price:** $32.50
**Last Year:** 1972
**Last Retail Price:** $32.50

**Ref. No.:** 5070
**Name:** Napping
**Height:** 6.75
**Status:** Open issue, retired
**Issue Year:** 1980
**Issue Price:** $240
**Last Year:** 1983
**Last Retail Price:** $240
**High Auction Price:** $750
**Low Auction Price:** $650

*Children*

Ref. No.: 5769
Name: Faithful Steed
Height: 6.75
Status: Open issue, retired
Issue Year: 1991
Issue Price: $370
Last Year: 1994
Last Retail Price: $310

Ref. No.: 6270
Name: Commencement
Height: 6.75
Status: Open issue, retired
Issue Year: 1996
Issue Price: $200
Last Year: 2001
Last Retail Price: $200

Ref. No.: 6272
Name: Going Forth
Height: 6.75
Status: Open issue, retired
Issue Year: 1996
Issue Price: $200
Last Year: 1999
Last Retail Price: $200

Ref. No.: 6275
Name: Rose
Height: 6.75
Status: Open issue, active
Issue Year: 1996
Issue Price: $150
2003 Retail Price: $150

Ref. No.: 6300
Name: Rubber Ducky
Height: 6.75
Status: Open issue, retired
Issue Year: 1996
Issue Price: $285
Last Year: 2000
Last Retail Price: $285

Ref. No.: 6801
Name: Sleepy Scholar
Height: 6.75
Status: Open issue, active
Issue Year: 2001
Issue Price: $325
2003 Retail Price: $350

**Ref. No.:** 6802
**Name:** Waiting for the Bell
**Height:** 6.75
**Status:** Open issue, active
**Issue Year:** 2001
**Issue Price:** $325
**2003 Retail Price:** $350

**Ref. No.:** 1083
**Name:** Girl with Doll
**Height:** 7
**Status:** Open issue, retired
**Issue Year:** 1969
**Issue Price:** $14.50
**Last Year:** 1985
**Last Retail Price:** $100
**High Auction Price:** $350
**Low Auction Price:** $185

**Ref. No.:** 4566
**Name:** Student
**Height:** 7
**Status:** Open issue, retired
**Issue Year:** 1969
**Issue Price:** $32.50
**Last Year:** 1972
**Last Retail Price:** $35

**Ref. No.:** 4714
**Name:** Boy Jewelry Dish
**Height:** 7
**Status:** Open issue, retired
**Issue Year:** 1970
**Issue Price:** $30
**Last Year:** 1978
**Last Retail Price:** $80
**Auction Price:** $700

**Ref. No.:** 4980
**Name:** Three On a Bench
**Height:** 7
**Status:** Open issue, retired
**Issue Year:** 1977
**Issue Price:** $145
**Last Year:** 1979
**Last Retail Price:** $160

**Ref. No.:** 5106
**Name:** Natalia
**Height:** 7
**Status:** Open issue, retired
**Issue Year:** 1982
**Issue Price:** $85
**Last Year:** 1985
**Last Retail Price:** $85
**High Auction Price:** $450
**Low Auction Price:** $300

*Children*

**Ref. No.:** 5212
**Name:** Evita
**Height:** 7
**Status:** Open edition, retired
**Issue Year:** 1984
**Issue Price:** $105
**Last Year:** 1998
**Last Retail Price:** $195

**Ref. No.:** 5647
**Name:** Sara
**Height:** 7
**Status:** Open edition, retired
**Issue Year:** 1990
**Issue Price:** $200
**Last Year:** 1998
**Last Retail Price:** $230

**Ref. No.:** 5720
**Name:** Sharing Secrets
**Height:** 7
**Status:** Open issue, retired
**Issue Year:** 1990
**Issue Price:** $290
**Last Year:** 1997
**Last Retail Price:** $335

**Ref. No.:** 6274
**Name:** Daisy
**Height:** 7
**Status:** Open edition, retired
**Issue Year:** 1996
**Issue Price:** $150
**Last Year:** 2002
**Last Retail Price:** $150

**Ref. No.:** 6440
**Name:** Time for Bed
**Height:** 7
**Status:** Open issue, retired
**Issue Year:** 1997
**Issue Price:** $160
**Last Year:** 1999
**Last Retail Price:** $160

**Ref. No.:** 6481
**Name:** Just Resting
**Height:** 7
**Status:** Open issue, retired
**Issue Year:** 1997
**Issue Price:** $125
**Last Year:** 2000
**Last Retail Price:** $145

**Ref. No.:** 6457
**Name:** Bathing Beauties
**Height:** 7
**Status:** Open issue, active
**Issue Year:** 1997
**Issue Price:** $240
**2003 Retail Price:** $250

**Ref. No.:** 6581
**Name:** Nighttime Blessings
**Height:** 7
**Status:** Open issue, active
**Issue Year:** 1998
**Issue Price:** $135
**2003 Retail Price:** $165

**Ref. No.:** 6124
**Name:** Traveler's Rest
**Height:** 7.25
**Status:** Open issue, retired
**Issue Year:** 1994
**Issue Price:** $275
**Last Year:** 1997
**Last Retail Price:** $295

**Ref. No.:** 6683
**Name:** Romance
**Height:** 7.25
**Status:** Open issue, active
**Issue Year:** 2000
**Issue Price:** $195
**2003 Retail Price:** $195

**Ref. No.:** 6685
**Name:** Happiness
**Height:** 7.25
**Status:** Open issue, active
**Issue Year:** 2000
**Issue Price:** $195
**2003 Retail Price:** $195

**Ref. No.:** 1082
**Name:** Girl Manicuring
**Height:** 7.5
**Status:** Open issue, retired
**Issue Year:** 1969
**Issue Price:** $14.50
**Last Year:** 1985
**Last Retail Price:** $100
**High Auction Price:** $275
**Low Auction Price:** $150

*Children*

**Ref. No.:** 1084
**Name:** Girl with Mother's Shoe
**Height:** 7.5
**Status:** Open issue, retired
**Issue Year:** 1969
**Issue Price:** $14.50
**Last Year:** 1985
**Last Retail Price:** $100
**High Auction Price:** $325
**Low Auction Price:** $150

**Ref. No.:** 4636
**Name:** Girl with Child
**Height:** 7.5
**Status:** Open issue, retired
**Issue Year:** 1969
**Issue Price:** $13
**Last Year:** 1979
**Last Retail Price:** $38.50
**High Auction Price:** $275
**Low Auction Price:** $250

**Ref. No.:** 4838
**Name:** Clean Up Time
**Height:** 7.5
**Status:** Open issue, retired
**Issue Year:** 1973
**Issue Price:** $36
**Last Year:** 1993
**Last Retail Price:** $170
**Auction Price:** $250

**Ref. No.:** 4873
**Name:** Girl Kissing
**Height:** 7.5
**Status:** Open edition, retired
**Issue Year:** 1974
**Issue Price:** $13
**Last Year:** 1997
**Last Retail Price:** $90

**Ref. No.:** 5210
**Name:** Jolie
**Height:** 7.5
**Status:** Open edition, retired
**Issue Year:** 1984
**Issue Price:** $105
**Last Year:** 2002
**Last Retail Price:** $270

**Ref. No.:** 5608
**Name:** Baby Doll
**Height:** 7.5
**Status:** Open edition, retired
**Issue Year:** 1989
**Issue Price:** $150
**Last Year:** 1998
**Last Retail Price:** $180

**Ref. No.:** 5643
**Name:** Cathy
**Height:** 7.5
**Status:** Open edition, retired
**Issue Year:** 1990
**Issue Price:** $200
**Last Year:** 1998
**Last Retail Price:** $235

**Ref. No.:** 6036
**Name:** Young Princess
**Height:** 7.5
**Status:** Open edition, retired
**Issue Year:** 1993
**Issue Price:** $240
**Last Year:** 1996
**Last Issue Price:** $240

**Ref. No.:** 6271
**Name:** Cap and Gown
**Height:** 7.5
**Status:** Open issue, retired
**Issue Year:** 1996
**Issue Price:** $200
**Last Year:** 2001
**Last Retail Price:** $200

**Ref. No.:** 6684
**Name:** Dreams
**Height:** 7.5
**Status:** Open issue, retired
**Issue Year:** 2000
**Issue Price:** $195
**Last Year:** 2002
**Last Retail Price:** $195

**Ref. No.:** 6799
**Name:** Just Like New
**Height:** 7.5
**Status:** Open issue, active
**Issue Year:** 2001
**Issue Price:** $100
**2003 Retail Price:** $125

**Ref. No.:** 6800
**Name:** Bundled Bather
**Height:** 7.5
**Status:** Open issue, active
**Issue Year:** 2001
**Issue Price:** $100
**2003 Retail Price:** $125

*Children*

**Ref. No.:** 4869
**Name:** Boy Blowing
**Height:** 7.75
**Status:** Open issue, retired
**Issue Year:** 1974
**Issue Price:** $13
**Last Year:** 1997
**Last Retail Price:** $90

**Ref. No.:** 4871
**Name:** Girl with Guitar
**Height:** 7.75
**Status:** Open edition, retired
**Issue Year:** 1974
**Issue Price:** $13
**Last Year:** 2000
**Last Retail Price:** $90

**Ref. No.:** 4872
**Name:** Girl Stretching
**Height:** 7.75
**Status:** Open edition, retired
**Issue Year:** 1974
**Issue Price:** $13
**Last Year:** 1999
**Last Retail Price:** $90

**Ref. No.:** 4874
**Name:** Children in Nightshirts
**Height:** 7.75
**Status:** Open issue, retired
**Issue Year:** 1974
**Issue Price:** $25
**Auction Price:** $425
**Last Year:** 1997
**Last Retail Price:** $150

**Ref. No.:** 4900
**Name:** Boy with Smoking Jacket
**Height:** 7.75
**Status:** Open issue, retired
**Issue Year:** 1974
**Issue Price:** $45
**Last Year:** 1983
**Last Retail Price:** $82.50
**High Auction Price:** $350
**Low Auction Price:** $275

**Ref. No.:** 5147
**Name:** "I" is for Ivy
**Height:** 7.75
**Status:** Open issue, retired
**Issue Year:** 1982
**Issue Price:** $100
**Last Year:** 1985
**Last Retail Price:** $110
**High Auction Price:** $600
**Low Auction Price:** $300

**Ref. No.:** 5149
**Name:** "U" is for Ursula
**Height:** 7.75
**Status:** Open issue, retired
**Issue Year:** 1982
**Issue Price:** $100
**Last Year:** 1985
**Last Retail Price:** $100
**High Auction Price:** $600
**Low Auction Price:** $275

**Ref. No.:** 5218
**Name:** Autumn
**Height:** 7.75
**Status:** Open edition, retired
**Issue Year:** 1984
**Issue Price:** $90
**Last Year:** 1999
**Last Retail Price:** $210

**Ref. No.:** 5219
**Name:** Summer
**Height:** 7.75
**Status:** Open edition, retired
**Issue Year:** 1984
**Issue Price:** $90
**Last Year:** 1999
**Last Retail Price:** $195

**Ref. No.:** 5606
**Name:** Quiet Evening
**Height:** 7.75
**Status:** Open issue, retired
**Issue Year:** 1989
**Issue Price:** $125
**Last Year:** 1993
**Last Retail Price:** $165

**Ref. No.:** 5607
**Name:** Calling a Friend
**Height:** 7.75
**Status:** Open edition, retired
**Issue Year:** 1989
**Issue Price:** $125
**Last Year:** 1997
**Last Retail Price:** $165

**Ref. No.:** 5648
**Name:** Courtney
**Height:** 7.75
**Status:** Open edition, active
**Issue Year:** 1990
**Issue Price:** $200
**2003 Retail Price:** $245

*Children*

**Ref. No.:** 6155
**Name:** European Love
**Height:** 7.75
**Status:** Open edition, retired
**Issue Year:** 1994
**Issue Price:** $225
**Last Year:** 1998
**Last Retail Price:** $235

**Ref. No.:** 1109
**Name:** Girl's Head
**Height:** 8
**Status:** Open edition, retired
**Issue Year:** 1971
**Issue Price:** $70
**Last Year:** 1975
**Last Retail Price:** $70
**Auction Price:** $700

**Ref. No.:** 5646
**Name:** Cindy
**Height:** 8
**Status:** Open edition, retired
**Issue Year:** 1990
**Issue Price:** $190
**Last Year:** 1998
**Last Retail Price:** $215

**Ref. No.:** 5877
**Name:** Guest of Honor
**Height:** 8
**Status:** Open issue, retired
**Issue Year:** 1992
**Issue Price:** $195
**Last Year:** 1996
**Last Retail Price:** $200

**Ref. No.:** 6419
**Name:** Arms Full of Love
**Height:** 8
**Status:** Open issue, active
**Issue Year:** 1997
**Issue Price:** $180
**2003 Retail Price:** $195

**Ref. No.:** 6465
**Name:** Bedtime Prayers
**Height:** 8
**Status:** Open issue, active
**Issue Year:** 1997
**Issue Price:** $105
**2003 Retail Price:** $125

**Ref. No.:** 6582
**Name:** Bless Us All
**Height:** 8
**Status:** Open issue, active
**Issue Year:** 1998
**Issue Price:** $170
**2003 Retail Price:** $195

**Ref. No.:** 4868
**Name:** Girl with Candle
**Height:** 8.25
**Status:** Open edition, retired
**Issue Year:** 1974
**Issue Price:** $13
**Last Year:** 2000
**Last Retail Price:** $90

**Ref. No.:** 4876
**Name:** Thinker, Little Boy
**Height:** 8.25
**Status:** Open issue, retired
**Issue Year:** 1974
**Issue Price:** $20
**Last Year:** 1993
**Last Retail Price:** $135
**High Auction Price:** $225
**Low Auction Price:** $175

**Ref. No.:** 4899
**Name:** Punishment
**Height:** 8.25
**Status:** Open issue, retired
**Issue Year:** 1974
**Issue Price:** $45
**Last Year:** 1983
**Last Retail Price:** $82.50

**Ref. No.:** 5145
**Name:** "A" is for Amy
**Height:** 8.25
**Status:** Open issue, retired
**Issue Year:** 1982
**Issue Price:** $110
**Last Year:** 1985
**Last Retail Price:** $110
**High Auction Price:** $1600
**Low Auction Price:** $1050

**Ref. No.:** 5146
**Name:** "E" is for Ellen
**Height:** 8.25
**Status:** Open issue, retired
**Issue Year:** 1982
**Issue Price:** $110
**Last Year:** 1985
**Last Retail Price:** $110
**Auction Price:** $750

*Children*

**Ref. No.:** 5400
**Name:** The Wanderer
**Height:** 8.25
**Status:** Open issue, retired
**Issue Year:** 1987
**Issue Price:** $150
**Last Year:** 1998
**Last Retail Price:** $245

**Ref. No.:** 5429
**Name:** Happy Birthday
**Height:** 8.25
**Status:** Open edition, active
**Issue Year:** 1987
**Issue Price:** $100
**2003 Retail Price:** $165

**Ref. No.:** 6123
**Name:** Out For a Stroll
**Height:** 8.25
**Status:** Open issue, retired
**Issue Year:** 1994
**Issue Price:** $198
**Last Year:** 1997
**Last Retail Price:** $215

**Ref. No.:** 1081
**Name:** Girl with Brush
**Height:** 8.5
**Status:** Open issue, retired
**Issue Year:** 1969
**Issue Price:** $14.50
**Last Year:** 1985
**Last Retail Price:** $100

**Ref. No.:** 1147
**Name:** Girl with Bonnet
**Height:** 8.5
**Status:** Open issue, retired
**Issue Year:** 1971
**Issue Price:** $20
**Last Year:** 1985
**Last Retail Price:** $100
**High Auction Price:** $350
**Low Auction Price:** $225

**Ref. No.:** 1148
**Name:** Girl Shampooing
**Height:** 8.5
**Status:** Open issue, retired
**Issue Year:** 1971
**Issue Price:** $20
**Last Year:** 1985
**Last Retail Price:** $100
**High Auction Price:** $375
**Low Auction Price:** $225

**Ref. No.:** 1211
**Name:** Girl with Doll
**Height:** 8.5
**Status:** Open issue, retired
**Issue Year:** 1972
**Issue Price:** $72
**Last Year:** 1994
**Last Retail Price:** $440
**Auction Price:** $450

**Ref. No.:** 1481
**Name:** Sunning
**Height:** 8.5
**Status:** Open issue, retired
**Issue Year:** 1985
**Issue Price:** $145
**Last Year:** 1988
**Last Retail Price:** $175

**Ref. No.:** 4779
**Name:** Teaching to Pray
**Height:** 8.5
**Status:** Open issue, retired
**Issue Year:** 1971
**Issue Price:** $32
**Last Year:** 1997
**Last Retail Price:** $210

**Ref. No.:** 4870
**Name:** Boy Awakening
**Height:** 8.5
**Status:** Open issue, retired
**Issue Year:** 1974
**Issue Price:** $13
**Last Year:** 1999
**Last Retail Price:** $90
**High Auction Price:** $200
**Low Auction Price:** $175

**Ref. No.:** 4898
**Name:** Boy from Madrid
**Height:** 8.5
**Status:** Open issue, retired
**Issue Year:** 1974
**Issue Price:** $45
**Last Year:** 1997
**Last Retail Price:** $150
**Auction Price:** $375
(sold w/4897)

**Ref. No.:** 5026
**Name:** Planning the Day
**Height:** 8.5
**Status:** Open issue, retired
**Issue Year:** 1980
**Issue Price:** $90
**Last Year:** 1985
**Last Retail Price:** $100
**High Auction Price:** $325
**Low Auction Price:** $200

*Children*

Ref. No.: 5158
Name: A Step in Time
Height: 8.5
Status: Open edition, retired
Issue Year: 1982
Issue Price: $90
Last Year: 1998
Last Retail Price: $200

Ref. No.: 5211
Name: Angela
Height: 8.5
Status: Open edition, retired
Issue Year: 1984
Issue Price: $105
Last Year: 2002
Last Retail Price: $270

Ref. No.: 5237
Name: School Chums
Height: 8.5
Status: Open issue, retired
Issue Year: 1984
Issue Price: $225
Last Year: 1996
Last Retail Price: $485

Ref. No.: 5380
Name: Sweet Harvest
Height: 8.5
Status: Open issue, retired
Issue Year: 1986
Issue Price: $450
Last Year: 1990
Last Retail Price: $610
Auction Price: $900

Ref. No.: 5716
Name: Land of the Giants
Height: 8.5
Status: Open issue, retired
Issue Year: 1990
Issue Price: $275
Last Year: 1994
Last Retail Price: $315

Ref. No.: 6031
Name: On the Go
Height: 8.5
Status: Open issue, retired
Issue Year: 1993
Issue Price: $475
Last Year: 1995
Last Retail Price: $485

**Ref. No.:** 6122
**Name:** A Great Adventure
**Height:** 8.5
**Status:** Open issue, retired
**Issue Year:** 1994
**Issue Price:** $198
**Last Year:** 1997
**Last Retail Price:** $215

**Ref. No.:** 5852
**Name:** Easter Bonnets
**Height:** 8.75
**Status:** Open issue, retired
**Issue Year:** 1992
**Issue Price:** $265
**Last Year:** 1993
**Last Retail Price:** $275
**High Auction Price:** $550
**Low Auction Price:** $450

**Ref. No.:** 4810
**Name:** Boy with Yacht
**Height:** 9
**Status:** Open issue, retired
**Issue Year:** 1972
**Issue Price:** $30
**Last Year:** 1998
**Last Retail Price:** $175

**Ref. No.:** 5009
**Name:** Curious Girl with Straw
Hat
**Height:** 9
**Status:** Open edition, active
**Issue Year:** 1978
**Issue Price:** $55
**2003 Retail Price:** $165

**Ref. No.:** 5025
**Name:** A Clean Sweep
**Height:** 9
**Status:** Open issue, retired
**Issue Year:** 1980
**Issue Price:** $100
**Last Year:** 1985
**Last Retail Price:** $112.50
**Auction Price:** $450

**Ref. No.:** 5164
**Name:** Cat Girl
**Height:** 9
**Status:** Open issue, retired
**Issue Year:** 1982
**Issue Price:** $125
**Last Year:** 1985
**Last Retail Price:** $125
**High Auction Price:** $600
**Low Auction Price:** $225

*Children*

**Ref. No.:** 5344
**Name:** A Stitch in Time
**Height:** 9
**Status:** Open issue, retired
**Issue Year:** 1986
**Issue Price:** $425
**Last Year:** 1997
**Last Retail Price:** $810

**Ref. No.:** 5909
**Name:** All Dressed Up
**Height:** 9
**Status:** Open edition, retired
**Issue Year:** 1992
**Issue Price:** $440
**Last Year:** 1997
**Last Retail Price:** $450

**Ref. No.:** 6412
**Name:** Joy of Life
**Height:** 9
**Status:** Open issue, retired
**Issue Year:** 1997
**Issue Price:** $215
**Last Year:** 2001
**Last Retail Price:** $220

**Ref. No.:** 6413
**Name:** Spirit of Youth
**Height:** 9
**Status:** Open issue, retired
**Issue Year:** 1997
**Issue Price:** $215
**Last Year:** 2001
**Last Retail Price:** $220

**Ref. No.:** 6421
**Name:** Off to Bed
**Height:** 9
**Status:** Open issue, retired
**Issue Year:** 1997
**Issue Price:** $145
**Last Year:** 1999
**Last Retail Price:** $145

**Ref. No.:** 6420
**Name:** My Favorite Slippers
**Height:** 9
**Status:** Open issue, retired
**Issue Year:** 1997
**Issue Price:** $145
**Last Year:** 1999
**Last Retail Price:** $145

**Ref. No.:** 6464
**Name:** Who's There?
**Height:** 9
**Status:** Open issue, retired
**Issue Year:** 1997
**Issue Price:** $115
**Last Year:** 2002
**Last Retail Price:** $125

**Ref. No.:** 6495
**Name:** The Road To Success
**Height:** 9
**Status:** Open issue, active
**Issue Year:** 1998
**Issue Price:** $155
**2003 Retail Price:** $175

**Ref. No.:** 5038
**Name:** Girl Bowing
**Height:** 9.25
**Status:** Open issue, retired
**Issue Year:** 1979
**Issue Price:** $185
**Last Year:** 1981
**Last Retail Price:** $240

**Ref. No.:** 5709
**Name:** Between Classes
**Height:** 9.25
**Status:** Open issue, retired
**Issue Year:** 1990
**Issue Price:** $280
**Last Year:** 1993
**Last Retail Price:** $315
**Auction Price:** $200

**Ref. No.:** 6117
**Name:** Constance
**Height:** 9.25
**Status:** Open edition, retired
**Issue Year:** 1994
**Issue Price:** $195
**Last Year:** 1997
**Last Retail Price:** $205

**Ref. No.:** 118.06
**Name:** Girl with Pitcher
**Height:** 9.5
**Status:** Very rare
**Issue Year:** 1956
**Issue Price:** Unknown
**Last Year:** Unknown
**Last Retail Price:** Unknown

*Children*

**Ref. No.:** 5040
**Name:** Girl Walking
**Height:** 9.5
**Status:** Open issue, retired
**Issue Year:** 1979
**Issue Price:** $150
**Last Year:** 1981
**Last Retail Price:** $192.50
**High Auction Price:** $425
**Low Auction Price:** $400

**Ref. No.:** 5084
**Name:** A Good Book
**Height:** 9.5
**Status:** Open issue, retired
**Issue Year:** 1980
**Issue Price:** $175
**Last Year:** 1985
**Last Retail Price:** $190
**High Auction Price:** $600
**Low Auction Price:** $450

**Ref. No.:** 5162
**Name:** Mouse Girl
**Height:** 9.5
**Status:** Open issue, retired
**Issue Year:** 1982
**Issue Price:** $125
**Last Year:** 1985
**Last Retail Price:** $125
**High Auction Price:** $300
**Low Auction Price:** $175

**Ref. No.:** 5708
**Name:** My First Class
**Height:** 9.5
**Status:** Open issue, retired
**Issue Year:** 1990
**Issue Price:** $280
**Last Year:** 1993
**Last Retail Price:** $315
**Auction Price:** $250

**Ref. No.:** 6806
**Name:** Delightful
**Height:** 9.5
**Status:** Open issue, active
**Issue Year:** 2001
**Issue Price:** $190
**2003 Retail Price:** $195

**Ref. No.:** 4925
**Name:** Laziness
**Height:** 9.75
**Status:** Open issue, retired
**Issue Year:** 1974
**Issue Price:** $140
**Last Year:** 1980
**Last Retail Price:** $235
**Auction Price:** $650

**Ref. No.:** 5006
**Name:** Naughty Girl
**Height:** 9.75
**Status:** Open edition, retired
**Issue Year:** 1978
**Issue Price:** $55
**Last Year:** 1998
**Last Retail Price:** $155

**Ref. No.:** 5007
**Name:** Bashful
**Height:** 9.75
**Status:** Open edition, retired
**Issue Year:** 1978
**Issue Price:** $55
**Last Year:** 1997
**Last Retail Price:** $155

**Ref. No.:** 5008
**Name:** The Dreamer
**Height:** 9.75
**Status:** Open edition, retired
**Issue Year:** 1978
**Issue Price:** $55
**Last Year:** 1999
**Last Retail Price:** $155

**Ref. No.:** 5010
**Name:** Prissy
**Height:** 9.75
**Status:** Open edition, retired
**Issue Year:** 1978
**Issue Price:** $55
**Last Year:** 1997
**Last Retail Price:** $155

**Ref. No.:** 5039
**Name:** Candid
**Height:** 9.75
**Status:** Open issue, retired
**Issue Year:** 1979
**Issue Price:** $145
**Last Year:** 1981
**Last Retail Price:** $185
**High Auction Price:** $500
**Low Auction Price:** $375

**Ref. No.:** 5199
**Name:** Girl Graduate
**Height:** 9.75
**Status:** Open edition, active
**Issue Year:** 1984
**Issue Price:** $160
**2003 Retail Price:** $295

*Children*

**Ref. No.:** 5287
**Name:** Winter Frost
**Height:** 9.75
**Status:** Open issue, active
**Issue Year:** 1985
**Issue Price:** $270
**2003 Retail Price:** $525

**Ref. No.:** 5615
**Name:** Bathing Beauty
**Height:** 9.75
**Status:** Open issue, retired
**Issue Year:** 1989
**Issue Price:** $265
**Last Year:** 1991
**Last Retail Price:** $300
**Auction Price:** $475

**Ref. No.:** 5702
**Name:** Back to School
**Height:** 9.75
**Status:** Open issue, retired
**Issue Year:** 1990
**Issue Price:** $350
**Last Year:** 1993
**Last Retail Price:** $405

**Ref. No.:** 5707
**Name:** After School
**Height:** 9.75
**Status:** Open issue, retired
**Issue Year:** 1990
**Issue Price:** $280
**Last Year:** 1993
**Last Retail Price:** $315
**Auction Price:** $275

**Ref. No.:** 1108
**Name:** Girl's Head
**Height:** 10
**Status:** Open edition, retired
**Issue Year:** 1971
**Issue Price:** $70
**Last Year:** 1973
**Last Retail Price:** $85

**Ref. No.:** 5092
**Name:** After the Dance
**Height:** 10
**Status:** Open issue, retired
**Issue Year:** 1980
**Issue Price:** $165
**Last Year:** 1983
**Last Retail Price:** $165
**High Auction Price:** $475
**Low Auction Price:** $200

**Ref. No.:** 5095
**Name:** Taking a Bow
**Height:** 10
**Status:** Open issue, retired
**Issue Year:** 1980
**Issue Price:** $165
**Last Year:** 1983
**Last Retail Price:** $165
**High Auction Price:** $375
**Low Auction Price:** $175

**Ref. No.:** 5118
**Name:** Daisy
**Height:** 10
**Status:** Open issue, retired
**Issue Year:** 1982
**Issue Price:** $170
**Last Year:** 1985
**Last Retail Price:** $170
**High Auction Price:** $900
**Low Auction Price:** $475

**Ref. No.:** 6353
**Name:** A World of Love
**Height:** 10
**Status:** Open issue, retired
**Issue Year:** 1997
**Issue Price:** $450
**Last Year:** 1999
**Last Retail Price:** $475
**Comment:** Created for UNICEF

**Ref. No.:** 6463
**Name:** My Cuddly Puppy
**Height:** 10
**Status:** Open issue, active
**Issue Year:** 1997
**Issue Price:** $110
**2003 Retail Price:** $125

**Ref. No.:** 6482
**Name:** Little Sleepwalker
**Height:** 10
**Status:** Open issue, retired
**Issue Year:** 1997
**Issue Price:** $110
**Last Year:** 2001
**Last Retail Price:** $120

**Ref. No.:** 6494
**Name:** Onward and Upward
**Height:** 10
**Status:** Open issue, active
**Issue Year:** 1998
**Issue Price:** $170
**2003 Retail Price:** $175

*Children*

**Ref. No.:** 6584
**Name:** Sunday Prayer
**Height:** 10
**Status:** Open issue, retired
**Issue Year:** 1998
**Issue Price:** $200
**Last Year:** 2001
**Last Retail Price:** $230

**Ref. No.:** 6813
**Name:** Little School Boy
**Height:** 10
**Status:** Open issue, active
**Issue Year:** 2002
**Issue Price:** $300
**2003 Retail Price:** $300

**Ref. No.:** 4981
**Name:** Ironing Time
**Height:** 10.25
**Status:** Open issue, retired
**Issue Year:** 1977
**Issue Price:** $80
**Last Year:** 1985
**Last Retail Price:** $107.5
**High Auction Price:** $375
**Low Auction Price:** $350

**Ref. No.:** 5011
**Name:** Coy
**Height:** 10.25
**Status:** Open edition, retired
**Issue Year:** 1978
**Issue Price:** $55
**Last Year:** 1998
**Last Retail Price:** $155

**Ref. No.:** 5119
**Name:** Lily
**Height:** 10.25
**Status:** Open issue, retired
**Issue Year:** 1982
**Issue Price:** $170
**Last Year:** 1985
**Last Retail Price:** $170
**High Auction Price:** $875
**Low Auction Price:** $750

**Ref. No.:** 5120
**Name:** Rose
**Height:** 10.25
**Status:** Open issue, retired
**Issue Year:** 1982
**Issue Price:** $170
**Last Year:** 1985
**Last Retail Price:** $170

**Ref. No.:** 5163
**Name:** Bunny Girl
**Height:** 10.25
**Status:** Open issue, retired
**Issue Year:** 1982
**Issue Price:** $125
**Last Year:** 1985
**Last Retail Price:** $125
**High Auction Price:** $525
**Low Auction Price:** $225

**Ref. No.:** 1379
**Name:** Debbie and Her Doll
**Height:** 10.5
**Status:** Open issue, retired
**Issue Year:** 1978
**Issue Price:** $215
**Last Year:** 1985
**Last Retail Price:** $285
**High Auction Price:** $1000
**Low Auction Price:** $700

**Ref. No.:** 1416
**Name:** Budding Blossoms
**Height:** 10.5
**Status:** Open edition, retired
**Issue Year:** 1982
**Issue Price:** $140
**Last Year:** 1997
**Last Retail Price:** $315

**Ref. No.:** 1417
**Name:** Nature's Bounty
**Height:** 10.5
**Status:** Open issue, retired
**Issue Year:** 1982
**Issue Price:** $160
**Last Year:** 1995
**Last Retail Price:** $340

**Ref. No.:** 4510
**Name:** Girl with Umbrella
**Height:** 10.5
**Status:** Open issue, retired
**Issue Year:** 1969
**Last Year:** 1993
**Issue Price:** $37.50
**Last Retail Price:** $245
**Auction Price:** $350

**Ref. No.:** 4985
**Name:** Mimi
**Height:** 10.5
**Status:** Open issue, retired
**Issue Year:** 1978
**Issue Price:** $110
**Last Year:** 1980
**Last Retail Price:** $125
**Auction Price:** $650

*Children*

**Ref. No.:** 4987
**Name:** Sweet Girl
**Height:** 10.5
**Status:** Open issue, retired
**Issue Year:** 1978
**Issue Price:** $110
**Last Year:** 1980
**Last Retail Price:** $125
**High Auction Price:** $425
**Low Auction Price:** $250

**Ref. No.:** 5079
**Name:** Pottery Seller
**Height:** 10.5
**Status:** Open issue, retired
**Issue Year:** 1980
**Issue Price:** $300
**Last Year:** 1985
**Last Retail Price:** $225
**High Auction Price:** $750
**Low Auction Price:** $650

**Ref. No.:** 5093
**Name:** A Dancing Partner
**Height:** 10.5
**Status:** Open issue, retired
**Issue Year:** 1980
**Issue Price:** $165
**Last Year:** 1983
**Last Retail Price:** $165
**High Auction Price:** $300
**Low Auction Price:** $175

**Ref. No.:** 5121
**Name:** Iris
**Height:** 10.5
**Status:** Open issue, retired
**Issue Year:** 1982
**Issue Price:** $170
**Last Year:** 1985
**Last Retail Price:** $170

**Ref. No.:** 5141
**Name:** Balloon Seller
**Height:** 10.5
**Status:** Open edition, retired
**Issue Year:** 1982
**Issue Price:** $145
**Last Year:** 1996
**Last Retail Price:** $250

**Ref. No.:** 5198
**Name:** Boy Graduate
**Height:** 10.5
**Status:** Open issue, active
**Issue Year:** 1984
**Issue Price:** $160
**2003 Retail Price:** $295

**Ref. No.:** 5768
**Name:** Academy Days
**Height:** 10.5
**Status:** Open issue, retired
**Issue Year:** 1991
**Issue Price:** $280
**Last Year:** 1993
**Last Retail Price:** $310
**Auction Price:** $150

**Ref. No.:** 6814
**Name:** Little School Girl
**Height:** 10.5
**Status:** Open issue, active
**Issue Year:** 2002
**Issue Price:** $300
**2003 Retail Price:** $300

**Ref. No.:** 1374
**Name:** Waiting in the Park
**Height:** 10.75
**Status:** Open issue, retired
**Issue Year:** 1978
**Issue Price:** $235
**Last Year:** 1993
**Last Retail Price:** $450
**Auction Price:** $550

**Ref. No.:** 1107
**Name:** Girl's Head
**Height:** 11
**Status:** Open edition, retired
**Issue Year:** 1971
**Issue Price:** $95
**Last Year:** 1975
**Last Retail Price:** $155

**Ref. No.:** 1378
**Name:** Suzy and Her Doll
**Height:** 11
**Status:** Open issue, retired
**Issue Year:** 1978
**Issue Price:** $215
**Last Year:** 1985
**Last Retail Price:** $285
**High Auction Price:** $800
**Low Auction Price:** $650

**Ref. No.:** 4931
**Name:** Children with Fruit
**Height:** 11
**Status:** Open issue, retired
**Issue Year:** 1974
**Issue Price:** $210
**Last Year:** 1981
**Last Retail Price:** $510
**High Auction Price:** $600
**Low Auction Price:** $450

*Children*

**Ref. No.:** 4939
**Name:** Milkmaid
**Height:** 11
**Status:** Open issue, retired
**Issue Year:** 1976
**Issue Price:** $70
**Last Year:** 1981
**Last Retail Price:** $110
**High Auction Price:** $350
**Low Auction Price:** $200

**Ref. No.:** 5044
**Name:** Girl With Toy Wagon
**Height:** 11
**Status:** Open edition, retired
**Issue Year:** 1980
**Issue Price:** $115
**Last Year:** 1997
**Last Retail Price:** $260

**Ref. No.:** 6483
**Name:** It's Morning Already?
**Height:** 11
**Status:** Open issue, retired
**Issue Year:** 1997
**Issue Price:** $105
**Last Year:** 2001
**Last Retail Price:** $110

**Ref. No.:** 5045
**Name:** Belinda with Her Doll
**Height:** 11.25
**Status:** Open issue, retired
**Issue Year:** 1980
**Issue Price:** $115
**Last Year:** 1995
**Last Retail Price:** $215

**Ref. No.:** 5081
**Name:** Girl Pottery Seller
**Height:** 11.75
**Status:** Open issue, retired
**Issue Year:** 1980
**Issue Price:** $300
**Last Year:** 1985
**Last Retail Price:** $225
**High Auction Price:** $725
**Low Auction Price:** $600

**Ref. No.:** 5150
**Name:** Girl's Head
**Height:** 12
**Status:** Open edition, retired
**Issue Year:** 1982
**Issue Price:** $435
**Last Year:** 1983
**Last Retail Price:** $435

**Ref. No.:** 5151
**Name:** Girl's Head
**Height:** 12
**Status:** Open edition, retired
**Issue Year:** 1982
**Issue Price:** $380
**Last Year:** 1983
**Last Retail Price:** $380
**Auction Price:** $1400

**Ref. No.:** 1125
**Name:** Pelusa
**Height:** 12.25
**Status:** Open issue, retired
**Issue Year:** 1971
**Issue Price:** $70
**Last Year:** 1978
**Last Retail Price:** $72.5
**High Auction Price:** $1800
**Low Auction Price:** $1150

**Ref. No.:** 6244
**Name:** Pumpkin Ride
**Height:** 12.25
**Status:** Open issue, retired
**Issue Year:** 1996
**Issue Price:** $695
**Last Year:** 1999
**Last Retail Price:** $695

**Ref. No.:** 1380
**Name:** Cathy and Her Doll
**Height:** 12.25
**Status:** Open issue, retired
**Issue Year:** 1978
**Issue Price:** $215
**Last Year:** 1985
**Last Retail Price:** $285
**High Auction Price:** $950
**Low Auction Price:** $775

**Ref. No.:** 3506
**Name:** Maiden
**Height:** 12.5
**Status:** Open issue, retired
**Issue Year:** 1978
**Issue Price:** $230
**Last Year:** 1988
**Last Retail Price:** $350
**Auction Price:** $375

**Ref. No.:** 6182
**Name:** Wanda
**Height:** 12.5
**Status:** Open issue, active
**Issue Year:** 1996
**Issue Price:** $205
**2003 Retail Price:** $225

*Children*

**Ref. No.:** 1028
**Name:** Girl with Heart
**Height:** 13
**Status:** Open issue, retired
**Issue Year:** 1969
**Issue Price:** $37.50
**Last Year:** 1970
**Last Retail Price:** $37.50

**Ref. No.:** 5153
**Name:** Girl's Head
**Height:** 13
**Status:** Open edition, retired
**Issue Year:** 1982
**Issue Price:** $475
**Last Year:** 1983
**Last Retail Price:** $475
**Auction Price:** $575

**Ref. No.:** 5286
**Name:** Fall Clean-Up
**Height:** 13
**Status:** Open issue, active
**Issue Year:** 1985
**Issue Price:** $295
**2003 Retail Price:** $575

**Ref. No.:** 6186
**Name:** For a Better World
**Height:** 13.5
**Status:** Open issue, retired
**Issue Year:** 1995
**Issue Price:** $575
**Last Year:** 1997
**Last Retail Price:** $575

**Ref. No.:** 1469
**Name:** Girl On Carousel Horse
**Height:** 15
**Status:** Open issue, retired
**Issue Year:** 1985
**Issue Price:** $470
**Last Year:** 2000
**Last Retail Price:** $945

**Ref. No.:** 1470
**Name:** Boy On Carousel Horse
**Height:** 15
**Status:** Open issue, retired
**Issue Year:** 1985
**Issue Price:** $470
**Last Year:** 2000
**Last Retail Price:** $945

**Ref. No.:** 5731
**Name:** Carousel Charm
**Height:** 16.5
**Status:** Open issue, retired
**Issue Year:** 1991
**Issue Price:** $1700
**Last Year:** 1994
**Last Retail Price:** $1850

**Ref. No.:** 5732
**Name:** Carousel Canter
**Height:** 16.5
**Status:** Open issue, retired
**Issue Year:** 1991
**Issue Price:** $1700
**Last Year:** 1994
**Last Retail Price:** $1850

*Children*

# *Families*

**Mothers and Children**

**Ref. No.:** 1606
**Name:** Latest Addition
**Height:** 6.25
**Status:** Open issue, active
**Issue Year:** 1989
**Issue Price:** $385
**2003 Retail Price:** $495

**Ref. No.:** 6713
**Name:** An Embroidery Lesson
**Height:** 7.25
**Status:** Open issue, retired
**Issue Year:** 2000
**Issue Price:** $545
**Last Year:** 2002
**Last Retail Price:** $575

**Ref. No.:** 5845
**Name:** Dressing the Baby
**Height:** 7.5
**Status:** Open issue, active
**Issue Year:** 1992
**Issue Price:** $295
**2003 Retail Price:** $295

**Ref. No.:** 5715
**Name:** Mommy, It's Cold!
**Height:** 7.75
**Status:** Open issue, retired
**Issue Year:** 1990
**Issue Price:** $360
**Last Year:** 1994
**Last Retail Price:** $415

**Ref. No.:** 5900
**Name:** Sleep Tight
**Height:** 8
**Status:** Open issue, retired
**Issue Year:** 1992
**Issue Price:** $450
**Last Year:** 1997
**Last Retail Price:** $495

**Ref. No.:** 5449
**Name:** Good Night
**Height:** 8.25
**Status:** Open issue, active
**Issue Year:** 1987
**Issue Price:** $225
**2003 Retail Price:** $395

**Ref. No.:** 1527
**Name:** Tenderness
**Height:** 8.5
**Status:** Open issue, active
**Issue Year:** 1987
**Issue Price:** $260
**2003 Retail Price:** $450

**Ref. No.:** 5140
**Name:** Feeding Her Son
**Height:** 9
**Status:** Open issue, retired
**Issue Year:** 1982
**Issue Price:** $170
**Last Year:** 1991
**Last Retail Price:** $280
**High Auction Price:** $400
**Low Auction Price:** $350

**Ref. No.:** 5995
**Name:** Soft Meow
**Height:** 9
**Status:** Open issue, retired
**Issue Year:** 1993
**Issue Price:** $550
**Last Year:** 1998
**Last Retail Price:** $515

**Ref. No.:** 6503
**Name:** My Little Treasure
**Height:** 9
**Status:** Open issue, active
**Issue Year:** 1998
**Issue Price:** $295
**2003 Retail Price:** $395

**Ref. No.:** 6506
**Name:** Guess Who?
**Height:** 9
**Status:** Open issue, retired
**Issue Year:** 1998
**Issue Price:** $430
**Last Year:** 2000
**Last Retail Price:** $490

**Ref. No.:** 5994
**Name:** Meet My Friend
**Height:** 9.25
**Status:** Open issue, retired
**Issue Year:** 1993
**Issue Price:** $695
**Last Year:** 1996
**Last Retail Price:** $695

*Families*

**Ref. No.:** 5299
**Name:** Mother with Child
and Lamb
**Height:** 9.5
**Status:** Open issue, retired
**Issue Year:** 1985
**Issue Price:** $180
**Last Year:** 1988
**Last Retail Price:** $210
**High Auction Price:** $750
**Low Auction Price:** $325

**Ref. No.:** 4890
**Name:** Bathing the Girl
**Height:** 9.5
**Status:** Open issue, retired
**Issue Year:** 1974
**Issue Price:** $165
**Last Year:** 1978
**Last Retail Price:** $285
**Auction Price:** $650

**Ref. No.:** 4993
**Name:** Gypsy Vendors
**Height:** 9.5
**Status:** Open issue, retired
**Issue Year:** 1978
**Issue Price:** $165
**Last Year:** 1985
**Last Retail Price:** $220
**High Auction Price:** $625
**Low Auction Price:** $450

**Ref. No.:** 5596
**Name:** Mother's Day
**Height:** 9.5
**Status:** Open issue, retired
**Issue Year:** 1989
**Issue Price:** $400
**Last Year:** 1998
**Last Retail Price:** $495

**Ref. No.:** 5650
**Name:** Anticipation
**Height:** 9.5
**Status:** Open issue, retired
**Issue Year:** 1990
**Issue Price:** $300
**Last Year:** 1993
**Last Retail Price:** $340

**Ref. No.:** 5989
**Name:** A Mother's Touch
**Height:** 9.5
**Status:** Open issue, retired
**Issue Year:** 1993
**Issue Price:** $495
**Last Year:** 1996
**Last Retail Price:** $470

**Ref. No.:** 4843
**Name:** Donkey Ride
**Height:** 9.75
**Status:** Open issue, retired
**Issue Year:** 1973
**Issue Price:** $86
**Last Year:** 1981
**Last Retail Price:** $155
**High Auction Price:** $700
**Low Auction Price:** $450

**Ref. No.:** 5721
**Name:** Once Upon A Time
**Height:** 10.25
**Status:** Open issue, retired
**Issue Year:** 1990
**Issue Price:** $550
**Last Year:** 1997
**Last Retail Price:** $650

**Ref. No.:** 5758
**Name:** Sunday Best
**Height:** 10.25
**Status:** Open issue, retired
**Issue Year:** 1991
**Issue Price:** $725
**Last Year:** 1997
**Last Retail Price:** $785

**Ref. No.:** 5786
**Name:** Story Hour
**Height:** 10.25
**Status:** Open issue, retired
**Issue Year:** 1991
**Issue Price:** $550
**Last Year:** 1997
**Last Retail Price:** $625

**Ref. No.:** 5793
**Name:** Precocious Ballerina
**Height:** 10.25
**Status:** Open issue, retired
**Issue Year:** 1991
**Issue Price:** $575
**Last Year:** 1995
**Last Retail Price:** $625

**Ref. No.:** 5142
**Name:** Solace
**Height:** 10.5
**Status:** Open issue, retired
**Issue Year:** 1982
**Issue Price:** $195
**Last Year:** 1991
**Last Retail Price:** $310
**Auction Price:** $475

*Families*

**Ref. No.:** 5457
**Name:** Bedtime Story
**Height:** 10.5
**Status:** Open issue, active
**Issue Year:** 1988
**Issue Price:** $275
**2003 Retail Price:** $360

**Ref. No.:** 5085
**Name:** Woman and Sleeping Girl
**Height:** 10.75
**Status:** Open issue, retired
**Issue Year:** 1980
**Issue Price:** Unknown
**Last Year:** 1985
**Last Retail Price:** $422.50
**Auction Price:** $800

**Ref. No.:** 6705
**Name:** One For You, One For Me
**Height:** 10.75
**Status:** Open issue, active
**Issue Year:** 2000
**Issue Price:** $370
**2003 Retail Price:** $395

**Ref. No.:** 5371
**Name:** Family Roots
**Height:** 11
**Status:** Open issue, active
**Issue Year:** 1986
**Issue Price:** $575
**2003 Retail Price:** $950

**Ref. No.:** 5874
**Name:** Off We Go
**Height:** 11.25
**Status:** Open issue, retired
**Issue Year:** 1992
**Issue Price:** $365
**Last Year:** 1994
**Last Retail Price:** $385

**Ref. No.:** 5946
**Name:** A Mother's Way
**Height:** 11.25
**Status:** Open issue, retired
**Issue Year:** 1993
**Issue Price:** $1350
**Last Year:** 1996
**Last Retail Price:** $1350

**Ref. No.:** 5757
**Name:** Beautiful Tresses
**Height:** 11.5
**Status:** Open issue, retired
**Issue Year:** 1991
**Issue Price:** $725
**Last Year:** 1993
**Last Retail Price:** $785

**Ref. No.:** 6634
**Name:** A Mother's Love
**Height:** 11.5
**Status:** Open issue, active
**Issue Year:** 1999
**Issue Price:** $335
**2003 Retail Price:** $350

**Ref. No.:** 6765
**Name:** An Afternoon Nap
**Height:** 11.5
**Status:** Open issue, active
**Issue Year:** 2001
**Issue Price:** $485
**2003 Retail Price:** $575

**Ref. No.:** 5083
**Name:** Lullabye and Goodnight
**Height:** 11.75
**Status:** Open issue, retired
**Issue Year:** 1980
**Issue Price:** $485
**Last Year:** 1983
**Last Retail Price:** $485
**Auction Price:** $1450

**Ref. No.:** 5873
**Name:** Modern Mother
**Height:** 11.75
**Status:** Open issue, retired
**Issue Year:** 1992
**Issue Price:** $325
**Last Year:** 1996
**Last Retail Price:** $335

**Ref. No.:** 5767
**Name:** First Sampler
**Height:** 12
**Status:** Open issue, retired
**Issue Year:** 1991
**Issue Price:** $625
**Last Year:** 1995
**Last Retail Price:** $680

*Families*

**Ref. No.:** 6851
**Name:** A Mother's Embrace
**Height:** 12
**Status:** Open issue, active
**Issue Year:** 2002
**Issue Price:** $370
**2003 Retail Price:** $375

**Ref. No.:** 6003
**Name:** Ready to Learn
**Height:** 12.25
**Status:** Open issue, retired
**Issue Year:** 1993
**Issue Price:** $650
**Last Year:** 1999
**Last Retail Price:** $650

**Ref. No.:** 4938
**Name:** Baby's Outing
**Height:** 12.5
**Status:** Open edition, retired
**Issue Year:** 1976
**Issue Price:** $250
**Last Year:** 2000
**Last Retail Price:** $775

**Ref. No.:** 5425
**Name:** Studying in the Park
**Height:** 12.5
**Status:** Open issue, retired
**Issue Year:** 1987
**Issue Price:** $675
**Last Year:** 1991
**Last Retail Price:** $950
**High Auction Price:** $925
**Low Auction Price:** $700

**Ref. No.:** 4575
**Name:** Mother and Child
**Height:** 13
**Status:** Open issue, retired
**Issue Year:** 1969
**Issue Price:** $47.50
**Last Year:** 1997
**Last Retail Price:** $265

**Ref. No.:** 6544
**Name:** On Our Way
**Height:** 13
**Status:** Open issue, retired
**Issue Year:** 1998
**Issue Price:** $340
**Last Year:** 2001
**Last Retail Price:** $375

**Ref. No.:** 4666
**Name:** Woman with Girl
    and Donkey
**Height:** 13.25
**Status:** Open issue, retired
**Issue Year:** 1969
**Issue Price:** $130
**Last Year:** 1979
**Last Retail Price:** $225

**Ref. No.:** 4701
**Name:** Mother and Child
**Height:** 13.25
**Status:** Open issue, retired
**Issue Year:** 1970
**Issue Price:** $45
**Last Year:** 1997
**Last Retail Price:** $295

**Ref. No.:** 6781
**Name:** Sunset in the Country
**Height:** 13.5
**Status:** Open issue, active
**Issue Year:** 2001
**Issue Price:** $325
**2003 Retail Price:** $350
**Comment:** To be retired as of
    December 31, 2003

**Ref. No.:** 6179
**Name:** Peaceful Moment
**Height:** 14
**Status:** Open issue, retired
**Issue Year:** 1995
**Issue Price:** $385
**Last Year:** 2002
**Last Retail Price:** $385

**Ref. No.:** 1353
**Name:** Lady with Girl
**Height:** 14.25
**Status:** Open issue, retired
**Issue Year:** 1978
**Issue Price:** $175
**Last Year:** 1985
**Last Retail Price:** $230
**High Auction Price:** $750
**Low Auction Price:** $450

**Ref. No.:** 4658
**Name:** Bolivian Mother
**Height:** 14.25
**Status:** Open issue, retired
**Issue Year:** 1969
**Issue Price:** $70
**Last Year:** 1972
**Last Retail Price:** $75

*Families*

**Ref. No.:** 6648
**Name:** Flowers In Bloom
**Height:** 14.5
**Status:** Open issue, retired
**Issue Year:** 2000
**Issue Price:** $545
**Last Year:** 2002
**Last Retail Price:** $550
**Comment:** Introduced by select
  dealers in 1999

**Ref. No.:** 6771
**Name:** Someone To Look Up To
**Height:** 14.5
**Status:** Open issue, active
**Issue Year:** 2001
**Issue Price:** $270
**2003 Retail Price:** $295

**Ref. No.:** 6301
**Name:** Care and Tenderness
**Height:** 14.75
**Status:** Open issue, retired
**Issue Year:** 1996
**Issue Price:** $850
**Last Year:** 2001
**Last Retail Price:** $850

**Ref. No.:** 4864
**Name:** Mother
**Height:** 15
**Status:** Open issue, retired
**Issue Year:** 1974
**Issue Price:** $190
**Last Year:** 1979
**Last Retail Price:** $450
**Auction Price:** $850

**Ref. No.:** 1429
**Name:** Winter Wonderland
**Height:** 15.75
**Status:** Open issue, retired
**Issue Year:** 1982
**Issue Price:** $1025
**Last Year:** 2001
**Last Retail Price:** $2230

**Ref. No.:** 5086
**Name:** Mother Amabilis
**Height:** 15.75
**Status:** Open issue, retired
**Issue Year:** 1980
**Issue Price:** $275
**Last Year:** 1983
**Last Retail Price:** $275
**High Auction Price:** $450
**Low Auction Price:** $425

## Fathers and Children

**Ref. No.:** 6858
**Name:** My Little Sweetie
**Height:** 18.5
**Status:** Open issue, active
**Issue Year:** 2002
**Issue Price:** $690
**2003 Retail Price:** $690

**Ref. No.:** 5139
**Name:** A New Doll House
**Height:** 7
**Status:** Open issue, retired
**Issue Year:** 1982
**Issue Price:** $185
**Last Year:** 1985
**Last Retail Price:** $185
**High Auction Price:** $950
**Low Auction Price:** $700

**Ref. No.:** 5584
**Name:** Daddy's Girl
**Height:** 8.5
**Status:** Open issue, retired
**Issue Year:** 1989
**Issue Price:** $315
**Last Year:** 1996
**Last Retail Price:** $395

**Ref. No.:** 5899
**Name:** Just One More
**Height:** 8.5
**Status:** Open issue, retired
**Issue Year:** 1992
**Issue Price:** $450
**Last Year:** 1997
**Last Retail Price:** $495

**Ref. No.:** 6001
**Name:** My Dad
**Height:** 9
**Status:** Open issue, retired
**Issue Year:** 1993
**Issue Price:** $550
**Last Year:** 1995
**Last Retail Price:** $550

**Ref. No.:** 6504
**Name:** Daddy's Blessing
**Height:** 9
**Status:** Open issue, active
**Issue Year:** 1998
**Issue Price:** $340
**2003 Retail Price:** $395

*Families*

**Ref. No.:** 6770
**Name:** Reading With Daddy
**Height:** 9.25
**Status:** Open issue, retired
**Issue Year:** 2001
**Issue Price:** $380
**Last Year:** 2002
**Last Retail Price:** $395

**Ref. No.:** 5082
**Name:** Little Flower Seller
**Height:** 10.75
**Status:** Open issue, retired
**Issue Year:** 1980
**Issue Price:** $750
**Last Year:** 1985
**Last Retail Price:** $820
**High Auction Price:** $3500
**Low Auction Price:** $1800

**Ref. No.:** 6793
**Name:** A Day With Dad
**Height:** 10.75
**Status:** Open issue, active
**Issue Year:** 2001
**Issue Price:** $395
**2003 Retail Price:** $450

**Ref. No.:** 6202
**Name:** Daddy's Little Sweetheart
**Height:** 12.5
**Status:** Open issue, active
**Issue Year:** 1995
**Issue Price:** $595
**2003 Retail Price:** $595

**Ref. No.:** 6609
**Name:** Like Father, Like Son
**Height:** 12.5
**Status:** Open issue, retired
**Issue Year:** 1999
**Issue Price:** $440
**Last Year:** 2002
**Last Retail Price:** $450

**Ref. No.:** 4888
**Name:** The Kiss
**Height:** 13
**Status:** Open issue, retired
**Issue Year:** 1974
**Issue Price:** $150
**Last Year:** 1983
**Last Retail Price:** $250
**High Auction Price:** $700
**Low Auction Price:** $550

**Ref. No.:** 5751
**Name:** Walk with Father
**Height:** 13.5
**Status:** Open issue, retired
**Issue Year:** 1991
**Issue Price:** $375
**Last Year:** 1994
**Last Retail Price:** $410

**Ref. No.:** 4974
**Name:** Dutch Children
**Height:** 13.75
**Status:** Open issue, retired
**Issue Year:** 1977
**Issue Price:** $375
**Last Year:** 1981
**Last Retail Price:** $535
**Auction Price:** $1150

**Ref. No.:** 6467
**Name:** A Father's Pride
**Height:** 14
**Status:** Open issue, retired
**Issue Year:** 1998
**Issue Price:** $475
**Last Year:** 2002
**Last Retail Price:** $550

### Grandparents and Grandchildren

**Ref. No.:** 5780
**Name:** Walking the Fields
**Height:** 15.5
**Status:** Open issue, retired
**Issue Year:** 1991
**Issue Price:** $725
**Last Year:** 1993
**Last Retail Price:** $795

**Ref. No.:** 5215
**Name:** Fishing with Gramps
**Height:** 7.5
**Status:** Open issue, active
**Issue Year:** 1984
**Issue Price:** $410
**2003 Retail Price:** $925

**Ref. No.:** 5305
**Name:** Visit with Granny
**Height:** 9
**Status:** Open issue, retired
**Issue Year:** 1985
**Issue Price:** $275
**Last Year:** 1993
**Last Retail Price:** $515

*Families*

**Ref. No.:** 5677
**Name:** Twilight Years
**Height:** 10.75
**Status:** Open Issue, retired
**Issue Year:** 1990
**Issue Price:** $370
**Last Year:** 1997
**Last Retail Price:** $420

**Ref. No.:** 5207
**Name:** A Tall Yarn
**Height:** 11
**Status:** Open issue, retired
**Issue Year:** 1984
**Issue Price:** $260
**Last Year:** 2002
**Last Retail Price:** $575

**Ref. No.:** 6468
**Name:** A Fishing Lesson
**Height:** 12
**Status:** Open issue, retired
**Issue Year:** 2000
**Issue Price:** $530
**Last Year:** 2002
**Last Retail Price:** $545

**Ref. No.:** 4654
**Name:** The Grandfather
**Height:** 13.75
**Status:** Open issue, retired
**Issue Year:** 1969
**Issue Price:** $75
**Last Year:** 1979
**Last Retail Price:** $220
**High Auction Price:** $1400
**Low Auction Price:** $700

**Ref. No.:** 6553
**Name:** Grandparents' Joy
**Height:** 14
**Status:** Open issue, retired
**Issue Year:** 1998
**Issue Price:** $645
**Last Year:** 2000
**Last Retail Price:** $700

**Ref. No.:** 1033
**Name:** Old Folks
**Height:** 19
**Status:** Open issue, retired
**Issue Year:** 1969
**Issue Price:** $140
**Last Year:** 1985
**Last Retail Price:** $410
**High Auction Price:** $1650
**Low Auction Price:** $1250

**Other Family**

**Ref. No.:** 5974
**Name:** Family Outing
**Height:** 12.75
**Status:** Open issue, retired
**Issue Year:** 1993
**Issue Price:** $4275
**Last Year:** 1997
**Last Retail Price:** $4275

**Ref. No.:** 6005
**Name:** Christening Day
**Height:** 14.25
**Status:** Open issue, retired
**Issue Year:** 1993
**Issue Price:** $1425
**Last Year:** 1995
**Last Retail Price:** $1425

**Ref. No.:** 1201
**Name:** The Family
**Height:** 21.5
**Status:** Open issue, retired
**Issue Year:** 1971
**Issue Price:** $245
**Last Year:** 1979
**Last Retail Price:** $450
**Auction Price:** $1300

# Women

**Young Women**

**Ref. No.:** 244.1
**Name:** Grace
**Height:** 4
**Status:** Very rare
**Issue Year:** 1958
**Issue Price:** Unknown
**Last Year:** Unknown
**Last Retail Price:** Unknown

**Ref. No.:** 296.13
**Name:** Country Girl
**Height:** 4.5
**Status:** Very rare
**Issue Year:** 1961
**Issue Price:** Unknown
**Last Year:** Unknown
**Last Retail Price:** Unknown

**Ref. No.:** 1661
**Name:** Mardi Gras Bust
**Height:** 6
**Status:** Open edition, retired
**Issue Year:** 1989
**Issue Price:** $500
**Last Year:** 1991
**Last Retail Price:** $595

**Ref. No.:** 1663
**Name:** Mardi Gras Bust
**Height:** 6
**Status:** Open edition, retired
**Issue Year:** 1989
**Issue Price:** $460
**Last Year:** 1991
**Last Retail Price:** $460

**Ref. No.:** 1023
**Name:** Girl with Daisy
**Height:** 6.25
**Status:** Open issue, retired
**Issue Year:** 1969
**Issue Price:** $47.50
**Last Year:** 1971
**Last Retail Price:** $47.50

**Ref. No.:** 1662
**Name:** Mardi Gras Bust
**Height:** 6.25
**Status:** Open edition, retired
**Issue Year:** 1989
**Issue Price:** $465
**Last Year:** 1991
**Last Retail Price:** $550
**Auction Price:** $600

**Ref. No.:** 1664
**Name:** Mardi Gras Bust
**Height:** 6.25
**Status:** Open edition, retired
**Issue Year:** 1989
**Issue Price:** $465
**Last Year:** 1991
**Last Retail Price:** $550

**Ref. No.:** 1672
**Name:** Kerchief's Lady
**Height:** 6.25
**Status:** Open edition, retired
**Issue Year:** 1989
**Issue Price:** $240
**Last Year:** 1991
**Last Retail Price:** $285

**Ref. No.:** 4713
**Name:** Girl Jewelry Dish
**Height:** 6.75
**Status:** Open issue, retired
**Issue Year:** 1970
**Issue Price:** $30
**Last Year:** 1978
**Last Retail Price:** $75

**Ref. No.:** 1665
**Name:** Lady With Hat
**Height:** 7
**Status:** Open edition, retired
**Issue Year:** 1989
**Issue Price:** $300
**Last Year:** 1991
**Last Retail Price:** $350

**Ref. No.:** 1671
**Name:** Lady of Style
**Height:** 7
**Status:** Open edition, retired
**Issue Year:** 1989
**Issue Price:** $235
**Last Year:** 1991
**Last Retail Price:** $275

**Ref. No.:** 6487
**Name:** New Shoes
**Height:** 7
**Status:** Open issue, retired
**Issue Year:** 1998
**Issue Price:** $150
**Last Year:** 2001
**Last Retail Price:** $170

*Women*

**Ref. No.:** 1212
**Name:** Woman Carrying Water
**Height:** 7.75
**Status:** Open issue, retired
**Issue Year:** 1972
**Issue Price:** $100
**Last Year:** 1983
**Last Retail Price:** $140
**High Auction Price:** $550
**Low Auction Price:** $500

**Ref. No.:** 6489
**Name:** Tailor Made
**Height:** 8
**Status:** Open edition, retired
**Issue Year:** 1997
**Issue Price:** $130
**Last Year:** 1997
**Last Retail Price:** $150
**Comment:** Lladró Special
    Edition Figurine

**Ref. No.:** 7525
**Name:** Ingenue
**Height:** 8
**Status:** Limited edition, sold out
**Issue Year:** 1993
**Issue Price:** $150
**Last Year:** 1994
**Last Retail Price:** $150
**Comment:** Exclusive to Princess
    House, USA

**Ref. No.:** 6488
**Name:** Gone Shopping
**Height:** 8
**Status:** Open issue, retired
**Issue Year:** 1998
**Issue Price:** $150
**Last Year:** 2001
**Last Retail Price:** $185

**Ref. No.:** 5598
**Name:** Bridesmaid
**Height:** 8.25
**Status:** Open edition, active
**Issue Year:** 1989
**Issue Price:** $150
**2003 Retail Price:** $195

**Ref. No.:** 5024
**Name:** Woman with Scarf
**Height:** 8.5
**Status:** Open issue, retired
**Issue Year:** 1978
**Issue Price:** $140.90
**Last Year:** 1985
**Last Retail Price:** $122.5
**High Auction Price:** $450
**Low Auction Price:** $275

**Ref. No.:** 6768
**Name:** Reading Companion
**Height:** 8.75
**Status:** Open issue, retired
**Issue Year:** 2001
**Issue Price:** $345
**Last Year:** 2002
**Last Retail Price:** $375

**Ref. No.:** 1669
**Name:** Turbanned Beauty
**Height:** 9
**Status:** Open edition, retired
**Issue Year:** 1989
**Issue Price:** $410
**Last Year:** 1991
**Last Retail Price:** $485

**Ref. No.:** 1670
**Name:** Spring Lady
**Height:** 9
**Status:** Open edition, retired
**Issue Year:** 1989
**Issue Price:** $1200
**Last Year:** 1991
**Last Retail Price:** $1400

**Ref. No.:** 5090
**Name:** Girl's Head
**Height:** 9
**Status:** Open edition, retired
**Issue Year:** 1980
**Issue Price:** $130
**Last Year:** 1981
**Last Retail Price:** $140

**Ref. No.:** 5428
**Name:** Feeding the Pigeons
**Height:** 9
**Status:** Open issue, retired
**Issue Year:** 1987
**Issue Price:** $490
**Last Year:** 1990
**Last Retail Price:** $590
**High Auction Price:** $700
**Low Auction Price:** $650

**Ref. No.:** 5614
**Name:** Startled
**Height:** 9
**Status:** Open issue, retired
**Issue Year:** 1989
**Issue Price:** $265
**Last Year:** 1991
**Last Retail Price:** $300
**Auction Price:** $425

*Women*

**Ref. No.:** 6130
**Name:** Spring Enchantment
**Height:** 9
**Status:** Open issue, active
**Issue Year:** 1996
**Issue Price:** $245
**2003 Retail Price:** $250

**Ref. No.:** 4918
**Name:** A Girl at the Pond
**Height:** 9
**Status:** Open issue, retired
**Issue Year:** 1974
**Issue Price:** $85
**Last Year:**1985
**Last Retail Price:** $190
**High Auction Price:** $500
**Low Auction Price:** $250

**Ref. No.:** 7617
**Name:** Garden Classic
**Height:** 9
**Status:** Limited edition, sold out
**Issue Year:** 1991
**Issue Price:** $295
**Last Year:** 1991
**Last Retail Price:** $295
**High Auction Price:** $1150
**Low Auction Price:** $600
**Comment:** Special event

**Ref. No.:** 6638
**Name:** A Quiet Evening
**Height:** 9.25
**Status:** Open issue, retired
**Issue Year:** 1999
**Issue Price:** $495
**Last Year:** 2001
**Last Retail Price:** $495

**Ref. No.:** 6754
**Name:** Sweet & Shy
**Height:** 9.25
**Status:** Open issue, active
**Issue Year:** 2001
**Issue Price:** $175
**2003 Retail Price:** $195

**Ref. No.:** 6755
**Name:** A Proper Pose
**Height:** 9.25
**Status:** Open issue, active
**Issue Year:** 2001
**Issue Price:** $175
**2003 Retail Price:** $195

**Ref. No.:** 362.13
**Name:** Farmer with Cow
**Height:** 9.5
**Status:** Very rare
**Issue Year:** 1967
**Issue Price:** Unknown
**Last Year:** Unknown
**Last Retail Price:** Unknown

**Ref. No.:** 4568
**Name:** Shepherdess with Ducks
**Height:** 9.5
**Status:** Open issue, retired
**Issue Year:** 1969
**Issue Price:** $45
**Last Year:** 1993
**Last Retail Price:** $220
**Auction Price:** $300

**Ref. No.:** 4576
**Name:** New Shepherdess
**Height:** 9.5
**Status:** Open issue, retired
**Issue Year:** 1969
**Issue Price:** $37.50
**Last Year:** 1985
**Last Retail Price:** $135
**High Auction Price:** $300
**Low Auction Price:** $275

**Ref. No.:** 5659
**Name:** Barnyard Scene
**Height:** 9.5
**Status:** Open issue, retired
**Issue Year:** 1990
**Issue Price:** $200
**Last Year:** 1998
**Last Retail Price:** $245

**Ref. No.:** 5666
**Name:** Trino at the Beach
**Height:** 9.5
**Status:** Open issue, retired
**Issue Year:** 1990
**Issue Price:** $390
**Last Year:** 1995
**Last Retail Price:** $460
**Auction Price:** $625

**Ref. No.:** 4682
**Name:** Girl with Milk Pail
**Height:** 9.5
**Status:** Open issue, retired
**Issue Year:** 1970
**Issue Price:** $26.50
**Last Year:** 1991
**Last Retail Price:** $175
**High Auction Price:** $350
**Low Auction Price:** $300

*Women*

**Ref. No.:** 6543
**Name:** Summer Breeze
**Height:** 9.5
**Status:** Open issue, active
**Issue Year:** 1998
**Issue Price:** $198
**2003 Retail Price:** $225
**Comment:** Federated Exclusive
until 2001

**Ref. No.:** 5546
**Name:** Reaching the Goal
**Height:** 9.75
**Status:** Open edition, retired
**Issue Year:** 1989
**Issue Price:** $215
**Last Year:** 1997
**Last Retail Price:** $275

**Ref. No.:** 4591
**Name:** Girl with Cockerel
**Height:** 9.75
**Status:** Open issue, retired
**Issue Year:** 1969
**Issue Price:** $20
**Last Year:** 1993
**Last Retail Price:** $140
**Auction Price:** $275

**Ref. No.:** 4686
**Name:** Girl's Head with Cap
**Height:** 9.75
**Status:** Open issue, retired
**Issue Year:** 1970
**Issue Price:** $25
**Last Year:** 1984
**Last Retail Price:** $85

**Ref. No.:** 5385
**Name:** Scarecrow and the Lady
**Height:** 9.75
**Status:** Open issue, retired
**Issue Year:** 1986
**Issue Price:** $350
**Last Year:** 1996
**Last Retail Price:** $680

**Ref. No.:** 6313
**Name:** Lost in Dreams
**Height:** 10
**Status:** Open edition, active
**Issue Year:** 1996
**Issue Price:** $420
**2003 Retail Price:** $425

**Ref. No.:** 6346
**Name:** Petals of Love
**Height:** 10
**Status:** Open issue, active
**Issue Year:** 1998
**Issue Price:** $350
**2003 Retail Price:** $375
**Comment:** Introduced by select
    dealers in 1997

**Ref. No.:** 6401
**Name:** Dreams of a Summer Past
**Height:** 10
**Status:** Open edition, retired
**Issue Year:** 1997
**Last Year:** 1997
**Last Retail Price:** $310
**Comment:** 1997 Special Events
    Sculpture

**Ref. No.:** 6252
**Name:** Nature's Beauty
**Height:** 10.25
**Status:** Open issue, retired
**Issue Year:** 1996
**Issue Price:** $770
**Last Year:** 1999
**Last Retail Price:** $770

**Ref. No.:** 1034
**Name:** Girl with Basket
**Height:** 10.5
**Status:** Open issue, retired
**Issue Year:** 1969
**Issue Price:** $30
**Last Year:** 1991
**Last Retail Price:** $160
**High Auction Price:** $400
**Low Auction Price:** $225

**Ref. No.:** 5855
**Name:** Afternoon Jaunt
**Height:** 10.5
**Status:** Open issue, retired
**Issue Year:** 1992
**Issue Price:** $420
**Last Year:** 1993
**Last Retail Price:** $440
**Auction Price:** $575

**Ref. No.:** 6106
**Name:** Spring Joy
**Height:** 10.5
**Status:** Open issue, active
**Issue Year:** 1994
**Issue Price:** $795
**2003 Retail Price:** $795

*Women*

**Ref. No.:** 5143
**Name:** Scooting
**Height:** 10.5
**Status:** Open issue, retired
**Issue Year:** 1982
**Issue Price:** $575
**Last Year:** 1988
**Last Retail Price:** $675
**High Auction Price:** $1800
**Low Auction Price:** $1200

**Ref. No.:** 6709
**Name:** Pensive Traveler
**Height:** 10.75
**Status:** Open issue, retired
**Issue Year:** 2000
**Issue Price:** $400
**Last Year:** 2001
**Last Retail Price:** $400

**Ref. No.:** 1158
**Name:** Shepherdess with
  Traditional Dress
**Height:** 11
**Status:** Very rare
**Issue Year:** 1971
**Issue Price:** $35
**Last Year:** 1975
**Last Retail Price:** Unknown

**Ref. No.:** 1391
**Name:** Girl's Head with Flowers
**Height:** 11
**Status:** Open edition, retired
**Issue Year:** 1981
**Issue Price:** $1250
**Last Year:** 1983
**Last Retail Price:** $1250

**Ref. No.:** 4865
**Name:** Embroiderer
**Height:** 11
**Status:** Open issue, retired
**Issue Year:** 1974
**Issue Price:** $115
**Last Year:** 1994
**Last Retail Price:** $645

**Ref. No.:** 4978
**Name:** In the Garden
**Height:** 11
**Status:** Open issue, retired
**Issue Year:** 1977
**Issue Price:** $160
**Last Year:** 1981
**Last Retail Price:** $230
**Auction Price:** $900

**Ref. No.:** 5337
**Name:** La Gioconda
**Height:** 11
**Status:** Open edition, retired
**Issue Year:** 1985
**Issue Price:** $350
**Last Year:** 1988
**Last Retail Price:** $410
**High Auction Price:** $800
**Low Auction Price:** $400

**Ref. No.:** 6181
**Name:** Velisa
**Height:** 11
**Status:** Open edition, active
**Issue Year:** 1995
**Issue Price:** $180
**2003 Retail Price:** $195

**Ref. No.:** 4689
**Name:** Gothic Queen
**Height:** 11
**Status:** Open issue, retired
**Issue Year:** 1970
**Issue Price:** $20
**Last Year:** 1975
**Last Retail Price:** $35

**Ref. No.:** 6767
**Name:** Petals on the Wind
**Height:** 11.25
**Status:** Open issue, active
**Issue Year:** 2001
**Issue Price:** $395
**2003 Retail Price:** $425

**Ref. No.:** 1160
**Name:** Shepherdess with
    Traditional Dress
**Height:** 11.5
**Status:** Very rare
**Issue Year:** 1971
**Issue Price:** $35
**Last Year:** 1975
**Last Retail Price:** Unknown

**Ref. No.:** 4665
**Name:** Girl with Basket
**Height:** 11.5
**Status:** Open issue, retired
**Issue Year:** 1969
**Issue Price:** $50
**Last Year:** 1979
**Last Retail Price:** $145
**Auction Price:** $550

*Women*

**Ref. No.:** 5126
**Name:** Sewing a Trousseau
**Height:** 11.5
**Status:** Open issue, retired
**Issue Year:** 1982
**Issue Price:** $185
**Last Year:** 1990
**Last Retail Price:** $240
**High Auction Price:** $750
**Low Auction Price:** $350

**Ref. No.:** 5660
**Name:** Sunning in Ipanema
**Height:** 11.5
**Status:** Open issue, retired
**Issue Year:** 1990
**Issue Price:** $370
**Last Year:** 1993
**Last Retail Price:** $420

**Ref. No.:** 5851
**Name:** Feathered Fantasy w/base
**Height:** 11.5
**Status:** Open issue, retired
**Issue Year:** 1992
**Issue Price:** $1200
**Last Year:** 1996
**Last Retail Price:** $1250

**Ref. No.:** 6284
**Name:** Quione
**Height:** 11.5
**Status:** Open issue, retired
**Issue Year:** 1996
**Issue Price:** $435
**Last Year:** 1998
**Last Retail Price:** $435

**Ref. No.:** 6712
**Name:** Lady In Love
**Height:** 11.5
**Status:** Open issue, active
**Issue Year:** 2000
**Issue Price:** $330
**2003 Retail Price:** $345

**Ref. No.:** 1271
**Name:** Pleasure
**Height:** 11.75
**Status:** Open issue, retired
**Issue Year:** 1974
**Issue Price:** $65
**Last Year:** 1981
**Last Retail Price:** $660

**Ref. No.:** 1381
**Name:** Medieval Girl
**Height:** 11.75
**Status:** Open issue, retired
**Issue Year:** 1978
**Issue Price:** $195
**Last Year:** 1985
**Last Retail Price:** $260
**Auction Price:** $600

**Ref. No.:** 4645
**Name:** Meditating
**Height:** 11.75
**Status:** Open issue, retired
**Issue Year:** 1969
**Issue Price:** $50
**Last Year:** 1975
**Last Retail Price:** $90

**Ref. No.:** 4953
**Name:** Woman with Cow
    and Calf
**Height:** 11.75
**Status:** Open issue, retired
**Issue Year:** 1977
**Issue Price:** $400
**Last Year:** 1979
**Last Retail Price:** $460

**Ref. No.:** 4984
**Name:** The Gossips
**Height:** 11.75
**Status:** Open issue, retired
**Issue Year:** 1978
**Issue Price:** $215
**Last Year:** 1985
**Last Retail Price:** $285
**High Auction Price:** $1100
**Low Auction Price:** $750

**Ref. No.:** 4994
**Name:** "My Little Pet"
**Height:** 11.75
**Status:** Open issue, retired
**Issue Year:** 1978
**Issue Price:** $92.50
**Last Year:** 1985
**Last Retail Price:** $122

**Ref. No.:** 5061
**Name:** March Winds
**Height:** 11.75
**Status:** Open issue, retired
**Issue Year:** 1980
**Issue Price:** $370
**Last Year:** 1983
**Last Retail Price:** $282.50
**High Auction Price:** $600
**Low Auction Price:** $350

*Women*

**Ref. No.:** 5152
**Name:** Girl's Head
**Height:** 11.75
**Status:** Open edition, retired
**Issue Year:** 1982
**Issue Price:** $535
**Last Year:** 1983
**Last Retail Price:** $535

**Ref. No.:** 6213
**Name:** Lady of Nice
**Height:** 11.75
**Status:** Open edition, retired
**Issue Year:** 1995
**Issue Price:** $198
**Last Year:** 1999
**Last Retail Price:** $210

**Ref. No.:** 6750
**Name:** Evening Light
**Height:** 12
**Status:** Open issue, active
**Issue Year:** 2001
**Issue Price:** $1100
**2003 Retail Price:** $1150

**Ref. No.:** 4668
**Name:** Maja Head
**Height:** 12.25
**Status:** Open edition, retired
**Issue Year:** 1969
**Issue Price:** $50
**Last Year:** 1985
**Last Retail Price:** $250
**High Auction Price:** $850
**Low Auction Price:** $500

**Ref. No.:** 4979
**Name:** Milkmaid with
Wheelbarrow
**Height:** 12.25
**Status:** Open issue, retired
**Issue Year:** 1977
**Issue Price:** $220
**Last Year:** 1981
**Last Retail Price:** $315
**Auction Price:** $950

**Ref. No.:** 4986
**Name:** Attentive Lady
**Height:** 12.25
**Status:** Open issue, retired
**Issue Year:** 1978
**Issue Price:** $635
**Last Year:** 1981
**Last Retail Price:** $825
**Auction Price:** $2200

**Ref. No.:** 5159
**Name:** Harmony
**Height:** 12.25
**Status:** Open issue, retired
**Issue Year:** 1982
**Issue Price:** $270
**Last Year:** 1998
**Last Retail Price:** $495

**Ref. No.:** 101.06
**Name:** Charm
**Height:** 12.5
**Status:** Very rare
**Issue Year:** 1958
**Issue Price:** Unknown
**Last Year:** Unknown
**Last Retail Price:** Unknown

**Ref. No.:** 357.13
**Name:** Girl with Pigtails
**Height:** 12.5
**Status:** Very rare
**Issue Year:** 1970
**Issue Price:** Unknown
**Last Year:** Unknown
**Last Retail Price:** Unknown

**Ref. No.:** 4599
**Name:** He Loves Me
**Height:** 12.5
**Status:** Open issue, retired
**Issue Year:** 1969
**Issue Price:** $47.50
**Last Year:** 1972
**Last Retail Price:** $47.50

**Ref. No.:** 4875
**Name:** The Jug Carrier
**Height:** 12.5
**Status:** Open issue, retired
**Issue Year:** 1974
**Issue Price:** $40
**Last Year:** 1985
**Last Retail Price:** $95
**High Auction Price:** $375
**Low Auction Price:** $300

**Ref. No.:** 5417
**Name:** Artist Model
**Height:** 12.5
**Status:** Open issue, retired
**Issue Year:** 1987
**Issue Price:** $425
**Last Year:** 1990
**Last Retail Price:** $500
**Auction Price:** $550

*Women*

**Ref. No.:** 347.13
**Name:** Spain-USA
**Height:** 12.75
**Status:** Very rare
**Issue Year:** 1973
**Issue Price:** Unknown
**Last Year:** Unknown
**Last Retail Price:** Unknown
**Auction Price:** $5500

**Ref. No.:** 6708
**Name:** Serene Moment
**Height:** 12.75
**Status:** Open issue, retired
**Issue Year:** 2000
**Issue Price:** $585
**Last Year:** 2002
**Last Retail Price:** $595

**Ref. No.:** 6777
**Name:** Butterfly Treasures
**Height:** 12.75
**Status:** Open issue, active
**Issue Year:** 2001
**Issue Price:** $265
**2003 Retail Price:** $295

**Ref. No.:** 1157
**Name:** Woman with Traditional
  Dress
**Height:** 13
**Status:** Very rare
**Issue Year:** 1971
**Issue Price:** $25
**Last Year:** 1975
**Last Retail Price:** Unknown
**Auction Price:** $600

**Ref. No.:** 4501
**Name:** A Basket of Goodies
**Height:** 13
**Status:** Open issue, retired
**Issue Year:** 1969
**Issue Price:** $37.50
**Last Year:** 1985
**Last Retail Price:** $115
**Auction Price:** $475

**Ref. No.:** 5174
**Name:** Roaring Twenties
**Height:** 13
**Status:** Open issue, retired
**Issue Year:** 1982
**Issue Price:** $172.50
**Last Year:** 1985
**Last Retail Price:** $295
**High Auction Price:** $450
**Low Auction Price:** $400

**Ref. No.:** 5370
**Name:** Can Can
**Height:** 13
**Status:** Open issue, retired
**Issue Year:** 1986
**Issue Price:** $700
**Last Year:** 1990
**Last Retail Price:** $925
**High Auction Price:** $1600
**Low Auction Price:** $1000

**Ref. No.:** 359.13
**Name:** Insular Lady
**Height:** 13.25
**Status:** Open issue, retired
**Issue Year:** 1969
**Issue Price:** Unknown
**Last Year:** Unknown
**Last Retail Price:** Unknown

**Ref. No.:** 1537
**Name:** Stepping Out
**Height:** 13.25
**Status:** Open issue, retired
**Issue Year:** 1988
**Issue Price:** $230
**Last Year:** 2000
**Last Retail Price:** $335

**Ref. No.:** 3505
**Name:** Fiesta
**Height:** 13.25
**Status:** Open issue, retired
**Issue Year:** 1978
**Issue Price:** $230
**Last Year:** 1988
**Last Retail Price:** $330
**Auction Price:** $475

**Ref. No.:** 4604
**Name:** Bread and Water
**Height:** 13.25
**Status:** Open issue, retired
**Issue Year:** 1969
**Issue Price:** $55
**Last Year:** 1972
**Last Retail Price:** $65

**Ref. No.:** 5651
**Name:** Musical Muse
**Height:** 13.25
**Status:** Open edition, retired
**Issue Year:** 1990
**Issue Price:** $375
**Last Year:** 1996
**Last Retail Price:** $440

*Women*

**Ref. No.:** 6682
**Name:** Ocean Offering
**Height:** 13.25
**Status:** Open issue, retired
**Issue Year:** 2000
**Issue Price:** $470
**Last Year:** 2001
**Last Retail Price:** $470

**Ref. No.:** 6687
**Name:** Sweet Sixteen
**Height:** 13.25
**Status:** Open issue, active
**Issue Year:** 2000
**Issue Price:** $450
**2003 Retail Price:** $475

**Ref. No.:** 6751
**Name:** Morning Dew
**Height:** 13.25
**Status:** Open issue, active
**Issue Year:** 2001
**Issue Price:** $1500
**2003 Retail Price:** $1575

**Ref. No.:** 4502
**Name:** Marketing Day
**Height:** 13.75
**Status:** Open issue, retired
**Issue Year:** 1969
**Issue Price:** $40
**Last Year:** 1985
**Last Retail Price:** $127.50
**High Auction Price:** $350
**Low Auction Price:** $225

**Ref. No.:** 4761
**Name:** Woman
**Height:** 13.75
**Status:** Open issue, retired
**Issue Year:** 1971
**Issue Price:** $60
**Last Year:** 1993
**Last Retail Price:** $260

**Ref. No.:** 4922
**Name:** Sea Breeze (Wind Blown
 Girl)
**Height:** 13.75
**Status:** Open edition, retired
**Issue Year:** 1974
**Issue Price:** $150
**Last Year:** 2002
**Last Retail Price:** $375

**Ref. No.:** 4922.3
**Name:** Wind Blown Girl (White)
**Height:** 13.75
**Status:** Open issue, retired
**Issue Year:** 1983
**Issue Price:** $155
**Last Year:** 1985
**Last Retail Price:** $155

**Ref. No.:** 6384
**Name:** A Quiet Moment
**Height:** 14
**Status:** Open issue, retired
**Issue Year:** 1997
**Issue Price:** $270
**Last Year:** 1999
**Last Retail Price:** $275

**Ref. No.:** 6370
**Name:** Country Chores
**Height:** 14
**Status:** Open issue, retired
**Issue Year:** 1997
**Issue Price:** $260
**Last Year:** 2000
**Last Retail Price:** $260

**Ref. No.:** 6752
**Name:** On My Way Home
**Height:** 14
**Status:** Open issue, active
**Issue Year:** 2001
**Issue Price:** $375
**2003 Retail Price:** $395

**Ref. No.:** 343.13
**Name:** Greek Shepherdess
**Height:** 14.25
**Status:** Very rare
**Issue Year:** 1963
**Issue Price:** Unknown
**Last Year:** Unknown
**Last Retail Price:** Unknown

**Ref. No.:** 5042
**Name:** Friends
**Height:** 14.25
**Status:** Open issue, retired
**Issue Year:** 1980
**Issue Price:** $385
**Last Year:** 1983
**Last Retail Price:** $422.50

*Women*

**Ref. No.:** 5755
**Name:** Claudette
**Height:** 14.25
**Status:** Open issue, retired
**Issue Year:** 1991
**Issue Price:** $265
**Last Year:** 1993
**Last Retail Price:** $285

**Ref. No.:** 5756
**Name:** Ashley
**Height:** 14.25
**Status:** Open issue, retired
**Issue Year:** 1991
**Issue Price:** $265
**Last Year:** 1993
**Last Retail Price:** $290
**Auction Price:** $300

**Ref. No.:** 4928
**Name:** Medieval Lady
**Height:** 14.5
**Status:** Open issue, retired
**Issue Year:** 1974
**Issue Price:** $275
**Last Year:** 1980
**Last Retail Price:** $500
**High Auction Price:** $825
**Low Auction Price:** $600

**Ref. No.:** 4893
**Name:** Walk with the Dog
**Height:** 14.5
**Status:** Open issue, active
**Issue Year:** 1974
**Issue Price:** $85
**2003 Retail Price:** $250

**Ref. No.:** 1049
**Name:** Girl with Basket
**Height:** 15
**Status:** Very rare
**Issue Year:** 1969
**Issue Price:** $60
**Last Year:** 1978
**Last Retail Price:** Unknown

**Ref. No.:** 6376
**Name:** Light and Life
**Height:** 15
**Status:** Open issue, retired
**Issue Year:** 1997
**Issue Price:** $220
**Last Year:** 2000
**Last Retail Price:** $220

**Ref. No.:** 6377
**Name:** Unity
**Height:** 15
**Status:** Open issue, retired
**Issue Year:** 1997
**Issue Price:** $220
**Last Year:** 1999
**Last Retail Price:** $220

**Ref. No.:** 6378
**Name:** Beginning and End
**Height:** 15
**Status:** Open issue, retired
**Issue Year:** 1997
**Issue Price:** $220
**Last Year:** 1999
**Last Retail Price:** $220

**Ref. No.:** 6379
**Name:** Love
**Height:** 15
**Status:** Open issue, retired
**Issue Year:** 1997
**Issue Price:** $220
**Last Year:** 2000
**Last Retail Price:** $220

**Ref. No.:** 6448
**Name:** Sweet Verses
**Height:** 15
**Status:** Open issue, retired
**Issue Year:** 1997
**Issue Price:** $280
**Last Year:** 1999
**Last Retail Price:** $295

**Ref. No.:** 6505
**Name:** On The Farm
**Height:** 15
**Status:** Open issue, retired
**Issue Year:** 1998
**Issue Price:** $325
**Last Year:** 2000
**Last Retail Price:** $345

**Ref. No.:** 353.13
**Name:** Country Woman
**Height:** 15.25
**Status:** Very rare
**Issue Year:** 1965
**Issue Price:** Unknown
**Last Year:** Unknown
**Last Retail Price:** Unknown

Women

**Ref. No.:** 6809
**Name:** Flowers for Everyone
**Height:** 15.25
**Status:** Open issue, active
**Issue Year:** 2002
**Issue Price:** $2875
**2003 Retail Price:** $2995

**Ref. No.:** 1040
**Name:** Girl with Letter
**Height:** 15.5
**Status:** Open issue, retired
**Issue Year:** 1969
**Issue Price:** $57.50
**Last Year:** 1978
**Last Retail Price:** $60

**Ref. No.:** 369.13
**Name:** Farmer with Pitcher
**Height:** 15.5
**Status:** Very rare
**Issue Year:** 1961
**Issue Price:** Unknown
**Last Year:** Unknown
**Last Retail Price:** Unknown

**Ref. No.:** 5069
**Name:** Spring Dance
**Height:** 15.5
**Status:** Open issue, retired
**Issue Year:** 1980
**Issue Price:** $555
**Last Year:** 1981
**Last Retail Price:** $555
**Auction Price:** $1550

**Ref. No.:** 1297
**Name:** Swinging
**Height:** 15.75
**Status:** Open issue, retired
**Issue Year:** 1974
**Issue Price:** $520
**Last Year:** 1990
**Last Retail Price:** $1350
**High Auction Price:** $2150
**Low Auction Price:** $1250

**Ref. No.:** 4518
**Name:** Girl Student
**Height:** 15.75
**Status:** Open issue, retired
**Issue Year:** 1969
**Issue Price:** $57.50
**Last Year:** 1978
**Last Retail Price:** $95

**Ref. No.:** 4582
**Name:** Harvester, Woman
**Height:** 15.75
**Status:** Open issue, retired
**Issue Year:** 1969
**Issue Price:** Unknown
**Last Year:** 1975
**Last Retail Price:** $100

**Ref. No.:** 1036
**Name:** Horsewoman
**Height:** 16
**Status:** Very rare
**Issue Year:** 1969
**Issue Price:** $170
**Last Year:** 1970
**Last Retail Price:** Unknown

**Ref. No.:** 6649
**Name:** Allegory Of Youth
**Height:** 16
**Status:** Open issue, active
**Issue Year:** 2000
**Issue Price:** $635
**2003 Retail Price:** $675

**Ref. No.:** 4514
**Name:** Diana
**Height:** 16.5
**Status:** Open issue, retired
**Issue Year:** 1969
**Issue Price:** $65
**Last Year:** 1981
**Last Retail Price:** $450

**Ref. No.:** 6884
**Name:** Serena
**Height:** 16.5
**Status:** Open issue, active
**Issue Year:** 2002
**Issue Price:** $550
**2003 Retail Price:** $550

**Ref. No.:** 6773
**Name:** The Encounter
**Height:** 16.75
**Status:** Open issue, retired
**Issue Year:** 2001
**Issue Price:** $775
**Last Year:** 2003
**Last Retail Price:** $775

*Women*

**Ref. No.:** 6773
**Name:** The Encounter
**Height:** 16.75
**Status:** Open issue, active
**Issue Year:** 2002
**Issue Price:** $1175
**2003 Retail Price:** $1175
**Comment:** Matte version.
  To be retired as of
  December 31, 2003

**Ref. No.:** 1346
**Name:** Under the Willow
**Height:** 18.5
**Status:** Open issue, retired
**Issue Year:** 1978
**Issue Price:** $1600
**Last Year:** 1990
**Last Retail Price:** $2400
**Auction Price:** $2000

**Ref. No.:** 1014
**Name:** Two Women Carrying
  Water Jugs
**Height:** 18.75
**Status:** Open issue, retired
**Issue Year:** 1969
**Issue Price:** $85
**Last Year:** 1985
**Last Retail Price:** $350
**High Auction Price:** $700
**Low Auction Price:** $550

**Elegant Ladies**

**Ref. No.:** 1272
**Name:** Thoughts
**Height:** 19.25
**Status:** Open issue, retired
**Issue Year:** 1974
**Issue Price:** $87.50
**Last Year:** 1998
**Last Retail Price:** $3490

**Ref. No.:** 98.06
**Name:** Vanity
**Height:** 5.75
**Status:** Very rare
**Issue Year:** 1957
**Issue Price:** Unknown
**Last Year:** Unknown
**Last Retail Price:** Unknown

**Ref. No.:** 95.06
**Name:** Going For a Walk
**Height:** 6
**Status:** Very rare
**Issue Year:** 1957
**Issue Price:** Unknown
**Last Year:** Unknown
**Last Retail Price:** Unknown

**Ref. No.:** 5412
**Name:** Isabel
**Height:** 6
**Status:** Open issue, retired
**Issue Year:** 1987
**Issue Price:** $225
**Last Year:** 1990
**Last Retail Price:** $290
**High Auction Price:** $500
**Low Auction Price:** $350

**Ref. No.:** 5588
**Name:** Blustery Day
**Height:** 6
**Status:** Open issue, retired
**Issue Year:** 1989
**Issue Price:** $185
**Last Year:** 1993
**Last Retail Price:** $230

**Ref. No.:** 110.06
**Name:** Louis XV Lady
**Height:** 6.25
**Status:** Very rare
**Issue Year:** 1958
**Issue Price:** Unknown
**Last Year:** Unknown
**Last Retail Price:** Unknown

**Ref. No.:** 5859
**Name:** At the Ball
**Height:** 6.25
**Status:** Open issue, active
**Issue Year:** 1992
**Issue Price:** $295
**2003 Retail Price:** $345

**Ref. No.:** 109.06
**Name:** Noble Lady
**Height:** 6.5
**Status:** Very rare
**Issue Year:** 1958
**Issue Price:** Unknown
**Last Year:** Unknown
**Last Retail Price:** Unknown

**Ref. No.:** 361.13
**Name:** Lady in Blue
**Height:** 6.5
**Status:** Very rare
**Issue Year:** 1959
**Issue Price:** Unknown
**Last Year:** Unknown
**Last Retail Price:** Unknown

*Women*

**Ref. No.:** 5590
**Name:** Spring Breeze
**Height:** 7
**Status:** Open issue, retired
**Issue Year:** 1989
**Issue Price:** $185
**Last Year:** 1993
**Last Retail Price:** $230

**Ref. No.:** 212.08
**Name:** The Prom
**Height:** 7.75
**Status:** Very rare
**Issue Year:** 1958
**Issue Price:** Unknown
**Last Year:** Unknown
**Last Retail Price:** Unknown

**Ref. No.:** 5487
**Name:** Ingenue
**Height:** 8
**Status:** Open edition, active
**Issue Year:** 1988
**Issue Price:** $110
**2003 Retail Price:** $150

**Ref. No.:** 5644
**Name:** Susan
**Height:** 8
**Status:** Open edition, active
**Issue Year:** 1990
**Issue Price:** $190
**2003 Retail Price:** $225

**Ref. No.:** 6594
**Name:** A Night Out
**Height:** 8
**Status:** Open issue, retired
**Issue Year:** 1999
**Issue Price:** $135
**Last Year:** 2001
**Last Retail Price:** $135

**Ref. No.:** 6595
**Name:** On The Runway
**Height:** 8
**Status:** Open issue, retired
**Issue Year:** 1999
**Issue Price:** $135
**Last Year:** 2001
**Last Retail Price:** $135

**Ref. No.:** 93.06
**Name:** The Ball
**Height:** 8.25
**Status:** Very rare
**Issue Year:** 1957
**Issue Price:** Unknown
**Last Year:** Unknown
**Last Retail Price:** Unknown

**Ref. No.:** 5486
**Name:** Debutantes
**Height:** 8.25
**Status:** Open issue, retired
**Issue Year:** 1988
**Issue Price:** $490
**Last Year:** 1997
**Last Retail Price:** $695

**Ref. No.:** 5597
**Name:** Summer Soiree
**Height:** 8.25
**Status:** Open edition, retired
**Issue Year:** 1989
**Issue Price:** $150
**Last Year:** 1998
**Last Retail Price:** $180

**Ref. No.:** 5599
**Name:** Coquette
**Height:** 8.25
**Status:** Open edition, active
**Issue Year:** 1989
**Issue Price:** $150
**2003 Retail Price:** $195

**Ref. No.:** 5686
**Name:** On the Avenue
**Height:** 8.25
**Status:** Open issue, retired
**Issue Year:** 1990
**Issue Price:** $275
**Last Year:** 1994
**Last Retail Price:** $325

**Ref. No.:** 5687
**Name:** Afternoon Stroll
**Height:** 8.25
**Status:** Open issue, retired
**Issue Year:** 1990
**Issue Price:** $275
**Last Year:** 1994
**Last Retail Price:** $325

*Women*

**Ref. No.:** 5365
**Name:** Sunday in the Park
**Height:** 8.5
**Status:** Open issue, retired
**Issue Year:** 1986
**Issue Price:** $375
**Last Year:** 1996
**Last Retail Price:** $625

**Ref. No.:** 5424
**Name:** Intermezzo
**Height:** 8.5
**Status:** Open issue, retired
**Issue Year:** 1987
**Issue Price:** $325
**Last Year:** 1990
**Last Retail Price:** $400
**High Auction Price:** $725
**Low Auction Price:** $500

**Ref. No.:** 5662
**Name:** May Dance
**Height:** 8.5
**Status:** Open edition, active
**Issue Year:** 1990
**Issue Price:** $170
**2003 Retail Price:** $225

**Ref. No.:** 5685
**Name:** Promenade
**Height:** 8.5
**Status:** Open issue, retired
**Issue Year:** 1990
**Issue Price:** $275
**Last Year:** 1994
**Last Retail Price:** $325

**Ref. No.:** 6653
**Name:** Elegance On Ice
**Height:** 8.5
**Status:** Open issue, active
**Issue Year:** 2000
**Issue Price:** $365
**2003 Retail Price:** $375

**Ref. No.:** 5663
**Name:** Spring Dance
**Height:** 8.75
**Status:** Open edition, retired
**Issue Year:** 1990
**Issue Price:** $170
**Last Year:** 2000
**Last Retail Price:** $210

**Ref. No.:** 5858
**Name:** Waiting to Dance
**Height:** 8.75
**Status:** Open issue, retired
**Issue Year:** 1992
**Issue Price:** $295
**Last Year:** 1995
**Last Retail Price:** $335

**Ref. No.:** 5176
**Name:** Lady Lying on Divan
**Height:** 9
**Status:** Open issue, retired
**Issue Year:** 1982
**Issue Price:** $325
**Last Year:** 1985
**Last Retail Price:** $325
**Auction Price:** $1150

**Ref. No.:** 5789
**Name:** The Flirt
**Height:** 9.25
**Status:** Open edition, retired
**Issue Year:** 1991
**Issue Price:** $185
**Last Year:** 1998
**Last Retail Price:** $195

**Ref. No.:** 5857
**Name:** Grand Entrance
**Height:** 9.25
**Status:** Open issue, retired
**Issue Year:** 1992
**Issue Price:** $265
**Last Year:** 1994
**Last Retail Price:** $275

**Ref. No.:** 5700
**Name:** Southern Charm
**Height:** 9.5
**Status:** Open issue, retired
**Issue Year:** 1990
**Issue Price:** $775
**Last Year:** 1997
**Last Retail Price:** $1025

**Ref. No.:** 5321
**Name:** Parisian Lady
**Height:** 9.75
**Status:** Open issue, retired
**Issue Year:** 1985
**Issue Price:** $192.50
**Last Year:** 1995
**Last Retail Price:** $325

*Women*

**Ref. No.:** 5322
**Name:** Viennese Lady
**Height:** 10.25
**Status:** Open issue, retired
**Issue Year:** 1985
**Issue Price:** $160
**Last Year:** 1994
**Last Retail Price:** $295

**Ref. No.:** 5323
**Name:** Milanese Lady
**Height:** 10.25
**Status:** Open issue, retired
**Issue Year:** 1985
**Issue Price:** $180
**Last Year:** 1994
**Last Retail Price:** $340

**Ref. No.:** 5324
**Name:** English Lady
**Height:** 10.25
**Status:** Open issue, retired
**Issue Year:** 1985
**Issue Price:** $225
**Last Year:** 1994
**Last Retail Price:** $410

**Ref. No.:** 5766
**Name:** Charming Duet
**Height:** 10.25
**Status:** Open issue, retired
**Issue Year:** 1991
**Issue Price:** $575
**Last Year:** 1996
**Last Retail Price:** $625

**Ref. No.:** 5787
**Name:** Sophisticate
**Height:** 10.25
**Status:** Open edition, retired
**Issue Year:** 1991
**Issue Price:** $185
**Last Year:** 1998
**Last Retail Price:** $195

**Ref. No.:** 5788
**Name:** Talk of the Town
**Height:** 10.25
**Status:** Open edition, retired
**Issue Year:** 1991
**Issue Price:** $185
**Last Year:** 1998
**Last Retail Price:** $195

**Ref. No.:** 5957
**Name:** The Glass Slipper
**Height:** 10.25
**Status:** Open edition, retired
**Issue Year:** 1993
**Issue Price:** $475
**Last Year:** 2001
**Last Retail Price:** $475

**Ref. No.:** 4912
**Name:** Young Lady in Trouble
**Height:** 10.5
**Status:** Open issue, retired
**Issue Year:** 1974
**Issue Price:** $110
**Last Year:** 1985
**Last Retail Price:** $192.50
**High Auction Price:** $600
**Low Auction Price:** $400

**Ref. No.:** 5408
**Name:** Sunday Stroll
**Height:** 10.5
**Status:** Open issue, retired
**Issue Year:** 1987
**Issue Price:** $250
**Last Year:** 1990
**Last Retail Price:** $300
**High Auction Price:** $600
**Low Auction Price:** $450

**Ref. No.:** 111.06
**Name:** Lady With Umbrella
**Height:** 11
**Status:** Very rare
**Issue Year:** 1958
**Issue Price:** Unknown
**Last Year:** Unknown
**Last Retail Price:** Unknown

**Ref. No.:** 6246
**Name:** Sunday's Best
**Height:** 11
**Status:** Open issue, retired
**Issue Year:** 1996
**Issue Price:** $370
**Last Year:** 1999
**Last Retail Price:** $370

**Ref. No.:** 6548
**Name:** Love Poems
**Height:** 11
**Status:** Open issue, retired
**Issue Year:** 1998
**Issue Price:** $470
**Last Year:** 2001
**Last Retail Price:** $495

*Women*

**Ref. No.:** 6180
**Name:** Sharia
**Height:** 11.5
**Status:** Open edition, active
**Issue Year:** 1995
**Issue Price:** $235
**2003 Retail Price:** $250

**Ref. No.:** 6279
**Name:** Flowers of Paris
**Height:** 11.5
**Status:** Open issue, retired
**Issue Year:** 1996
**Issue Price:** $525
**Last Year:** 1999
**Last Retail Price:** $525

**Ref. No.:** 6280
**Name:** Paris in Bloom
**Height:** 11.5
**Status:** Open issue, retired
**Issue Year:** 1996
**Issue Price:** $525
**Last Year:** 1999
**Last Retail Price:** $525

**Ref. No.:** 1242
**Name:** Lady at Dressing Table
**Height:** 11.75
**Status:** Open issue, retired
**Issue Year:** 1973
**Issue Price:** $320
**Last Year:** 1978
**Last Retail Price:** $650
**High Auction Price:** $3750
**Low Auction Price:** $2500

**Ref. No.:** 5898
**Name:** Spring Splendor
**Height:** 11.75
**Status:** Open edition, active
**Issue Year:** 1992
**Issue Price:** $440
**2003 Retail Price:** $450

**Ref. No.:** 6315
**Name:** Dreaming of You
**Height:** 11.75
**Status:** Open edition, retired
**Issue Year:** 1996
**Issue Price:** $1280
**Last Year:** 1999
**Last Retail Price:** $1280

**Ref. No.:** 4879
**Name:** Aranjuez Little Lady
**Height:** 12.25
**Status:** Open issue, retired
**Issue Year:** 1974
**Issue Price:** $48
**Last Year:** 1996
**Last Retail Price:** $325

**Ref. No.:** 5003
**Name:** A Sunny Day
**Height:** 12.25
**Status:** Open issue, retired
**Issue Year:** 1978
**Issue Price:** $192.50
**Last Year:** 1993
**Last Retail Price:** $360
**Auction Price:** $375

**Ref. No.:** 5297
**Name:** Girl Standing Under
    Trellis
**Height:** 12.25
**Status:** Open issue, retired
**Issue Year:** 1985
**Issue Price:** $340
**Last Year:** 1988
**Last Retail Price:** $390
**High Auction Price:** $1000
**Low Auction Price:** $700

**Ref. No.:** 5682
**Name:** Breezy Afternoon
**Height:** 12.25
**Status:** Open edition, active
**Issue Year:** 1990
**Issue Price:** $180
**2003 Retail Price:** $195

**Ref. No.:** 4999
**Name:** Miss Teresa
**Height:** 12.5
**Status:** Open issue, retired
**Issue Year:** 1978
**Issue Price:** $150
**Last Year:** 1983
**Last Retail Price:** $200
**High Auction Price:** $600
**Low Auction Price:** $325

**Ref. No.:** 5125
**Name:** Goya Lady
**Height:** 12.5
**Status:** Open issue, retired
**Issue Year:** 1982
**Issue Price:** $130
**Last Year:** 1990
**Last Retail Price:** $175
**Auction Price:** $350

*Women*

**Ref. No.:** 5345
**Name:** A New Hat
**Height:** 12.5
**Status:** Open issue, retired
**Issue Year:** 1986
**Issue Price:** $200
**Last Year:** 1990
**Last Retail Price:** $270
**High Auction Price:** $475
**Low Auction Price:** $375

**Ref. No.:** 6193
**Name:** Summer Serenade
**Height:** 12.5
**Status:** Open issue, active
**Issue Year:** 1995
**Issue Price:** $375
**2003 Retail Price:** $395

**Ref. No.:** 6283
**Name:** Temis
**Height:** 12.75
**Status:** Open issue, retired
**Issue Year:** 1996
**Issue Price:** $435
**Last Year:** 1998
**Last Retail Price:** $435

**Ref. No.:** 6576
**Name:** Autumn Romance
**Height:** 12.75
**Status:** Open issue, active
**Issue Year:** 1999
**Issue Price:** $335
**2003 Retail Price:** $395
**Comment:** Introduced by select
dealers in 1998

**Ref. No.:** 6621
**Name:** Winter Love
**Height:** 12.75
**Status:** Open issue, retired
**Issue Year:** 1999
**Issue Price:** $345
**Last Year:** 2002
**Last Retail Price:** $345

**Ref. No.:** 6783
**Name:** Winds of Romance
**Height:** 12.75
**Status:** Open issue, active
**Issue Year:** 2001
**Issue Price:** $290
**2003 Retail Price:** $325

**Ref. No.:** 4594
**Name:** Lady with Greyhound
**Height:** 13
**Status:** Open issue, retired
**Issue Year:** 1969
**Issue Price:** $60
**Last Year:** 1981
**Last Retail Price:** $330
**Auction Price:** $825

**Ref. No.:** 5156
**Name:** Susan and the Doves
**Height:** 13
**Status:** Open issue, retired
**Issue Year:** 1982
**Issue Price:** $202.50
**Last Year:** 1991
**Last Retail Price:** $360

**Ref. No.:** 6302
**Name:** Thena
**Height:** 13
**Status:** Open issue, retired
**Issue Year:** 1996
**Issue Price:** $485
**Last Year:** 1998
**Last Retail Price:** $485

**Ref. No.:** 6351
**Name:** Tokens of Love
**Height:** 13
**Status:** Open issue, retired
**Issue Year:** 1997
**Issue Price:** $385
**Last Year:** 2000
**Last Retail Price:** $425

**Ref. No.:** 6365
**Name:** Spring Flirtation
**Height:** 13
**Status:** Open issue, active
**Issue Year:** 1997
**Issue Price:** $395
**2003 Retail Price:** $395
**Comment:** Introduced by select
dealers in 1996

**Ref. No.:** 6366
**Name:** Summer Infatuation
**Height:** 13
**Status:** Open issue, active
**Issue Year:** 1998
**Issue Price:** $325
**2003 Retail Price:** $325
**Comment:** Introduced by select
dealers in 1997

*Women*

**Ref. No.:** 6403
**Name:** Breathless
**Height:** 13
**Status:** Open issue, retired
**Issue Year:** 1997
**Issue Price:** $235
**Last Year:** 2000
**Last Retail Price:** $235

**Ref. No.:** 6418
**Name:** So Beautiful!
**Height:** 13
**Status:** Open issue, retired
**Issue Year:** 1997
**Issue Price:** $325
**Last Year:** 2000
**Last Retail Price:** $325

**Ref. No.:** 6518
**Name:** A Lovely Thought
**Height:** 13
**Status:** Open issue, retired
**Issue Year:** 1998
**Issue Price:** $580
**Last Year:** 2000
**Last Retail Price:** $580

**Ref. No.:** 6542
**Name:** A Stroll In The Sun
**Height:** 13
**Status:** Open issue, retired
**Issue Year:** 1998
**Issue Price:** $450
**Last Year:** 2001
**Last Retail Price:** $500

**Ref. No.:** 6608
**Name:** Anticipation
**Height:** 13
**Status:** Open issue, retired
**Issue Year:** 1999
**Issue Price:** $275
**Last Year:** 1999
**Last Retail Price:** $275
**Comment:** 1999 Vanguard Dealer
  Exclusive

**Ref. No.:** 1568
**Name:** Grand Dame
**Height:** 13.25
**Status:** Open edition, retired
**Issue Year:** 1987
**Issue Price:** $290
**Last Year:** 2000
**Last Retail Price:** $515

**Ref. No.:** 4934
**Name:** Dainty Lady
**Height:** 13.25
**Status:** Open issue, retired
**Issue Year:** 1974
**Issue Price:** $60
**Last Year:** 1985
**Last Retail Price:** $147.50
**Auction Price:** $725

**Ref. No.:** 4936
**Name:** Spring Breeze
**Height:** 13.25
**Status:** Open edition, active
**Issue Year:** 1974
**Issue Price:** $145
**2003 Retail Price:** $425

**Ref. No.:** 5283
**Name:** Socialite of the 20s
**Height:** 13.25
**Status:** Open edition, retired
**Issue Year:** 1985
**Issue Price:** $175
**Last Year:** 2001
**Last Retail Price:** $350

**Ref. No.:** 5378
**Name:** Time for Reflection
**Height:** 13.25
**Status:** Open edition, active
**Issue Year:** 1986
**Issue Price:** $425
**2003 Retail Price:** $750

**Ref. No.:** 6236
**Name:** Lady of Monaco
**Height:** 13.5
**Status:** Open edition, retired
**Issue Year:** 1995
**Issue Price:** $260
**Last Year:** 1999
**Last Retail Price:** $260

**Ref. No.:** 6251
**Name:** Wind of Peace
**Height:** 13.5
**Status:** Open issue, retired
**Issue Year:** 1997
**Issue Price:** $310
**Last Year:** 1999
**Last Retail Price:** $310
**Comment:** 1996 Vanguard
　　　　　 Dealer Exclusive

*Women*

**Ref. No.:** 6281
**Name:** Coqueta
**Height:** 13.5
**Status:** Open issue, retired
**Issue Year:** 1996
**Issue Price:** $435
**Last Year:** 1998
**Last Retail Price:** $435

**Ref. No.:** 6753
**Name:** Traveling Companions
**Height:** 13.5
**Status:** Open issue, active
**Issue Year:** 2001
**Issue Price:** $235
**2003 Retail Price:** $250

**Ref. No.:** 6857
**Name:** The Lady of the Rose
**Height:** 13.5
**Status:** Open issue, active
**Issue Year:** 2002
**Issue Price:** $235
**2003 Retail Price:** $245

**Ref. No.:** 1428
**Name:** Afternoon Tea
**Height:** 13.75
**Status:** Open edition, retired
**Issue Year:** 1982
**Issue Price:** $115
**Last Year:** 1998
**Last Retail Price:** $300

**Ref. No.:** 1431
**Name:** The Debutante
**Height:** 13.75
**Status:** Open edition, retired
**Issue Year:** 1982
**Issue Price:** $115
**Last Year:** 1998
**Last Retail Price:** $300

**Ref. No.:** 6592
**Name:** An Expression Of Love
**Height:** 14
**Status:** Open issue, retired
**Issue Year:** 1999
**Issue Price:** $295
**Last Year:** 2002
**Last Retail Price:** $295

**Ref. No.:** 6610
**Name:** Faithful Companion
**Height:** 14
**Status:** Open issue, retired
**Issue Year:** 1999
**Issue Price:** $675
**Last Year:** 2001
**Last Retail Price:** $675

**Ref. No.:** 6760
**Name:** Walking the Dogs
**Height:** 14
**Status:** Open issue, active
**Issue Year:** 2001
**Issue Price:** $365
**2003 Retail Price:** $375

**Ref. No.:** 1270
**Name:** Reminiscing
**Height:** 14.25
**Status:** Open issue, retired
**Issue Year:** 1974
**Issue Price:** $975
**Last Year:** 1988
**Last Retail Price:** $1200
**Auction Price:** $900

**Ref. No.:** 4700
**Name:** Dressmaker
**Height:** 14.25
**Status:** Open issue, retired
**Issue Year:** 1970
**Issue Price:** $40
**Last Year:** 1993
**Last Retail Price:** $360
**High Auction Price:** $425
**Low Auction Price:** $400

**Ref. No.:** 4995
**Name:** Coquetry
**Height:** 14.25
**Status:** Open issue, retired
**Issue Year:** 1978
**Issue Price:** $140
**Last Year:** 1979
**Last Retail Price:** $145

**Ref. No.:** 4997
**Name:** Frustrated Walk
**Height:** 14.25
**Status:** Open issue, retired
**Issue Year:** 1978
**Issue Price:** $130
**Last Year:** 1979
**Last Retail Price:** $135

*Women*

**Ref. No.:** 5000
**Name:** Reading
**Height:** 14.25
**Status:** Open edition, retired
**Issue Year:** 1978
**Issue Price:** $150
**Last Year:** 2002
**Last Retail Price:** $285

**Ref. No.:** 5470
**Name:** Tea Time
**Height:** 14.25
**Status:** Open edition, retired
**Issue Year:** 1988
**Issue Price:** $260
**Last Year:** 1997
**Last Retail Price:** $410

**Ref. No.:** 1495
**Name:** A Lady of Taste
**Height:** 14.5
**Status:** Open edition, active
**Issue Year:** 1986
**Issue Price:** $575
**2003 Retail Price:** $1100

**Ref. No.:** 4698
**Name:** Lady with Fan
**Height:** 14.5
**Status:** Open issue, retired
**Issue Year:** 1970
**Issue Price:** $75
**Last Year:** 1975
**Last Retail Price:** $130

**Ref. No.:** 5377
**Name:** A Touch of Class
**Height:** 14.5
**Status:** Open edition, retired
**Issue Year:** 1986
**Issue Price:** $475
**Last Year:** 2000
**Last Retail Price:** $795

**Ref. No.:** 6863
**Name:** A Sign of the Season
**Height:** 14.5
**Status:** Open issue, retired
**Issue Year:** 2002
**Issue Price:** $375
**Last Year:** 2002
**Last Retail Price:** $375
**Comment:** Event Piece 2002

**Ref. No.:** 6545
**Name:** On The Boulevard
**Height:** 14.75
**Status:** Open issue, retired
**Issue Year:** 2000
**Issue Price:** $585
**Last Year:** 2001
**Last Retail Price:** $585

**Ref. No.:** 6622
**Name:** A Sunny Afternoon
**Height:** 14.75
**Status:** Open issue, active
**Issue Year:** 1999
**Issue Price:** $675
**2003 Retail Price:** $695

**Ref. No.:** 6782
**Name:** Blossom of the Heart
**Height:** 14.75
**Status:** Open issue, active
**Issue Year:** 2001
**Issue Price:** $345
**2003 Retail Price:** $375

**Ref. No.:** 1519
**Name:** A Stroll in the Park
**Height:** 15
**Status:** Open issue, retired
**Issue Year:** 1987
**Issue Price:** $1600
**Last Year:** 1997
**Last Retail Price:** $2600

**Ref. No.:** 4850
**Name:** Aesthetic Pose
**Height:** 15
**Status:** Open issue, retired
**Issue Year:** 1973
**Issue Price:** $110
**Last Year:** 1985
**Last Retail Price:** $265
**High Auction Price:** $900
**Low Auction Price:** $650

**Ref. No.:** 6427
**Name:** A Flower for You
**Height:** 15
**Status:** Open issue, retired
**Issue Year:** 1997
**Issue Price:** $320
**Last Year:** 2000
**Last Retail Price:** $320

*Women*

**Ref. No.:** 5175
**Name:** Flapper
**Height:** 15.25
**Status:** Open issue, retired
**Issue Year:** 1982
**Issue Price:** $185
**Last Year:** 1995
**Last Retail Price:** $365

**Ref. No.:** 5802
**Name:** Elegant Promenade
**Height:** 15.25
**Status:** Open issue, active
**Issue Year:** 1991
**Issue Price:** $775
**2003 Retail Price:** $825

**Ref. No.:** 6639
**Name:** Sunday Stroll
**Height:** 15.25
**Status:** Open issue, retired
**Issue Year:** 1999
**Issue Price:** $925
**Last Year:** 2002
**Last Retail Price:** $950

**Ref. No.:** 6805
**Name:** Romantica
**Height:** 16
**Status:** Open issue, active
**Issue Year:** 2002
**Issue Price:** $445
**2003 Retail Price:** $450

**Ref. No.:** 6847
**Name:** Aurora
**Height:** 16
**Status:** Open issue, active
**Issue Year:** 2002
**Issue Price:** $795
**2003 Retail Price:** $795

**Ref. No.:** 4914
**Name:** Lady with Shawl
**Height:** 16.5
**Status:** Open issue, retired
**Issue Year:** 1974
**Issue Price:** $220
**Last Year:** 1998
**Last Retail Price:** $730

**Ref. No.:** 5005
**Name:** Eloise
**Height:** 16.5
**Status:** Open issue, retired
**Issue Year:** 1978
**Issue Price:** $175
**Last Year:** 1981
**Last Retail Price:** $230
**High Auction Price:** $550
**Low Auction Price:** $475

**Ref. No.:** 6562
**Name:** A Wish For Love
**Height:** 16.5
**Status:** Open issue, active
**Issue Year:** 1999
**Issue Price:** $1875
**2003 Retail Price:** $1875
**Comment:** Introduced by select dealers in 1998

**Ref. No.:** 6655
**Name:** Cocktail Party
**Height:** 16.5
**Status:** Open issue, retired
**Issue Year:** 2000
**Issue Price:** $265
**Last Year:** 2002
**Last Retail Price:** $275

**Ref. No.:** 6866
**Name:** Fragrances And Colors
**Height:** 16.5
**Status:** Open issue, active
**Issue Year:** 2002
**Issue Price:** $550
**2003 Retail Price:** $575

**Ref. No.:** 1440
**Name:** Pleasantries
**Height:** 17
**Status:** Open issue, retired
**Issue Year:** 1983
**Issue Price:** $960
**Last Year:** 1991
**Last Retail Price:** $1400
**High Auction Price:** $2000
**Low Auction Price:** $1700

**Ref. No.:** 6848
**Name:** Alborada
**Height:** 17.25
**Status:** Open issue, active
**Issue Year:** 2002
**Issue Price:** $695
**2003 Retail Price:** $695

*Women*

**Ref. No.:** 4719
**Name:** Lady Empire
**Height:** 18
**Status:** Open issue, retired
**Issue Year:** 1970
**Issue Price:** $150
**Last Year:** 1979
**Last Retail Price:** $340
**Auction Price:** $850

**Ref. No.:** 4804
**Name:** Harmony Group
**Height:** 19.25
**Status:** Open issue, retired
**Issue Year:** 1972
**Issue Price:** $165
**Last Year:** 1981
**Last Retail Price:** $495

**Ref. No.:** 4805
**Name:** Woman with Umbrella
**Height:** 19.25
**Status:** Open issue, retired
**Issue Year:** 1972
**Issue Price:** $100
**Last Year:** 1981
**Last Retail Price:** $467.50
**High Auction Price:** $850
**Low Auction Price:** $600

*Men*

**Ref. No.:** 4685
**Name:** Tricornered Hat
**Height:** 9
**Status:** Open edition, retired
**Issue Year:** 1970
**Issue Price:** $25
**Last Year:** 1984
**Last Retail Price:** $85

**Ref. No.:** 5547
**Name:** Only the Beginning
**Height:** 9.5
**Status:** Open issue, retired
**Issue Year:** 1989
**Issue Price:** $215
**Last Year:** 1996
**Last Retail Price:** $275

**Ref. No.:** 5676
**Name:** Wandering Minstrel
**Height:** 9.5
**Status:** Open issue, retired
**Issue Year:** 1990
**Issue Price:** $270
**Last Year:** 1993
**Last Retail Price:** $310

**Ref. No.:** 5355
**Name:** Consideration
**Height:** 10
**Status:** Open edition, retired
**Issue Year:** 1986
**Issue Price:** $100
**Last Year:** 1988
**Last Retail Price:** $125
**High Auction Price:** $300
**Low Auction Price:** $200

**Ref. No.:** 4637
**Name:** Caped Gentleman
**Height:** 10.25
**Status:** Open issue, retired
**Issue Year:** 1969
**Issue Price:** $25
**Last Year:** 1972
**Last Retail Price:** $25

**Ref. No.:** 4859
**Name:** Peddler
**Height:** 10.25
**Status:** Open issue, retired
**Issue Year:** 1974
**Issue Price:** $180
**Last Year:** 1985
**Last Retail Price:** $410
**High Auction Price:** $1200
**Low Auction Price:** $800

**Ref. No.:** 1094
**Name:** Beggar
**Height:** 10.5
**Status:** Open issue, retired
**Issue Year:** 1969
**Issue Price:** $65
**Last Year:** 1981
**Last Retail Price:** $95

**Ref. No.:** 4688
**Name:** Gothic King
**Height:** 11
**Status:** Open issue, retired
**Issue Year:** 1970
**Issue Price:** $20
**Last Year:** 1975
**Last Retail Price:** $35

**Ref. No.:** 5233
**Name:** Charlie the Tramp
**Height:** 11
**Status:** Open issue, retired
**Issue Year:** 1984
**Issue Price:** $150
**Last Year:** 1991
**Last Retail Price:** $245
**High Auction Price:** $1100
**Low Auction Price:** $375

**Ref. No.:** 5661
**Name:** Travelling Artist
**Height:** 11.25
**Status:** Open issue, retired
**Issue Year:** 1990
**Issue Price:** $250
**Last Year:** 1994
**Last Retail Price:** $290

**Ref. No.:** 4664
**Name:** Countryman
**Height:** 11.5
**Status:** Open issue, retired
**Issue Year:** 1969
**Issue Price:** $50
**Last Year:** 1979
**Last Retail Price:** $145
**High Auction Price:** $500
**Low Auction Price:** $425

**Ref. No.:** 4684
**Name:** Hebrew Student
**Height:** 11.5
**Status:** Open issue, retired
**Issue Year:** 1970
**Issue Price:** $33
**Last Year:** 1985
**Last Retail Price:** $145
**High Auction Price:** $750
**Low Auction Price:** $500

*Men*

**Ref. No.:** 5397
**Name:** The Poet
**Height:** 11.75
**Status:** Open issue, retired
**Issue Year:** 1986
**Issue Price:** $425
**Last Year:** 1988
**Last Retail Price:** $475
**High Auction Price:** $900
**Low Auction Price:** $550

**Ref. No.:** 5280
**Name:** Hiker
**Height:** 12.25
**Status:** Open issue, retired
**Issue Year:** 1985
**Issue Price:** $195
**Last Year:** 1988
**Last Retail Price:** $225

**Ref. No.:** 1029
**Name:** Boy with Bowler
**Height:** 12.5
**Status:** Open issue, retired
**Issue Year:** 1969
**Issue Price:** $37.50
**Last Year:** 1970
**Last Retail Price:** $37.50

**Ref. No.:** 1351
**Name:** Botanic
**Height:** 12.5
**Status:** Open issue, retired
**Issue Year:** 1978
**Issue Price:** $400
**Last Year:** 1979
**Last Retail Price:** $420

**Ref. No.:** 4823
**Name:** Legionary
**Height:** 12.5
**Status:** Open issue, retired
**Issue Year:** 1972
**Issue Price:** $55
**Last Year:** 1978
**Last Retail Price:** $125
**High Auction Price:** $550
**Low Auction Price:** $475

**Ref. No.:** 5359
**Name:** El Greco
**Height:** 12.5
**Status:** Open issue, retired
**Issue Year:** 1986
**Issue Price:** $300
**Last Year:** 1990
**Last Retail Price:** $410

**Ref. No.:** 4600
**Name:** Man with Heart
**Height:** 13
**Status:** Open issue, retired
**Issue Year:** 1969
**Issue Price:** $47.50
**Last Year:** 1972
**Last Retail Price:** $50

**Ref. No.:** 5681
**Name:** On the Road
**Height:** 13.5
**Status:** Open issue, retired
**Issue Year:** 1990
**Issue Price:** $320
**Last Year:** 1991
**Last Retail Price:** $345
**Auction Price:** $550

**Ref. No.:** 4927
**Name:** Minstrel
**Height:** 13.75
**Status:** Open issue, retired
**Issue Year:** 1974
**Issue Price:** $375
**Last Year:** 1980
**Last Retail Price:** $500
**Auction Price:** $725

**Ref. No.:** 4933
**Name:** Fernando of Aragon
**Height:** 13.75
**Status:** Open issue, retired
**Issue Year:** 1974
**Issue Price:** $525
**Last Year:** 1981
**Last Retail Price:** $950
**Auction Price:** $2000

**Ref. No.:** 6317
**Name:** Making House Calls
**Height:** 14
**Status:** Open issue, retired
**Issue Year:** 1996
**Issue Price:** $250
**Last Year:** 1998
**Last Retail Price:** $260

**Ref. No.:** 4732
**Name:** Artist
**Height:** 14.25
**Status:** Open issue, retired
**Issue Year:** 1970
**Issue Price:** $75
**Last Year:** 1976
**Last Retail Price:** $80
**Auction Price:** $650

**Ref. No.:** 4652
**Name:** Happy Travelers
**Height:** 14.25
**Status:** Open issue, retired
**Issue Year:** 1969
**Issue Price:** $115
**Last Year:** 1978
**Last Retail Price:** $320
**Auction Price:** $775

**Ref. No.:** 5642
**Name:** The King's Guard
**Height:** 14.25
**Status:** Open issue, retired
**Issue Year:** 1990
**Issue Price:** $950
**Last Year:** 1993
**Last Retail Price:** $1100
**Auction Price:** $1000

**Ref. No.:** 4956
**Name:** Tavern Drinkers
**Height:** 14.5
**Status:** Open issue, retired
**Issue Year:** 1977
**Issue Price:** $1125
**Last Year:** 1985
**Last Retail Price:** $1645
**High Auction Price:** $3500
**Low Auction Price:** $2750

**Ref. No.:** 1050
**Name:** Boy with Pouch
**Height:** 15
**Status:** Open issue, retired
**Issue Year:** 1969
**Issue Price:** $65
**Last Year:** 1978
**Last Retail Price:** $65

**Ref. No.:** 1086
**Name:** Pregonero
**Height:** 15
**Status:** Very rare
**Issue Year:** 1969
**Issue Price:** $120
**Last Year:** 1975
**Last Retail Price:** Unknown
**High Auction Price:** $1050
**Low Auction Price:** $750

**Ref. No.:** 1037
**Name:** Horseman
**Height:** 16
**Status:** Very rare
**Issue Year:** 1969
**Issue Price:** $170
**Last Year:** 1970
**Last Retail Price:** Unknown
**Auction Price:** $2500

**Ref. No.:** 1078
**Name:** Herald
**Height:** 17
**Status:** Open issue, retired
**Issue Year:** 1969
**Issue Price:** $110
**Last Year:** 1980
**Last Retail Price:** $110

**Ref. No.:** 4517
**Name:** Boy Student
**Height:** 17
**Status:** Open issue, retired
**Issue Year:** 1969
**Issue Price:** $57.5
**Last Year:** 1978
**Last Retail Price:** $95

**Ref. No.:** 4515
**Name:** Man on Horse
**Height:** 19
**Status:** Open issue, retired
**Issue Year:** 1969
**Issue Price:** $180
**Last Year:** 1985
**Last Retail Price:** $490
**High Auction Price:** $1300

**Ref. No.:** 1328
**Name:** Man with Lamb
    on Shoulders
**Height:** 27.5
**Status:** Open issue, retired
**Issue Year:** 1976
**Issue Price:** $1100
**Last Year:** 1981
**Last Retail Price:** $1860

*Men*

**Ref. No.:** 4659
**Name:** Shepherd
**Height:** 7.5
**Status:** Open issue, retired
**Issue Year:** 1969
**Issue Price:** $25.50
**Last Year:** 1985
**Last Retail Price:** $132
**High Auction Price:** $325
**Low Auction Price:** $175

**Ref. No.:** 5733
**Name:** Horticulturist
**Height:** 8.5
**Status:** Open issue, retired
**Issue Year:** 1991
**Issue Price:** $450
**Last Year:** 1993
**Last Retail Price:** $495

**Ref. No.:** 1373
**Name:** Chestnut Seller
**Height:** 9.5
**Status:** Open issue, retired
**Issue Year:** 1978
**Issue Price:** $800
**Last Year:** 1981
**Last Retail Price:** $1000
**Auction Price:** $950

**Ref. No.:** 4577
**Name:** New Shepherd
**Height:** 9.75
**Status:** Open issue, retired
**Issue Year:** 1969
**Issue Price:** $35
**Last Year:** 1983
**Last Retail Price:** $100
**High Auction Price:** $550
**Low Auction Price:** $400

**Ref. No.:** 4853
**Name:** Cobbler
**Height:** 9.75
**Status:** Open issue, retired
**Issue Year:** 1973
**Issue Price:** $100
**Last Year:** 1985
**Last Retail Price:** $285
**High Auction Price:** $750
**Low Auction Price:** $450

**Ref. No.:** 4571
**Name:** Shepherd Resting
**Height:** 10.25
**Status:** Open issue, retired
**Issue Year:** 1969
**Issue Price:** $60
**Last Year:** 1981
**Last Retail Price:** $90
**Auction Price:** $450

**Ref. No.:** 1089
**Name:** Lawyer
**Height:** 11
**Status:** Very rare
**Issue Year:** 1971
**Issue Price:** $35
**Last Year:** 1973
**Last Retail Price:** Unknown
**Auction Price:** $700

**Ref. No.:** 1090
**Name:** Lawyer
**Height:** 11
**Status:** Very rare
**Issue Year:** 1971
**Issue Price:** $35
**Last Year:** 1973
**Last Retail Price:** Unknown
**Auction Price:** $700

**Ref. No.:** 4718
**Name:** Cadet
**Height:** 11
**Status:** Open issue, retired
**Issue Year:** 1970
**Issue Price:** $25
**Last Year:** 1971
**Last Retail Price:** $25

**Ref. No.:** 6749
**Name:** Always on the Go
**Height:** 11.25
**Status:** Open issue, active
**Issue Year:** 2001
**Issue Price:** $265
**2003 Retail Price:** $295

**Ref. No.:** 1305
**Name:** Viviandiere and Soldier
**Height:** 11.5
**Status:** Open issue, retired
**Issue Year:** 1974
**Issue Price:** $550
**Last Year:** 1979
**Last Retail Price:** $1000
**High Auction Price:** $800
**Low Auction Price:** $775

**Ref. No.:** 4620
**Name:** Policeman
**Height:** 11.5
**Status:** Open issue, retired
**Issue Year:** 1969
**Issue Price:** $16
**Last Year:** 1972
**Last Retail Price:** $200

**Ref. No.:** 4834
**Name:** Shepherd
**Height:** 11.5
**Status:** Open issue, retired
**Issue Year:** 1972
**Issue Price:** $40
**Last Year:** 1981
**Last Retail Price:** $57.50

**Ref. No.:** 5204
**Name:** Sharpening Cutlery
**Height:** 11.5
**Status:** Open issue, retired
**Issue Year:** 1984
**Issue Price:** $210
**Last Year:** 1988
**Last Retail Price:** $275
**High Auction Price:** $1200
**Low Auction Price:** $750

**Ref. No.:** 5234
**Name:** Artistic Endeavor
**Height:** 11.5
**Status:** Open issue, retired
**Issue Year:** 1984
**Issue Price:** $225
**Last Year:** 1988
**Last Retail Price:** $275
**High Auction Price:** $825
**Low Auction Price:** $400

**Ref. No.:** 5273
**Name:** Civil Guard at Attention
**Height:** 11.5
**Status:** Open issue, retired
**Issue Year:** 1985
**Issue Price:** $170
**Last Year:** 1988
**Last Retail Price:** $200
**Auction Price:** $500

**Ref. No.:** 1252
**Name:** Shepherd's Rest
**Height:** 11.75
**Status:** Open issue, retired
**Issue Year:** 1974
**Issue Price:** $100
**Last Year:** 1981
**Last Retail Price:** $130

**Ref. No.:** 4554
**Name:** Shepherd with Girl
and Lamb
**Height:** 11.75
**Status:** Open issue, retired
**Issue Year:** 1969
**Issue Price:** $65
**Last Year:** 1972
**Last Retail Price:** $75

**Ref. No.:** 4889
**Name:** Spanish Policeman
**Height:** 11.75
**Status:** Open issue, retired
**Issue Year:** 1974
**Issue Price:** $55
**Last Year:** 2002
**Last Retail Price:** $315

**Ref. No.:** 5191
**Name:** Cookies for Sale
**Height:** 11.75
**Status:** Open issue, retired
**Issue Year:** 1984
**Issue Price:** $135
**Last Year:** 1985
**Last Retail Price:** $135
**High Auction Price:** $600
**Low Auction Price:** $250

**Ref. No.:** 5194
**Name:** Roving Photographer
**Height:** 11.75
**Status:** Open issue, retired
**Issue Year:** 1984
**Issue Price:** $145
**Last Year:** 1985
**Last Retail Price:** $145
**High Auction Price:** $2500
**Low Auction Price:** $1450

**Ref. No.:** 5255
**Name:** Spanish Soldier
**Height:** 11.75
**Status:** Open issue, retired
**Issue Year:** 1984
**Issue Price:** $185
**Last Year:** 1988
**Last Retail Price:** $230
**High Auction Price:** $650
**Low Auction Price:** $350

**Ref. No.:** 5325
**Name:** Ice Cream Vendor
**Height:** 11.75
**Status:** Open issue, retired
**Issue Year:** 1985
**Issue Price:** $380
**Last Year:** 1995
**Last Retail Price:** $650

**Ref. No.:** 6450
**Name:** Dentist
**Height:** 12
**Status:** Open issue, retired
**Issue Year:** 1997
**Issue Price:** $225
**Last Year:** 2000
**Last Retail Price:** $250

**Ref. No.:** 4839
**Name:** Soldier
**Height:** 12.25
**Status:** Open issue, retired
**Issue Year:** 1973
**Issue Price:** $65
**Last Year:** 1976
**Last Retail Price:** $95
**High Auction Price:** $650
**Low Auction Price:** $525

**Ref. No.:** 5214
**Name:** The Architect
**Height:** 12.25
**Status:** Open issue, retired
**Issue Year:** 1984
**Issue Price:** $140
**Last Year:** 1990
**Last Retail Price:** $220
**High Auction Price:** $625
**Low Auction Price:** $400

**Ref. No.:** 5253
**Name:** Cadet
**Height:** 12.25
**Status:** Open issue, retired
**Issue Year:** 1984
**Issue Price:** $150
**Last Year:** 1984
**Last Retail Price:** $150
**Auction Price:** $525

**Ref. No.:** 5326
**Name:** The Tailor
**Height:** 12.25
**Status:** Open issue, retired
**Issue Year:** 1985
**Issue Price:** $335
**Last Year:** 1988
**Last Retail Price:** $390
**High Auction Price:** $975
**Low Auction Price:** $750

**Ref. No.:** 4844
**Name:** Pharmacist
**Height:** 12.5
**Status:** Open issue, retired
**Issue Year:** 1973
**Issue Price:** $70
**Last Year:** 1985
**Last Retail Price:** $235
**High Auction Price:** $2150
**Low Auction Price:** $625

**Ref. No.:** 5976
**Name:** The Fireman
**Height:** 12.5
**Status:** Open issue, retired
**Issue Year:** 1993
**Issue Price:** $490
**Last Year:** 1997
**Last Retail Price:** $465

**Ref. No.:** 5195
**Name:** Say Cheese
**Height:** 13
**Status:** Open issue, retired
**Issue Year:** 1984
**Issue Price:** $170
**Last Year:** 1990
**Last Retail Price:** $250
**High Auction Price:** $600
**Low Auction Price:** $350

**Ref. No.:** 5208
**Name:** The Professor
**Height:** 13
**Status:** Open issue, retired
**Issue Year:** 1984
**Issue Price:** $205
**Last Year:** 1990
**Last Retail Price:** $340
**High Auction Price:** $900
**Low Auction Price:** $450

**Ref. No.:** 5209
**Name:** School Marm
**Height:** 13
**Status:** Open issue, retired
**Issue Year:** 1984
**Issue Price:** $205
**Last Year:** 1990
**Last Retail Price:** $340
**High Auction Price:** $1000
**Low Auction Price:** $700

**Ref. No.:** 5213
**Name:** Attorney
**Height:** 13
**Status:** Open issue, retired
**Issue Year:** 1984
**Issue Price:** $250
**Last Year:** 1997
**Last Retail Price:** $620

**Ref. No.:** 5431
**Name:** Midwife
**Height:** 13
**Status:** Open issue, retired
**Issue Year:** 1987
**Issue Price:** $175
**Last Year:** 1990
**Last Retail Price:** $215
**Auction Price:** $400

**Ref. No.:** 6273
**Name:** Pharmacist
**Height:** 13
**Status:** Open issue, retired
**Issue Year:** 1996
**Issue Price:** $290
**Last Year:** 2000
**Last Retail Price:** $290

**Ref. No.:** 4663
**Name:** Painter
**Height:** 13.25
**Status:** Open issue, retired
**Issue Year:** 1969
**Issue Price:** $45
**Last Year:** 1972
**Last Retail Price:** $55

**Ref. No.:** 4825
**Name:** Veterinarian
**Height:** 13.25
**Status:** Open issue, retired
**Issue Year:** 1972
**Issue Price:** $35
**Last Year:** 1985
**Last Retail Price:** $147.5
**High Auction Price:** $525
**Low Auction Price:** $350

**Ref. No.:** 5197
**Name:** Female Physician
**Height:** 13.25
**Status:** Open edition, active
**Issue Year:** 1984
**Issue Price:** $120
**2003 Retail Price:** $295

**Ref. No.:** 5206
**Name:** Yachtsman
**Height:** 13.25
**Status:** Open issue, retired
**Issue Year:** 1984
**Issue Price:** $110
**Last Year:** 1994
**Last Retail Price:** $210

**Ref. No.:** 5489
**Name:** Justice
**Height:** 13.25
**Status:** Open issue, retired
**Issue Year:** 1988
**Issue Price:** $675
**Last Year:** 1993
**Last Retail Price:** $825

**Ref. No.:** 5948
**Name:** Physician
**Height:** 13.5
**Status:** Open issue, active
**Issue Year:** 1993
**Issue Price:** $375
**2003 Retail Price:** $375

**Ref. No.:** 6654
**Name:** On Shore Leave
**Height:** 13.5
**Status:** Open issue, active
**Issue Year:** 2000
**Issue Price:** $285
**2003 Retail Price:** $295

**Ref. No.:** 4762.3
**Name:** Dentist (Reduced)
**Height:** 13.75
**Status:** Open issue, retired
**Issue Year:** 1971
**Issue Price:** $30
**Last Year:** 1985
**Last Retail Price:** $132
**High Auction Price:** $500
**Low Auction Price:** $450

**Ref. No.:** 4763.3
**Name:** Obstetrician (Reduced)
**Height:** 13.75
**Status:** Open issue, retired
**Issue Year:** 1971
**Issue Price:** $40
**Last Year:** Unknown
**Last Retail Price:** Unknown

**Ref. No.:** 4892
**Name:** Watching the Pigs
**Height:** 13.75
**Status:** Open issue, retired
**Issue Year:** 1974
**Issue Price:** $160
**Last Year:** 1978
**Last Retail Price:** $275

**Ref. No.:** 5947
**Name:** General Practitioner
**Height:** 13.75
**Status:** Open issue, retired
**Issue Year:** 1993
**Issue Price:** $360
**Last Year:** 1997
**Last Retail Price:** $370

**Ref. No.:** 5960
**Name:** On Patrol
**Height:** 13.75
**Status:** Open issue, retired
**Issue Year:** 1993
**Issue Price:** $395
**Last Year:** 1997
**Last Retail Price:** $445

**Ref. No.:** 6256
**Name:** Making Rounds
**Height:** 13.75
**Status:** Open edition, active
**Issue Year:** 1996
**Issue Price:** $295
**2003 Retail Price:** $295

**Ref. No.:** 1104
**Name:** Shepherd Sleeping
**Height:** 14
**Status:** Open issue, retired
**Issue Year:** 1971
**Issue Price:** $225
**Last Year:** 1978
**Last Retail Price:** $650

**Ref. No.:** 6282
**Name:** Medic
**Height:** 14
**Status:** Open issue, retired
**Issue Year:** 1996
**Issue Price:** $225
**Last Year:** 1999
**Last Retail Price:** $225

**Ref. No.:** 6320
**Name:** Architect
**Height:** 14
**Status:** Open issue, retired
**Issue Year:** 1996
**Issue Price:** $330
**Last Year:** 1999
**Last Retail Price:** $330

**Ref. No.:** 6425
**Name:** Female Attorney
**Height:** 14
**Status:** Open issue, retired
**Issue Year:** 1997
**Issue Price:** $300
**Last Year:** 2000
**Last Retail Price:** $320

**Ref. No.:** 6659
**Name:** Today's Lesson
**Height:** 14
**Status:** Open issue, active
**Issue Year:** 2000
**Issue Price:** $265
**2003 Retail Price:** $295

**Ref. No.:** 1325
**Name:** Seaman
**Height:** 14.25
**Status:** Open edition, retired
**Issue Year:** 1976
**Issue Price:** $600
**Last Year:** 1988
**Last Retail Price:** $1100
**High Auction Price:** $1200
**Low Auction Price:** $950

**Ref. No.:** 4603
**Name:** Nurse
**Height:** 14.25
**Status:** Open issue, active
**Issue Year:** 1971
**Issue Price:** $35
**2003 Retail Price:** $250

**Ref. No.:** 342.13
**Name:** Greek Shepherd
**Height:** 14.5
**Status:** Very rare
**Issue Year:** 1963
**Issue Price:** Unknown
**Last Year:** Unknown
**Last Retail Price:** Unknown

**Ref. No.:** 1355
**Name:** Astronomy Lesson
**Height:** 14.5
**Status:** Open issue, retired
**Issue Year:** 1978
**Issue Price:** $550
**Last Year:** 1979
**Last Retail Price:** $575

**Ref. No.:** 4621
**Name:** Sea Captain
**Height:** 14.5
**Status:** Open issue, retired
**Issue Year:** 1969
**Issue Price:** $42.50
**Last Year:** 1993
**Last Retail Price:** $265
**Auction Price:** $300

**Ref. No.:** 4644
**Name:** Village Mayor
**Height:** 14.5
**Status:** Open issue, retired
**Issue Year:** 1969
**Issue Price:** $35
**Last Year:** 1972
**Last Retail Price:** $40

**Ref. No.:** 4656
**Name:** Woodcutter
**Height:** 14.5
**Status:** Open issue, retired
**Issue Year:** 1969
**Issue Price:** $80
**Last Year:** 1978
**Last Retail Price:** $220

**Ref. No.:** 4657
**Name:** Sailor
**Height:** 14.5
**Status:** Open issue, retired
**Issue Year:** 1969
**Issue Price:** $35
**Last Year:** 1978
**Last Retail Price:** $75

**Ref. No.:** 4802
**Name:** Fisherman
**Height:** 14.5
**Status:** Open issue, retired
**Issue Year:** 1972
**Issue Price:** $70
**Last Year:** 1979
**Last Retail Price:** $95
**Auction Price:** $700

**Ref. No.:** 5048
**Name:** Teacher Woman
**Height:** 14.5
**Status:** Open issue, retired
**Issue Year:** 1980
**Issue Price:** $115
**Last Year:** 1981
**Last Retail Price:** $125
**High Auction Price:** $650
**Low Auction Price:** $600

**Ref. No.:** 4602
**Name:** Doctor
**Height:** 14.75
**Status:** Open issue, retired
**Issue Year:** 1971
**Issue Price:** $33
**Last Year:** 1999
**Last Retail Price:** $230

**Ref. No.:** 6625
**Name:** The Master Chef
**Height:** 14.75
**Status:** Open issue, retired
**Issue Year:** 1999
**Issue Price:** $240
**Last Year:** 2001
**Last Retail Price:** $240

**Ref. No.:** 4801
**Name:** The Teacher
**Height:** 15
**Status:** Open issue, retired
**Issue Year:** 1972
**Issue Price:** $45
**Last Year:** 1978
**Last Retail Price:** $105
**High Auction Price:** $500
**Low Auction Price:** $250

**Ref. No.:** 6426
**Name:** Male Attorney
**Height:** 15
**Status:** Open issue, retired
**Issue Year:** 1997
**Issue Price:** $300
**Last Year:** 2000
**Last Retail Price:** $320

**Ref. No.:** 345.13
**Name:** Shepherd, Contemplative
**Height:** 15.25
**Status:** Very rare
**Issue Year:** 1968
**Issue Price:** Unknown
**Last Year:** Unknown
**Last Retail Price:** Unknown

**Ref. No.:** 346.13
**Name:** Allegory
**Height:** 15.25
**Status:** Very rare
**Issue Year:** 1965
**Issue Price:** Unknown
**Last Year:** Unknown
**Last Retail Price:** Unknown

**Ref. No.:** 5891
**Name:** The Aviator
**Height:** 15.5
**Status:** Open issue, retired
**Issue Year:** 1992
**Issue Price:** $375
**Last Year:** 1997
**Last Retail Price:** $425

**Ref. No.:** 4602.1
**Name:** Doctor
**Height:** 15.75
**Status:** Open issue, retired
**Issue Year:** 1969
**Issue Price:** $33
**Last Year:** 1978
**Last Retail Price:** Unknown

**Ref. No.:** 4603.1
**Name:** Nurse
**Height:** 15.75
**Status:** Open issue, retired
**Issue Year:** 1969
**Issue Price:** $35
**Last Year:** 1978

**Ref. No.:** 4762
**Name:** Dentist
**Height:** 15.75
**Status:** Open issue, retired
**Issue Year:** 1971
**Issue Price:** $30
**Last Year:** 1978
**Last Retail Price:** $75
**Auction Price:** $425

**Ref. No.:** 4803
**Name:** Sorian Shepherd with
   Flock
**Height:** 15.75
**Status:** Open issue, retired
**Issue Year:** 1972
**Issue Price:** $195
**Last Year:** 1975
**Last Retail Price:** $300

**Ref. No.:** 4908
**Name:** The Barrister
**Height:** 15.75
**Status:** Open issue, retired
**Issue Year:** 1974
**Issue Price:** $100
**Last Year:** 1985
**Last Retail Price:** $250
**Auction Price:** $425

**Ref. No.:** 4581
**Name:** The Harvester
**Height:** 16
**Status:** Open issue, retired
**Issue Year:** 1969
**Issue Price:** $60
**Last Year:** 1975
**Last Retail Price:** $110

**Ref. No.:** 4763
**Name:** Obstetrician
**Height:** 16.5
**Status:** Open issue, retired
**Issue Year:** 1971
**Issue Price:** $47.50
**Last Year:** 1997
**Last Retail Price:** 255
**Auction Price:** $450

**Ref. No.:** 1253
**Name:** Sad Chimney Sweep
**Height:** 17
**Status:** Open issue, retired
**Issue Year:** 1974
**Issue Price:** $180
**Last Year:** 1983
**Last Retail Price:** $220

**Ref. No.:** 1075
**Name:** Knight
**Height:** 17.25
**Status:** Open issue, retired
**Issue Year:** 1969
**Issue Price:** $170
**Last Year:** 1970
**Last Retail Price:** $170

**Ref. No.:** 5087
**Name:** The Watchman
**Height:** 17.25
**Status:** Open issue, retired
**Issue Year:** 1980
**Issue Price:** $225
**Last Year:** 1983
**Last Retail Price:** $250
**High Auction Price:** $1350
**Low Auction Price:** $1125

### Sports

**Ref. No.:** 4623
**Name:** Shepherd
**Height:** 18.5
**Status:** Open issue, retired
**Issue Year:** 1969
**Issue Price:** $80
**Last Year:** 1975
**Last Retail Price:** $80
**Auction Price:** $900

**Ref. No.:** 5205
**Name:** Lamplighter
**Height:** 18.5
**Status:** Open issue, active
**Issue Year:** 1984
**Issue Price:** $170
**2003 Retail Price:** $450

**Ref. No.:** 5335
**Name:** Aerobics Floor Exerciser
**Height:** 4.25
**Status:** Open issue, retired
**Issue Year:** 1985
**Issue Price:** $110
**Last Year:** 1988
**Last Retail Price:** $125
**High Auction Price:** $300
**Low Auction Price:** $166

**Ref. No.:** 5331
**Name:** Gymnast with Ring
**Height:** 4.75
**Status:** Open issue, retired
**Issue Year:** 1985
**Issue Price:** $95
**Last Year:** 1988
**Last Retail Price:** $110
**Auction Price:** $425
**Low Auction Price:** $150

**Ref. No.:** 5336
**Name:** Aerobics Scissor Figure
**Height:** 6
**Status:** Open issue, retired
**Issue Year:** 1985
**Issue Price:** $110
**Last Year:** 1988
**Last Retail Price:** $125
**High Auction Price:** $375
**Low Auction Price:** $166

**Ref. No.:** 5332
**Name:** Gymnast Balancing Ball
**Height:** 6.25
**Status:** Open issue, retired
**Issue Year:** 1985
**Issue Price:** $95
**Last Year:** 1988
**Last Retail Price:** $110
**High Auction Price:** $325
**Low Auction Price:** $175

**Ref. No.:** 5333
**Name:** Gymnast Exercising
with Ball
**Height:** 6.5
**Status:** Open issue, retired
**Issue Year:** 1985
**Issue Price:** $95
**Last Year:** 1988
**Last Retail Price:** $110
**High Auction Price:** $325
**Low Auction Price:** $150

**Ref. No.:** 85.06
**Name:** The Hunter
**Height:** 8.25
**Status:** Very rare
**Issue Year:** 1956
**Issue Price:** Unknown
**Last Year:** Unknown
**Last Retail Price:** Unknown

**Ref. No.:** 5200
**Name:** Soccer Player
**Height:** 8.5
**Status:** Open issue, retired
**Issue Year:** 1984
**Issue Price:** $155
**Last Year:** 1988
**Last Retail Price:** $170
**High Auction Price:** $725
**Low Auction Price:** $450

**Ref. No.:** 5200.3
**Name:** Special Male Soccer Player
**Height:** 8.5
**Status:** Open issue, retired
**Issue Year:** 1984
**Issue Price:** $150
**Last Year:** 1988
**Last Retail Price:** $185
**High Auction Price:** $750
**Low Auction Price:** $450

**Ref. No.:** 6096
**Name:** The Sportsman
**Height:** 8.75
**Status:** Open issue, retired
**Issue Year:** 1994
**Issue Price:** $495
**Last Year:** 1997
**Last Retail Price:** $540

**Ref. No.:** 5334
**Name:** Aerobics Pull-Ups
**Height:** 9
**Status:** Open issue, retired
**Issue Year:** 1985
**Issue Price:** $110
**Last Year:** 1988
**Last Retail Price:** $125
**High Auction Price:** $325
**Low Auction Price:** $150

**Ref. No.:** 5328
**Name:** Lady Equestrian
**Height:** 9.75
**Status:** Open issue, retired
**Issue Year:** 1985
**Issue Price:** $160
**Last Year:** 1988
**Last Retail Price:** $190
**High Auction Price:** $550
**Low Auction Price:** $375

**Ref. No.:** 4851
**Name:** Golf Player (Woman)
**Height:** 10.25
**Status:** Open edition, active
**Issue Year:** 1973
**Issue Price:** $70
**2003 Retail Price:** $295

**Ref. No.:** 5270
**Name:** Racing Motorcyclist
**Height:** 10.25
**Status:** Open issue, retired
**Issue Year:** 1985
**Issue Price:** $360
**Last Year:** 1988
**Last Retail Price:** $425
**High Auction Price:** $1050
**Low Auction Price:** $575

**Ref. No.:** 5272
**Name:** Biking in the Country
**Height:** 10.25
**Status:** Open issue, retired
**Issue Year:** 1985
**Issue Price:** $295
**Last Year:** 1990
**Last Retail Price:** $430
**High Auction Price:** $825
**Low Auction Price:** $500

**Ref. No.:** 5329
**Name:** Gentleman Equestrian
**Height:** 10.25
**Status:** Open issue, retired
**Issue Year:** 1985
**Issue Price:** $160
**Last Year:** 1988
**Last Retail Price:** $190
**High Auction Price:** $525
**Low Auction Price:** $275

**Ref. No.:** 4824
**Name:** Golfer
**Height:** 10.5
**Status:** Open issue, active
**Issue Year:** 1972
**Issue Price:** $66
**2003 Retail Price:** $295

**Ref. No.:** 4894
**Name:** Boy Tennis Player
**Height:** 10.5
**Status:** Open issue, retired
**Issue Year:** 1974
**Issue Price:** $75
**Last Year:** 1980
**Last Retail Price:** $125
**High Auction Price:** $425
**Low Auction Price:** $350

**Ref. No.:** 5879
**Name:** Shot On Goal
**Height:** 10.75
**Status:** Open issue, retired
**Issue Year:** 1992
**Issue Price:** $1100
**Last Year:** 1996
**Last Retail Price:** $1150

**Ref. No.:** 1427
**Name:** Female Tennis Player
**Height:** 11
**Status:** Open issue, retired
**Issue Year:** 1982
**Issue Price:** $200
**Last Year:** 1988
**Issue Price:** $200
**Last Retail Price:** $250
**Auction Price:** $450

**Ref. No.:** 1426
**Name:** Male Tennis Player
**Height:** 11.5
**Status:** Open issue, retired
**Issue Year:** 1982
**Issue Price:** $200
**Last Year:** 1988
**Last Retail Price:** $250
**High Auction Price:** $325
**Low Auction Price:** $150

**Ref. No.:** 5301
**Name:** Waiting to Tee Off
**Height:** 11.5
**Status:** Open issue, retired
**Issue Year:** 1985
**Issue Price:** $145
**Last Year:** 1999
**Last Retail Price:** $295

**Ref. No.:** 1162
**Name:** Seated Torero
**Height:** 11.75
**Status:** Very rare
**Issue Year:** 1971
**Issue Price:** $35
**Last Year:** 1973
**Last Retail Price:** Unknown
**Auction Price:** $400

**Ref. No.:** 1341
**Name:** Jockey
**Height:** 12.25
**Status:** Open issue, retired
**Issue Year:** 1977
**Issue Price:** $120
**Last Year:** 1979
**Last Retail Price:** $140
**Auction Price:** $500

**Ref. No.:** 4798
**Name:** Girl Tennis Player
**Height:** 12.50
**Status:** Open issue, retired
**Issue Year:** 1972
**Issue Price:** $50
**Last Year:** 1981
**Last Retail Price:** $187.5
**High Auction Price:** $450
**Low Auction Price:** $300

**Ref. No.:** 1249
**Name:** The Race
**Height:** 13
**Status:** Open issue, retired
**Issue Year:** 1974
**Issue Price:** $410
**Last Year:** 1988
**Last Retail Price:** $1210
**High Auction Price:** $3200
**Low Auction Price:** $2200

Ref. No.: 1453
Name: Golfing Couple
Height: 13.25
Status: Open issue, active
Issue Year: 1983
Issue Price: $248
2003 Retail Price: $550

Ref. No.: 5089
Name: The Jockey
Height: 13.25
Status: Open issue, retired
Issue Year: 1980
Issue Price: $660
Last Year: 1985
Last Retail Price: $730
High Auction Price: $1150
Low Auction Price: $900

Ref. No.: 6286
Name: Tennis Champion
Height: 14
Status: Open issue, retired
Issue Year: 1996
Issue Price: $350
Last Year: 1999
Last Retail Price: $390

Ref. No.: 6466
Name: A Prize Catch
Height: 14
Status: Open issue, retired
Issue Year: 1998
Issue Price: $340
Last Year: 2000
Last Retail Price: $355

Ref. No.: 5002
Name: Hunter with Dog
Height: 14.25
Status: Open issue, retired
Issue Year: 1978
Issue Price: $325
Last Year: 1979
Last Retail Price: $340

Ref. No.: 6248
Name: Regatta
Height: 14.5
Status: Open issue, retired
Issue Year: 1995
Issue Price: $695
Last Year: 1996
Last Retail Price: $695

**Ref. No.:** 6689
**Name:** A Perfect Drive
**Height:** 14.75
**Status:** Open issue, active
**Issue Year:** 2000
**Issue Price:** $335
**2003 Retail Price:** $350

**Ref. No.:** 1344
**Name:** Derby
**Height:** 15.5
**Status:** Open issue, retired
**Issue Year:** 1977
**Issue Price:** $1125
**Last Year:** 1985
**Last Retail Price:** $1675
**High Auction Price:** $2300
**Low Auction Price:** $1800

**Ref. No.:** 6032
**Name:** On the Green
**Height:** 15.5
**Status:** Open issue, retired
**Issue Year:** 1993
**Issue Price:** $645
**Last Year:** 2002
**Last Retail Price:** $645

**Ref. No.:** 1061
**Name:** Campero
**Height:** 15.75
**Status:** Open issue, retired
**Issue Year:** 1969
**Issue Price:** $180
**Last Year:** 1975
**Last Retail Price:** $275

**Ref. No.:** 4940
**Name:** Torch Bearer
**Height:** 16.5
**Status:** Open issue, retired
**Issue Year:** 1974
**Issue Price:** $80
**Last Year:** 1978
**Last Retail Price:** $135

**Ref. No.:** 5251
**Name:** Torch Bearer
**Height:** 16.5
**Status:** Open issue, retired
**Issue Year:** 1984
**Issue Price:** $100
**Last Year:** 1988
**Last Retail Price:** $120
**High Auction Price:** $675
**Low Auction Price:** $200

**Ref. No.:** 6845
**Name:** The Perfect Swing
**Height:** 16.75
**Status:** Open issue, active
**Issue Year:** 2002
**Issue Price:** $395
**2003 Retail Price:** $395

**Ref. No.:** 6865
**Name:** Cricket Player
**Height:** 16.75
**Status:** Open issue, active
**Issue Year:** 2002
**Issue Price:** $525
**2003 Retail Price:** $525

**Ref. No.:** 349.13
**Name:** Tempting the Bull
**Height:** 17.25
**Status:** Very rare
**Issue Year:** 1965
**Issue Price:** Unknown
**Last Year:** Unknown
**Last Retail Price:** Unknown
**Auction Price:** $5000

**Ref. No.:** 4516
**Name:** Woman on Horse
**Height:** 17.25
**Status:** Open issue, active
**Issue Year:** 1969
**Issue Price:** $170
**2003 Retail Price:** $795

**Ref. No.:** 1048
**Name:** Hunters
**Height:** 18
**Status:** Open issue, retired
**Issue Year:** 1969
**Issue Price:** $115
**Last Year:** 1986
**Last Retail Price:** $460
**High Auction Price:** $1875
**Low Auction Price:** $900

**Ref. No.:** 5017
**Name:** Horsewoman and Jockey
**Height:** 20.5
**Status:** Open issue, retired
**Issue Year:** 1978
**Issue Price:** $2700
**Last Year:** 1981
**Last Retail Price:** $2700

**Ref. No.:** 1266
**Name:** Soccer Players
**Height:** 27.5
**Status:** Sold out
**Issue Year:** 1974
**Issue Price:** Unknown
**Last Year:** Unknown
**Last Retail Price:** Unknown

# The World

**European**

**Ref. No.:** 5668
**Name:** Valencian Harvest
**Height:** 5
**Status:** Open edition, retired
**Issue Year:** 1990
**Issue Price:** $175
**Last Year:** 1993
**Last Retail Price:** $205
**High Auction Price:** $675
**Low Auction Price:** $400

**Ref. No.:** 5669
**Name:** Valencian Flowers
**Height:** 6
**Status:** Open edition, retired
**Issue Year:** 1990
**Issue Price:** $370
**Last Year:** 1993
**Last Retail Price:** $420
**Auction Price:** $500

**Ref. No.:** 5670
**Name:** Valencian Beauty
**Height:** 6
**Status:** Open edition, retired
**Issue Year:** 1990
**Issue Price:** $175
**Last Year:** 1993
**Last Retail Price:** $205

**Ref. No.:** 83.06
**Name:** Regional Dress
**Height:** 6.5
**Status:** Very rare
**Issue Year:** 1956
**Issue Price:** Unknown
**Last Year:** Unknown
**Last Retail Price:** Unknown

**Ref. No.:** 84.06
**Name:** Balearic Lady
**Height:** 6.5
**Status:** Very rare
**Issue Year:** 1956
**Issue Price:** Unknown
**Last Year:** Unknown
**Last Retail Price:** Unknown

**Ref. No.:** 201.07
**Name:** Lady From Menorca
**Height:** 6.5
**Status:** Very rare
**Issue Year:** 1956
**Issue Price:** Unknown
**Last Year:** Unknown
**Last Retail Price:** Unknown

**Ref. No.:** 90.06
**Name:** Regional Dance
**Height:** 7.5
**Status:** Very rare
**Issue Year:** 1956
**Issue Price:** Unknown
**Last Year:** Unknown
**Last Retail Price:** Unknown

**Ref. No.:** 6480
**Name:** A Perfect Day
**Height:** 8
**Status:** Open issue, active
**Issue Year:** 1998
**Issue Price:** $495
**2003 Retail Price:** $525

**Ref. No.:** 5254
**Name:** Making Paella
**Height:** 8.5
**Status:** Open issue, retired
**Issue Year:** 1984
**Issue Price:** $215
**Last Year:** 1993
**Last Retail Price:** $400
**High Auction Price:** $525
**Low Auction Price:** $500

*The World*

**Ref. No.:** 1077
**Name:** Dutch Girl
**Height:** 9.25
**Status:** Open issue, retired
**Issue Year:** 1969
**Issue Price:** $57.50
**Last Year:** 1981
**Last Retail Price:** $130
**High Auction Price:** $ 575
**Low Auction Price:** $400

**Ref. No.:** 5601
**Name:** "Olé"
**Height:** 9.25
**Status:** Open issue, active
**Issue Year:** 1989
**Issue Price:** $365
**2003 Retail Price:** $475

**Ref. No.:** 54.04
**Name:** Valencian Girl
**Height:** 9.75
**Status:** Very rare
**Issue Year:** 1957
**Issue Price:** Unknown
**Last Year:** Unknown
**Last Retail Price:** Unknown

**Ref. No.:** 5062
**Name:** Kristina
**Height:** 10
**Status:** Open issue, retired
**Issue Year:** 1980
**Issue Price:** $255
**Last Year:** 1985
**Last Retail Price:** $195
**High Auction Price:** $400
**Low Auction Price:** $300

**Ref. No.:** 1213
**Name:** Girl Offering Ceramic
**Height:** 10.25
**Status:** Very rare
**Issue Year:** 1972
**Issue Price:** $55
**Last Year:** 1975
**Last Retail Price:** Unknown

**Ref. No.:** 4860
**Name:** Dutch Girl
**Height:** 10.25
**Status:** Open issue, retired
**Issue Year:** 1974
**Issue Price:** $45
**Last Year:** 1985
**Last Retail Price:** $115
**High Auction Price:** $450
**Low Auction Price:** $225

**Ref. No.:** 1399
**Name:** Dutch Girl
**Height:** 10.5
**Status:** Open issue, retired
**Issue Year:** 1982
**Issue Price:** $750
**Last Year:** 1988
**Last Retail Price:** $935
**High Auction Price:** $850
**Low Auction Price:** $700

**Ref. No.:** 1518
**Name:** Valencian Garden
**Height:** 10.5
**Status:** Open issue, retired
**Issue Year:** 1987
**Issue Price:** $1100
**Last Year:** 1991
**Last Retail Price:** $1650
**Auction Price:** $1950

**Ref. No.:** 5240
**Name:** Lady from Majorca
**Height:** 11.5
**Status:** Open issue, retired
**Issue Year:** 1984
**Issue Price:** $120
**Last Year:** 1990
**Last Retail Price:** $180
**High Auction Price:** $475
**Low Auction Price:** $375

**Ref. No.:** 6086
**Name:** Allow Me
**Height:** 11.75
**Status:** Open edition, retired
**Issue Year:** 1994
**Issue Price:** $1625
**Last Year:** 1997
**Last Retail Price:** $1625

**Ref. No.:** 6163
**Name:** Fiesta Dancer
**Height:** 12.5
**Status:** Open edition, retired
**Issue Year:** 1995
**Issue Price:** $285
**Last Year:** 1998
**Last Retail Price:** $305

**Ref. No.:** 6328
**Name:** Venice Festival
**Height:** 12.5
**Status:** Open issue, retired
**Issue Year:** 1996
**Issue Price:** $5350
**Last Year:** 1999
**Last Retail Price:** $5350

**Ref. No.:** 6650
**Name:** Quinceañera
**Height:** 12.75
**Status:** Open issue, active
**Issue Year:** 2000
**Issue Price:** $450
**2003 Retail Price:** $450

**Ref. No.:** 1511
**Name:** Cafe De Paris
**Height:** 13.25
**Status:** Open issue, retired
**Issue Year:** 1987
**Issue Price:** $1900
**Last Year:** 1995
**Last Retail Price:** $2950

**Ref. No.:** 370.13
**Name:** Valencian Girl
**Height:** 13.75
**Status:** Very rare
**Issue Year:** 1970
**Issue Price:** Unknown
**Last Year:** Unknown
**Last Retail Price:** Unknown

*The World*

**Ref. No.:** 4937
**Name:** Golden Wedding
**Height:** 14.25
**Status:** Open issue, retired
**Issue Year:** 1976
**Issue Price:** $285
**Last Year:** 1981
**Last Retail Price:** $485
**High Auction Price:** $700
**Low Auction Price:** $650

**Ref. No.:** 5239
**Name:** Wine Taster
**Height:** 14.25
**Status:** Open issue, retired
**Issue Year:** 1984
**Issue Price:** $190
**Last Year:** 2002
**Last Retail Price:** $475

**Ref. No.:** 298.13
**Name:** Lady from Valencia
**Height:** 14.5
**Status:** Very rare
**Issue Year:** 1963
**Issue Price:** Unknown
**Last Year:** Unknown
**Last Retail Price:** Unknown

**Ref. No.:** 4919
**Name:** Gypsy Woman
**Height:** 15
**Status:** Open issue, retired
**Issue Year:** 1974
**Issue Price:** $165
**Last Year:** 1981
**Last Retail Price:** $325
**High Auction Price:** $1500
**Low Auction Price:** $950

**Ref. No.:** 1315
**Name:** Scottish Lass
**Height:** 15.5
**Status:** Open issue, retired
**Issue Year:** 1974
**Issue Price:** $450
**Last Year:** 1979
**Last Retail Price:** $800

**Ref. No.:** 5269
**Name:** Lady from Elche
**Height:** 15.75
**Status:** Open edition, retired
**Issue Year:** 1985
**Issue Price:** $432.50
**Last Year:** 1988
**Last Retail Price:** $490

**Ref. No.:** 4647
**Name:** Andalucians Group
**Height:** 17
**Status:** Open issue, retired
**Issue Year:** 1969
**Issue Price:** $250
**Last Year:** 1990
**Last Retail Price:** $925
**High Auction Price:** $1400
**Low Auction Price:** $950

**Ref. No.:** 4648
**Name:** Valencians Group
**Height:** 17
**Status:** Open issue, retired
**Issue Year:** 1969
**Issue Price:** $250
**Last Year:** 1990
**Last Retail Price:** $1250
**Auction Price:** $1000

**Ref. No.:** 1350
**Name:** In the Gondola
**Height:** 17.75
**Status:** Numbered series, active
**Issue Year:** 1978
**Issue Price:** $1350
**2003 Retail Price:** $3250

*The World*

### Asian

**Ref. No.:** 100.06
**Name:** Hawaiian
**Height:** 5.75
**Status:** Very rare
**Issue Year:** 1959
**Issue Price:** Unknown
**Last Year:** Unknown
**Last Retail Price:** Unknown

**Ref. No.:** 1479
**Name:** In A Tropical Garden
**Height:** 6
**Status:** Open issue, retired
**Issue Year:** 1985
**Issue Price:** $230
**Last Year:** 1995
**Last Retail Price:** $440

**Ref. No.:** 1450
**Name:** Kiyoko
**Height:** 7
**Status:** Open edition, retired
**Issue Year:** 1983
**Issue Price:** $235
**Last Year:** 1998
**Last Retail Price:** $550

**Ref. No.:** 1448
**Name:** Yuki
**Height:** 7.5
**Status:** Open edition, retired
**Issue Year:** 1983
**Issue Price:** $285
**Last Year:** 1997
**Last Retail Price:** $550

**Ref. No.:** 4840
**Name:** Oriental Girl
**Height:** 7.5
**Status:** Open edition, retired
**Issue Year:** 1973
**Issue Price:** $90
**Last Year:** 1997
**Last Retail Price:** $515

**Ref. No.:** 6151
**Name:** Bearing Flowers
**Height:** 7.5
**Status:** Open edition, retired
**Issue Year:** 1994
**Issue Price:** $175
**Last Year:** 1998
**Last Retail Price:** $190

**Ref. No.:** 6230
**Name:** Oriental Dance
**Height:** 7.5
**Status:** Open edition, active
**Issue Year:** 1995
**Issue Price:** $198
**2003 Retail Price:** $225

**Ref. No.:** 6231
**Name:** Oriental Lantern
**Height:** 7.5
**Status:** Open edition, active
**Issue Year:** 1995
**Issue Price:** $198
**2003 Retail Price:** $225

**Ref. No.:** 6232
**Name:** Oriental Beauty
**Height:** 7.5
**Status:** Open edition, retired
**Issue Year:** 1995
**Issue Price:** $198
**Last Year:** 2000
**Last Retail Price:** $210

**The World**

**Ref. No.:** 6152
**Name:** Flower Gazer
**Height:** 7.75
**Status:** Open edition, retired
**Issue Year:** 1994
**Issue Price:** $190
**Last Year:** 1999
**Last Retail Price:** $190

**Ref. No.:** 6156
**Name:** Asian Love
**Height:** 8
**Status:** Open edition, retired
**Issue Year:** 1994
**Issue Price:** $225
**Last Year:** 1998
**Last Retail Price:** $235

**Ref. No.:** 1447
**Name:** Michiko
**Height:** 8.25
**Status:** Open edition, active
**Issue Year:** 1983
**Issue Price:** $235
**2003 Retail Price:** $525

**Ref. No.:** 1182
**Name:** Manchurian Girl
**Height:** 8.5
**Status:** Open issue, retired
**Issue Year:** 1971
**Issue Price:** $60
**Last Year:** 1975
**Last Retail Price:** $105

**Ref. No.:** 5122
**Name:** August Moon
**Height:** 8.5
**Status:** Open issue, retired
**Issue Year:** 1982
**Issue Price:** $185
**Last Year:** 1993
**Last Retail Price:** $310

**Ref. No.:** 5775
**Name:** Gift of Beauty
**Height:** 8.75
**Status:** Open issue, retired
**Issue Year:** 1991
**Issue Price:** $850
**Last Year:** 1995
**Last Retail Price:** $895

**Ref. No.:** 6142
**Name:** Indian Pose
**Height:** 8.75
**Status:** Open edition, retired
**Issue Year:** 1994
**Issue Price:** $475
**Last Year:** 1997
**Last Retail Price:** $475

**Ref. No.:** 1480
**Name:** Aroma of the Islands
**Height:** 9
**Status:** Open edition, active
**Issue Year:** 1985
**Issue Price:** $260
**2003 Retail Price:** $495

**Ref. No.:** 5172
**Name:** Fish a' Plenty
**Height:** 9
**Status:** Open issue, retired
**Issue Year:** 1982
**Issue Price:** $190
**Last Year:** 1994
**Last Retail Price:** $385

**Ref. No.:** 5327
**Name:** Nippon Lady
**Height:** 9
**Status:** Open edition, retired
**Issue Year:** 1985
**Issue Price:** $325
**Last Year:** 2000
**Last Retail Price:** $595

**Ref. No.:** 6188
**Name:** Asian Boy
**Height:** 9.25
**Status:** Open issue, retired
**Issue Year:** 1995
**Issue Price:** $225
**Last Year:** 1998
**Last Retail Price:** $225

**Ref. No.:** 6748
**Name:** Mirror Mirror...
**Height:** 9.25
**Status:** Open issue, active
**Issue Year:** 2001
**Issue Price:** $395
**2003 Retail Price:** $425

**Ref. No.:** 1449
**Name:** Mayumi
**Height:** 9.5
**Status:** Open edition, retired
**Issue Year:** 1983
**Issue Price:** $235
**Last Year:** 1997
**Last Retail Price:** $525

**Ref. No.:** 6177
**Name:** Asian Scholar
**Height:** 9.5
**Status:** Open issue, retired
**Issue Year:** 1995
**Issue Price:** $315
**Last Year:** 2002
**Last Retail Price:** $325

**Ref. No.:** 1488
**Name:** Lady of the East
**Height:** 9.75
**Status:** Open edition, retired
**Issue Year:** 1986
**Issue Price:** $625
**Last Year:** 1993
**Last Retail Price:** $1100
**Auction Price:** $700

*The World*

**Ref. No.:** 1451
**Name:** Teruko
**Height:** 10.25
**Status:** Open edition, active
**Issue Year:** 1983
**Issue Price:** $235
**2003 Retail Price:** $550

**Ref. No.:** 1530
**Name:** Leilani
**Height:** 10.25
**Status:** Open issue, retired
**Issue Year:** 1987
**Issue Price:** $275
**Last Year:** 1990
**Last Retail Price:** $340
**High Auction Price:** $700
**Low Auction Price:** $500

**Ref. No.:** 1531
**Name:** Malia
**Height:** 10.25
**Status:** Open issue, retired
**Issue Year:** 1987
**Issue Price:** $275
**Last Year:** 1990
**Last Retail Price:** $340
**Auction Price:** $625

**Ref. No.:** 4989
**Name:** Sayonara
**Height:** 10.25
**Status:** Open edition, retired
**Issue Year:** 1978
**Issue Price:** $125
**Last Year:** 1996
**Last Retail Price:** $300

**Ref. No.:** 5123
**Name:** My Precious Bundle
**Height:** 10.25
**Status:** Open issue, retired
**Issue Year:** 1982
**Issue Price:** $150
**Last Year:** 1998
**Last Retail Price:** $245

**Ref. No.:** 1183
**Name:** Oriental Man on Horse
**Height:** 10.5
**Status:** Very Rare
**Issue Year:** 1971
**Issue Price:** $60
**Last Year:** 1973
**Last Retail Price:** Unknown

**Ref. No.:** 1216
**Name:** Hindu Dancer
**Height:** 10.5
**Status:** Open issue, retired
**Issue Year:** 1972
**Issue Price:** $60
**Last Year:** 1975
**Last Retail Price:** $67.50

**Ref. No.:** 4799
**Name:** Japanese Woman
**Height:** 10.5
**Status:** Open issue, retired
**Issue Year:** 1972
**Issue Price:** $45
**Last Year:** 1975
**Last Retail Price:** $70
**Auction Price:** $700

**Ref. No.:** 1532
**Name:** Lehua
**Height:** 11
**Status:** Open issue, retired
**Issue Year:** 1987
**Issue Price:** $275
**Last Year:** 1990
**Last Retail Price:** $340
**High Auction Price:** $575
**Low Auction Price:** $450

**Ref. No.:** 1529
**Name:** Momi
**Height:** 11.5
**Status:** Open issue, retired
**Issue Year:** 1987
**Issue Price:** $275
**Last Year:** 1990
**Last Retail Price:** $340

**Ref. No.:** 4988
**Name:** Oriental Spring
**Height:** 11.5
**Status:** Open edition, retired
**Issue Year:** 1978
**Issue Price:** $125
**Last Year:** 1996
**Last Retail Price:** $325

**Ref. No.:** 4990
**Name:** Chrysanthemum
**Height:** 11.5
**Status:** Open edition, retired
**Issue Year:** 1978
**Issue Price:** $125
**Last Year:** 1998
**Last Retail Price:** $310

**Ref. No.:** 1498
**Name:** Tahitian Dancing Girls
**Height:** 11.75
**Status:** Open issue, retired
**Issue Year:** 1986
**Issue Price:** $750
**Last Year:** 1995
**Last Retail Price:** $1325

**Ref. No.:** 1174
**Name:** Young Sultan
**Height:** 11.75
**Status:** Very rare
**Issue Year:** 1971
**Issue Price:** $40
**Last Year:** 1975
**Last Retail Price:** Unknown

**Ref. No.:** 1445
**Name:** Springtime in Japan
**Height:** 11.75
**Status:** Open issue, active
**Issue Year:** 1983
**Issue Price:** $965
**2003 Retail Price:** $1800

**Ref. No.:** 4991
**Name:** Madame Butterfly
**Height:** 11.75
**Status:** Open edition, retired
**Issue Year:** 1978
**Issue Price:** $125
**Last Year:** 1998
**Last Retail Price:** $295

**Ref. No.:** 5773
**Name:** Graceful Offering
**Height:** 12
**Status:** Open issue, retired
**Issue Year:** 1991
**Issue Price:** $850
**Last Year:** 1995
**Last Retail Price:** $895

**Ref. No.:** 4807
**Name:** Geisha
**Height:** 12.25
**Status:** Open issue, retired
**Issue Year:** 1972
**Issue Price:** $190
**Last Year:** 1993
**Last Retail Price:** $440

**Ref. No.:** 1383
**Name:** Ride in China
**Height:** 12.5
**Status:** Open issue, active
**Issue Year:** 1978
**Issue Price:** $1500
**2003 Retail Price:** $2150

**Ref. No.:** 4916
**Name:** Chinese Noblewoman
**Height:** 13
**Status:** Open issue, retired
**Issue Year:** 1974
**Issue Price:** $300
**Last Year:** 1978
**Last Retail Price:** $550

**Ref. No.:** 4921
**Name:** Chinese Nobleman
**Height:** 13
**Status:** Open issue, retired
**Issue Year:** 1974
**Issue Price:** $325
**Last Year:** 1978
**Last Retail Price:** $550

**Ref. No.:** 5592
**Name:** Male Siamese Dancer
**Height:** 13
**Status:** Open issue, retired
**Issue Year:** 1989
**Issue Price:** $345
**Last Year:** 1993
**Last Retail Price:** $420
**High Auction Price:** $425
**Low Auction Price:** $400

**Ref. No.:** 5593
**Name:** Siamese Dancer
**Height:** 13
**Status:** Open issue, retired
**Issue Year:** 1989
**Issue Price:** $345
**Last Year:** 1993
**Last Retail Price:** $420
**Auction Price:** $400

**Ref. No.:** 6396
**Name:** Oriental Forest
**Height:** 13
**Status:** Open issue, retired
**Issue Year:** 1997
**Issue Price:** $565
**Last Year:** 2001
**Last Retail Price:** $565

**Ref. No.:** 5774
**Name:** Nature's Gifts
**Height:** 13.25
**Status:** Open issue, retired
**Issue Year:** 1991
**Issue Price:** $900
**Last Year:** 1994
**Last Retail Price:** $975

**Ref. No.:** 6143
**Name:** Indian Dancer
**Height:** 13.25
**Status:** Open edition, retired
**Issue Year:** 1994
**Issue Price:** $475
**Last Year:** 1997
**Last Retail Price:** $475

**Ref. No.:** 4565
**Name:** Oriental Lady
**Height:** 15
**Status:** Open issue, retired
**Issue Year:** 1969
**Issue Price:** $65
**Last Year:** 1972
**Last Retail Price:** $75

*The World*

**Ref. No.:** 344.13
**Name:** Nanki Poo
**Height:** 15.5
**Status:** Very rare
**Issue Year:** 1965
**Issue Price:** Unknown
**Last Year:** Unknown
**Last Retail Price:** Unknown

**Ref. No.:** 6572
**Name:** In Touch With Nature
**Height:** 15.5
**Status:** Open issue, active
**Issue Year:** 1999
**Issue Price:** $625
**2003 Retail Price:** $650

**Ref. No.:** 1421
**Name:** Mariko
**Height:** 16
**Status:** Open issue, retired
**Issue Year:** 1982
**Issue Price:** $860
**Last Year:** 1995
**Last Retail Price:** $1575

## World Children

**Ref. No.:** 5754
**Name:** Singapore Dancers
**Height:** 16.75
**Status:** Open issue, retired
**Issue Year:** 1991
**Issue Price:** $950
**Last Year:** 1993
**Last Retail Price:** $1025
**Auction Price:** $800

**Ref. No.:** 1525
**Name:** Valencian Dreams
**Height:** 3.5
**Status:** Open issue, retired
**Issue Year:** 1987
**Issue Price:** $240
**Last Year:** 1991
**Last Retail Price:** $360
**High Auction Price:** $450
**Low Auction Price:** $425

**Ref. No.:** 5389
**Name:** Deep in Thought
**Height:** 4.25
**Status:** Open issue, retired
**Issue Year:** 1986
**Issue Price:** $170
**Last Year:** 1990
**Last Retail Price:** $225
**High Auction Price:** $500
**Low Auction Price:** $250

**Ref. No.:** 1195
**Name:** Eskimo
**Height:** 4.75
**Status:** Open issue, active
**Issue Year:** 1972
**Issue Price:** $30
**2003 Retail Price:** $145

**Ref. No.:** 5372
**Name:** Lolita
**Height:** 4.75
**Status:** Open issue, retired
**Issue Year:** 1986
**Issue Price:** $120
**Last Year:** 1993
**Last Retail Price:** $200
**Auction Price:** $350

**Ref. No.:** 5391
**Name:** A Time to Rest
**Height:** 4.75
**Status:** Open issue, retired
**Issue Year:** 1986
**Issue Price:** $170
**Last Year:** 1990
**Last Retail Price:** $225
**High Auction Price:** $350
**Low Auction Price:** $225

**Ref. No.:** 305.13
**Name:** Young Valencian Girl
**Height:** 5
**Status:** Very rare
**Issue Year:** 1963
**Issue Price:** Unknown
**Last Year:** Unknown
**Last Retail Price:** Unknown

**Ref. No.:** 5373
**Name:** Carmencita
**Height:** 5
**Status:** Open issue, retired
**Issue Year:** 1986
**Issue Price:** $120
**Last Year:** 1993
**Last Retail Price:** $200
**Auction Price:** $400

**Ref. No.:** 5375
**Name:** Teresita
**Height:** 5
**Status:** Open issue, retired
**Issue Year:** 1986
**Issue Price:** $120
**Last Year:** 1993
**Last Retail Price:** $200
**Auction Price:** $400

*The World*

**Ref. No.:** 5869
**Name:** Fallas Queen
**Height:** 5.25
**Status:** Open issue, retired
**Issue Year:** 1992
**Issue Price:** $420
**Last Year:** 1995
**Last Retail Price:** $440

**Ref. No.:** 1524
**Name:** Valencian Bouquet
**Height:** 5.5
**Status:** Open issue, retired
**Issue Year:** 1987
**Issue Price:** $250
**Last Year:** 1991
**Last Retail Price:** $375
**High Auction Price:** $450
**Low Auction Price:** $400

**Ref. No.:** 5374
**Name:** Pepita
**Height:** 5.5
**Status:** Open issue, retired
**Issue Year:** 1986
**Issue Price:** $120
**Last Year:** 1993
**Last Retail Price:** $200
**Auction Price:** $325

**Ref. No.:** 5390
**Name:** Spanish Dancer
**Height:** 5.5
**Status:** Open issue, retired
**Issue Year:** 1986
**Issue Price:** $170
**Last Year:** 1990
**Last Retail Price:** $225
**High Auction Price:** $550
**Low Auction Price:** $250

**Ref. No.:** 5238
**Name:** Eskimo Boy with Pet
**Height:** 5.5
**Status:** Open issue, active
**Issue Year:** 1984
**Issue Price:** $55
**2003 Retail Price:** $125

**Ref. No.:** 5867
**Name:** Serene Valencia
**Height:** 5.5
**Status:** Open issue, retired
**Issue Year:** 1992
**Issue Price:** $365
**Last Year:** 1994
**Last Retail Price:** $385

**Ref. No.:** 5868
**Name:** Loving Valencia
**Height:** 5.75
**Status:** Open issue, retired
**Issue Year:** 1992
**Issue Price:** $365
**Last Year:** 1995
**Last Retail Price:** $385

**Ref. No.:** 6308
**Name:** Natural Wonder
**Height:** 6.25
**Status:** Open issue, retired
**Issue Year:** 1996
**Last Year:** 1999
**Last Retail Price:** $220

**Ref. No.:** 4841
**Name:** Valencian Girl
**Height:** 6.5
**Status:** Open issue, active
**Issue Year:** 1973
**Issue Price:** $35
**2003 Retail Price:** $250

**Ref. No.:** 5193
**Name:** Juanita
**Height:** 6.5
**Status:** Open issue, active
**Issue Year:** 1984
**Issue Price:** $80
**2003 Retail Price:** $165

**Ref. No.:** 5353
**Name:** Eskimo Riders
**Height:** 6.5
**Status:** Open issue, active
**Issue Year:** 1986
**Issue Price:** $150
**2003 Retail Price:** $275

**Ref. No.:** 6309
**Name:** Nature's Treasures
**Height:** 6.5
**Status:** Open issue, retired
**Issue Year:** 1996
**Issue Price:** $220
**Last Year:** 1998
**Last Retail Price:** $220

**Ref. No.:** 6310
**Name:** Nature's Song
**Height:** 6.5
**Status:** Open issue, retired
**Issue Year:** 1996
**Issue Price:** $230
**Last Year:** 1998
**Last Retail Price:** $230

**Ref. No.:** 1422
**Name:** Miss Valencia
**Height:** 7.5
**Status:** Open edition, retired
**Issue Year:** 1982
**Issue Price:** $175
**Last Year:** 1997
**Last Retail Price:** $415

**Ref. No.:** 5192
**Name:** Lolita
**Height:** 7.5
**Status:** Open edition, active
**Issue Year:** 1984
**Issue Price:** $80
**2003 Retail Price:** $165

**Ref. No.:** 1058
**Name:** Lupita
**Height:** 7.75
**Status:** Open issue, retired
**Issue Year:** 1969
**Issue Price:** $28
**Last Year:** 1980
**Last Retail Price:** $130

**Ref. No.:** 1526
**Name:** Valencian Flowers
**Height:** 7.75
**Status:** Open issue, retired
**Issue Year:** 1987
**Issue Price:** $375.50
**Last Year:** 1991
**Last Retail Price:** $550
**High Auction Price:** $600
**Low Auction Price:** $500

**Ref. No.:** 6150
**Name:** Playing the Flute
**Height:** 7.75
**Status:** Open edition, retired
**Issue Year:** 1994
**Issue Price:** $175
**Last Year:** 1999
**Last Retail Price:** $190

**Ref. No.:** 6157
**Name:** Polynesian Love
**Height:** 8
**Status:** Open issue, retired
**Issue Year:** 1994
**Issue Price:** $225
**Last Year:** 1998
**Last Retail Price:** $235

**Ref. No.:** 1478
**Name:** Aloha
**Height:** 8.25
**Status:** Open edition, active
**Issue Year:** 1985
**Issue Price:** $230
**2003 Retail Price:** $450

**Ref. No.:** 4811
**Name:** Dutch Boy
**Height:** 8.25
**Status:** Open issue, retired
**Issue Year:** 1972
**Issue Price:** $30
**Last Year:** 1988
**Last Retail Price:** $60
**High Auction Price:** $425
**Low Auction Price:** $250

*The World*

**Ref. No.:** 5671
**Name:** Little Dutch Gardener
**Height:** 8.5
**Status:** Open issue, retired
**Issue Year:** 1990
**Issue Price:** $400
**Last Year:** 1993
**Last Retail Price:** $475
**Auction Price:** $450

**Ref. No.:** 6153
**Name:** American Love
**Height:** 8.75
**Status:** Open issue, retired
**Issue Year:** 1994
**Issue Price:** $225
**Last Year:** 1998
**Last Retail Price:** $235

**Ref. No.:** 5352
**Name:** Hindu Children
**Height:** 9
**Status:** Open issue, active
**Issue Year:** 1986
**Issue Price:** $250
**2003 Retail Price:** $450

**Ref. No.:** 4822
**Name:** Peruvian Girl with Baby
**Height:** 9
**Status:** Open issue, retired
**Issue Year:** 1972
**Issue Price:** $65
**Last Year:** 1981
**Last Retail Price:** $160
**High Auction Price:** $775
**Low Auction Price:** $550

**Ref. No.:** 6437
**Name:** Timid Torero
**Height:** 9
**Status:** Open issue, retired
**Issue Year:** 1997
**Issue Price:** $195
**Last Year:** 1999
**Last Retail Price:** $195

**Ref. No.:** 6438
**Name:** Young Torero
**Height:** 9
**Status:** Open issue, retired
**Issue Year:** 1997
**Issue Price:** $240
**Last Year:** 2001
**Last Retail Price:** $240

**Ref. No.:** 5115
**Name:** Reverent Matador
**Height:** 9.5
**Status:** Open issue, retired
**Issue Year:** 1982
**Issue Price:** $122.50
**Last Year:** 1985
**Last Retail Price:** $122.50

**Ref. No.:** 5395
**Name:** Valencian Boy
**Height:** 9.5
**Status:** Open issue, retired
**Issue Year:** 1986
**Issue Price:** $200
**Last Year:** 1991
**Last Retail Price:** $325
**High Auction Price:** $400
**Low Auction Price:** $300

**Ref. No.:** 5490
**Name:** Flor Maria
**Height:** 9.5
**Status:** Open edition, active
**Issue Year:** 1988
**Issue Price:** $500
**2003 Retail Price:** $650

**Ref. No.:** 6187
**Name:** European Boy
**Height:** 9.5
**Status:** Open issue, retired
**Issue Year:** 1995
**Issue Price:** $185
**Last Year:** 1998
**Last Retail Price:** $185

**Ref. No.:** 6190
**Name:** Polynesian Boy
**Height:** 9.5
**Status:** Open issue, retired
**Issue Year:** 1995
**Issue Price:** $250
**Last Year:** 1998
**Last Retail Price:** $250

**Ref. No.:** 1304
**Name:** Valencian Girl with
  Flowers
**Height:** 9.5
**Status:** Open edition, active
**Issue Year:** 1974
**Issue Price:** $200
**2003 Retail Price:** $625

*The World*

**Ref. No.:** 5066
**Name:** Ilsa
**Height:** 9.75
**Status:** Open issue, retired
**Issue Year:** 1980
**Issue Price:** $275
**Last Year:** 1990
**Last Retail Price:** $300
**High Auction Price:** $600
**Low Auction Price:** $425

**Ref. No.:** 5117
**Name:** Proud Matador
**Height:** 9.75
**Status:** Open issue, retired
**Issue Year:** 1982
**Issue Price:** $122.50
**Last Year:** 1985
**Last Retail Price:** $122.50

**Ref. No.:** 6178
**Name:** Little Matador
**Height:** 9.75
**Status:** Open issue, active
**Issue Year:** 1995
**Issue Price:** $245
**2003 Retail Price:** $250

**Ref. No.:** 6189
**Name:** African Boy
**Height:** 9.75
**Status:** Open issue, retired
**Issue Year:** 1995
**Issue Price:** $195
**Last Year:** 1999
**Last Retail Price:** $195

**Ref. No.:** 5063
**Name:** Margaretta
**Height:** 9.75
**Status:** Open issue, retired
**Issue Year:** 1980
**Issue Price:** $265
**Last Year:** 1985
**Last Retail Price:** $200
**High Auction Price:** $600
**Low Auction Price:** $425

**Ref. No.:** 5064
**Name:** Gretel
**Height:** 9.75
**Status:** Open issue, retired
**Issue Year:** 1980
**Issue Price:** $255
**Last Year:** 1990
**Last Retail Price:** $280
**High Auction Price:** $450
**Low Auction Price:** $400

**Ref. No.:** 5127
**Name:** Marcelina
**Height:** 10
**Status:** Open issue, retired
**Issue Year:** 1982
**Issue Price:** $255
**Last Year:** 1985
**Last Retail Price:** $255
**High Auction Price:** $750
**Low Auction Price:** $600

**Ref. No.:** 6424
**Name:** Ceremonial Princess
**Height:** 10
**Status:** Open issue, retired
**Issue Year:** 1997
**Issue Price:** $240
**Last Year:** 2000
**Last Retail Price:** $240

**Ref. No.:** 1214
**Name:** Country Girl
**Height:** 10.25
**Status:** Very rare
**Issue Year:** 1972
**Issue Price:** $55
**Last Year:** 1975
**Last Retail Price:** Unknown

**Ref. No.:** 1159
**Name:** Girl with Traditional
    Dress and Bowl
**Height:** 10.25
**Status:** Very rare
**Issue Year:** 1971
**Issue Price:** $40
**Last Year:** 1975
**Last Retail Price:** Unknown

**Ref. No.:** 5116
**Name:** Young Matador
**Height:** 10.25
**Status:** Open issue, retired
**Issue Year:** 1982
**Issue Price:** $122.50
**Last Year:** 1985
**Last Retail Price:** $122.50
**High Auction Price:** $525
**Low Auction Price:** $350

**Ref. No.:** 1395
**Name:** Full of Mischief
**Height:** 10.5
**Status:** Open edition, retired
**Issue Year:** 1982
**Issue Price:** $420
**Last Year:** 1997
**Last Retail Price:** $865

**Ref. No.:** 1396
**Name:** Appreciation
**Height:** 10.5
**Status:** Open edition, retired
**Issue Year:** 1982
**Issue Price:** $420
**Last Year:** 1997
**Last Retail Price:** $860

**Ref. No.:** 1397
**Name:** Second Thoughts
**Height:** 10.5
**Status:** Open edition, retired
**Issue Year:** 1982
**Issue Price:** $420
**Last Year:** 1997
**Last Retail Price:** $880

**Ref. No.:** 1398
**Name:** Reverie
**Height:** 10.5
**Status:** Open edition, retired
**Issue Year:** 1982
**Issue Price:** $490
**Last Year:** 1997
**Last Retail Price:** $970

*The World*

**Ref. No.:** 5053
**Name:** Festival Time
**Height:** 10.5
**Status:** Open issue, retired
**Issue Year:** 1980
**Issue Price:** $250
**Last Year:** 1985
**Last Retail Price:** $190
**High Auction Price:** $450
**Low Auction Price:** $375

**Ref. No.:** 5054
**Name:** Little Senorita
**Height:** 10.5
**Status:** Open issue, retired
**Issue Year:** 1980
**Issue Price:** $235
**Last Year:** 1985
**Last Retail Price:** $177.50
**High Auction Price:** $600
**Low Auction Price:** $500

**Ref. No.:** 6192
**Name:** American Indian Boy
**Height:** 10.75
**Status:** Open issue, retired
**Issue Year:** 1995
**Issue Price:** $225
**Last Year:** 1998
**Last Retail Price:** $225

**Ref. No.:** 5124
**Name:** Dutch Couple with Tulips
**Height:** 11
**Status:** Open issue, retired
**Issue Year:** 1982
**Issue Price:** $310
**Last Year:** 1985
**Last Retail Price:** $325
**Auction Price:** $1350

**Ref. No.:** 1489
**Name:** Valencian Children
**Height:** 11
**Status:** Open issue, active
**Issue Year:** 1986
**Issue Price:** $700
**2003 Retail Price:** $1250

**Ref. No.:** 6423
**Name:** Precious Papoose
**Height:** 11
**Status:** Open issue, retired
**Issue Year:** 1997
**Issue Price:** $240
**Last Year:** 1999
**Last Retail Price:** $240

**Ref. No.:** 1059
**Name:** Panchito
**Height:** 11
**Status:** Open issue, retired
**Issue Year:** 1969
**Issue Price:** $20
**Last Year:** 1980
**Last Retail Price:** $100
**Auction Price:** $400

**Ref. No.:** 1400
**Name:** Valencian Boy
**Height:** 11.5
**Status:** Open issue, retired
**Issue Year:** 1982
**Issue Price:** $297.50
**Last Year:** 1988
**Last Retail Price:** $360
**High Auction Price:** $500
**Low Auction Price:** $400

**Ref. No.:** 5080
**Name:** Boy Pottery Seller
**Height:** 11.5
**Status:** Open issue, retired
**Issue Year:** 1980
**Issue Price:** $320
**Last Year:** 1985
**Last Retail Price:** $245
**High Auction Price:** $850
**Low Auction Price:** $600

## Other World

**Ref. No.:** 5402
**Name:** Desert Tour
**Height:** 11.75
**Status:** Open issue, retired
**Issue Year:** 1987
**Issue Price:** $950
**Last Year:** 1990
**Last Retail Price:** $1150
**High Auction Price:** $1050
**Low Auction Price:** $900

**Ref. No.:** 2148
**Name:** Head of Congolese Woman
**Height:** 8
**Status:** Open issue, retired
**Issue Year:** 1984
**Issue Price:** $55
**Last Year:** 1988
**Last Retail Price:** $65
**Auction Price:** $600

**Ref. No.:** 6369
**Name:** Indian Maiden
**Height:** 10
**Status:** Open issue, retired
**Issue Year:** 1997
**Issue Price:** $600
**Last Year:** 1999
**Last Retail Price:** $600

*The World*

**Ref. No.:** 1173
**Name:** Sultanita
**Height:** 10.5
**Status:** Very rare
**Issue Year:** 1971
**Issue Price:** $40
**Last Year:** 1975
**Last Retail Price:** Unknown

**Ref. No.:** 1512
**Name:** Hawaiian Beauty
**Height:** 11
**Status:** Open issue, retired
**Issue Year:** 1987
**Issue Price:** $575
**Last Year:** 1990
**Last Retail Price:** $700
**Auction Price:** $1100

**Ref. No.:** 5415
**Name:** Mexican Dancers
**Height:** 12
**Status:** Open issue, active
**Issue Year:** 1987
**Issue Price:** $800
**2003 Retail Price:** $1195

**Ref. No.:** 1310
**Name:** Arabian Knight
**Height:** 14.25
**Status:** Open issue, retired
**Issue Year:** 1974
**Issue Price:** $285
**Last Year:** 1979
**Last Retail Price:** $570
**Auction Price:** $1900

**Ref. No.:** 4610
**Name:** Peruvian Group
**Height:** 14.25
**Status:** Open issue, retired
**Issue Year:** 1969
**Issue Price:** $180
**Last Year:** 1970
**Last Retail Price:** $190

**Ref. No.:** 4768
**Name:** Woman from Guadalupe
**Height:** 16
**Status:** Open edition, retired
**Issue Year:** 1971
**Issue Price:** $75
**Last Year:** 1973
**Last Retail Price:** $95
**Auction Price:** $300

**Ref. No.:** 6527
**Name:** Hindu Dancer
**Height:** 18
**Status:** Open issue, retired
**Issue Year:** 1998
**Issue Price:** $700
**Last Year:** 2000
**Last Retail Price:** $795

**Ref. No.:** 3524
**Name:** Watusi Queen
**Height:** 23.25
**Status:** Limited edition, sold out
**Edition Size:** 1500
**Issue Year:** 1981
**Issue Price:** $1875
**Last Year:** 1994
**Last Retail Price:** $3050

*The World*

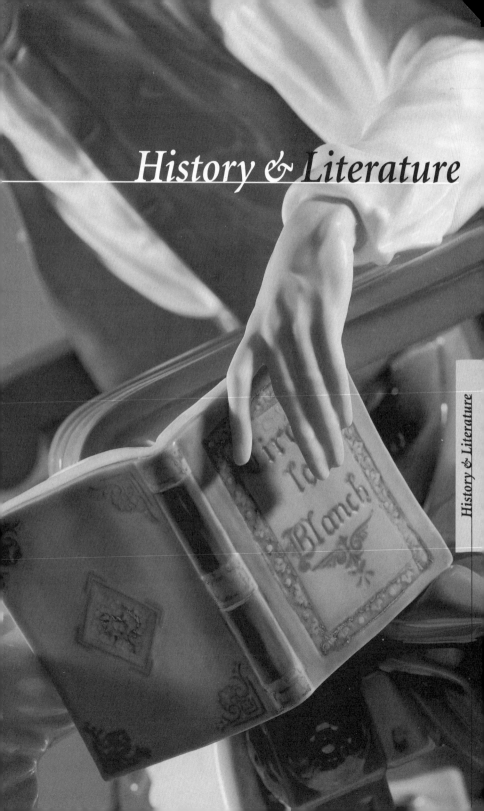

# History & Literature

# History

**Ref. No.:** 348.13
**Name:** Prince Charles
**Height:** 11.5
**Status:** Very Rare
**Issue Year:** 1975
**Issue Price:** Unknown
**Last Year:** Unknown
**Last Retail Price:** Unknown

**Ref. No.:** 5734
**Name:** Pilgrim Couple
**Height:** 11.75
**Status:** Open issue, retired
**Issue Year:** 1991
**Issue Price:** $490
**Last Year:** 1993
**Last Retail Price:** $525
**Auction Price:** $425

**Ref. No.:** 5944
**Name:** The Great Adventurer
**Height:** 12
**Status:** Open issue, retired
**Issue Year:** 1993
**Issue Price:** $315
**Last Year:** 1994
**Last Retail Price:** $325

## Literature

**Ref. No.:** 7528
**Name:** Dr. Martin Luther King, Jr.
**Height:** 12.5
**Status:** Open issue, active
**Issue Year:** 1994
**Issue Price:** $345
**2003 Retail Price:** $375

**Ref. No.:** 4976
**Name:** Augustine of Aragon
**Height:** 13.75
**Status:** Open issue, retired
**Issue Year:** 1977
**Issue Price:** $475
**Last Year:** 1979
**Last Retail Price:** $550
**Auction Price:** $1800

**Ref. No.:** 5165
**Name:** A Toast by Sancho
**Height:** 8.25
**Status:** Open issue, retired
**Issue Year:** 1982
**Issue Price:** $100
**Last Year:** 1990
**Last Retail Price:** $150
**High Auction Price:** $500
**Low Auction Price:** $375

**Ref. No.:** 5357
**Name:** Oration
**Height:** 8.5
**Status:** Open issue, active
**Issue Year:** 1986
**Issue Price:** $170
**2003 Retail Price:** $300

**Ref. No.:** 5740
**Name:** Alice in Wonderland
**Height:** 8.75
**Status:** Open issue, retired
**Issue Year:** 1991
**Issue Price:** $440
**Last Year:** 1998
**Last Retail Price:** $485

**Ref. No.:** 5396
**Name:** The Puppet Painter
**Height:** 9.5
**Status:** Open issue, active
**Issue Year:** 1986
**Issue Price:** $500
**2003 Retail Price:** $850

**Ref. No.:** 4828
**Name:** Cinderella
**Height:** 9.75
**Status:** Open edition, retired
**Issue Year:** 1972
**Issue Price:** $47
**Last Year:** 1998
**Last Retail Price:** $245

**Ref. No.:** 6633
**Name:** Sancho
**Height:** 10
**Status:** Open issue, active
**Issue Year:** 1999
**Issue Price:** $255
**2003 Retail Price:** $275

**Ref. No.:** 4965
**Name:** Little Red Riding Hood
**Height:** 10.25
**Status:** Open issue, retired
**Issue Year:** 1977
**Issue Price:** $210
**Last Year:** 1983
**Last Retail Price:** $285
**High Auction Price:** $825
**Low Auction Price:** $500

*History & Literature*

**Ref. No.:** 1031
**Name:** Sancho Panza
**Height:** 10.5
**Status:** Open issue, retired
**Issue Year:** 1969
**Issue Price:** $65
**Last Year:** 1989
**Last Retail Price:** $400
**High Auction Price:** $525
**Low Auction Price:** $400

**Ref. No.:** 6092
**Name:** The Prince
**Height:** 10.5
**Status:** Open issue, retired
**Issue Year:** 1994
**Issue Price:** $325
**Last Year:** 1997
**Last Retail Price:** $325

**Ref. No.:** 5224
**Name:** The Quest
**Height:** 11
**Status:** Open issue, retired
**Issue Year:** 1984
**Issue Price:** $125
**Last Year:** 1998
**Last Retail Price:** $310

**Ref. No.:** 5791
**Name:** Fairy Godmother
**Height:** 11
**Status:** Open issue, retired
**Issue Year:** 1991
**Issue Price:** $375
**Last Year:** 1994
**Last Retail Price:** $410

**Ref. No.:** 6364
**Name:** A Dream Come True
**Height:** 11
**Status:** Open issue, retired
**Issue Year:** 1997
**Issue Price:** $550
**Last Year:** 2000
**Last Retail Price:** $550

**Ref. No.:** 1254
**Name:** Hamlet and Yorick
**Height:** 11.75
**Status:** Open issue, retired
**Issue Year:** 1974
**Issue Price:** $325
**Last Year:** 1983
**Last Retail Price:** $740
**High Auction Price:** $1200
**Low Auction Price:** $900

**Ref. No.:** 4854
**Name:** Quixote Standing Up
**Height:** 11.75
**Status:** Open issue, active
**Issue Year:** 1973
**Issue Price:** $40
**2003 Retail Price:** $225

**Ref. No.:** 4932
**Name:** Isabel of Castilla
**Height:** 13.75
**Status:** Open issue, retired
**Issue Year:** 1974
**Issue Price:** $525
**Last Year:** 1981
**Last Retail Price:** $950
**Auction Price:** $2250

**Ref. No.:** 5051
**Name:** Samson and Delilah
**Height:** 13.75
**Status:** Open issue, retired
**Issue Year:** 1980
**Issue Price:** $350
**Last Year:** 1981
**Last Retail Price:** $380
**High Auction Price:** $1600
**Low Auction Price:** $1500

**Ref. No.:** 5177
**Name:** Dante
**Height:** 13.75
**Status:** Open issue, retired
**Issue Year:** 1982
**Issue Price:** $262.50
**Last Year:** 1983
**Last Retail Price:** $262.50
**High Auction Price:** $700
**Low Auction Price:** $500

**Ref. No.:** 5132
**Name:** Miguel de Cervantes
**Height:** 14.25
**Status:** Open issue, retired
**Issue Year:** 1982
**Issue Price:** $925
**Last Year:** 1988
**Last Retail Price:** $1075

**Ref. No.:** 1030
**Name:** Quixote
**Height:** 14.5
**Status:** Open issue, active
**Issue Year:** 1969
**Issue Price:** $225
**2003 Retail Price:** $1450

**Ref. No.:** 1455
**Name:** Reflections of Hamlet
**Height:** 15
**Status:** Open issue, retired
**Issue Year:** 1983
**Issue Price:** $1000
**Last Year:** 1988
**Last Retail Price:** $1150
**High Auction Price:** $1600
**Low Auction Price:** $1400

**Ref. No.:** 1385
**Name:** Quixote on Guard
**Height:** 15.5
**Status:** Open issue, retired
**Issue Year:** 1978
**Issue Price:** $175
**Last Year:** 1991
**Last Retail Price:** $425
**High Auction Price:** $1050
**Low Auction Price:** $700

**Ref. No.:** 4998
**Name:** Don Quixote and
      Sancho Panza
**Height:** 15.5
**Status:** Open issue, retired
**Issue Year:** 1978
**Issue Price:** $875
**Last Year:** 1983
**Last Retail Price:** $1275
**High Auction Price:** $3300
**Low Auction Price:** $2625

**Ref. No.:** 4729
**Name:** Hamlet
**Height:** 15.75
**Status:** Open issue, retired
**Issue Year:** 1970
**Issue Price:** $85
**Last Year:** 1980
**Last Retail Price:** $200
**High Auction Price:** $800
**Low Auction Price:** $600

**Ref. No.:** 6285
**Name:** Dreams of Aladdin
**Height:** 15.75
**Status:** Open issue, retired
**Issue Year:** 1996
**Issue Price:** $1440
**Last Year:** 1999
**Last Retail Price:** $1440

**Ref. No.:** 6373
**Name:** Palace Dance
**Height:** 16
**Status:** Open issue, retired
**Issue Year:** 1997
**Issue Price:** $700
**Last Year:** 1999
**Last Retail Price:** $700

**Ref. No.:** 1343
**Name:** Wrath of Don Quixote
**Height:** 16.5
**Status:** Open issue, retired
**Issue Year:** 1977
**Issue Price:** $250
**Last Year:** 1990
**Last Retail Price:** $490
**High Auction Price:** $1600
**Low Auction Price:** $700

**Ref. No.:** 4750
**Name:** Romeo and Juliet
**Height:** 17.75
**Status:** Open issue, active
**Issue Year:** 1971
**Issue Price:** $150
**2003 Retail Price:** $1250

**Ref. No.:** 3510
**Name:** Othello
**Height:** 18
**Status:** Open issue, retired
**Issue Year:** 1978
**Issue Price:** $450
**Last Year:** 1981
**Last Retail Price:** $575

**Ref. No.:** 3518
**Name:** Lady Macbeth
**Height:** 18.5
**Status:** Open issue, retired
**Issue Year:** 1980
**Issue Price:** $385
**Last Year:** 1981
**Last Retail Price:** $420
**Auction Price:** $600

**Ref. No.:** 1497
**Name:** Quixote and Windmill
**Height:** 21.25
**Status:** Open issue, retired
**Issue Year:** 1986
**Issue Price:** $1100
**Last Year:** 1996
**Last Retail Price:** $2050

**Ref. No.:** 1522
**Name:** I Am Don Quixote!
**Height:** 21.5
**Status:** Open issue, active
**Issue Year:** 1987
**Issue Price:** $2600
**2003 Retail Price:** $3950

**Ref. No.:** 4609
**Name:** Don Juan
**Height:** 22.5
**Status:** Open issue, retired
**Issue Year:** 1969
**Issue Price:** $135
**Last Year:** 1970
**Last Retail Price:** $145

# Entertainment & the Arts

# Dance

**Ref. No.:** 115.06
**Name:** Bouquet Ballerina
**Height:** 3
**Status:** Very rare
**Issue Year:** 1958
**Issue Price:** Unknown
**Last Year:** Unknown
**Last Retail Price:** Unknown

**Ref. No.:** 96.06
**Name:** Ballerina Resting
**Height:** 3.25
**Status:** Very rare
**Issue Year:** 1957
**Issue Price:** Unknown
**Last Year:** Unknown
**Last Retail Price:** Unknown

**Ref. No.:** 1502
**Name:** Forgotten
**Height:** 3.5
**Status:** Open issue, retired
**Issue Year:** 1986
**Issue Price:** $125
**Last Year:** 1991
**Last Retail Price:** $200
**Auction Price:** $275

**Ref. No.:** 1501
**Name:** Rag Doll
**Height:** 4
**Status:** Open issue, retired
**Issue Year:** 1986
**Issue Price:** $125
**Last Year:** 1991
**Last Retail Price:** $200
**Auction Price:** $250

**Ref. No.:** 92.06
**Name:** Ballerina with Squirrel
**Height:** 4.75
**Status:** Very rare
**Issue Year:** 1957
**Issue Price:** Unknown
**Last Year:** Unknown
**Last Retail Price:** Unknown

**Ref. No.:** 125.06
**Name:** Ballet
**Height:** 5
**Status:** Very rare
**Issue Year:** 1959
**Issue Price:** Unknown
**Last Year:** Unknown
**Last Retail Price:** Unknown

**Ref. No.:** 213.08
**Name:** Young Ballerina
**Height:** 5
**Status:** Very rare
**Issue Year:** 1956
**Issue Price:** $275
**Last Year:** Unknown
**Last Retail Price:** Unknown

**Ref. No.:** 1359
**Name:** Heather
**Height:** 5
**Status:** Open issue, retired
**Issue Year:** 1978
**Issue Price:** $75
**Last Year:** 1993
**Last Retail Price:** $170
**Auction Price:** $200

**Ref. No.:** 4855
**Name:** Death of the Swan
**Height:** 5
**Status:** Open issue, retired
**Issue Year:** 1973
**Issue Price:** $45
**Last Year:** 2000
**Last Retail Price:** $330

**Ref. No.:** 4855.3
**Name:** Death of the Swan (White)
**Height:** 5
**Status:** Open issue, retired
**Issue Year:** 1983
**Issue Price:** $110
**Last Year:** 1987
**Last Retail Price:** $130

**Ref. No.:** 5919
**Name:** Rose Ballet
**Height:** 5
**Status:** Open issue, active
**Issue Year:** 1992
**Issue Price:** $210
**2003 Retail Price:** $225

**Ref. No.:** 6174
**Name:** Graceful Pose
**Height:** 5
**Status:** Open issue, active
**Issue Year:** 1995
**Issue Price:** $195
**2003 Retail Price:** $195

*Entertainment & the Arts*

**Ref. No.:** 91.06
**Name:** Ballerina with Rose
**Height:** 5.25
**Status:** Very rare
**Issue Year:** 1957
**Issue Price:** Unknown
**Last Year:** Unknown
**Last Retail Price:** Unknown

**Ref. No.:** 97.06
**Name:** Tying the Slipper
**Height:** 5.5
**Status:** Very rare
**Issue Year:** 1957
**Issue Price:** Unknown
**Last Year:** Unknown
**Last Retail Price:** Unknown

**Ref. No.:** 107.06
**Name:** Dancers
**Height:** 5.5
**Status:** Very rare
**Issue Year:** 1958
**Issue Price:** Unknown
**Last Year:** Unknown
**Last Retail Price:** Unknown

**Ref. No.:** 5496
**Name:** Recital
**Height:** 5.75
**Status:** Open issue, active
**Issue Year:** 1988
**Issue Price:** $190
**2003 Retail Price:** $295

**Ref. No.:** 1356
**Name:** Phyllis
**Height:** 6
**Status:** Open issue, retired
**Issue Year:** 1978
**Issue Price:** $75
**Last Year:** 1993
**Last Retail Price:** $170

**Ref. No.:** 5499
**Name:** Pretty Ballerina
**Height:** 6
**Status:** Open issue, retired
**Issue Year:** 1988
**Issue Price:** $190
**Last Year:** 1998
**Last Retail Price:** $285

**Ref. No.:** 108.06
**Name:** Kneeling Ballerina
**Height:** 6.25
**Status:** Very rare
**Issue Year:** 1958
**Issue Price:** Unknown
**Last Year:** Unknown
**Last Retail Price:** Unknown

**Ref. No.:** 1357
**Name:** Shelley
**Height:** 6.25
**Status:** Open issue, retired
**Issue Year:** 1978
**Issue Price:** $75
**Last Year:** 1993
**Last Retail Price:** $170

**Ref. No.:** 5498
**Name:** Opening Night
**Height:** 6.25
**Status:** Open issue, active
**Issue Year:** 1988
**Issue Price:** $190
**2003 Retail Price:** $295

**Ref. No.:** 5920
**Name:** Swan Ballet
**Height:** 6.25
**Status:** Open issue, active
**Issue Year:** 1992
**Issue Price:** $210
**2003 Retail Price:** $225

**Ref. No.:** 6325
**Name:** Curtains Up
**Height:** 6.25
**Status:** Open issue, retired
**Issue Year:** 1996
**Issue Price:** $255
**Last Year:** 1999
**Last Retail Price:** $255

**Ref. No.:** 5105
**Name:** Giselle
**Height:** 6.5
**Status:** Open issue, retired
**Issue Year:** 1982
**Issue Price:** $85
**Last Year:** 1985
**Last Retail Price:** $85

*Entertainment & the Arts*

**Ref. No.:** 5817
**Name:** Backstage Preparation
**Height:** 6.5
**Status:** Open issue, retired
**Issue Year:** 1991
**Issue Price:** $490
**Last Year:** 1994
**Last Retail Price:** $520

**Ref. No.:** 5107
**Name:** Karena
**Height:** 6.75
**Status:** Open issue, retired
**Issue Year:** 1982
**Issue Price:** $85
**Last Year:** 1985
**Last Retail Price:** $85
**Auction Price:** $425

**Ref. No.:** 5741
**Name:** Dancing Class
**Height:** 6.75
**Status:** Open issue, retired
**Issue Year:** 1991
**Issue Price:** $340
**Last Year:** 1996
**Last Retail Price:** $365

**Ref. No.:** 94.06
**Name:** Ballet
**Height:** 7
**Status:** Very rare
**Issue Year:** 1957
**Issue Price:** Unknown
**Last Year:** Unknown
**Last Retail Price:** Unknown

**Ref. No.:** 1358
**Name:** Beth
**Height:** 7.5
**Status:** Open issue, retired
**Issue Year:** 1978
**Issue Price:** $75
**Last Year:** 1993
**Last Retail Price:** $170

**Ref. No.:** 5104
**Name:** Sallie
**Height:** 7.5
**Status:** Open issue, retired
**Issue Year:** 1982
**Issue Price:** $85
**Last Year:** 1985
**Last Retail Price:** $85
**High Auction Price:** $350
**Low Auction Price:** $300

**Ref. No.:** 5497
**Name:** Dress Rehearsal
**Height:** 7.5
**Status:** Open issue, retired
**Issue Year:** 1988
**Issue Price:** $290
**Last Year:** 2002
**Last Retail Price:** $425

**Ref. No.:** 5714
**Name:** First Ballet
**Height:** 7.75
**Status:** Open issue, active
**Issue Year:** 1990
**Issue Price:** $370
**2003 Retail Price:** $425

**Ref. No.:** 5814
**Name:** Curtain Call
**Height:** 7.75
**Status:** Open issue, retired
**Issue Year:** 1991
**Issue Price:** $490
**Last Year:** 1994
**Last Retail Price:** $520

**Ref. No.:** 4504
**Name:** Seated Ballerina
**Height:** 8.25
**Status:** Open issue, retired
**Issue Year:** 1969
**Issue Price:** $110
**Last Year:** 1975
**Last Retail Price:** $200
**High Auction Price:** $350
**Low Auction Price:** $275

**Ref. No.:** 6103
**Name:** Beautiful Ballerina
**Height:** 8.5
**Status:** Open edition, retired
**Issue Year:** 1994
**Issue Price:** $250
**Last Year:** 1999
**Last Retail Price:** $285

**Ref. No.:** 6104
**Name:** Finishing Touches
**Height:** 8.5
**Status:** Open edition, retired
**Issue Year:** 1994
**Issue Price:** $240
**Last Year:** 1999
**Last Retail Price:** $250

*Entertainment & the Arts*

**Ref. No.:** 1360
**Name:** Laura
**Height:** 9
**Status:** Open issue, retired
**Issue Year:** 1978
**Issue Price:** $75
**Last Year:** 1993
**Last Retail Price:** $170

**Ref. No.:** 1361
**Name:** Julia
**Height:** 9
**Status:** Open issue, retired
**Issue Year:** 1978
**Issue Price:** $75
**Last Year:** 1993
**Last Retail Price:** $170

**Ref. No.:** 5160
**Name:** Rhumba
**Height:** 9
**Status:** Open edition, retired
**Issue Year:** 1982
**Issue Price:** $112.50
**Last Year:** 1998
**Last Retail Price:** $185

**Ref. No.:** 4847
**Name:** Classic Dance
**Height:** 9.5
**Status:** Open issue, retired
**Issue Year:** 1973
**Issue Price:** $80
**Last Year:** 1985
**Last Retail Price:** $247.50
**High Auction Price:** $675
**Low Auction Price:** $400

**Ref. No.:** 4935
**Name:** Closing Scene
**Height:** 9.5
**Status:** Open issue, retired
**Issue Year:** 1974
**Issue Price:** $180
**Last Year:** 1996
**Last Retail Price:** $520

**Ref. No.:** 4935.3
**Name:** Closing Scene (White)
**Height:** 9.5
**Status:** Open issue, retired
**Issue Year:** 1983
**Issue Price:** $212.50
**Last Year:** 1987
**Last Retail Price:** $240

**Ref. No.:** 5865
**Name:** Dressing for the Ballet
**Height:** 9.5
**Status:** Open issue, retired
**Issue Year:** 1992
**Issue Price:** $395
**Last Year:** 1995
**Last Retail Price:** $415

**Ref. No.:** 5866
**Name:** Final Touches
**Height:** 10
**Status:** Open issue, retired
**Issue Year:** 1992
**Issue Price:** $395
**Last Year:** 1995
**Last Retail Price:** $415

**Ref. No.:** 6323
**Name:** Stage Presence
**Height:** 10
**Status:** Open issue, retired
**Issue Year:** 1996
**Issue Price:** $355
**Last Year:** 2000
**Last Retail Price:** $355

**Ref. No.:** 7641
**Name:** For a Perfect Performance
**Height:** 10.25
**Status:** Limited edition, sold out
**Issue Year:** 1995
**Issue Price:** $310
**Last Year:** 1995
**Last Retail Price:** $310
**High Auction Price:** $550
**Low Auction Price:** $450
**Comment:** Special Event

**Ref. No.:** 5799
**Name:** Shall We Dance?
**Height:** 10.5
**Status:** Open issue, retired
**Issue Year:** 1991
**Issue Price:** $600
**Last Year:** 1993
**Last Retail Price:** $650

**Ref. No.:** 5816
**Name:** Prima Ballerina
**Height:** 10.5
**Status:** Open issue, retired
**Issue Year:** 1991
**Issue Price:** $490
**Last Year:** 1994
**Last Retail Price:** $520

*Entertainment & the Arts*

**Ref. No.:** 5818
**Name:** On Her Toes
**Height:** 10.5
**Status:** Open issue, retired
**Issue Year:** 1991
**Issue Price:** $490
**Last Year:** 1994
**Last Retail Price:** $520

**Ref. No.:** 5094
**Name:** Ballet First Step
**Height:** 11
**Status:** Open issue, retired
**Issue Year:** 1980
**Issue Price:** $165
**Last Year:** 1983
**Last Retail Price:** $165
**High Auction Price:** $400
**Low Auction Price:** $200

**Ref. No.:** 5275
**Name:** Weary Ballerina
**Height:** 11
**Status:** Open issue, retired
**Issue Year:** 1985
**Issue Price:** $175
**Last Year:** 1995
**Last Retail Price:** $310

**Ref. No.:** 6484
**Name:** After The Show
**Height:** 11
**Status:** Open issue, retired
**Issue Year:** 1998
**Issue Price:** $350
**Last Year:** 2000
**Last Retail Price:** $375

**Ref. No.:** 6485
**Name:** In Admiration
**Height:** 11
**Status:** Open issue, retired
**Issue Year:** 1998
**Issue Price:** $370
**Last Year:** 2000
**Last Retail Price:** $400

**Ref. No.:** 6486
**Name:** Posing For A Portrait
**Height:** 11
**Status:** Open issue, retired
**Issue Year:** 1998
**Issue Price:** $380
**Last Year:** 2000
**Last Retail Price:** $410

**Ref. No.:** 5050
**Name:** Dancer
**Height:** 11.5
**Status:** Open edition, active
**Issue Year:** 1979
**Issue Price:** $85
**2003 Retail Price:** $225

**Ref. No.:** 5256
**Name:** Folk Dancing
**Height:** 11.75
**Status:** Open issue, retired
**Issue Year:** 1984
**Issue Price:** $205
**Last Year:** 1990
**Last Retail Price:** $300
**High Auction Price:** $550
**Low Auction Price:** $475

**Ref. No.:** 5815
**Name:** In Full Relave
**Height:** 11.75
**Status:** Open issue, retired
**Issue Year:** 1991
**Issue Price:** $490
**Last Year:** 1994
**Last Retail Price:** $520

**Ref. No.:** 5935
**Name:** Nutcracker Suite
**Height:** 11.75
**Status:** Open issue, retired
**Issue Year:** 1993
**Issue Price:** $620
**Last Year:** 1998
**Last Retail Price:** $620

**Ref. No.:** 4520
**Name:** Flamenco Dancer
**Height:** 12.25
**Status:** Open issue, retired
**Issue Year:** 1969
**Issue Price:** $70
**Last Year:** 1970
**Last Retail Price:** $70

**Ref. No.:** 4992
**Name:** Dancers Resting
**Height:** 12.25
**Status:** Open issue, retired
**Issue Year:** 1978
**Issue Price:** $350
**Last Year:** 1983
**Last Retail Price:** $460
**High Auction Price:** $575
**Low Auction Price:** $550

*Entertainment & the Arts*

**Ref. No.:** 5252
**Name:** Dancing the Polka
**Height:** 12.25
**Status:** Open issue, retired
**Issue Year:** 1984
**Issue Price:** $205
**Last Year:** 1994
**Last Retail Price:** $340

**Ref. No.:** 310.13
**Name:** Behind the Screen
**Height:** 12.75
**Status:** Very rare
**Issue Year:** 1966
**Issue Price:** Unknown
**Last Year:** Unknown
**Last Retail Price:** Unknown

**Ref. No.:** 6371
**Name:** En Pointe
**Height:** 13
**Status:** Open issue, retired
**Issue Year:** 1997
**Issue Price:** $390
**Last Year:** 2000
**Last Retail Price:** $390

**Ref. No.:** 6374
**Name:** Pas de Deux
**Height:** 13
**Status:** Open issue, retired
**Issue Year:** 1997
**Issue Price:** $725
**Last Year:** 2000
**Last Retail Price:** $745

**Ref. No.:** 4559
**Name:** Ballerina
**Height:** 13.75
**Status:** Open issue, retired
**Issue Year:** 1969
**Issue Price:** $110
**Last Year:** 1993
**Last Retail Price:** $440
**High Auction Price:** $525
**Low Auction Price:** $500

**Ref. No.:** 5459
**Name:** Graduation Dance
**Height:** 14.25
**Status:** Open issue, retired
**Issue Year:** 1988
**Last Year:** 1990
**Last Retail Price:** $370
**Auction Price:** $450

**Ref. No.:** 5972
**Name:** Before the Dance
**Height:** 15.5
**Status:** Open issue, active
**Issue Year:** 1993
**Issue Price:** $3550
**2003 Retail Price:** $3550

**Ref. No.:** 4556
**Name:** Profound Contemplation
**Height:** 15.75
**Status:** Open issue, retired
**Issue Year:** 1969
**Issue Price:** $195
**Last Year:** 1974
**Last Retail Price:** $315
**Auction Price:** $1000

**Ref. No.:** 4557
**Name:** Musical Contemplation
**Height:** 15.75
**Status:** Open issue, retired
**Issue Year:** 1969
**Issue Price:** $170
**Last Year:** 1970
**Last Retail Price:** $180

**Ref. No.:** 1123
**Name:** La Tarantella
**Height:** 16
**Status:** Very rare
**Issue Year:** 1971
**Issue Price:** $550
**Last Year:** 1975
**Last Retail Price:** Unknown
**Auction Price:** $2400

**Ref. No.:** 6240
**Name:** Graceful Ballet
**Height:** 16.75
**Status:** Open edition, retired
**Issue Year:** 1995
**Issue Price:** $795
**Last Year:** 1998
**Last Retail Price:** $815

**Ref. No.:** 5235
**Name:** Ballet Trio
**Height:** 17
**Status:** Open issue, retired
**Issue Year:** 1984
**Issue Price:** $785
**Last Year:** 1998
**Last Retail Price:** $1675

*Entertainment & the Arts*

**Ref. No.:** 6387
**Name:** A Passionate Dance
**Height:** 17
**Status:** Open issue, active
**Issue Year:** 1997
**Issue Price:** $890
**2003 Retail Price:** $975

**Ref. No.:** 6444
**Name:** Spanish Dance
**Height:** 19
**Status:** Open issue, retired
**Issue Year:** 1997
**Issue Price:** $445
**Last Year:** 2000
**Last Retail Price:** $545

**Ref. No.:** 4519
**Name:** Flamenco Dancers
**Height:** 19.75
**Status:** Open issue, retired
**Issue Year:** 1969
**Issue Price:** $150
**Last Year:** 1993
**Last Retail Price:** $1100
**Auction Price:** $1200

Music

**Ref. No.:** 5035
**Name:** Act II
**Height:** 25.5
**Status:** Open issue, active
**Issue Year:** 1979
**Issue Price:** $700
**2003 Retail Price:** $1425

**Ref. No.:** 4616
**Name:** Boy with Drum
**Height:** 4.25
**Status:** Open issue, retired
**Issue Year:** 1969
**Issue Price:** $16.50
**Last Year:** 1979
**Last Retail Price:** $55
**High Auction Price:** $625
**Low Auction Price:** $350

**Ref. No.:** 4613
**Name:** Boy with Cymbals
**Height:** 5
**Status:** Open issue, retired
**Issue Year:** 1969
**Issue Price:** $14
**Last Year:** 1979
**Last Retail Price:** $37.5
**High Auction Price:** $400
**Low Auction Price:** $250

**Ref. No.:** 5929
**Name:** Jazz Drums
**Height:** 7.25
**Status:** Open issue, active
**Issue Year:** 1992
**Issue Price:** $595
**2003 Retail Price:** $625

**Ref. No.:** 4612
**Name:** Girl Singer
**Height:** 7.5
**Status:** Open issue, retired
**Issue Year:** 1969
**Issue Price:** $14
**Last Year:** 1979
**Last Retail Price:** $35
**High Auction Price:** $450
**Low Auction Price:** $350

**Ref. No.:** 4614
**Name:** Boy with Guitar
**Height:** 7.5
**Status:** Open issue, retired
**Issue Year:** 1969
**Issue Price:** $19.50
**Last Year:** 1979
**Last Retail Price:** $65
**High Auction Price:** $425
**Low Auction Price:** $350

**Ref. No.:** 5430
**Name:** Music Time
**Height:** 7.5
**Status:** Open issue, retired
**Issue Year:** 1987
**Issue Price:** $500
**Last Year:** 1990
**Last Retail Price:** $610
**High Auction Price:** $700
**Low Auction Price:** $675

**Ref. No.:** 6332
**Name:** Concerto
**Height:** 7.5
**Status:** Open issue, retired
**Issue Year:** 1996
**Issue Price:** $490
**Last Year:** 2002
**Last Retail Price:** $490

**Ref. No.:** 117.06
**Name:** Young Harpist
**Height:** 8
**Status:** Very rare
**Issue Year:** 1965
**Issue Price:** Unknown
**Last Year:** Unknown
**Last Retail Price:** Unknown

*Entertainment & the Arts*

**Ref. No.:** 6452
**Name:** Spring Recital
**Height:** 8
**Status:** Open issue, active
**Issue Year:** 1998
**Issue Price:** $685
**2003 Retail Price:** $775

**Ref. No.:** 1105
**Name:** Boy with Cornet
**Height:** 8.25
**Status:** Very Rare
**Issue Year:** 1971
**Issue Price:** $30
**Last Year:** 1973
**Last Retail Price:** Unknown
**High Auction Price:** $450
**Low Auction Price:** $400

**Ref. No.:** 4837
**Name:** Student Flute Player
**Height:** 8.25
**Status:** Open issue, retired
**Issue Year:** 1973
**Issue Price:** $66
**Last Year:** 1983
**Last Retail Price:** $125
**High Auction Price:** $625
**Low Auction Price:** $375

**Ref. No.:** 4615
**Name:** Boy with Double Bass
**Height:** 8.5
**Status:** Open issue, retired
**Issue Year:** 1969
**Issue Price:** $22.50
**Last Year:** 1979
**Last Retail Price:** $55
**High Auction Price:** $600
**Low Auction Price:** $350

**Ref. No.:** 4617
**Name:** Group of Musicians
**Height:** 8.5
**Status:** Open issue, retired
**Issue Year:** 1969
**Issue Price:** $33
**Last Year:** 1979
**Last Retail Price:** $85
**High Auction Price:** $550
**Low Auction Price:** $350

**Ref. No.:** 5930
**Name:** Jazz Duo
**Height:** 8.5
**Status:** Open issue, active
**Issue Year:** 1992
**Issue Price:** $795
**2003 Retail Price:** $995

**Ref. No.:** 5462
**Name:** Practice Makes Perfect
**Height:** 8.5
**Status:** Open edition, retired
**Issue Year:** 1988
**Issue Price:** $375
**Last Year:** 1998
**Last Retail Price:** $545

**Ref. No.:** 5833
**Name:** Jazz Sax
**Height:** 8.5
**Status:** Open issue, active
**Issue Year:** 1991
**Issue Price:** $295
**2003 Retail Price:** $325

**Ref. No.:** 5928
**Name:** Jazz Clarinet
**Height:** 8.5
**Status:** Open issue, active
**Issue Year:** 1992
**Issue Price:** $295
**2003 Retail Price:** $295

**Ref. No.:** 5810
**Name:** Musically Inclined
**Height:** 8.75
**Status:** Open issue, retired
**Issue Year:** 1991
**Issue Price:** $235
**Last Year:** 1993
**Last Retail Price:** $250
**Auction Price:** $225

**Ref. No.:** 5832
**Name:** Jazz Horn
**Height:** 8.75
**Status:** Open issue, active
**Issue Year:** 1991
**Issue Price:** $295
**2003 Retail Price:** $325

**Ref. No.:** 4877
**Name:** Boy with Flute
**Height:** 9
**Status:** Open issue, retired
**Issue Year:** 1974
**Issue Price:** $60
**Last Year:** 1981
**Last Retail Price:** $135
**High Auction Price:** $600
**Low Auction Price:** $350

*Entertainment & the Arts*

**Ref. No.:** 5157
**Name:** Bongo Beat
**Height:** 9
**Status:** Open issue, retired
**Issue Year:** 1982
**Issue Price:** $135
**Last Year:** 1998
**Last Retail Price:** $230

**Ref. No.:** 6319
**Name:** Beautiful Rhapsody
**Height:** 9
**Status:** Open edition, retired
**Issue Year:** 1996
**Issue Price:** $450
**Last Year:** 2001
**Last Retail Price:** $450

**Ref. No.:** 6408
**Name:** Sweet Song
**Height:** 9
**Status:** Open issue, retired
**Issue Year:** 1997
**Issue Price:** $480
**Last Year:** 2001
**Last Retail Price:** $480

**Ref. No.:** 6243
**Name:** Sweet Symphony
**Height:** 9.25
**Status:** Open issue, active
**Issue Year:** 1996
**Issue Price:** $450
**2003 Retail Price:** $450

**Ref. No.:** 1026
**Name:** Girl with Mandolin
**Height:** 9.5
**Status:** Open issue, retired
**Issue Year:** 1969
**Issue Price:** $52.50
**Last Year:** 1978
**Last Retail Price:** $150

**Ref. No.:** 5306
**Name:** Young Street Musicians
**Height:** 9.5
**Status:** Open issue, retired
**Issue Year:** 1985
**Issue Price:** $300
**Last Year:** 1988
**Last Retail Price:** $360
**High Auction Price:** $1200
**Low Auction Price:** $750

**Ref. No.:** 6304
**Name:** Bass Drummer
**Height:** 9.5
**Status:** Open issue, retired
**Issue Year:** 1996
**Issue Price:** $400
**Last Year:** 1998
**Last Retail Price:** $400

**Ref. No.:** 5834
**Name:** Jazz Bass
**Height:** 10
**Status:** Open issue, active
**Issue Year:** 1991
**Issue Price:** $395
**2003 Retail Price:** $425

**Ref. No.:** 6306
**Name:** Majorette
**Height:** 10
**Status:** Open issue, retired
**Issue Year:** 1996
**Issue Price:** $310
**Last Year:** 1998
**Last Retail Price:** $310

**Ref. No.:** 6303
**Name:** Tuba Player
**Height:** 10.5
**Status:** Open issue, retired
**Issue Year:** 1996
**Issue Price:** $315
**Last Year:** 1998
**Last Retail Price:** $315

**Ref. No.:** 6305
**Name:** Trumpet Player
**Height:** 10.5
**Status:** Open issue, retired
**Issue Year:** 1996
**Issue Price:** $270
**Last Year:** 1998
**Last Retail Price:** $270

**Ref. No.:** 5850
**Name:** Inspiring Muse
**Height:** 11
**Status:** Open issue, retired
**Issue Year:** 1992
**Issue Price:** $1200
**Last Year:** 1994
**Last Retail Price:** $1250

**Ref. No.:** 4842
**Name:** Viola Lesson
**Height:** 11.75
**Status:** Open issue, retired
**Issue Year:** 1973
**Issue Price:** $66
**Last Year:** 1981
**Last Retail Price:** $130
**Auction Price:** $450

**Ref. No.:** 5692
**Name:** Street Harmonies
**Height:** 11.75
**Status:** Open issue, retired
**Issue Year:** 1990
**Issue Price:** $3200
**Last Year:** 1993
**Last Retail Price:** $3750

**Ref. No.:** 4651
**Name:** Cellist
**Height:** 12.5
**Status:** Open issue, retired
**Issue Year:** 1969
**Issue Price:** $70
**Last Year:** 1978
**Last Retail Price:** $220
**High Auction Price:** $800
**Low Auction Price:** $625

**Ref. No.:** 5388
**Name:** Sidewalk Serenade
**Height:** 12.5
**Status:** Open issue, retired
**Issue Year:** 1986
**Issue Price:** $750
**Last Year:** 1988
**Last Retail Price:** $850
**High Auction Price:** $1750
**Low Auction Price:** $1200

**Ref. No.:** 5196
**Name:** Music Maestro Please
**Height:** 13
**Status:** Open issue, retired
**Issue Year:** 1984
**Issue Price:** $135
**Last Year:** 1988
**Last Retail Price:** $160
**High Auction Price:** $675
**Low Auction Price:** $350

**Ref. No.:** 4622
**Name:** Old Man with Violin
**Height:** 13
**Status:** Open issue, retired
**Issue Year:** 1969
**Issue Price:** $45
**Last Year:** 1982
**Last Retail Price:** $165
**High Auction Price:** $1100
**Low Auction Price:** $700

**Ref. No.:** 4606
**Name:** Accordion Player
**Height:** 13.25
**Status:** Open issue, retired
**Issue Year:** 1969
**Issue Price:** $60
**Last Year:** 1978
**Last Retail Price:** $130
**Auction Price:** $500

**Ref. No.:** 5330
**Name:** Concert Violinist
**Height:** 13.25
**Status:** Open issue, retired
**Issue Year:** 1985
**Issue Price:** $220
**Last Year:** 1988
**Last Retail Price:** $250
**High Auction Price:** $500
**Low Auction Price:** $350

**Ref. No.:** 6312
**Name:** The Harpist
**Height:** 13.25
**Status:** Open edition, retired
**Issue Year:** 1996
**Issue Price:** $820
**Last Year:** 1999
**Last Retail Price:** $820

**Ref. No.:** 5046
**Name:** Organ Grinder
**Height:** 13.5
**Status:** Open issue, retired
**Issue Year:** 1980
**Issue Price:** $327.50
**Last Year:** 1981
**Last Retail Price:** $360
**High Auction Price:** $1650
**Low Auction Price:** $1600

**Ref. No.:** 6340
**Name:** Sweet Country
**Height:** 13.5
**Status:** Open issue, retired
**Issue Year:** 1996
**Issue Price:** $750
**Last Year:** 1998
**Last Retail Price:** $750

**Ref. No.:** 4887
**Name:** Violinist
**Height:** 13.75
**Status:** Open issue, retired
**Issue Year:** 1974
**Issue Price:** $110
**Last Year:** 1981
**Last Retail Price:** $130

*Entertainment & the Arts*

**Ref. No.:** 6339
**Name:** Country Sounds
**Height:** 14.25
**Status:** Open issue, retired
**Issue Year:** 1996
**Issue Price:** $750
**Last Year:** 1998
**Last Retail Price:** $750

**Ref. No.:** 1025
**Name:** Flute Player
**Height:** 14.5
**Status:** Open issue, retired
**Issue Year:** 1969
**Issue Price:** $72.50
**Last Year:** 1978
**Last Retail Price:** $72.50
**High Auction Price:** $800
**Low Auction Price:** $700

**Ref. No.:** 4653
**Name:** Orchestra Conductor
**Height:** 15.5
**Status:** Open issue, retired
**Issue Year:** 1969
**Issue Price:** $95
**Last Year:** 1979
**Last Retail Price:** $200
**High Auction Price:** $900
**Low Auction Price:** $850

**Circus and Clowns**

**Ref. No.:** 1085
**Name:** Musical, 19th Century
**Height:** 17
**Status:** Very rare
**Issue Year:** 1969
**Issue Price:** $180
**Last Year:** 1973
**Last Retail Price:** Unknown

**Ref. No.:** 1039
**Name:** Violinist and Girl
**Height:** 17.75
**Status:** Open issue, retired
**Issue Year:** 1969
**Issue Price:** $120
**Last Year:** 1991
**Last Retail Price:** $825
**High Auction Price:** $1000
**Low Auction Price:** $700

**Ref. No.:** 5277
**Name:** Pierrot with Puppy
**Height:** 4.25
**Status:** Open issue, active
**Issue Year:** 1985
**Issue Price:** $95
**2003 Retail Price:** $165

**Ref. No.:** 5278
**Name:** Pierrot with Puppy
and Ball
**Height:** 4.25
**Status:** Open issue, active
**Issue Year:** 1985
**Issue Price:** $95
**2003 Retail Price:** $165

**Ref. No.:** 5764
**Name:** Seeds of Laughter
**Height:** 4.75
**Status:** Open issue, retired
**Issue Year:** 1991
**Issue Price:** $525
**Last Year:** 1995
**Last Retail Price:** $575

**Ref. No.:** 5812
**Name:** Tired Friend
**Height:** 5
**Status:** Open issue, active
**Issue Year:** 1991
**Issue Price:** $225
**2003 Retail Price:** $250

**Ref. No.:** 5279
**Name:** Pierrot with Concertina
**Height:** 5.5
**Status:** Open issue, active
**Issue Year:** 1985
**Issue Price:** $95
**2003 Retail Price:** $165

**Ref. No.:** 6913
**Name:** The Magic of Comedy
**Height:** 5.5
**Status:** Open issue, active
**Issue Year:** 2002
**Issue Price:** $525
**2003 Retail Price:** $525

**Ref. No.:** 5600
**Name:** The Blues
**Height:** 6
**Status:** Open edition, retired
**Issue Year:** 1989
**Issue Price:** $265
**Last Year:** 1993
**Last Retail Price:** $340

*Entertainment & the Arts*

**Ref. No.:** 4618
**Name:** Clown
**Height:** 6.25
**Status:** Open issue, active
**Issue Year:** 1969
**Issue Price:** $70
**2003 Retail Price:** $425

**Ref. No.:** 5813
**Name:** Having a Ball
**Height:** 6.75
**Status:** Open issue, active
**Issue Year:** 1991
**Issue Price:** $225
**2003 Retail Price:** $250

**Ref. No.:** 5585
**Name:** Fine Melody
**Height:** 7
**Status:** Open edition, retired
**Issue Year:** 1989
**Issue Price:** $225
**Last Year:** 1993
**Last Retail Price:** $295
**Auction Price:** $325

**Ref. No.:** 5811
**Name:** Littlest Clown
**Height:** 7.25
**Status:** Open issue, active
**Issue Year:** 1991
**Issue Price:** $225
**2003 Retail Price:** $250

**Ref. No.:** 6245
**Name:** Destination Big Top
**Height:** 7.75
**Status:** Limited edition, sold out
**Issue Year:** 1996
**Issue Price:** $225
**Last Year:** 1996
**Last Retail Price:** $225
**Auction Price:** $650
**Comment:** Special Event

**Ref. No.:** 5610
**Name:** Star Struck
**Height:** 8
**Status:** Open issue, retired
**Issue Year:** 1989
**Issue Price:** $335
**Last Year:** 1997
**Last Retail Price:** $420

**Ref. No.:** 5611
**Name:** Sad Clown
**Height:** 8.25
**Status:** Open issue, retired
**Issue Year:** 1989
**Issue Price:** $335
**Last Year:** 1997
**Last Retail Price:** $420

**Ref. No.:** 5763
**Name:** Musical Partners
**Height:** 8.25
**Status:** Open issue, retired
**Issue Year:** 1991
**Issue Price:** $625
**Last Year:** 1995
**Last Retail Price:** $675

**Ref. No.:** 5471
**Name:** Sad Sax
**Height:** 8.5
**Status:** Open issue, active
**Issue Year:** 1988
**Issue Price:** $175
**2003 Retail Price:** $225

**Ref. No.:** 5472
**Name:** Circus Sam
**Height:** 8.5
**Status:** Open issue, active
**Issue Year:** 1988
**Issue Price:** $175
**2003 Retail Price:** $225

**Ref. No.:** 5612
**Name:** Reflecting
**Height:** 9
**Status:** Open edition, retired
**Issue Year:** 1989
**Issue Price:** $335
**Last Year:** 1994
**Last Retail Price:** $420

**Ref. No.:** 5762
**Name:** Checking the Time
**Height:** 9.5
**Status:** Open issue, retired
**Issue Year:** 1991
**Issue Price:** $560
**Last Year:** 1995
**Last Retail Price:** $595

*Entertainment & the Arts*

**Ref. No.:** 1517
**Name:** Circus Train
**Height:** 9.75
**Status:** Open issue, retired
**Issue Year:** 1987
**Issue Price:** $2900
**Last Year:** 1994
**Last Retail Price:** $4350

**Ref. No.:** 5130
**Name:** Pensive Clown
**Height:** 9.75
**Status:** Open issue, retired
**Issue Year:** 1982
**Issue Price:** $250
**Last Year:** 2000
**Last Retail Price:** $475

**Ref. No.:** 5901
**Name:** Surprise
**Height:** 9.75
**Status:** Open issue, active
**Issue Year:** 1992
**Issue Price:** $325
**2003 Retail Price:** $350

**Ref. No.:** 5059
**Name:** Clown with Saxophone
**Height:** 10.25
**Status:** Open issue, retired
**Issue Year:** 1980
**Issue Price:** $320
**Last Year:** 1985
**Last Retail Price:** $245
**High Auction Price:** $750
**Low Auction Price:** $475

**Ref. No.:** 5856
**Name:** Circus Concert
**Height:** 10.25
**Status:** Open issue, retired
**Issue Year:** 1992
**Issue Price:** $570
**Last Year:** 1996
**Last Retail Price:** $585

**Ref. No.:** 5892
**Name:** Circus Magic
**Height:** 10.5
**Status:** Open issue, retired
**Issue Year:** 1992
**Issue Price:** $470
**Last Year:** 1997
**Last Retail Price:** $495

**Ref. No.:** 5771
**Name:** The Magic of Laughter
**Height:** 10.5
**Status:** Open issue, retired
**Issue Year:** 1991
**Issue Price:** $950
**Last Year:** 1996
**Last Retail Price:** $1065

**Ref. No.:** 5542
**Name:** Melancholy
**Height:** 11
**Status:** Open issue, retired
**Issue Year:** 1989
**Issue Price:** $375
**Last Year:** 2000
**Last Retail Price:** $460

**Ref. No.:** 5838
**Name:** On the Move
**Height:** 11
**Status:** Open issue, retired
**Issue Year:** 1991
**Issue Price:** $340
**Last Year:** 1997
**Last Retail Price:** $395

**Ref. No.:** 6900
**Name:** Music for a Dream
**Height:** 11.5
**Status:** Open issue, active
**Issue Year:** 2002
**Issue Price:** $490
**2003 Retail Price:** $495

**Ref. No.:** 5056
**Name:** Clown with Clock
**Height:** 11.75
**Status:** Open issue, retired
**Issue Year:** 1980
**Issue Price:** $290
**Last Year:** 1985
**Last Retail Price:** $220
**High Auction Price:** $950
**Low Auction Price:** $600

**Ref. No.:** 5129
**Name:** Jester with Base
**Height:** 12.25
**Status:** Open issue, retired
**Issue Year:** 1982
**Issue Price:** $220
**Last Year:** 2000
**Last Retail Price:** $475

*Entertainment & the Arts*

**Ref. No.:** 5057
**Name:** Clown with Violin
**Height:** 12.5
**Status:** Open issue, retired
**Issue Year:** 1980
**Issue Price:** $270
**Last Year:** 1985
**Last Retail Price:** $200
**Auction Price:** $850

**Ref. No.:** 5052
**Name:** At the Circus
**Height:** 13
**Status:** Open issue, retired
**Issue Year:** 1979
**Issue Price:** $525
**Last Year:** 1985
**Last Retail Price:** $665
**High Auction Price:** $1500
**Low Auction Price:** $1000

**Ref. No.:** 5060
**Name:** Clown with Trumpet
**Height:** 13.25
**Status:** Open issue, retired
**Issue Year:** 1980
**Issue Price:** $290
**Last Year:** 1985
**Last Retail Price:** $220
**High Auction Price:** $800
**Low Auction Price:** $350

**Ref. No.:** 1126
**Name:** Clown with Violin
**Height:** 13.75
**Status:** Open issue, retired
**Issue Year:** 1971
**Issue Price:** $71
**Last Year:** 1978
**Last Retail Price:** $190
**High Auction Price:** $2350
**Low Auction Price:** $650

**Ref. No.:** 6507
**Name:** A Mile Of Style
**Height:** 14
**Status:** Open issue, retired
**Issue Year:** 1998
**Issue Price:** $275
**Last Year:** 1998
**Last Retail Price:** $275
**Comment:** 1998 Vanguard
      Dealer Exclusive

**Ref. No.:** 4605
**Name:** Magic
**Height:** 15.5
**Status:** Open issue, retired
**Issue Year:** 1969
**Issue Price:** $160
**Last Year:** 1985
**Last Retail Price:** $600
**High Auction Price:** $1100
**Low Auction Price:** $725

**Ref. No.:** 4924
**Name:** Languid Clown
**Height:** 16
**Status:** Open issue, retired
**Issue Year:** 1974
**Issue Price:** $200
**Last Year:** 1983
**Last Retail Price:** $260
**Auction Price:** $1100

**Ref. No.:** 5765
**Name:** Hats Off to Fun
**Height:** 16.25
**Status:** Open issue, retired
**Issue Year:** 1991
**Issue Price:** $475
**Last Year:** 1995
**Last Retail Price:** $510

**Ref. No.:** 1076
**Name:** Court Jester
**Height:** 17
**Status:** Open issue, retired
**Issue Year:** 1969
**Issue Price:** $120
**Last Year:** 1970
**Last Retail Price:** $120

**Ref. No.:** 6316
**Name:** Carnevale
**Height:** 17.5
**Status:** Open issue, retired
**Issue Year:** 1996
**Issue Price:** $840
**Last Year:** 1998
**Last Retail Price:** $840

**Ref. No.:** 1027
**Name:** Clown with Concertina
**Height:** 17.75
**Status:** Open issue, retired
**Issue Year:** 1969
**Issue Price:** $95
**Last Year:** 1993
**Last Retail Price:** $735
**High Auction Price:** $700
**Low Auction Price:** $475

**Ref. No.:** 5058
**Name:** Clown with Concertina
**Height:** 19.25
**Status:** Open issue, retired
**Issue Year:** 1980
**Issue Price:** $290
**Last Year:** 1985
**Last Retail Price:** $227.50
**High Auction Price:** $625
**Low Auction Price:** $425

*Entertainment & the Arts*

## Harlequins and Columbinas

**Ref. No.:** 1503
**Name:** Neglected
**Height:** 2.25
**Status:** Open issue, retired
**Issue Year:** 1986
**Issue Price:** $125
**Last Year:** 1991
**Last Retail Price:** $200
**Auction Price:** $450

**Ref. No.:** 1500
**Name:** Ragamuffin
**Height:** 4
**Status:** Open issue, retired
**Issue Year:** 1986
**Issue Price:** $125
**Last Year:** 1991
**Last Retail Price:** $200

**Ref. No.:** 1178
**Name:** Girl with Accordion
**Height:** 6
**Status:** Open issue, retired
**Issue Year:** 1971
**Issue Price:** $34
**Last Year:** 1981
**Last Retail Price:** $60

**Ref. No.:** 6257
**Name:** Pierrot In Preparation
**Height:** 6
**Status:** Open issue, retired
**Issue Year:** 1996
**Issue Price:** $195
**Last Year:** 1999
**Last Retail Price:** $195

**Ref. No.:** 1177
**Name:** Girl with Ball
**Height:** 6.5
**Status:** Open issue, retired
**Issue Year:** 1971
**Issue Price:** $27.50
**Last Year:** 1981
**Last Retail Price:** $85

**Ref. No.:** 5694
**Name:** Circus Serenade
**Height:** 6.5
**Status:** Open issue, retired
**Issue Year:** 1990
**Issue Price:** $300
**Last Year:** 1994
**Last Retail Price:** $360

**Ref. No.:** 5696
**Name:** Mandolin Serenade
**Height:** 6.5
**Status:** Open issue, retired
**Issue Year:** 1990
**Issue Price:** $300
**Last Year:** 1994
**Last Retail Price:** $360

**Ref. No.:** 1179
**Name:** Boy with Concertina
**Height:** 7
**Status:** Open issue, retired
**Issue Year:** 1971
**Issue Price:** $34
**Last Year:** 1981
**Last Retail Price:** $60

**Ref. No.:** 4503
**Name:** Seated Harlequin
**Height:** 7
**Status:** Open issue, retired
**Issue Year:** 1969
**Issue Price:** $110
**Last Year:** 1975
**Last Retail Price:** $200

**Ref. No.:** 5586
**Name:** Sad Note
**Height:** 7
**Status:** Open edition, retired
**Issue Year:** 1989
**Issue Price:** $185
**Last Year:** 1993
**Last Retail Price:** $275

**Ref. No.:** 5695
**Name:** Concertina
**Height:** 7
**Status:** Open issue, retired
**Issue Year:** 1990
**Issue Price:** $300
**Last Year:** 1995
**Last Retail Price:** $360
**Auction Price:** $325

**Ref. No.:** 6258
**Name:** Pierrot In Love
**Height:** 7.25
**Status:** Open issue, retired
**Issue Year:** 1996
**Issue Price:** $195
**Last Year:** 1999
**Last Retail Price:** $195

**Ref. No.:** 6259
**Name:** Pierrot Rehearsing
**Height:** 7.25
**Status:** Open issue, retired
**Issue Year:** 1996
**Issue Price:** $195
**Last Year:** 1999
**Last Retail Price:** $195

**Ref. No.:** 1175
**Name:** Girl with Domino
**Height:** 7.75
**Status:** Open issue, retired
**Issue Year:** 1971
**Issue Price:** $25
**Last Year:** 1981
**Last Retail Price:** $35
**Auction Price:** $350

**Ref. No.:** 1176
**Name:** Girl with Dice
**Height:** 7.75
**Status:** Open issue, retired
**Issue Year:** 1971
**Issue Price:** $25
**Last Year:** 1981
**Last Retail Price:** $35
**Auction Price:** $325

**Ref. No.:** 5203
**Name:** Little Jester
**Height:** 7.75
**Status:** Open issue, retired
**Issue Year:** 1984
**Issue Price:** $75
**Last Year:** 1993
**Last Retail Price:** $140
**Auction Price:** $325

**Ref. No.:** 5077
**Name:** Harlequin "C"
**Height:** 7.75
**Status:** Open issue, retired
**Issue Year:** 1980
**Issue Price:** $185
**Last Year:** 1985
**Last Retail Price:** $142.5
**High Auction Price:** $500
**Low Auction Price:** $250

**Ref. No.:** 6239
**Name:** Young Jester-Singer
**Height:** 7.75
**Status:** Open issue, retired
**Issue Year:** 1995
**Issue Price:** $235
**Last Year:** 1997
**Last Retail Price:** $235

**Ref. No.:** 5076
**Name:** Harlequin "B"
**Height:** 8
**Status:** Open issue, retired
**Issue Year:** 1980
**Issue Price:** $185
**Last Year:** 1985
**Last Retail Price:** $142.50
**High Auction Price:** $425
**Low Auction Price:** $275

**Ref. No.:** 6237
**Name:** Young Jester with
  Mandolin
**Height:** 8
**Status:** Open issue, retired
**Issue Year:** 1995
**Issue Price:** $235
**Last Year:** 1997
**Last Retail Price:** $235

**Ref. No.:** 6278
**Name:** Young Mandolin Player
**Height:** 8.25
**Status:** Open issue, retired
**Issue Year:** 1996
**Issue Price:** $330
**Last Year:** 2000
**Last Retail Price:** $330

**Ref. No.:** 4883
**Name:** Lady with Young
  Harlequin
**Height:** 8.5
**Status:** Open issue, retired
**Issue Year:** 1974
**Issue Price:** $100
**Last Year:** 1975
**Last Retail Price:** $130

**Ref. No.:** 5075
**Name:** Harlequin "A"
**Height:** 8.5
**Status:** Open issue, retired
**Issue Year:** 1980
**Issue Price:** $217.50
**Last Year:** 1985
**Last Retail Price:** $165
**High Auction Price:** $500
**Low Auction Price:** $350

**Ref. No.:** 6238
**Name:** Young Jester–Trumpet
**Height:** 8.75
**Status:** Open issue, retired
**Issue Year:** 1995
**Issue Price:** $235
**Last Year:** 1997
**Last Retail Price:** $235

*Entertainment & the Arts*

**Ref. No.:** 5452
**Name:** Masquerade Ball
**Height:** 9
**Status:** Open issue, retired
**Issue Year:** 1988
**Issue Price:** $220
**Last Year:** 1993
**Last Retail Price:** $290

**Ref. No.:** 4548
**Name:** Troubadour
**Height:** 9.5
**Status:** Open issue, retired
**Issue Year:** 1969
**Issue Price:** $67.50
**Last Year:** 1978
**Last Retail Price:** $175

**Ref. No.:** 1229
**Name:** Young Harlequin
**Height:** 9.75
**Status:** Open issue, retired
**Issue Year:** 1972
**Issue Price:** $70
**Last Year:** 1999
**Last Retail Price:** $520

**Ref. No.:** 4848
**Name:** Charm
**Height:** 9.75
**Status:** Open issue, retired
**Issue Year:** 1973
**Issue Price:** $45
**Last Year:** 1985
**Last Retail Price:** $140
**High Auction Price:** $350
**Low Auction Price:** $300

**Ref. No.:** 4882
**Name:** Carnival Couple
**Height:** 10.25
**Status:** Open issue, retired
**Issue Year:** 1974
**Issue Price:** $60
**Last Year:** 1995
**Last Retail Price:** $300

**Ref. No.:** 6322
**Name:** Serenading Colombina
**Height:** 10.25
**Status:** Open issue, retired
**Issue Year:** 1996
**Issue Price:** $415
**Last Year:** 1998
**Last Retail Price:** $415

**Ref. No.:** 5128
**Name:** Lost Love
**Height:** 10.5
**Status:** Open issue, retired
**Issue Year:** 1982
**Issue Price:** $400
**Last Year:** 1988
**Last Retail Price:** $460

**Ref. No.:** 5658
**Name:** Venetian Carnival
**Height:** 10.5
**Status:** Open issue, retired
**Issue Year:** 1990
**Issue Price:** $500
**Last Year:** 1993
**Last Retail Price:** $575
**Auction Price:** $750

**Ref. No.:** 5844
**Name:** Flirtatious Jester
**Height:** 10.5
**Status:** Open issue, retired
**Issue Year:** 1992
**Issue Price:** $890
**Last Year:** 1997
**Last Retail Price:** $925

**Ref. No.:** 4580
**Name:** Mardi Gras
**Height:** 11
**Status:** Open issue, retired
**Issue Year:** 1969
**Issue Price:** $57.50
**Last Year:** 1975
**Last Retail Price:** $100
**High Auction Price:** $2500
**Low Auction Price:** $1800

**Ref. No.:** 4963
**Name:** Infantile Candor
**Height:** 11
**Status:** Open issue, retired
**Issue Year:** 1977
**Issue Price:** $285
**Last Year:** 1979
**Last Retail Price:** $330
**Auction Price:** $1350

**Ref. No.:** 4646
**Name:** Pierrot with Mandolin
**Height:** 11.75
**Status:** Open issue, retired
**Issue Year:** 1969
**Issue Price:** $60
**Last Year:** 1970
**Last Retail Price:** $65

*Entertainment & the Arts*

**Ref. No.:** 1382
**Name:** Medieval Boy
**Height:** 12.25
**Status:** Open issue, retired
**Issue Year:** 1978
**Issue Price:** $235
**Last Year:** 1985
**Last Retail Price:** $310
**High Auction Price:** $700
**Low Auction Price:** $450

**Ref. No.:** 5821
**Name:** Minstrel's Love
**Height:** 12.25
**Status:** Open issue, retired
**Issue Year:** 1991
**Issue Price:** $525
**Last Year:** 1993
**Last Retail Price:** $575

**Ref. No.:** 6195
**Name:** Carnival Companions
**Height:** 12.25
**Status:** Open issue, retired
**Issue Year:** 1995
**Issue Price:** $650
**Last Year:** 1998
**Last Retail Price:** $685

**Ref. No.:** 4977
**Name:** Harlequin Serenade
**Height:** 12.5
**Status:** Open issue, retired
**Issue Year:** 1977
**Issue Price:** $185
**Last Year:** 1979
**Last Retail Price:** $215
**Auction Price:** $675

**Ref. No.:** 1314
**Name:** Little Troubadour
**Height:** 13
**Status:** Open issue, retired
**Issue Year:** 1974
**Issue Price:** $240
**Last Year:** 1979
**Last Retail Price:** $435

**Ref. No.:** 4923
**Name:** Serious Clown
**Height:** 13
**Status:** Open issue, retired
**Issue Year:** 1974
**Issue Price:** $150
**Last Year:** 1979
**Last Retail Price:** $240

**Ref. No.:** 6435
**Name:** Colombina
**Height:** 13
**Status:** Open issue, retired
**Issue Year:** 1997
**Issue Price:** $525
**Last Year:** 1998
**Last Retail Price:** $525

**Ref. No.:** 4558
**Name:** Sad Harlequin
**Height:** 13.75
**Status:** Open issue, retired
**Issue Year:** 1969
**Issue Price:** $65
**Last Year:** 1993
**Last Retail Price:** $510

**Ref. No.:** 6434
**Name:** Pensive Harlequin
**Height:** 14
**Status:** Open issue, retired
**Issue Year:** 1997
**Issue Price:** $495
**Last Year:** 1998
**Last Retail Price:** $495

**Ref. No.:** 1017
**Name:** Idyl
**Height:** 14.25
**Status:** Open issue, retired
**Issue Year:** 1969
**Issue Price:** $115
**Last Year:** 1991
**Last Retail Price:** $565

**Ref. No.:** 1247
**Name:** Happy Harlequin
**Height:** 14.5
**Status:** Open issue, retired
**Issue Year:** 1974
**Issue Price:** $220
**Last Year:** 1983
**Last Retail Price:** $300
**Auction Price:** $900

**Ref. No.:** 4943
**Name:** Troubadour
**Height:** 15
**Status:** Open edition, retired
**Issue Year:** 1976
**Issue Price:** $435
**Last Year:** 1981
**Last Retail Price:** $740

*Entertainment & the Arts*

**Ref. No.:** 6447
**Name:** Melancholy Musician
**Height:** 15
**Status:** Open issue, retired
**Issue Year:** 1997
**Issue Price:** $400
**Last Year:** 1999
**Last Retail Price:** $420

**Ref. No.:** 4560
**Name:** Pensive Pierrot
**Height:** 15.75
**Status:** Open issue, retired
**Issue Year:** 1969
**Issue Price:** $160
**Last Year:** 1975
**Last Retail Price:** $290

**Ref. No.:** 341.13
**Name:** Troubadour
**Height:** 17
**Status:** Very rare
**Issue Year:** 1972
**Issue Price:** Unknown
**Last Year:** Unknown
**Last Retail Price:** Unknown

**Ref. No.:** 4831
**Name:** Romance
**Height:** 17.75
**Status:** Open issue, retired
**Issue Year:** 1972
**Issue Price:** $175
**Last Year:** 1981
**Last Retail Price:** $570

**Ref. No.:** 4699
**Name:** Troubadour in Love
**Height:** 19
**Status:** Open issue, retired
**Issue Year:** 1970
**Issue Price:** $60
**Last Year:** 1975
**Last Retail Price:** $100
**Auction Price:** $1450

**Ref. No.:** 6375
**Name:** Pierrot's Proposal
**Height:** 19
**Status:** Open issue, retired
**Issue Year:** 1997
**Issue Price:** $1425
**Last Year:** 2000
**Last Retail Price:** $1475

# Bridal & Romance

**Bridal**

**Ref. No.:** 6585
**Name:** Endless Love
**Height:** 5.25
**Status:** Open issue, active
**Issue Year:** 1999
**Issue Price:** $175
**2003 Retail Price:** $175

**Ref. No.:** 5835
**Name:** "I Do"
**Height:** 7.25
**Status:** Open issue, active
**Issue Year:** 1991
**Issue Price:** $165
**2003 Retail Price:** $195

**Ref. No.:** 6620
**Name:** A Kiss To Remember
**Height:** 7.5
**Status:** Open issue, active
**Issue Year:** 1999
**Issue Price:** $250
**2003 Retail Price:** $250

**Ref. No.:** 4808
**Name:** Wedding
**Height:** 7.75
**Status:** Open issue, active
**Issue Year:** 1972
**Issue Price:** $50
**2003 Retail Price:** $195

**Ref. No.:** 5555
**Name:** Let's Make Up
**Height:** 7.75
**Status:** Open issue, active
**Issue Year:** 1989
**Issue Price:** $215
**2003 Retail Price:** $275

**Ref. No.:** 5885
**Name:** From This Day Forward
**Height:** 7.75
**Status:** Open issue, active
**Issue Year:** 1992
**Issue Price:** $265
**2003 Retail Price:** $295

**Ref. No.:** 5968
**Name:** Honeymoon Ride
**Height:** 8
**Status:** Open issue, retired
**Issue Year:** 1993
**Issue Price:** $2750
**Last Year:** 1995
**Last Retail Price:** $2750

**Ref. No.:** 6164
**Name:** Wedding Bells
**Height:** 8.25
**Status:** Open issue, active
**Issue Year:** 1994
**Issue Price:** $175
**2003 Retail Price:** $195

**Ref. No.:** 6199
**Name:** In The Procession
**Height:** 8.75
**Status:** Open issue, retired
**Issue Year:** 1995
**Issue Price:** $250
**Last Year:** 1998
**Last Retail Price:** $250

**Ref. No.:** 6028
**Name:** Mazel Tov!
**Height:** 9.25
**Status:** Open issue, active
**Issue Year:** 1993
**2003 Retail Price:** $395

**Ref. No.:** 5282
**Name:** Over the Threshold
**Height:** 10.25
**Status:** Open issue, active
**Issue Year:** 1985
**Issue Price:** $150
**2003 Retail Price:** $295

**Ref. No.:** 5903
**Name:** Down the Aisle
**Height:** 10.5
**Status:** Open edition, retired
**Issue Year:** 1992
**Issue Price:** $295
**Last Year:** 1996
**Last Retail Price:** $295

**Ref. No.:** 5274
**Name:** Wedding Day
**Height:** 11
**Status:** Open issue, retired
**Issue Year:** 1985
**Issue Price:** $240
**Last Year:** 1999
**Last Retail Price:** $435

**Ref. No.:** 5447
**Name:** Will You Marry Me?
**Height:** 11
**Status:** Open issue, retired
**Issue Year:** 1987
**Issue Price:** $750
**Last Year:** 1994
**Last Retail Price:** $1250
**Auction Price:** $1500

**Ref. No.:** 5439
**Name:** The Bride
**Height:** 11.75
**Status:** Open issue, retired
**Issue Year:** 1987
**Issue Price:** $250
**Last Year:** 1995
**Last Retail Price:** $425

**Ref. No.:** 1372
**Name:** Anniversary Dance
**Height:** 12.25
**Status:** Open issue, active
**Issue Year:** 1978
**Issue Price:** $260
**2003 Retail Price:** $575

**Ref. No.:** 1404
**Name:** Wedding
**Height:** 12.25
**Status:** Open issue, retired
**Issue Year:** 1982
**Issue Price:** $320
**Last Year:** 1997
**Last Retail Price:** $585

**Ref. No.:** 5587
**Name:** Wedding Cake
**Height:** 13.25
**Status:** Open issue, retired
**Issue Year:** 1989
**Issue Price:** $595
**Last Year:** 1996
**Last Retail Price:** $750

**Ref. No.:** 5742
**Name:** Bridal Portrait
**Height:** 13.25
**Status:** Open issue, retired
**Issue Year:** 1991
**Issue Price:** $480
**Last Year:** 1995
**Last Retail Price:** $560

**Ref. No.:** 1434
**Name:** Vows
**Height:** 13.75
**Status:** Open issue, retired
**Issue Year:** 1983
**Issue Price:** $300
**Last Year:** 1991
**Last Retail Price:** $875
**High Auction Price:** $925
**Low Auction Price:** $675

**Ref. No.:** 1446
**Name:** Here Comes the Bride
**Height:** 13.75
**Status:** Open issue, retired
**Issue Year:** 1983
**Issue Price:** $517.50
**Last Year:** 1997
**Last Retail Price:** $995

**Ref. No.:** 6329
**Name:** Blushing Bride
**Height:** 14
**Status:** Open edition, retired
**Issue Year:** 1996
**Issue Price:** $370
**Last Year:** 1999
**Last Retail Price:** $370

**Ref. No.:** 1528
**Name:** I Love You Truly
**Height:** 14.5
**Status:** Open issue, active
**Issue Year:** 1987
**Issue Price:** $375
**2003 Retail Price:** $595

**Ref. No.:** 1494
**Name:** My Wedding Day
**Height:** 15.5
**Status:** Open issue, retired
**Issue Year:** 1986
**Issue Price:** $800
**Last Year:** 1997
**Last Retail Price:** $1495

**Romance**

Ref. No.: 304.13
Name: Romantic Serenade
Height: 5.5
Status: Very rare
Issue Year: 1960
Issue Price: Unknown
Last Year: Unknown
Last Retail Price: Unknown

Ref. No.: 5047
Name: Couple
Height: 10.25
Status: Open issue, retired
Issue Year: 1980
Issue Price: $425
Last Year: 1981
Last Retail Price: $460
Auction Price: $1300

Ref. No.: 4830
Name: You and Me
Height: 10.5
Status: Open issue, retired
Issue Year: 1972
Issue Price: $112.50
Last Year: 1979
Last Retail Price: $290
High Auction Price: $750
Low Auction Price: $500

Ref. No.: 5381
Name: Serenade
Height: 11
Status: Open issue, retired
Issue Year: 1986
Issue Price: $450
Last Year: 1990
Last Retail Price: $610
Auction Price: $600

Ref. No.: 5820
Name: Dance of Love
Height: 11
Status: Open edition, retired
Issue Year: 1991
Issue Price: $575
Last Year: 1993
Last Retail Price: $625
Auction Price: $400

Ref. No.: 4662
Name: Romantic Group
Height: 11.5
Status: Open issue, retired
Issue Year: 1969
Issue Price: $100
Last Year: 1981
Last Retail Price: $300
High Auction Price: $800
Low Auction Price: $750

**Ref. No.:** 4669
**Name:** Couple Pastoral
**Height:** 11.5
**Status:** Open issue, retired
**Issue Year:** 1969
**Issue Price:** $100
**Last Year:** 1978
**Last Retail Price:** $350
**Auction Price:** $1250

**Ref. No.:** 6704
**Name:** Love's Embrace
**Height:** 11.5
**Status:** Open issue, sold out
**Issue Year:** 2000
**Last Year:** 2000
**Last Retail Price:** $485
**Comment:** 2000 Vanguard Dealer
    Exclusive

**Ref. No.:** 1274
**Name:** Lovers in the Park
**Height:** 11.75
**Status:** Open issue, retired
**Issue Year:** 1974
**Issue Price:** $450
**Last Year:** 1993
**Last Retail Price:** $1365
**Auction Price:** $1200

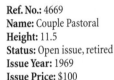

**Ref. No.:** 1521
**Name:** The Landau Carriage
**Height:** 11.75
**Status:** Open issue, retired
**Issue Year:** 1987
**Issue Price:** $2500
**Last Year:** 1997
**Last Retail Price:** $3850

**Ref. No.:** 6296
**Name:** Sweethearts
**Height:** 12.25
**Status:** Open issue, retired
**Issue Year:** 1996
**Issue Price:** $900
**Last Year:** 1999
**Last Retail Price:** $900

**Ref. No.:** 5276
**Name:** A Sailor's Serenade
**Height:** 12.5
**Status:** Open issue, retired
**Issue Year:** 1985
**Issue Price:** $315
**Last Year:** 1988
**Last Retail Price:** $360
**High Auction Price:** $950
**Low Auction Price:** $450

**Ref. No.:** 5540
**Name:** An Evening Out
**Height:** 12.5
**Status:** Open issue, retired
**Issue Year:** 1989
**Issue Price:** $350
**Last Year:** 1991
**Last Retail Price:** 400
**High Auction Price:** $700
**Low Auction Price:** $650

**Ref. No.:** 5843
**Name:** A Quiet Afternoon
**Height:** 12.5
**Status:** Open issue, retired
**Issue Year:** 1992
**Issue Price:** $1050
**Last Year:** 1995
**Last Retail Price:** $1125

**Ref. No.:** 5583
**Name:** Sad Parting
**Height:** 13
**Status:** Open issue, retired
**Issue Year:** 1989
**Issue Price:** $375
**Last Year:** 1991
**Last Retail Price:** $430
**High Auction Price:** $525
**Low Auction Price:** $300

**Ref. No.:** 6475
**Name:** Happy Anniversary
**Height:** 13
**Status:** Open issue, active
**Issue Year:** 1998
**Issue Price:** $300
**2003 Retail Price:** $340
**Comment:** Introduced by select
    dealers in 1997

**Ref. No.:** 1504
**Name:** The Reception
**Height:** 13.25
**Status:** Open issue, retired
**Issue Year:** 1986
**Issue Price:** $625
**Last Year:** 1990
**Last Retail Price:** $850
**High Auction Price:** $1050
**Low Auction Price:** $650

**Ref. No.:** 5161
**Name:** Old Fashioned Motorist
**Height:** 13.25
**Status:** Open issue, retired
**Issue Year:** 1982
**Issue Price:** $2000
**Last Year:** 1985
**Last Retail Price:** $2000
**High Auction Price:** $3000
**Low Auction Price:** $2800

Bridal & Romance

**Ref. No.:** 1513
**Name:** Flower For My Lady
**Height:** 13.25
**Status:** Open issue, retired
**Issue Year:** 1987
**Issue Price:** $1150
**Last Year:** 1990
**Last Retail Price:** $1375
**High Auction Price:** $2000
**Low Auction Price:** $1350

**Ref. No.:** 6597
**Name:** Declaration Of Love
**Height:** 13.5
**Status:** Open issue, active
**Issue Year:** 1999
**Issue Price:** $550
**2003 Retail Price:** $550

**Ref. No.:** 6819
**Name:** A Lovers' Dance
**Height:** 13.5
**Status:** Open issue, active
**Issue Year:** 2002
**Issue Price:** $360
**2003 Retail Price:** $360

**Ref. No.:** 5216
**Name:** On the Lake
**Height:** 13.75
**Status:** Open issue, retired
**Issue Year:** 1984
**Issue Price:** $660
**Last Year:** 1988
**Last Retail Price:** $800
**High Auction Price:** $1100
**Low Auction Price:** $875

**Ref. No.:** 5300
**Name:** Medieval Courtship
**Height:** 13.75
**Status:** Open issue, retired
**Issue Year:** 1985
**Issue Price:** $735
**Last Year:** 1990
**Last Retail Price:** $990
**High Auction Price:** $1150
**Low Auction Price:** $850

**Ref. No.:** 5398
**Name:** At the Ball
**Height:** 13.75
**Status:** Open issue, retired
**Issue Year:** 1986
**Issue Price:** $375
**Last Year:** 1991
**Last Retail Price:** $620
**High Auction Price:** $700
**Low Auction Price:** $525

**Ref. No.:** 1430
**Name:** High Society
**Height:** 14.25
**Status:** Open issue, retired
**Issue Year:** 1982
**Issue Price:** $305
**Last Year:** 1993
**Last Retail Price:** $595
**High Auction Price:** $750
**Low Auction Price:** $550

**Ref. No.:** 5991
**Name:** Love Story
**Height:** 14.25
**Status:** Open issue, retired
**Issue Year:** 1993
**Issue Price:** $2800
**Last Year:** 2000
**Last Retail Price:** $2800

**Ref. No.:** 6327
**Name:** Medieval Romance
**Height:** 14.25
**Status:** Open issue, retired
**Issue Year:** 1996
**Issue Price:** $2250
**Last Year:** 1999
**Last Retail Price:** $2350

**Ref. No.:** 1452
**Name:** On The Town
**Height:** 14.5
**Status:** Open issue, retired
**Issue Year:** 1983
**Issue Price:** $220
**Last Year:** 1993
**Last Retail Price:** $440

**Ref. No.:** 4903
**Name:** Serenity
**Height:** 14.5
**Status:** Open issue, retired
**Issue Year:** 1974
**Issue Price:** $285
**Last Year:** 1979
**Last Retail Price:** $575
**Auction Price:** $750

**Ref. No.:** 6842
**Name:** You're Everything To Me
**Height:** 14.5
**Status:** Open issue, active
**Issue Year:** 2002
**Issue Price:** $590
**2003 Retail Price:** $590

**Ref. No.:** 6746
**Name:** Love's Little Surprises
**Height:** 14.75
**Status:** Open issue, active
**Issue Year:** 2001
**Issue Price:** $395
**2003 Retail Price:** $450

**Ref. No.:** 1250
**Name:** Lovers from Verona
**Height:** 15.5
**Status:** Open issue, retired
**Issue Year:** 1974
**Issue Price:** $330
**Last Year:** 1990
**Last Retail Price:** $1050
**Auction Price:** $850

**Ref. No.:** 4881
**Name:** Typical Group
**Height:** 15.5
**Status:** Open issue, retired
**Issue Year:** 1974
**Issue Price:** $560
**Last Year:** 1979
**Last Retail Price:** $1000

**Ref. No.:** 4996
**Name:** Ready To Go
**Height:** 15.5
**Status:** Open issue, retired
**Issue Year:** 1978
**Issue Price:** $425
**Last Year:** 1981
**Last Retail Price:** $550
**High Auction Price:** $1700
**Low Auction Price:** $850

**Ref. No.:** 5004
**Name:** Walk in Versailles
**Height:** 15.75
**Status:** Open issue, retired
**Issue Year:** 1978
**Issue Price:** $375
**Last Year:** 1981
**Last Retail Price:** $485
**Auction Price:** $875

**Ref. No.:** 5014
**Name:** Genteel
**Height:** 15.75
**Status:** Open issue, retired
**Issue Year:** 1978
**Issue Price:** $725
**Last Year:** 1981
**Last Retail Price:** $935
**Auction Price:** $2300

**Ref. No.:** 313.13
**Name:** Reposing
**Height:** 16
**Status:** Very Rare
**Issue Year:** 1970
**Issue Price:** Unknown
**Last Year:** Unknown
**Last Retail Price:** Unknown

**Ref. No.:** 5036
**Name:** Jockey with Lass
**Height:** 16.5
**Status:** Open issue, retired
**Issue Year:** 1979
**Issue Price:** $950
**Auction Price:** $1500
**Last Year:** 2000
**Last Retail Price:** $2590

**Ref. No.:** 5012
**Name:** Re-encounter
**Height:** 17
**Status:** Open issue, retired
**Issue Year:** 1978
**Issue Price:** $600
**Last Year:** 1981
**Last Retail Price:** $775

**Ref. No.:** 4564
**Name:** The Flirt
**Height:** 17.25
**Status:** Open issue, retired
**Issue Year:** 1969
**Issue Price:** $115
**Last Year:** 1978
**Last Retail Price:** $300
**Auction Price:** $850

**Ref. No.:** 5096
**Name:** A Summer Afternoon
**Height:** 17.75
**Status:** Open issue, retired
**Issue Year:** 1980
**Issue Price:** $2150
**Last Year:** 1985
**Last Retail Price:** $1830
**High Auction Price:** $2750
**Low Auction Price:** $2375

**Ref. No.:** 5097
**Name:** Sedan Chair Group
**Height:** 17.75
**Status:** Open issue, retired
**Issue Year:** 1980
**Issue Price:** $2950
**Last Year:** 1991
**Last Retail Price:** $6700
**Auction Price:** $4000

**Ref. No.:** 4598
**Name:** Sweethearts
**Height:** 19.5
**Status:** Open issue, retired
**Issue Year:** 1969
**Issue Price:** $85
**Last Year:** 1978
**Last Retail Price:** $220

**Ref. No.:** 4563
**Name:** Couple with Parasol
**Height:** 19.75
**Status:** Open issue, retired
**Issue Year:** 1969
**Issue Price:** $180
**Last Year:** 1985
**Last Retail Price:** $490
**High Auction Price:** $1100
**Low Auction Price:** $675

# Religion

Religion

**Christian**

**Ref. No.:** 4535
**Name:** Baby Jesus in box
**Height:** 2.25
**Status:** Open edition, retired
**Issue Year:** 1969
**Issue Price:** $6
**Last Year:** 1991
**Last Retail Price:** $65

**Ref. No.:** 5618
**Name:** Christening
**Height:** 2.75
**Status:** Open edition, retired
**Issue Year:** 1989
**Issue Price:** $365
**Last Year:** 1991
**Last Retail Price:** $420

**Ref. No.:** 103.06
**Name:** Choir Boy
**Height:** 3.5
**Status:** Very rare
**Issue Year:** 1957
**Issue Price:** Unknown
**Last Year:** Unknown
**Last Retail Price:** Unknown

**Ref. No.:** 104.06
**Name:** Choir Boy
**Height:** 3.5
**Status:** Very rare
**Issue Year:** 1957
**Issue Price:** Unknown
**Last Year:** Unknown
**Last Retail Price:** Unknown

**Ref. No.:** 116.06
**Name:** Choir Boy
**Height:** 4
**Status:** Very rare
**Issue Year:** 1956
**Issue Price:** Unknown
**Last Year:** Unknown
**Last Retail Price:** Unknown

**Ref. No.:** 306.13
**Name:** Choir Boy
**Height:** 4
**Status:** Very rare
**Issue Year:** 1961
**Issue Price:** Unknown
**Last Year:** Unknown
**Last Retail Price:** Unknown

**Ref. No.:** 7531
**Name:** Madonna of Orange
(reduced size)
**Height:** 7.25
**Status:** Open issue, active
**Issue Year:** 1993
**Comment:** Exclusive to Lladró
Valencia Gift Shop

**Ref. No.:** 1482
**Name:** Eve
**Height:** 7.5
**Status:** Open issue, retired
**Issue Year:** 1985
**Issue Price:** $145
**Last Year:** 1988
**Last Retail Price:** $175
**High Auction Price:** $675
**Low Auction Price:** $600

**Ref. No.:** 5684
**Name:** Barnyard Reflections
**Height:** 7.5
**Status:** Open issue, retired
**Issue Year:** 1990
**Issue Price:** $460
**Last Year:** 1993
**Last Retail Price:** $525
**High Auction Price:** $700
**Low Auction Price:** $650

**Ref. No.:** 6088
**Name:** Communion Prayer, Boy
**Height:** 7.5
**Status:** Open issue, active
**Issue Year:** 1994
**Issue Price:** $194
**2003 Retail Price:** $225

**Ref. No.:** 6089
**Name:** Communion Prayer, Girl
**Height:** 7.5
**Status:** Open edition, active
**Issue Year:** 1994
**2003 Retail Price:** $250

**Ref. No.:** 6203
**Name:** Boys' Choir
**Height:** 7.75
**Status:** Open issue, retired
**Issue Year:** 1995
**Issue Price:** $250
**Last Year:** 1999
**Last Retail Price:** $265

**Ref. No.:** 326.13
**Name:** Choir Boy
**Height:** 8
**Status:** Very rare
**Issue Year:** 1965
**Issue Price:** Unknown
**Last Year:** Unknown
**Last Retail Price:** Unknown

**Ref. No.:** 4649
**Name:** Madonna Head
**Height:** 8.25
**Status:** Open issue, retired
**Issue Year:** 1969
**Issue Price:** $25
**Last Year:** 2001
**Last Retail Price:** $185

**Ref. No.:** 5501
**Name:** Time to Sew (Blue)
**Height:** 8.25
**Status:** Open edition, active
**Issue Year:** 1988
**Issue Price:** $90
**2003 Retail Price:** $125

**Ref. No.:** 5501.3
**Name:** Time to Sew (White)
**Height:** 8.25
**Status:** Open edition, retired
**Issue Year:** 1988
**Last Year:** 1991
**Last Retail Price:** $100

**Ref. No.:** 5502
**Name:** Meditation (Blue)
**Height:** 8.25
**Status:** Open edition, active
**Issue Year:** 1988
**Issue Price:** $90
**2003 Retail Price:** $125

**Ref. No.:** 5502.3
**Name:** Meditation (White)
**Height:** 8.25
**Status:** Open edition, retired
**Issue Year:** 1988
**Last Year:** 1991
**Last Retail Price:** $100

**Ref. No.:** 4585
**Name:** Nativity
**Height:** 8.5
**Status:** Open issue, active
**Issue Year:** 1969
**Issue Price:** $18
**2003 Retail Price:** $135

**Ref. No.:** 5796
**Name:** Holy Night
**Height:** 9
**Status:** Open issue, retired
**Issue Year:** 1991
**Issue Price:** $330
**Last Year:** 1994
**Last Retail Price:** $360

**Ref. No.:** 6404
**Name:** Sister with Sax
**Height:** 9
**Status:** Open issue, retired
**Issue Year:** 1997
**Issue Price:** $180
**Last Year:** 1999
**Last Retail Price:** $180

**Ref. No.:** 6405
**Name:** Sister Singing
**Height:** 9
**Status:** Open issue, retired
**Issue Year:** 1997
**Issue Price:** $165
**Last Year:** 1999
**Last Retail Price:** $165

**Ref. No.:** 6406
**Name:** Sister with Guitar
**Height:** 9
**Status:** Open issue, retired
**Issue Year:** 1997
**Issue Price:** $200
**Last Year:** 1999
**Last Retail Price:** $200

**Ref. No.:** 5996
**Name:** Bless the Child
**Height:** 9.5
**Status:** Open issue, retired
**Issue Year:** 1993
**Issue Price:** $490
**Last Year:** 1994
**Last Retail Price:** $465

**Ref. No.:** 5961
**Name:** The Great Teacher
    with base
**Height:** 10
**Status:** Open issue, retired
**Issue Year:** 1996
**Issue Price:** $850
**Last Year:** 1996
**Last Retail Price:** $850

**Ref. No.:** 6084
**Name:** St. James
**Height:** 10
**Status:** Open issue, retired
**Issue Year:** 1994
**Issue Price:** $310
**Last Year:** 1997
**Last Retail Price:** $310

**Ref. No.:** 6407
**Name:** Sister with Tambourine
**Height:** 10
**Status:** Open issue, retired
**Issue Year:** 1997
**Issue Price:** $185
**Last Year:** 1999
**Last Retail Price:** $185

**Ref. No.:** 1499
**Name:** Blessed Family
**Height:** 10.25
**Status:** Open issue, retired
**Issue Year:** 1986
**Issue Price:** $200
**Last Year:** 1998
**Last Retail Price:** $395

**Ref. No.:** 5500
**Name:** Prayerful Moment (Blue)
**Height:** 10.25
**Status:** Open edition, active
**Issue Year:** 1988
**Issue Price:** $90
**2003 Retail Price:** $125

**Ref. No.:** 5500.3
**Name:** Prayerful Moment (White)
**Height:** 10.25
**Status:** Open edition, retired
**Issue Year:** 1988
**Last Year:** 1991
**Last Retail Price:** $100

**Ref. No.:** 5551
**Name:** Call to Prayer (Blue)
**Height:** 10.25
**Status:** Open issue, retired
**Issue Year:** 1989
**Issue Price:** $100
**Last Year:** 1993
**Last Retail Price:** $135

**Ref. No.:** 5551.3
**Name:** Call to Prayer (White)
**Height:** 10.25
**Status:** Open issue, retired
**Issue Year:** 1989
**Issue Price:** $100
**Last Year:** 1991
**Last Retail Price:** $120

**Ref. No.:** 5552
**Name:** Morning Chores (Blue)
**Height:** 10.25
**Status:** Open issue, retired
**Issue Year:** 1989
**Issue Price:** $115
**Last Year:** 1993
**Last Retail Price:** $140

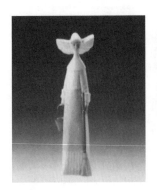

**Ref. No.:** 5552.3
**Name:** Morning Chores (White)
**Height:** 10.25
**Status:** Open issue, retired
**Issue Year:** 1989
**Issue Price:** $115
**Last Year:** 1991
**Last Retail Price:** $125

**Ref. No.:** 4619
**Name:** Seminarian
**Height:** 10.5
**Status:** Open issue, retired
**Issue Year:** 1969
**Issue Price:** $18.50
**Last Year:** 1972
**Last Retail Price:** $20

**Ref. No.:** 5550
**Name:** Serene Moment Blue
**Height:** 10.5
**Status:** Open issue, retired
**Issue Year:** 1989
**Issue Price:** $115
**Last Year:** 1993
**Last Retail Price:** $150

**Ref. No.:** 5550.3
**Name:** Serene Moment White
**Height:** 10.5
**Status:** Open issue, retired
**Issue Year:** 1989
**Issue Price:** $115
**Last Year:** 1991
**Last Retail Price:** $135

**Ref. No.:** 5848
**Name:** The Loving Family
**Height:** 10.75
**Status:** Open issue, retired
**Issue Year:** 1992
**Issue Price:** $950
**Last Year:** 1994
**Last Retail Price:** $985

**Ref. No.:** 1234
**Name:** Little Jesus of Prague
**Height:** 11.5
**Status:** Open edition, retired
**Issue Year:** 1972
**Issue Price:** $70
**Last Year:** 1978
**Last Retail Price:** $125

**Ref. No.:** 1610
**Name:** Flight to Egypt
**Height:** 11.5
**Status:** Open issue, retired
**Issue Year:** 1989
**Issue Price:** $885
**Last Year:** 2000
**Last Retail Price:** $1150

**Ref. No.:** 5168
**Name:** King Solomon
**Height:** 11.5
**Status:** Open issue, retired
**Issue Year:** 1982
**Issue Price:** $205
**Last Year:** 1985
**Last Retail Price:** $205
**Auction Price:** $850

**Ref. No.:** 5360
**Name:** Sewing Circle
**Height:** 11.5
**Status:** Open issue, retired
**Issue Year:** 1986
**Issue Price:** $600
**Last Year:** 1990
**Last Retail Price:** $850
**High Auction Price:** $1400
**Low Auction Price:** $1300

**Religion**

**Ref. No.:** 5171
**Name:** Our Lady with Flowers
**Height:** 12.25
**Status:** Open issue, active
**Issue Year:** 1982
**Issue Price:** $172.50
**2003 Retail Price:** $325

**Ref. No.:** 5986
**Name:** Sunday Sermon
**Height:** 12.25
**Status:** Open issue, active
**Issue Year:** 1993
**Issue Price:** $425
**2003 Retail Price:** $425
**Comment:** To be retired or sold
       out as of December 31, 2003

**Ref. No.:** 5387
**Name:** St. Vincent
**Height:** 12.5
**Status:** Open issue, retired
**Issue Year:** 1986
**Issue Price:** $190
**Last Year:** 1990
**Last Retail Price:** $275
**High Auction Price:** $550
**Low Auction Price:** $300

**Ref. No.:** 358.13
**Name:** Madonna
**Height:** 12.75
**Status:** Very rare
**Issue Year:** 1970
**Issue Price:** Unknown
**Last Year:** Unknown
**Last Retail Price:** Unknown

**Ref. No.:** 4611
**Name:** Nuns
**Height:** 13
**Status:** Open issue, active
**Issue Year:** 1969
**Issue Price:** $36.50
**2003 Retail Price:** $175

**Ref. No.:** 6565
**Name:** Gabriel The Archangel
**Height:** 13
**Status:** Open issue, retired
**Issue Year:** 1998
**Issue Price:** $475
**Last Year:** 2000
**Last Retail Price:** $520

**Ref. No.:** 4973
**Name:** Singing Lesson
**Height:** 13.25
**Status:** Open issue, retired
**Issue Year:** 1977
**Issue Price:** $350
**Last Year:** 1981
**Last Retail Price:** $500

**Ref. No.:** 5934
**Name:** The Holy Teacher
**Height:** 13.25
**Status:** Open issue, retired
**Issue Year:** 1993
**Issue Price:** $385
**Last Year:** 1996
**Last Retail Price:** $375

**Ref. No.:** 6268
**Name:** Our Lady of Caridid
   del Cobre
**Height:** 13.25
**Status:** Open issue, retired
**Issue Year:** 1996
**Issue Price:** $1355
**Last Year:** 1998
**Last Retail Price:** $1355

**Ref. No.:** 6834
**Name:** Mary and Baby Jesus
**Height:** 13.25
**Status:** Active
**Issue Year:** 2002
**Issue Price:** $575
**2003 Retail Price:** $575

**Ref. No.:** 5896
**Name:** The Loaves and Fishes
**Height:** 13.5
**Status:** Open issue, retired
**Issue Year:** 1992
**Issue Price:** $695
**Last Year:** 1997
**Last Retail Price:** $760

**Ref. No.:** 7517
**Name:** Madonna of Lareto
**Height:** 13.5
**Status:** Open issue, active
**Issue Year:** 1992
**Comment:** Exclusive to the
   Spanish Air Force

**Ref. No.:** 4586
**Name:** Madonna
**Height:** 13.75
**Status:** Open issue, retired
**Issue Year:** 1969
**Issue Price:** $32.50
**Last Year:** 1979
**Last Retail Price:** $92.50
**Auction Price:** $425

**Ref. No.:** 5167
**Name:** Jesus
**Height:** 14.25
**Status:** Open issue, active
**Issue Year:** 1982
**Issue Price:** $130
**2003 Retail Price:** $275

**Ref. No.:** 5169
**Name:** Abraham
**Height:** 14.25
**Status:** Open issue, retired
**Issue Year:** 1982
**Issue Price:** $155
**Last Year:** 1985
**Last Retail Price:** $155
**High Auction Price:** $900
**Low Auction Price:** $550

*Religion*

**Ref. No.:** 6008
**Name:** Joyful Event
**Height:** 14.5
**Status:** Open issue, active
**Issue Year:** 1993
**Issue Price:** $825
**2003 Retail Price:** $850

**Ref. No.:** 6631
**Name:** Sweet Mary
**Height:** 14.5
**Status:** Open issue, active
**Issue Year:** 1999
**Issue Price:** $220
**2003 Retail Price:** $225

**Ref. No.:** 1394
**Name:** Holy Mary
**Height:** 15
**Status:** Open issue, active
**Issue Year:** 1982
**Issue Price:** $1000
**2003 Retail Price:** $1475

**Ref. No.:** 5933
**Name:** The Ten Commandments
**Height:** 15
**Status:** Open issue, retired
**Issue Year:** 1993
**Issue Price:** $930
**Last Year:** 1996
**Last Retail Price:** $930

**Ref. No.:** 6761
**Name:** Blessed Family
**Height:** 15.25
**Status:** Open issue, active
**Issue Year:** 2001
**Issue Price:** $495
**2003 Retail Price:** $525

**Ref. No.:** 5170
**Name:** Moses
**Height:** 16.5
**Status:** Open issue, retired
**Issue Year:** 1982
**Issue Price:** $175
**Last Year:** 2000
**Last Retail Price:** $410

**Ref. No.:** 5246
**Name:** St. Cristobal
**Height:** 16.5
**Status:** Open issue, retired
**Issue Year:** 1984
**Issue Price:** $265
**Last Year:** 1988
**Last Retail Price:** $300
**High Auction Price:** $650
**Low Auction Price:** $450

**Ref. No.:** 6363
**Name:** St. Joseph the Carpenter
**Height:** 17
**Status:** Open issue, retired
**Issue Year:** 1997
**Issue Price:** $1050
**Last Year:** 1999
**Last Retail Price:** $1105

**Ref. No.:** 6145
**Name:** Heavenly Prayer
**Height:** 17.25
**Status:** Open issue, retired
**Issue Year:** 1994
**Issue Price:** $675
**Last Year:** 1997
**Last Retail Price:** $695

**Ref. No.:** 7530
**Name:** Madonna of Orange
**Height:** 17.25
**Status:** Open issue, active
**Issue Year:** 1993
**Comment:** Exclusive to Lladró Valencia Gift Shop

**Ref. No.:** 1345
**Name:** Sacristan
**Height:** 18
**Status:** Open issue, retired
**Issue Year:** 1978
**Issue Price:** $385
**Last Year:** 1979
**Last Retail Price:** $400

**Ref. No.:** 6383
**Name:** The Ascension with base
**Height:** 19
**Status:** Open issue, retired
**Issue Year:** 1997
**Issue Price:** $775
**Last Year:** 1999
**Last Retail Price:** $775

**Ref. No.:** 6326
**Name:** Virgin of Carmen
**Height:** 19.5
**Status:** Open issue, retired
**Issue Year:** 1996
**Issue Price:** $1270
**Last Year:** 1999
**Last Retail Price:** $1270

**Ref. No.:** 7584
**Name:** Christus
**Height:** 21
**Status:** Open issue, active
**Issue Year:** 1999
**Issue Price:** $495
**2003 Retail Price:** $495

**Ref. No.:** 3516
**Name:** Jesus Christ
**Height:** 42
**Status:** Open issue, retired
**Issue Year:** 1978
**Issue Price:** $1050
**Last Year:** 1988
**Last Retail Price:** $1700
**Auction Price:** $1450

Religion

## Judaic

**Ref. No.:** 6027
**Name:** Hanukkah Lights
**Height:** 4.25
**Status:** Open issue, retired
**Issue Year:** 1993
**Issue Price:** $395
**Last Year:** 1999
**Last Retail Price:** $395

**Ref. No.:** 6183
**Name:** Preparing for the Sabbath
**Height:** 7.25
**Status:** Open edition, retired
**Issue Year:** 1995
**Issue Price:** $385
**Last Year:** 1999
**Last Retail Price:** $385

**Ref. No.:** 6004
**Name:** Bar Mitzvah Day
**Height:** 8.25
**Status:** Open issue, active
**Issue Year:** 1993
**Issue Price:** $395
**2003 Retail Price:** $445

**Ref. No.:** 6029
**Name:** Hebrew Scholar
**Height:** 9.25
**Status:** Open issue, retired
**Issue Year:** 1993
**Issue Price:** $265
**Last Year:** 1996
**Last Retail Price:** $265

**Ref. No.:** 6593
**Name:** My Bat Mitzvah
**Height:** 9.25
**Status:** Open issue, active
**Issue Year:** 1999
**Issue Price:** $345
**2003 Retail Price:** $345

**Ref. No.:** 6172
**Name:** Coming Of Age
**Height:** 10.5
**Status:** Open issue, retired
**Issue Year:** 1995
**Issue Price:** $345
**Last Year:** 1998
**Last Retail Price:** $345

**Other Religions**

**Ref. No.:** 6208
**Name:** Reading the Torah
**Height:** 14.25
**Status:** Open issue, retired
**Issue Year:** 1995
**Issue Price:** $535
**Last Year:** 2000
**Last Retail Price:** $535

**Ref. No.:** 6209
**Name:** The Rabbi
**Height:** 14.25
**Status:** Open issue, retired
**Issue Year:** 1995
**Issue Price:** $250
**Last Year:** 1997
**Last Retail Price:** $250

**Ref. No.:** 1215
**Name:** Hindu Goddess
**Height:** 10.5
**Status:** Open issue, retired
**Issue Year:** 1972
**Issue Price:** $110
**Last Year:** 1975
**Last Retail Price:** $125

**Ref. No.:** 1235
**Name:** Buddha
**Height:** 11.5
**Status:** Open issue, retired
**Issue Year:** 1972
**Issue Price:** $130
**Last Year:** 1976
**Last Retail Price:** $155

**Ref. No.:** 1236
**Name:** Disciple of Buddha
**Height:** 11.75
**Status:** Open issue, retired
**Issue Year:** 1972
**Issue Price:** $70
**Last Year:** 1975
**Last Retail Price:** $80
**Auction Price:** $500

**Ref. No.:** 1237
**Name:** The Wisdom of Buddha
**Height:** 20
**Status:** Open issue, retired
**Issue Year:** 1972
**Issue Price:** $350
**Last Year:** 1975
**Last Retail Price:** $350

**Nativity**

**Ref. No.:** 4535.3
**Name:** Little Jesus
**Height:** 1
**Status:** Open edition, active
**Issue Year:** 1971
**Issue Price:** $6
**2003 Retail Price:** $70

**Ref. No.:** 5750
**Name:** Little Lamb
**Height:** 1.25
**Status:** Open issue, retired
**Issue Year:** 1991
**Issue Price:** $40
**Last Year:** 1996
**Last Retail Price:** $42

**Ref. No.:** 4670
**Name:** Baby Jesus (Part of an 8-piece set)
**Height:** 2
**Status:** Open issue, retired
**Issue Year:** 1969
**Issue Price:** Unknown
**Last Year:** 2001
**Last Retail Price:** $55

**Ref. No.:** 5478
**Name:** Baby Jesus
**Height:** 2
**Status:** Open issue, active
**Issue Year:** 1988
**Issue Price:** $55
**2003 Retail Price:** $75

**Ref. No.:** 6094
**Name:** 1993 Three-piece Nativity set, without hooks
**Height:** 2
**Status:** Limited edition, sold out
**Issue Year:** 1993
**Last Year:** 1994
**Last Retail Price:** Not available in the United States

**Ref. No.:** 4680
**Name:** Cow
**Height:** 2.25
**Status:** Open issue, retired
**Issue Year:** 1969
**Issue Price:** $12
**Last Year:** 2001
**Last Retail Price:** $95

**Ref. No.:** 5482
**Name:** Ox
**Height:** 2.75
**Status:** Open issue, active
**Issue Year:** 1988
**Issue Price:** $125
**2003 Retail Price:** $180

**Ref. No.:** 1388
**Name:** Baby Jesus
**Height:** 3.25
**Status:** Open issue, active
**Issue Year:** 1981
**Issue Price:** $85
**2003 Retail Price:** $145

**Ref. No.:** 1388.3
**Name:** White Baby Jesus
**Height:** 3.25
**Status:** Open edition, retired
**Issue Year:** 1983
**Issue Price:** $50
**Last Year:** 1985
**Last Retail Price:** $50

**Ref. No.:** 5745
**Name:** Baby Jesus
**Height:** 3.25
**Status:** Open issue, retired
**Issue Year:** 1991
**Issue Price:** $170
**Last Year:** 1996
**Last Retail Price:** $185

**Ref. No.:** 4679
**Name:** Donkey
**Height:** 4.25
**Status:** Open issue, retired
**Issue Year:** 1969
**Issue Price:** $11.50
**Last Year:** 2001
**Last Retail Price:** $100

**Ref. No.:** 5744
**Name:** Bull and Donkey
**Height:** 4.5
**Status:** Open issue, retired
**Issue Year:** 1991
**Issue Price:** $250
**Last Year:** 1996
**Last Retail Price:** $275

*Christmas*

**Ref. No.:** 5483
**Name:** Donkey
**Height:** 4.75
**Status:** Open issue, active
**Issue Year:** 1988
**Issue Price:** $125
**2003 Retail Price:** $180

**Ref. No.:** 5748
**Name:** Shepherd Girl
**Height:** 4.75
**Status:** Open issue, retired
**Issue Year:** 1991
**Issue Price:** $150
**Last Year:** 1996
**Last Retail Price:** $165

**Ref. No.:** 5749
**Name:** Shepherd Boy
**Height:** 5
**Status:** Open issue, retired
**Issue Year:** 1991
**Issue Price:** $225
**Last Year:** 1996
**Last Retail Price:** $245

**Ref. No.:** 1390
**Name:** Cow
**Height:** 5.25
**Status:** Open issue, active
**Issue Year:** 1981
**Issue Price:** $95
**2003 Retail Price:** $245

**Ref. No.:** 1390.3
**Name:** Ox (White)
**Height:** 5.25
**Status:** Open edition, retired
**Issue Year:** 1983
**Issue Price:** $72
**Last Year:** 1985
**Last Retail Price:** $72

**Ref. No.:** 5484
**Name:** Lost Lamb
**Height:** 5.25
**Status:** Open issue, active
**Issue Year:** 1988
**Issue Price:** Unknown
**Issue Price:** $100
**2003 Retail Price:** $150

**Ref. No.:** 1389
**Name:** Donkey
**Height:** 6
**Status:** Open issue, active
**Issue Year:** 1981
**Issue Price:** $95
**2003 Retail Price:** $245

**Ref. No.:** 1389.3
**Name:** Donkey (White)
**Height:** 6
**Status:** Open edition, retired
**Issue Year:** 1983
**Issue Price:** $72
**Last Year:** 1985
**Last Retail Price:** $72

**Ref. No.:** 4671
**Name:** Mary
**Height:** 6
**Status:** Open issue, retired
**Issue Year:** 1969
**Issue Price:** $10
**Last Year:** 2001
**Last Retail Price:** $75

**Ref. No.:** 4676
**Name:** Shepherd with Lamb
**Height:** 6
**Status:** Open issue, retired
**Issue Year:** 1969
**Issue Price:** $14
**Last Year:** 2001
**Last Retail Price:** $110

**Ref. No.:** 5752
**Name:** Little Virgin
**Height:** 6
**Status:** Open issue, retired
**Issue Year:** 1991
**Issue Price:** $295
**Last Year:** 1994
**Last Retail Price:** $325

**Ref. No.:** 4672
**Name:** Saint Joseph
**Height:** 6.25
**Status:** Open issue, retired
**Issue Year:** 1969
**Issue Price:** $10.50
**Last Year:** 2001
**Last Retail Price:** $90

*Christmas*

**Ref. No.:** 4534
**Name:** Madonna
**Height:** 6.5
**Status:** Open issue, active
**Issue Year:** 1969
**Issue Price:** $15
**2003 Retail Price:** $90

**Ref. No.:** 4673
**Name:** King Melchior
**Height:** 6.5
**Status:** Open issue, retired
**Issue Year:** 1969
**Issue Price:** $11
**Auction Price:** $400
**Last Year:** 2001
**Last Retail Price:** $95

**Ref. No.:** 5477
**Name:** Mary
**Height:** 6.5
**Status:** Open issue, active
**Issue Year:** 1988
**Issue Price:** $130
**2003 Retail Price:** $175

**Ref. No.:** 5476
**Name:** St. Joseph
**Height:** 6.75
**Status:** Open issue, active
**Issue Year:** 1988
**Issue Price:** $210
**2003 Retail Price:** $295

**Ref. No.:** 5792
**Name:** Reverent Moment
**Height:** 6.75
**Status:** Open issue, retired
**Issue Year:** 1991
**Issue Price:** $295
**Last Year:** 1994
**Last Retail Price:** $320

**Ref. No.:** 4674
**Name:** King Gaspar
**Height:** 7.75
**Status:** Open issue, retired
**Issue Year:** 1969
**Issue Price:** $11
**Last Year:** 2001
**Last Retail Price:** $95

**Ref. No.:** 4677
**Name:** Girl with Rooster
**Height:** 7.75
**Status:** Open issue, retired
**Issue Year:** 1969
**Issue Price:** $14
**Last Year:** 2001
**Last Retail Price:** $90

**Ref. No.:** 5747
**Name:** Mary
**Height:** 7.75
**Status:** Open edition, retired
**Issue Year:** 1991
**Issue Price:** $275
**Last Year:** 1996
**Last Retail Price:** $295

**Ref. No.:** 4675
**Name:** King Balthasar
**Height:** 8.25
**Status:** Open issue, retired
**Issue Year:** 1969
**Issue Price:** $11
**Last Year:** 2001
**Last Retail Price:** $95

*Christmas*

**Ref. No.:** 5485
**Name:** Shepherd Boy
**Height:** 8.25
**Status:** Open issue, active
**Issue Year:** 1988
**Issue Price:** $140
**2003 Retail Price:** $225

**Ref. No.:** 4533
**Name:** Saint Joseph
**Height:** 8.5
**Status:** Open issue, active
**Issue Year:** 1969
**Issue Price:** $14
**2003 Retail Price:** $115

**Ref. No.:** 4678
**Name:** Girl with Basket
**Height:** 8.5
**Status:** Open edition, retired
**Issue Year:** 1969
**Issue Price:** $13
**Last Year:** 2001
**Last Retail Price:** $90

**Ref. No.:** 5746
**Name:** St. Joseph
**Height:** 8.5
**Status:** Open issue, retired
**Issue Year:** 1991
**Issue Price:** $350
**Last Year:** 1996
**Last Retail Price:** $375

**Ref. No.:** 5479
**Name:** King Melchior
**Height:** 9
**Status:** Open issue, active
**Issue Year:** 1988
**Issue Price:** $210
**2003 Retail Price:** $265

**Ref. No.:** 5480
**Name:** King Gaspar
**Height:** 9
**Status:** Open issue, active
**Issue Year:** 1988
**Issue Price:** $210
**2003 Retail Price:** $265

**Ref. No.:** 1387
**Name:** Virgin Mary
**Height:** 9.75
**Status:** Open edition, active
**Issue Year:** 1981
**Issue Price:** $240
**2003 Retail Price:** $390

**Ref. No.:** 1387.3
**Name:** Mary (White)
**Height:** 9.75
**Status:** Open issue, retired
**Issue Year:** 1983
**Issue Price:** $150
**Last Year:** 1985
**Last Retail Price:** $150

**Ref. No.:** 1423
**Name:** King Melchior
**Height:** 9.75
**Status:** Open issue, active
**Issue Year:** 1982
**Issue Price:** $225
**2003 Retail Price:** $440

**Ref. No.:** 1423.3
**Name:** King Melchior (White)
**Height:** 9.75
**Status:** Open issue, retired
**Issue Year:** 1983
**Issue Price:** $132
**Last Year:** 1985
**Last Retail Price:** $140

**Ref. No.:** 1424
**Name:** King Gaspar
**Height:** 10.25
**Status:** Open issue, active
**Issue Year:** 1982
**Issue Price:** $265
**2003 Retail Price:** $475

**Ref. No.:** 1424.3
**Name:** King Gaspar (White)
**Height:** 10.25
**Status:** Open issue, retired
**Issue Year:** 1983
**Issue Price:** $142.5
**Last Year:** 1985
**Last Retail Price:** $150

*Christmas*

**Ref. No.:** 1515
**Name:** Melchior's Page
**Height:** 12.25
**Status:** Open issue, retired
**Issue Year:** 1987
**Issue Price:** $290
**Last Year:** 1990
**Last Retail Price:** $360

**Ref. No.:** 5481
**Name:** King Balthasar
**Height:** 12.5
**Status:** Open issue, active
**Issue Year:** 1988
**Issue Price:** $210
**2003 Retail Price:** $265

**Ref. No.:** 1386
**Name:** St. Joseph
**Height:** 13
**Status:** Open issue, active
**Issue Year:** 1981
**Issue Price:** $250
**2003 Retail Price:** $390

**Ref. No.:** 1386.3
**Name:** Saint Joseph (White)
**Height:** 13
**Status:** Open issue, retired
**Issue Year:** 1981
**Issue Price:** $167.50
**Last Year:** 1985
**Last Retail Price:** $167.50

**Ref. No.:** 1514
**Name:** Gaspar's Page
**Height:** 13
**Status:** Open issue, retired
**Issue Year:** 1987
**Issue Price:** $275
**Last Year:** 1990
**Last Retail Price:** $340

**Ref. No.:** 1425
**Name:** King Balthasar
**Height:** 13.75
**Status:** Open issue, active
**Issue Year:** 1982
**Issue Price:** $315
**2003 Retail Price:** $585

**Ref. No.:** 1425.3
**Name:** King Balthasar (White)
**Height:** 13.75
**Status:** Open issue, retired
**Issue Year:** 1983
**Issue Price:** $142.5
**Last Year:** 1985
**Last Retail Price:** $150

**Ref. No.:** 1516
**Name:** Balthasar's Page
**Height:** 13.75
**Status:** Open issue, retired
**Issue Year:** 1987
**Issue Price:** $275
**Last Year:** 1990
**Last Retail Price:** $335

**Ref. No.:** 242.1
**Name:** Nativity Chorus
**Height:** 14.25
**Status:** Very rare
**Issue Year:** 1962
**Issue Price:** Unknown
**Last Year:** Unknown
**Last Retail Price:** Unknown

**Ref. No.:** 339.13
**Name:** Nativity Cone
**Height:** 15
**Status:** Very rare
**Issue Year:** 1964
**Issue Price:** Unknown
**Last Year:** Unknown
**Last Retail Price:** Unknown

**Ref. No.:** 1018
**Name:** King Gaspar
**Height:** 15.75
**Status:** Open issue, active
**Issue Year:** 1969
**Issue Price:** $345
**2003 Retail Price:** $1895

**Ref. No.:** 1019
**Name:** King Melchior
**Height:** 15.75
**Status:** Open issue, active
**Issue Year:** 1969
**Issue Price:** $345
**2003 Retail Price:** $1895

Ornaments

**Ref. No.:** 1020
**Name:** King Balthasar
**Height:** 15.75
**Status:** Open issue, active
**Issue Year:** 1969
**Issue Price:** $345
**2003 Retail Price:** $1895

**Ref. No.:** 6095
**Name:** Nativity Trio, set of three
**Height:** 1
**Status:** Limited edition, sold out
**Issue Year:** 1993
**Last Year:** 1993
**Issue Price:** $115
**Last Retail Price:** $115

**Ref. No.:** 1604
**Name:** Angels ornaments, Set of 3
**Height:** 2
**Status:** Limited edition, sold out
**Issue Year:** 1988
**Issue Price:** $75
**Last Year:** 1988
**Last Retail Price:** $75
**High Auction Price:** $375
**Low Auction Price:** $108

*Christmas*

**Ref. No.:** 5923
**Name:** Our First Christmas
**Height:** 2
**Status:** Limited edition, sold out
**Issue Year:** 1992
**Issue Price:** $50
**Last Year:** 1992
**Last Retail Price:** $50

**Ref. No.:** 6253
**Name:** Surprised Cherub
**Height:** 2
**Status:** Open issue, retired
**Issue Year:** 1995
**Last Year:** 1997
**Last Retail Price:** $120

**Ref. No.:** 6254
**Name:** Playing Cherub
**Height:** 2
**Status:** Open issue, retired
**Issue Year:** 1995
**Last Year:** 1997
**Last Retail Price:** $120

**Ref. No.:** 6264
**Name:** Train
**Height:** 2
**Status:** Open issue, retired
**Issue Year:** 1995
**Last Year:** 1997
**Last Retail Price:** $75

**Ref. No.:** 6266
**Name:** Landing Dove
**Height:** 2
**Status:** Open issue, retired
**Issue Year:** 1995
**Last Year:** 1997
**Last Retail Price:** $50

**Ref. No.:** 6343
**Name:** Little Aviator
**Height:** 2
**Status:** Open issue, retired
**Issue Year:** 1996
**Issue Price:** $79
**Last Year:** 1997
**Last Retail Price:** $79

**Ref. No.:** 6381
**Name:** Little Roadster
**Height:** 2
**Status:** Open issue, retired
**Issue Year:** 1997
**Issue Price:** $79
**Last Year:** 1998
**Last Retail Price:** $79

**Ref. No.:** 5458
**Name:** 1987 Christmas Bell
**Height:** 2.75
**Status:** Limited edition, sold out
**Issue Year:** 1987
**Issue Price:** $29.50
**Last Year:** 1987
**Last Retail Price:** $29.50

**Ref. No.:** 5641
**Name:** 1990 Christmas Bell
**Height:** 2.75
**Status:** Limited edition, sold out
**Issue Year:** 1990
**Issue Price:** $35
**Last Year:** 1990
**Last Retail Price:** $35
**High Auction Price:** $67
**Low Auction Price:** $38

*Christmas*

**Ref. No.:** 5803
**Name:** 1991 Christmas Bell
**Height:** 2.75
**Status:** Limited edition, sold out
**Issue Year:** 1991
**Issue Price:** $37.50
**Last Year:** 1991
**Last Retail Price:** $37.50
**High Auction Price:** $67
**Low Auction Price:** $50

**Ref. No.:** 5913
**Name:** 1992 Christmas Bell
**Height:** 2.75
**Status:** Limited edition, sold out
**Issue Year:** 1992
**Issue Price:** $37.50
**Last Year:** 1992
**Last Retail Price:** $37.50
**Auction Price:** $67

**Ref. No.:** 6265
**Name:** Santa's Journey
**Height:** 2.75
**Status:** Open issue, retired
**Issue Year:** 1996
**Issue Price:** $49
**Last Year:** 1997
**Last Retail Price:** $49

**Ref. No.:** 6267
**Name:** Flying Dove
**Height:** 2.75
**Status:** Open issue, retired
**Issue Year:** 1995
**Last Year:** 1997
**Last Retail Price:** $50

**Ref. No.:** 5525
**Name:** 1988 Christmas Bell
**Height:** 3
**Status:** Limited edition, sold out
**Issue Year:** 1988
**Issue Price:** $32.50
**Last Year:** 1988
**Last Retail Price:** $32.50
**High Auction Price:** $67
**Low Auction Price:** $38

**Ref. No.:** 5616
**Name:** 1989 Christmas Bell
**Height:** 3
**Status:** Limited edition, sold out
**Issue Year:** 1989
**Issue Price:** $35
**Last Year:** 1989
**Last Retail Price:** $32.50
**High Auction Price:** $150
**Low Auction Price:** $38

**Ref. No.:** 5938
**Name:** Elf Ornament
**Height:** 3
**Status:** Open issue, retired
**Issue Year:** 1992
**Issue Price:** $50
**Last Year:** 1993
**Last Retail Price:** $52
**Auction Price:** $400

**Ref. No.:** 5969
**Name:** Nativity Lamb
**Height:** 3
**Status:** Limited edition, sold out
**Issue Year:** 1993
**Issue Price:** $85
**Last Year:** 1993
**Last Retail Price:** $85

**Ref. No.:** 6009
**Name:** 1993 Christmas Ball
**Height:** 3
**Status:** Limited edition, sold out
**Issue Year:** 1993
**Issue Price:** $54
**Last Year:** 1993
**Last Retail Price:** $54

**Ref. No.:** 6010
**Name:** 1993 Christmas Bell
**Height:** 3
**Status:** Limited edition, sold out
**Issue Year:** 1993
**Issue Price:** $39.50
**Last Year:** 1993
**Last Retail Price:** $39.50

**Ref. No.:** 6139
**Name:** 1994 Christmas Bell
**Height:** 3
**Status:** Limited edition, sold out
**Issue Year:** 1994
**Issue Price:** $39.50
**Last Year:** 1994
**Last Retail Price:** $39.50

**Ref. No.:** 6206
**Name:** 1995 Christmas Bell
**Height:** 3
**Status:** Limited edition, sold out
**Issue Year:** 1995
**Issue Price:** $39.50
**Last Year:** 1995
**Last Retail Price:** $39.50

*Christmas*

**Ref. No.:** 6255
**Name:** Thinking Cherub
**Height:** 3
**Status:** Open issue, retired
**Issue Year:** 1995
**Issue Price:** Unknown
**Last Year:** 1997
**Last Retail Price:** $120

**Ref. No.:** 6297
**Name:** 1996 Christmas Bell
**Height:** 3
**Status:** Limited edition, sold out
**Issue Year:** 1996
**Issue Price:** $39.50
**Last Year:** 1996
**Last Retail Price:** $39.50

**Ref. No.:** 6335
**Name:** Welcome Home
**Height:** 3
**Status:** Open issue, retired
**Issue Year:** 1996
**Issue Price:** $85
**Last Year:** 1997
**Last Retail Price:** $85

**Ref. No.:** 6342
**Name:** Seraph with Bells
**Height:** 3
**Status:** Open issue, retired
**Issue Year:** 1996
**Issue Price:** $79
**Last Year:** 1997
**Last Retail Price:** $79

**Ref. No.:** 6344
**Name:** Teddy Bear
**Height:** 3
**Status:** Open issue, retired
**Issue Year:** 1996
**Issue Price:** $67
**Last Year:** 1997
**Last Retail Price:** $67

**Ref. No.:** 6336
**Name:** Home Sweet Home
**Height:** 3
**Status:** Open issue, retired
**Issue Year:** 1997
**Issue Price:** $85
**Last Year:** 1998
**Last Retail Price:** $85

**Ref. No.:** 6388
**Name:** Circus Star
**Height:** 3
**Status:** Open issue, retired
**Issue Year:** 1997
**Issue Price:** $79
**Last Year:** 1998
**Last Retail Price:** $79

**Ref. No.:** 6394
**Name:** Seraph with Holly
**Height:** 3
**Status:** Open issue, retired
**Issue Year:** 1997
**Issue Price:** $79
**Last Year:** 1998
**Last Retail Price:** $79

**Ref. No.:** 6441
**Name:** 1997 Christmas Bell
**Height:** 3
**Status:** Open issue, retired
**Issue Year:** 1997
**Issue Price:** $40
**Last Year:** 1997
**Last Retail Price:** $40

**Ref. No.:** 6445
**Name:** Seraph with Bow
**Height:** 3
**Status:** Open issue, retired
**Issue Year:** 1998
**Issue Price:** $79
**Last Year:** 1999
**Last Retail Price:** $80

**Ref. No.:** 6519
**Name:** Our Winter Home
**Height:** 3
**Status:** Open issue, retired
**Issue Year:** 1998
**Issue Price:** $85
**Last Year:** 1999
**Last Retail Price:** $85

**Ref. No.:** 6560
**Name:** 1998 Christmas Bell
**Height:** 3
**Status:** Open issue, retired
**Issue Year:** 1998
**Issue Price:** $40
**Last Year:** 1998
**Last Retail Price:** $40

Christmas

**Ref. No.:** 5809
**Name:** Holy Shepherds, set of 3
**Height:** 3.25
**Status:** Limited edition, sold out
**Issue Year:** 1991
**Issue Price:** $97.50
**Last Year:** 1991
**Last Retail Price:** $97.50
**High Auction Price:** $300
**Low Auction Price:** $175

**Ref. No.:** 5829
**Name:** 1991 Christmas Ball
**Height:** 3.25
**Status:** Limited edition, sold out
**Issue Year:** 1991
**Issue Price:** $52
**Last Year:** 1991
**Last Retail Price:** $52

**Ref. No.:** 5914
**Name:** 1992 Christmas Ball
**Height:** 3.25
**Status:** Limited edition, sold out
**Issue Year:** 1992
**Issue Price:** $52
**Last Year:** 1992
**Last Retail Price:** $52

**Ref. No.:** 5940
**Name:** Christmas Morning,
    Set of 3
**Height:** 3.25
**Status:** Limited edition, sold out
**Issue Year:** 1992
**Issue Price:** $97.50
**Last Year:** 1992
**Last Retail Price:** $97.50

**Ref. No.:** 6105
**Name:** 1994 Christmas Ball
**Height:** 3.25
**Status:** Limited edition, sold out
**Issue Year:** 1994
**Issue Price:** $55
**Last Year:** 1994
**Last Retail Price:** $55

**Ref. No.:** 6207
**Name:** 1995 Christmas Ball
**Height:** 3.25
**Status:** Limited edition, sold out
**Issue Year:** 1995
**Issue Price:** $55
**Last Year:** 1995
**Last Retail Price:** $55

**Ref. No.:** 6262
**Name:** Rocking Horse
**Height:** 3.25
**Status:** Open issue, retired
**Issue Year:** 1995
**Issue Price:** $75
**Last Year:** 1997
**Last Retail Price:** $75

**Ref. No.:** 6298
**Name:** 1996 Christmas Ball
**Height:** 3.25
**Status:** Limited edition, sold out
**Issue Year:** 1996
**Issue Price:** $55
**Last Year:** 1996
**Last Retail Price:** $55

**Ref. No.:** 6263
**Name:** Doll
**Height:** 3.25
**Status:** Open issue, retired
**Issue Year:** 1995
**Issue Price:** $75
**Last Year:** 1997
**Last Retail Price:** $75

**Ref. No.:** 6442
**Name:** 1997 Christmas Ball
**Height:** 3.25
**Status:** Open issue, retired
**Issue Year:** 1997
**Issue Price:** $55
**Last Year:** 1997
**Last Retail Price:** $55

**Ref. No.:** 6636
**Name:** 1999 Christmas Bell
**Height:** 3.25
**Status:** Open issue, retired
**Issue Year:** 1999
**Issue Price:** $40
**Last Year:** 1999
**Last Retail Price:** $40

**Ref. No.:** 6700
**Name:** 2000 Christmas Bell
**Height:** 3.25
**Status:** Open issue, sold out
**Issue Year:** 2000
**Last Year:** 2000
**Last Retail Price:** $45

**Ref. No.:** 6718
**Name:** 2001 Christmas Bell
**Height:** 3.25
**Status:** Limited edition, sold out
**Issue Year:** 2001
**Issue Price:** $40
**Last Year:** 2001
**Last Retail Price:** $40

**Ref. No.:** 6723
**Name:** 2002 Christmas Bell
**Height:** 3.25
**Status:** Limited Edition, retired
**Issue Year:** 2002
**Issue Price:** $40
**Last Year:** 2002
**Last Retail Price:** $40

**Ref. No.:** 6637
**Name:** 1999 Christmas Ball
**Height:** 3.5
**Status:** Open issue, retired
**Issue Year:** 1999
**Issue Price:** $55
**Last Year:** 1999
**Last Retail Price:** $55

*Christmas*

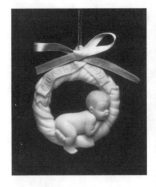

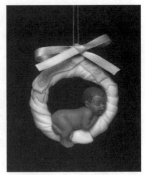

**Ref. No.:** 6694
**Name:** Baby's First Christmas
1999
**Height:** 3.5
**Status:** Open issue, retired
**Issue Year:** 1999
**Issue Price:** $55
**Last Year:** 1999
**Last Retail Price:** $55

**Ref. No.:** 6695
**Name:** Baby's First Christmas
1999 (Black Legacy)
**Height:** 3.5
**Status:** Open issue, retired
**Issue Year:** 1999
**Issue Price:** $55
**Last Year:** 1999
**Last Retail Price:** $55

**Ref. No.:** 6697
**Name:** Baby's First Christmas
2000
**Height:** 3.5
**Status:** Open issue, sold out
**Issue Year:** 2000
**Last Year:** 2000
**Last Retail Price:** $65

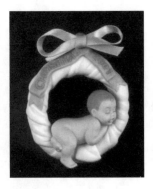

**Ref. No.:** 6699
**Name:** 2000 Christmas Ball
**Height:** 3.5
**Status:** Open issue, sold out
**Issue Year:** 2000
**Last Year:** 2000
**Last Retail Price:** $60

**Ref. No.:** 6711
**Name:** Baby's First Christmas
2000 (Black Legacy)
**Height:** 3.5
**Status:** Open issue, sold out
**Issue Year:** 2000
**Last Year:** 2000
**Last Retail Price:** $65

**Ref. No.:** 6719
**Name:** Baby's First Christmas
2001
**Height:** 3.5
**Status:** Sold Out
**Issue Year:** 2001
**Issue Price:** $65
**Last Year:** 2001
**Last Retail Price:** $65

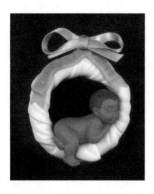

**Ref. No.:** 6720
**Name:** Baby's First Christmas
2001 (Black Legacy)
**Height:** 3.5
**Status:** Sold Out
**Issue Year:** 2001
**Issue Price:** $65
**Last Year:** 2001
**Last Retail Price:** $65

**Ref. No.:** 6724
**Name:** Baby's First Christmas
2002
**Height:** 3.5
**Status:** Limited Edition, retired
**Issue Year:** 2002
**Issue Price:** $65
**Last Year:** 2002
**Last Retail Price:** $65

**Ref. No.:** 6725
**Name:** Baby's First Christmas
2002 (Black Legacy)
**Height:** 3.5
**Status:** Limited Edition, retired
**Issue Year:** 2002
**Issue Price:** $65
**Last Year:** 2002
**Last Retail Price:** $65

**Ref. No.:** 1603
**Name:** 1988 Christmas Ball
**Height:** 4
**Status:** Limited edition, sold out
**Issue Year:** 1988
**Issue Price:** $60
**Last Year:** 1988
**Last Retail Price:** $60
**Auction Price:** $75

**Ref. No.:** 5656
**Name:** 1989 Christmas Ball
**Height:** 4
**Status:** Limited edition, sold out
**Issue Year:** 1989
**Issue Price:** $65
**Last Year:** 1989
**Last Retail Price:** $65
**Auction Price:** $75

**Ref. No.:** 5657
**Name:** Holy Family, set of three
**Height:** 4
**Status:** Limited edition, sold out
**Issue Year:** 1989
**Issue Price:** $79.50
**Last Year:** 1989
**Last Retail Price:** $79.50
**High Auction Price:** $250
**Low Auction Price:** $87.50

*Christmas*

**Ref. No.:** 5730
**Name:** 1990 Christmas Ball
**Height:** 4
**Status:** Limited edition, sold out
**Issue Year:** 1990
**Issue Price:** $70
**Last Year:** 1990
**Last Retail Price:** $70
**Auction Price:** $75

**Ref. No.:** 5841
**Name:** Snowman Ornament
**Height:** 4
**Status:** Open issue, retired
**Issue Year:** 1991
**Issue Price:** $50
**Last Year:** 1993
**Last Retail Price:** $52
**Auction Price:** $225

**Ref. No.:** 5939
**Name:** Mrs. Claus Ornament
**Height:** 4
**Status:** Open issue, retired
**Issue Year:** 1992
**Issue Price:** $55
**Last Year:** 1993
**Last Retail Price:** $57

**Ref. No.:** 6341
**Name:** King Melchior
**Height:** 4
**Status:** Open issue, retired
**Issue Year:** 1996
**Issue Price:** $75
**Last Year:** 1997
**Last Retail Price:** $75

**Ref. No.:** 6372
**Name:** Heavenly Tenor
**Height:** 4
**Status:** Open issue, retired
**Issue Year:** 1996
**Issue Price:** $98
**Last Year:** 1997
**Last Retail Price:** $98

**Ref. No.:** 6380
**Name:** King Gaspar
**Height:** 4
**Status:** Open issue, retired
**Issue Year:** 1997
**Issue Price:** $75
**Last Year:** 1998
**Last Retail Price:** $75

**Ref. No.:** 6386
**Name:** Little Harlequin
**Height:** 4
**Status:** Open issue, retired
**Issue Year:** 1997
**Issue Price:** $79
**Last Year:** 1998
**Last Retail Price:** $79

**Ref. No.:** 6393
**Name:** Heavenly Flutist
**Height:** 4
**Status:** Open issue, retired
**Issue Year:** 1997
**Issue Price:** $98
**Last Year:** 1998
**Last Retail Price:** $98

**Ref. No.:** 6498
**Name:** Heavenly Musician
**Height:** 4
**Status:** Open issue, retired
**Issue Year:** 1998
**Issue Price:** $98
**Last Year:** 1999
**Last Retail Price:** $100

*Christmas*

**Ref. No.:** 6509
**Name:** King Balthasar
**Height:** 4
**Status:** Open issue, retired
**Issue Year:** 1998
**Issue Price:** $75
**Last Year:** 1999
**Last Retail Price:** $75

**Ref. No.:** 6588
**Name:** Baby's First Christmas 1998
**Height:** 4
**Status:** Open issue, retired
**Issue Year:** 1998
**Issue Price:** $55
**Last Year:** 1998
**Last Retail Price:** $55

**Ref. No.:** 6716
**Name:** Our First Christmas 2000
**Height:** 4
**Status:** Open issue, sold out
**Issue Year:** 2000
**Last Year:** 2000
**Last Retail Price:** $65

**Ref. No.:** 6722
**Name:** 2002 Christmas Ball
**Height:** 4
**Status:** Limited Edition, retired
**Issue Year:** 2002
**Issue Price:** $55
**Last Year:** 2002
**Last Retail Price:** $55

**Ref. No.:** 5729
**Name:** Three Kings, set of three
**Height:** 4.25
**Status:** Limited edition, sold out
**Issue Year:** 1990
**Issue Price:** $87.50
**Last Year:** 1990
**Last Retail Price:** $87.50
**High Auction Price:** $225
**Low Auction Price:** $108

**Ref. No.:** 6717
**Name:** 2001 Christmas Ball
**Height:** 4.5
**Status:** Sold Out
**Issue Year:** 2001
**Issue Price:** $55
**Last Year:** 2001
**Last Retail Price:** $55

**Ref. No.:** 6721
**Name:** Our First Christmas 2001
**Height:** 4.5
**Status:** Sold Out
**Issue Year:** 2001
**Issue Price:** $65
**Last Year:** 2001
**Last Retail Price:** $65

**Ref. No.:** 6726
**Name:** Our First Christmas 2002
**Height:** 4.5
**Status:** Limited Edition, retired
**Issue Year:** 2002
**Issue Price:** $70
**Last Year:** 2002
**Last Retail Price:** $70

**Ref. No.:** 5842
**Name:** Santa Ornament
**Height:** 4.75
**Status:** Open issue, retired
**Issue Year:** 1991
**Issue Price:** $55
**Last Year:** 1993
**Last Retail Price:** $57
**Auction Price:** $125

**Ref. No.:** 6345
**Name:** Toy Soldier
**Height:** 5
**Status:** Open issue, retired
**Issue Year:** 1996
**Issue Price:** $90
**Last Year:** 1997
**Last Retail Price:** $90

**Ref. No.:** 6561
**Name:** 1998 Christmas Ball
**Height:** 5
**Status:** Open issue, retired
**Issue Year:** 1998
**Issue Price:** $55
**Last Year:** 1998
**Last Retail Price:** $55

**Ref. No.:** 5922
**Name:** Baby's First Christmas
**Height:** 5.25
**Status:** Limited edition, sold out
**Issue Year:** 1992
**Issue Price:** $55
**Last Year:** 1992
**Last Retail Price:** $55

**Treetoppers**

**Ref. No.:** 5839
**Name:** Baby's First Christmas
**Height:** 5.5
**Status:** Limited edition, sold out
**Issue Year:** 1991
**Issue Price:** $55
**Last Year:** 1991
**Last Retail Price:** $55

**Ref. No.:** 6037
**Name:** Baby's First Christmas
**Height:** 5.5
**Status:** Limited edition, sold out
**Issue Year:** 1993
**Issue Price:** $57
**Last Year:** 1993
**Last Retail Price:** $57

**Ref. No.:** 5719
**Name:** Angel Tree Topper
**Height:** 7
**Status:** Limited edition, sold out
**Issue Year:** 1990
**Issue Price:** $100
**Last Year:** 1990
**Last Retail Price:** $100
**High Auction Price:** $300
**Low Auction Price:** $150

*Christmas*

**Ref. No.:** 6126
**Name:** Angelic Violinist
**Height:** 7
**Status:** Open issue, retired
**Issue Year:** 1994
**Issue Price:** $150
**Last Year:** 1994
**Last Retail Price:** $150

**Ref. No.:** 5830
**Name:** Heavenly Harpist
**Height:** 7.25
**Status:** Limited edition, sold out
**Issue Year:** 1991
**Issue Price:** $135
**Last Year:** 1991
**Last Retail Price:** $135
**High Auction Price:** $275
**Low Auction Price:** $250

**Ref. No.:** 5831
**Name:** Angel Tree Topper
**Height:** 7.25
**Status:** Limited edition, sold out
**Issue Year:** 1991
**Issue Price:** $115
**Last Year:** 1991
**Last Retail Price:** $115
**High Auction Price:** $225
**Low Auction Price:** $150

**Ref. No.:** 5875
**Name:** Angel Tree Topper
**Height:** 7.25
**Status:** Limited edition, sold out
**Issue Year:** 1992
**Issue Price:** $120
**Last Year:** 1992
**Last Retail Price:** $120
**High Auction Price:** $225
**Low Auction Price:** $150

**Ref. No.:** 5876
**Name:** Angelic Cymbalist
**Height:** 7.25
**Status:** Limited edition, sold out
**Issue Year:** 1992
**Issue Price:** $140
**Last Year:** 1992
**Last Retail Price:** $140
**Auction Price:** $225

**Ref. No.:** 5962
**Name:** Angel Tree Topper
**Height:** 7.25
**Status:** Limited edition, sold out
**Issue Year:** 1993
**Issue Price:** $125
**Last Year:** 1993
**Last Retail Price:** $125
**Auction Price:** $150

**Ref. No.:** 5963
**Name:** Angelic Melody
**Height:** 7.25
**Status:** Open issue, retired
**Issue Year:** 1993
**Issue Price:** $145
**Last Year:** 1993
**Last Retail Price:** $145

**Ref. No.:** 6125
**Name:** Joyful Offering
**Height:** 8.25
**Status:** Open issue, retired
**Issue Year:** 1994
**Issue Price:** $245
**Last Year:** 1995
**Last Retail Price:** $245

**Ref. No.:** 6132
**Name:** Angel of the Stars
**Height:** 8.25
**Status:** Open issue, retired
**Issue Year:** 1995
**Issue Price:** $195
**Last Year:** 1995
**Last Retail Price:** $195

**Ref. No.:** 6321
**Name:** Rejoice
**Height:** 8.25
**Status:** Limited edition, sold out
**Issue Year:** 1996
**Issue Price:** $220
**Last Year:** 1996
**Last Retail Price:** $220

**Ref. No.:** 6835
**Name:** Heavenly Melodies
**Height:** 9.25
**Status:** Sold Out
**Issue Year:** 2001
**Issue Price:** $150
**Last Year:** 2001
**Last Retail Price:** $150
**Comment:** 2001 Tree Topper

**Ref. No.:** 6908
**Name:** Joy in My Heart
**Height:** 9.25
**Status:** Open issue, retired
**Issue Year:** 2002
**Issue Price:** $150
**Last Year:** 2002
**Last Retail Price:** $150

*Christmas*

**Ref. No.:** 6792
**Name:** Star of the Heavens —
    2001 Tree Topper
**Height:** 9.5
**Status:** Sold Out
**Issue Year:** 2000
**Issue Price:** $150
**Last Year:** 2001
**Last Retail Price:** $150
**Comment:** 2001 Tree topper

**Ref. No.:** 6747
**Name:** A Celestial Christmas —
    2000 Tree Topper
**Height:** 10.5
**Status:** Open issue, sold out
**Issue Year:** 2000
**Last Year:** 2000
**Last Retail Price:** $270

**Ref. No.:** 6501
**Name:** Angel of Light —
    1997 Tree Topper
**Height:** 10.75
**Status:** Sold out
**Issue Year:** 1997
**Last Year:** 1998

**Other Christmas**

**Ref. No.:** 6643
**Name:** Message Of Love —
    1999 Tree Topper
**Height:** 10.75
**Status:** Open issue, retired
**Issue Year:** 1999
**Issue Price:** $150
**Last Year:** 1999
**Last Retail Price:** $150

**Ref. No.:** 6587
**Name:** Message of Peace —
    1998 Tree Topper
**Height:** 11
**Status:** Open issue, retired
**Issue Year:** 1998
**Issue Price:** $150
**Last Year:** 1998
**Last Retail Price:** $150

**Ref. No.:** 5840
**Name:** Our First Christmas
**Height:** 2
**Status:** Limited edition, sold out
**Issue Year:** 1991
**Issue Price:** Unknown
**Last Year:** 1991
**Last Retail Price:** $50

**Ref. No.:** 6038
**Name:** Our First Christmas
**Height:** 2
**Status:** Limited edition, sold out
**Issue Year:** 1993
**Issue Price:** $52
**Last Year:** 1993
**Last Retail Price:** $52

**Ref. No.:** 6194
**Name:** Christmas Wishes
**Height:** 4
**Status:** Open issue, retired
**Issue Year:** 1996
**Issue Price:** $245
**Last Year:** 1998
**Last Retail Price:** $245

**Ref. No.:** 6261
**Name:** Christmas Tree
**Height:** 5
**Status:** Open issue, active
**Issue Year:** 1995
**Issue Price:** Unknown
**2003 Retail Price:** $95

**Ref. No.:** 335.13
**Name:** Merry Christmas
**Height:** 6
**Status:** Very rare
**Issue Year:** 1966
**Issue Price:** Unknown
**Last Year:** Unknown
**Last Retail Price:** Unknown

**Ref. No.:** 6774
**Name:** Santa's Magic Touch
**Height:** 6.75
**Status:** Open issue, active
**Issue Year:** 2001
**Issue Price:** $225
**2003 Retail Price:** $250

**Ref. No.:** 6575
**Name:** A Gift From Santa
**Height:** 7
**Status:** Open issue, retired
**Issue Year:** 1998
**Issue Price:** $180
**Last Year:** 1999
**Last Retail Price:** $200
**Comment:** Introduced by select
  dealers in 1998

*Christmas*

**Ref. No.:** 5711
**Name:** A Christmas Wish
**Height:** 7.5
**Status:** Open issue, retired
**Issue Year:** 1990
**Issue Price:** $350
**Last Year:** 1997
**Last Retail Price:** $410

**Ref. No.:** 4904
**Name:** Santa Claus
**Height:** 8.25
**Status:** Open issue, retired
**Issue Year:** 1974
**Last Year:** 1978
**Issue Price:** $100
**Last Retail Price:** $175
**Auction Price:** $1000

**Ref. No.:** 4905
**Name:** Santa Claus with Toys
**Height:** 8.25
**Status:** Open issue, retired
**Issue Year:** 1974
**Last Year:** 1978
**Issue Price:** $125
**Last Retail Price:** $215
**Auction Price:** $1250

**Ref. No.:** 5713
**Name:** The Snow Man
**Height:** 8.25
**Status:** Open issue, active
**Issue Year:** 1990
**Issue Price:** $300
**2003 Retail Price:** $350

**Ref. No.:** 6657
**Name:** Santa's List
**Height:** 8.5
**Status:** Open issue, sold out
**Issue Year:** 2000
**Last Year:** 2000
**Last Retail Price:** $210

**Ref. No.:** 6714
**Name:** A Christmas Duet
**Height:** 8.5
**Status:** Open issue, retired
**Issue Year:** 2000
**Issue Price:** $315
**Last Year:** 2002
**Last Retail Price:** $325

**Ref. No.:** 6779
**Name:** Santa's Busiest Hour
**Height:** 8.5
**Status:** Open issue, retired
**Issue Year:** 2001
**Issue Price:** $195
**Last Year:** 2001
**Last Retail Price:** $195

**Ref. No.:** 1239
**Name:** Christmas Carols
**Height:** 9
**Status:** Open issue, retired
**Issue Year:** 1973
**Issue Price:** $125
**Last Year:** 1981
**Last Retail Price:** $210
**High Auction Price:** $950
**Low Auction Price:** $650

**Ref. No.:** 6500
**Name:** Jolly Santa
**Height:** 9
**Status:** Open issue, retired
**Issue Year:** 1998
**Issue Price:** $180
**Last Year:** 1998
**Last Retail Price:** $180
**Comment:** Introduced by select
dealers in 1997

*Christmas*

**Ref. No.:** 6532
**Name:** A Christmas Song
**Height:** 10
**Status:** Open issue, retired
**Issue Year:** 1998
**Issue Price:** $198
**Last Year:** 2000
**Last Retail Price:** $200

**Ref. No.:** 6533
**Name:** The Christmas Caroler
**Height:** 10
**Status:** Open issue, retired
**Issue Year:** 1998
**Issue Price:** $175
**Last Year:** 2000
**Last Retail Price:** $175

**Ref. No.:** 6534
**Name:** The Spirit of Christmas
**Height:** 10
**Status:** Open issue, retired
**Issue Year:** 1998
**Issue Price:** $198
**Last Year:** 2000
**Last Retail Price:** $200

**Ref. No.:** 6128
**Name:** Christmas Melodies
**Height:** 10.5
**Status:** Open issue, retired
**Issue Year:** 1994
**Issue Price:** 375
**Last Year:** 1997
**Last Retail Price:** $385

**Ref. No.:** 5971
**Name:** A Special Toy
**Height:** 10.5
**Status:** Open issue, retired
**Issue Year:** 1993
**Issue Price:** $815
**Last Year:** 1996
**Last Retail Price:** $815

**Ref. No.:** 5897
**Name:** Trimming the Tree
**Height:** 12.75
**Status:** Open issue, active
**Issue Year:** 1992
**Issue Price:** $900
**2003 Retail Price:** $950

**Night Before Christmas Collection**

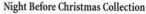

**Ref. No.:** 5975
**Name:** Up and Away
**Height:** 13.25
**Status:** Open issue, retired
**Issue Year:** 1993
**Issue Price:** $2850
**Last Year:** 1996
**Last Retail Price:** $2850

**Ref. No.:** 5427
**Name:** Saint Nicholas
**Height:** 15.5
**Status:** Open issue, retired
**Issue Year:** 1987
**Issue Price:** $425
**Last Year:** 1991
**Last Retail Price:** $635
**High Auction Price:** $900
**Low Auction Price:** $625

**Ref. No.:** 6673
**Name:** Christmas Buddies
**Height:** 3.5
**Status:** Sold Out
**Issue Year:** 2001
**Issue Price:** $245
**Last Year:** 2001
**Last Retail Price:** $245
**Comment:** The Night before
Christmas Collection

**Ref. No.:** 6671
**Name:** Ringing In The Season
**Height:** 6
**Status:** Open issue, sold out
**Issue Year:** 2000
**Last Year:** 2001
**Last Retail Price:** $245
**Comment:** The Night before
Christmas Collection

**Ref. No.:** 6667
**Name:** Visions Of Sugarplums
**Height:** 6.75
**Status:** Open issue, sold out
**Issue Year:** 1999
**Issue Price:** $260
**Last Year:** 2001
**Last Retail Price:** $260
**Comment:** The Night before
Christmas Collection

**Ref. No.:** 6675
**Name:** Cookies for Santa
**Height:** 7.25
**Status:** Open issue, sold out
**Issue Year:** 1999
**Issue Price:** $325
**Last Year:** 2001
**Last Retail Price:** $325
**Comment:** The Night before
Christmas Collection

*Christmas*

**Ref. No.:** 6668
**Name:** Up The Chimney He Rose
**Height:** 7.50
**Status:** Open issue, sold out
**Issue Year:** 1999
**Issue Price:** $370
**Last Year:** 2001
**Last Retail Price:** $370
**Comment:** The Night before
Christmas Collection

**Ref. No.:** 6676
**Name:** Santa Won't Notice
**Height:** 8
**Status:** Open issue, sold out
**Issue Year:** 2001
**Issue Price:** $175
**Last Year:** 2001
**Last Retail Price:** $175
**Comment:** The Night before
Christmas Collection

**Ref. No.:** 6669
**Name:** A Stocking For Kitty
**Height:** 8.50
**Status:** Open issue, sold out
**Issue Year:** 1999
**Issue Price:** $235
**Last Year:** 2001
**Last Retail Price:** $235
**Comment:** The Night before
Christmas Collection

**Ref. No.:** 6672
**Name:** I Love Christmas!
**Height:** 9.5
**Status:** Open issue, sold out
**Issue Year:** 2000
**Last Year:** 2001
**Last Retail Price:** $245
**Comment:** The Night before
  Christmas Collection

**Ref. No.:** 6670
**Name:** Christmas Is Here!
**Height:** 12.75
**Status:** Open issue, sold out
**Issue Year:** 2000
**Last Year:** 2001
**Last Retail Price:** $495
**Comment:** The Night before
  Christmas Collection

**Ref. No.:** 6892
**Name:** Where Presents Are Made
**Height:** 6.75
**Status:** Open issue, active
**Issue Year:** 2002
**Issue Price:** $300
**2003 Retail Price:** $300
**Comment:** Santa's Magical
  Workshop Collection

**Ref. No.:** 6891
**Name:** A Brushstroke of Dreams
**Height:** 8.5
**Status:** Open issue, active
**Issue Year:** 2002
**Issue Price:** $250
**2003 Retail Price:** $250
**Comment:** Santa's Magical
  Workshop Collection

**Ref. No.:** 6890
**Name:** Santa's Little Secret
**Height:** 9.25
**Status:** Open issue, active
**Issue Year:** 2002
**Issue Price:** $450
**2003 Retail Price:** $450
**Comment:** Santa's Magical
  Workshop Collection

*Angels*

**Ref. No.:** 4884
**Name:** Seraph's Head No. 1
**Height:** 2
**Status:** Open edition, retired
**Issue Year:** 1974
**Issue Price:** $10
**Last Year:** 1985
**Last Retail Price:** $25

**Ref. No.:** 4885
**Name:** Seraph's Head No. 2
**Height:** 2
**Status:** Open edition, retired
**Issue Year:** 1974
**Issue Price:** $10
**Last Year:** 1985
**Last Retail Price:** $25

**Ref. No.:** 4886
**Name:** Seraph's Head No. 3
**Height:** 2
**Status:** Open edition, retired
**Issue Year:** 1974
**Issue Price:** $10
**Last Year:** 1985
**Last Retail Price:** $25

**Ref. No.:** 4541
**Name:** Angel, Reclining
**Height:** 2.25
**Status:** Open issue, active
**Issue Year:** 1969
**Issue Price:** $13
**2003 Retail Price:** $95

**Ref. No.:** 5728
**Name:** Heavenly Dreamer
**Height:** 2.5
**Status:** Open issue, retired
**Issue Year:** 1990
**Issue Price:** $100
**Last Year:** 2000
**Last Retail Price:** $120

**Ref. No.:** 5723
**Name:** Heavenly Chimes
**Height:** 3
**Status:** Open issue, active
**Issue Year:** 1990
**Issue Price:** $100
**2003 Retail Price:** $125

**Ref. No.:** 5725
**Name:** Making a Wish
**Height:** 3
**Status:** Open issue, active
**Issue Year:** 1990
**Issue Price:** $125
**2003 Retail Price:** $145

**Ref. No.:** 4539
**Name:** Angel Thinking
**Height:** 4
**Status:** Open issue, active
**Issue Year:** 1969
**Issue Price:** $13
**2003 Retail Price:** $95

**Ref. No.:** 6491
**Name:** Heavenly Dreamer
**Height:** 4
**Status:** Open issue, active
**Issue Year:** 1997
**Issue Price:** $95
**2003 Retail Price:** $95

**Ref. No.:** 4537
**Name:** Angel
**Height:** 4.25
**Status:** Open issue, active
**Issue Year:** 1969
**Issue Price:** $13
**2003 Retail Price:** $95

**Ref. No.:** 4538
**Name:** Angel Praying
**Height:** 5
**Status:** Open issue, active
**Issue Year:** 1969
**Issue Price:** $13
**2003 Retail Price:** $95

**Ref. No.:** 5727
**Name:** Angel Care
**Height:** 5
**Status:** Open issue, retired
**Issue Year:** 1990
**Issue Price:** $185
**Last Year:** 2000
**Last Retail Price:** $210

*Angels*

**Ref. No.:** 6490
**Name:** An Angel's Tune
**Height:** 5
**Status:** Open issue, active
**Issue Year:** 1997
**Issue Price:** $115
**2003 Retail Price:** $120

**Ref. No.:** 6528
**Name:** Little Angel with Lyre
**Height:** 5
**Status:** Open issue, active
**Issue Year:** 1998
**Issue Price:** $120
**2003 Retail Price:** $125

**Ref. No.:** 6529
**Name:** Little Angel with Violin
**Height:** 5
**Status:** Open issue, active
**Issue Year:** 1998
**Issue Price:** $120
**2003 Retail Price:** $125

**Ref. No.:** 6530
**Name:** Little Angel with
    Tambourine
**Height:** 5
**Status:** Open issue, retired
**Issue Year:** 1998
**Issue Price:** $120
**Last Year:** 2002
**Last Retail Price:** $125

**Ref. No.:** 4536
**Name:** Chinese Angel
**Height:** 5.5
**Status:** Open issue, active
**Issue Year:** 1969
**Issue Price:** $45
**2003 Retail Price:** $95

**Ref. No.:** 6628
**Name:** Adagio
**Height:** 5.5
**Status:** Open issue, active
**Issue Year:** 1999
**Issue Price:** $160
**2003 Retail Price:** $165

**Ref. No.:** 6629
**Name:** Allegro
**Height:** 5.5
**Status:** Open issue, active
**Issue Year:** 1999
**Issue Price:** $160
**2003 Retail Price:** $165

**Ref. No.:** 4540
**Name:** Angel with Horn
**Height:** 6.25
**Status:** Open issue, active
**Issue Year:** 1969
**Issue Price:** $13
**2003 Retail Price:** $95

**Ref. No.:** 4962
**Name:** Angel Wondering
**Height:** 6.25
**Status:** Open issue, active
**Issue Year:** 1977
**Issue Price:** $40
**2003 Retail Price:** $145

**Ref. No.:** 5724
**Name:** Angelic Voice
**Height:** 6.25
**Status:** Open issue, retired
**Issue Year:** 1990
**Issue Price:** $125
**Last Year:** 2002
**Last Retail Price:** $145

**Ref. No.:** 4542
**Name:** Angels group
**Height:** 6.5
**Status:** Open issue, active
**Issue Year:** 1969
**Issue Price:** $31
**2003 Retail Price:** $200

**Ref. No.:** 4961
**Name:** Angel Dreaming
**Height:** 6.5
**Status:** Open issue, active
**Issue Year:** 1977
**Issue Price:** $40
**2003 Retail Price:** $145
**Comment:** To be retired as of
December 31, 2003

*Angels*

**Ref. No.:** 5726
**Name:** Sweep Away the Clouds
**Height:** 6.5
**Status:** Open issue, retired
**Issue Year:** 1990
**Issue Price:** $125
**Last Year:** 2002
**Last Retail Price:** $145

**Ref. No.:** 6772
**Name:** Heaven's Harvest
**Height:** 6.75
**Status:** Open issue, active
**Issue Year:** 2001
**Issue Price:** $295
**2003 Retail Price:** $325

**Ref. No.:** 4635
**Name:** Angel with Child
**Height:** 7
**Status:** Open issue, retired
**Issue Year:** 1969
**Issue Price:** $15
**Last Year:** 2002
**Last Retail Price:** $135

**Ref. No.:** 6492
**Name:** Your Special Angel
**Height:** 7
**Status:** Open issue, active
**Issue Year:** 1998
**Issue Price:** $92
**2003 Retail Price:** $95

**Ref. No.:** 6837
**Name:** Angelic Serenade
**Height:** 7.25
**Status:** Open issue, active
**Issue Year:** 2002
**Issue Price:** $235
**2003 Retail Price:** $245

**Ref. No.:** 6856
**Name:** Heavenly Love
**Height:** 7.25
**Status:** Open issue, active
**Issue Year:** 2002
**Issue Price:** $195
**2003 Retail Price:** $245
**Comment:** 2001 Federated
Exclusive

**Ref. No.:** 6871
**Name:** Celestial Harmony
**Height:** 7.25
**Status:** Open issue, active
**Issue Year:** 2002
**Issue Price:** $335
**2003 Retail Price:** $345

**Ref. No.:** 5491
**Name:** Heavenly Strings
**Height:** 7.75
**Status:** Open issue, retired
**Issue Year:** 1988
**Issue Price:** $140
**Last Year:** 1993
**Last Retail Price:** $185

**Ref. No.:** 6493
**Name:** Filled with Joy
**Height:** 8
**Status:** Open issue, active
**Issue Year:** 1998
**Issue Price:** $92
**2003 Retail Price:** $95

**Ref. No.:** 6838
**Name:** Angelic Music
**Height:** 8
**Status:** Open issue, active
**Issue Year:** 2002
**Issue Price:** $235
**2003 Retail Price:** $245

**Ref. No.:** 6840
**Name:** Dreaming of the Stars
**Height:** 8
**Status:** Open issue, active
**Issue Year:** 2002
**Issue Price:** $195
**2003 Retail Price:** $195
**Comment:** 2001 USA Exclusive

**Ref. No.:** 5492
**Name:** Heavenly Cellist
**Height:** 8.25
**Status:** Open issue, retired
**Issue Year:** 1988
**Issue Price:** $240
**Last Year:** 1993
**Last Retail Price:** $315

*Angels*

**Ref. No.:** 5493
**Name:** Angel with Lute
**Height:** 8.25
**Status:** Open issue, retired
**Issue Year:** 1988
**Issue Price:** $140
**Last Year:** 1993
**Last Retail Price:** $185

**Ref. No.:** 5494
**Name:** Angel with Clarinet
**Height:** 8.25
**Status:** Open issue, retired
**Issue Year:** 1988
**Issue Price:** $140
**Last Year:** 1993
**Last Retail Price:** $185

**Ref. No.:** 1231
**Name:** Angel with Lute
**Height:** 8.5
**Status:** Open issue, retired
**Issue Year:** 1972
**Issue Price:** $60
**Last Year:** 1988
**Last Retail Price:** $150
**Auction Price:** $425

**Ref. No.:** 1233
**Name:** Angel with Flute
**Height:** 8.5
**Status:** Open issue, retired
**Issue Year:** 1972
**Issue Price:** $60
**Last Year:** 1988
**Last Retail Price:** $150
**High Auction Price:** $500
**Low Auction Price:** $375

**Ref. No.:** 4959
**Name:** Mime Angel
**Height:** 8.5
**Status:** Open issue, active
**Issue Year:** 1977
**Issue Price:** $40
**2003 Retail Price:** $140

**Ref. No.:** 6839
**Name:** Exploring the Stars
**Height:** 8.5
**Status:** Open issue, active
**Issue Year:** 2002
**Issue Price:** $195
**2003 Retail Price:** $195
2001 USA Exclusive

**Ref. No.:** 6146
**Name:** Spring Angel
**Height:** 9
**Status:** Open issue, retired
**Issue Year:** 1994
**Issue Price:** $250
**Last Year:** 1997
**Last Retail Price:** $265

**Ref. No.:** 6148
**Name:** Summer Angel
**Height:** 9.25
**Status:** Open issue, retired
**Issue Year:** 1994
**Issue Price:** $220
**Last Year:** 1997
**Last Retail Price:** $220

**Ref. No.:** 6788
**Name:** An Angel's Wish
**Height:** 9.25
**Status:** Open issue, active
**Issue Year:** 2001
**Issue Price:** $125
**2003 Retail Price:** $130

Angels

**Ref. No.:** 6789
**Name:** An Angel's Song
**Height:** 9.25
**Status:** Open issue, active
**Issue Year:** 2001
**Issue Price:** $125
**2003 Retail Price:** $130

**Ref. No.:** 4960
**Name:** Curious Angel
**Height:** 9.5
**Status:** Open issue, active
**Issue Year:** 1977
**Issue Price:** $40
**2003 Retail Price:** $145

**Ref. No.:** 5495
**Name:** Angelic Choir
**Height:** 9.5
**Status:** Open issue, retired
**Issue Year:** 1988
**Issue Price:** $300
**Last Year:** 1993
**Last Retail Price:** $395

**Ref. No.:** 1232
**Name:** Angel with Clarinet
**Height:** 9.75
**Status:** Open issue, retired
**Issue Year:** 1972
**Issue Price:** $60
**Last Year:** 1988
**Last Retail Price:** $150
**High Auction Price:** $550
**Low Auction Price:** $400

**Ref. No.:** 1464
**Name:** Carefree Angel with Lyre
**Height:** 9.75
**Status:** Open issue, retired
**Issue Year:** 1985
**Issue Price:** $220
**Last Year:** 1988
**Last Retail Price:** $250
**High Auction Price:** $1000
**Low Auction Price:** $250

**Ref. No.:** 6085
**Name:** Angelic Harmony
**Height:** 10
**Status:** Open issue, retired
**Issue Year:** 1994
**Issue Price:** $495
**Last Year:** 1997
**Last Retail Price:** $575

**Ref. No.:** 1320
**Name:** Angel with Tambourine
**Height:** 10.5
**Status:** Open issue, retired
**Issue Year:** 1976
**Issue Price:** $125
**Last Year:** 1985
**Last Retail Price:** $192.5
**High Auction Price:** $350
**Low Auction Price:** $325

**Ref. No.:** 1322
**Name:** Angel Recital
**Height:** 10.5
**Status:** Open issue, retired
**Issue Year:** 1976
**Issue Price:** $125
**Last Year:** 1985
**Last Retail Price:** $192.5
**High Auction Price:** $500
**Low Auction Price:** $475

**Ref. No.:** 6147
**Name:** Fall Angel
**Height:** 11.25
**Status:** Open issue, retired
**Issue Year:** 1994
**Issue Price:** $250
**Last Year:** 1997
**Last Retail Price:** $265

**Ref. No.:** 6149
**Name:** Winter Angel
**Height:** 11.25
**Status:** Open issue, retired
**Issue Year:** 1994
**Issue Price:** $250
**Last Year:** 1997
**Last Retail Price:** $265

**Ref. No.:** 1463
**Name:** Carefree Angel with Flute
**Height:** 11.5
**Status:** Open issue, retired
**Issue Year:** 1985
**Issue Price:** $220
**Last Year:** 1988
**Last Retail Price:** $250
**High Auction Price:** $1000
**Low Auction Price:** $275

**Ref. No.:** 6849
**Name:** Heavenly Apprentice
**Height:** 11.5
**Status:** Open issue, active
**Issue Year:** 2002
**Issue Price:** $475
**2003 Retail Price:** $475

**Ref. No.:** 1321
**Name:** Angel with Lyre
**Height:** 11.75
**Status:** Open issue, retired
**Issue Year:** 1976
**Issue Price:** $125
**Last Year:** 1985
**Last Retail Price:** $192.5
**Auction Price:** $450

**Ref. No.:** 6131
**Name:** Angel of Peace
**Height:** 12
**Status:** Open issue, retired
**Issue Year:** 1994
**Issue Price:** $345
**Last Year:** 2002
**Last Retail Price:** $370

**Ref. No.:** 6870
**Name:** Love in the World
**Height:** 12
**Status:** Open issue, active
**Issue Year:** 2002
**Issue Price:** $345
**2003 Retail Price:** $350

*Angels*

**Ref. No.:** 1323
**Name:** Angel with Accordion
**Height:** 12.25
**Status:** Open issue, retired
**Issue Year:** 1976
**Issue Price:** $125
**Last Year:** 1985
**Last Retail Price:** $192.5
**High Auction Price:** $400
**Low Auction Price:** $275

**Ref. No.:** 1324
**Name:** Angel with Violin
**Height:** 12.25
**Status:** Open issue, retired
**Issue Year:** 1976
**Issue Price:** $125
**Last Year:** 1985
**Last Retail Price:** $192.5
**High Auction Price:** $625
**Low Auction Price:** $400

**Ref. No.:** 6133
**Name:** Angel with Garland
**Height:** 12.25
**Status:** Open issue, retired
**Issue Year:** 1994
**Issue Price:** $345
**Last Year:** 1999
**Last Retail Price:** $370

**Ref. No.:** 1721
**Name:** Leprechaun
**Height:** 3
**Status:** Open issue, active
**Issue Year:** 1990
**Issue Price:** $1200
**2003 Retail Price:** $1400

**Ref. No.:** 1720
**Name:** Sprite
**Height:** 3.75
**Status:** Open issue, active
**Issue Year:** 1990
**Issue Price:** $1200
**2003 Retail Price:** $1400

**Ref. No.:** 99.06
**Name:** Boys with Grapes
**Height:** 4.75
**Status:** Very Rare
**Issue Year:** 1958
**Issue Price:** Unknown
**Last Year:** Unknown
**Last Retail Price:** Unknown

**Ref. No.:** 6691
**Name:** Oopsy Daisy
**Height:** 4.75
**Status:** Open issue, active
**Issue Year:** 2000
**Issue Price:** $300
**2003 Retail Price:** $325

**Ref. No.:** 1401
**Name:** Butterfly Girl
**Height:** 5
**Status:** Open issue, retired
**Issue Year:** 1982
**Issue Price:** $210
**Last Year:** 1988
**Last Retail Price:** $275
**High Auction Price:** $750
**Low Auction Price:** $250

**Ref. No.:** 5320
**Name:** Demure Centaur Girl
**Height:** 5
**Status:** Open issue, retired
**Issue Year:** 1985
**Issue Price:** $157.50
**Last Year:** 1990
**Last Retail Price:** $225
**High Auction Price:** $350
**Low Auction Price:** $300

**Ref. No.:** 6690
**Name:** Rosy Posey
**Height:** 5.25
**Status:** Open issue, active
**Issue Year:** 2000
**Issue Price:** $300
**2003 Retail Price:** $325

**Ref. No.:** 5853
**Name:** Floral Admiration
**Height:** 5.25
**Status:** Open issue, retired
**Issue Year:** 1992
**Issue Price:** $690
**Last Year:** 1994
**Last Retail Price:** $725

**Ref. No.:** 6645
**Name:** Lillypad Love
**Height:** 5.25
**Status:** Open issue, active
**Issue Year:** 2000
**Issue Price:** $495
**2003 Retail Price:** $495
**Comment:** Introduced by select
dealers in 1999

**Ref. No.:** 5319
**Name:** Wistful Centaur Girl
**Height:** 5.5
**Status:** Open issue, retired
**Issue Year:** 1985
**Issue Price:** $157.50
**Last Year:** 1990
**Last Retail Price:** $225
**High Auction Price:** $450
**Low Auction Price:** $300

**Ref. No.:** 1403
**Name:** Butterfly Girl
**Height:** 6
**Status:** Open issue, retired
**Issue Year:** 1982
**Issue Price:** $210
**Last Year:** 1988
**Last Retail Price:** $275
**High Auction Price:** $550
**Low Auction Price:** $400

**Ref. No.:** 1415
**Name:** Mirage
**Height:** 6
**Status:** Open issue, active
**Issue Year:** 1982
**Issue Price:** $115
**2003 Retail Price:** $275

*Fantasy*

**Ref. No.:** 6787
**Name:** Dreaming on Dew Drops
**Height:** 6
**Status:** Open issue, active
**Issue Year:** 2001
**Issue Price:** $495
**2003 Retail Price:** $495

**Ref. No.:** 1402
**Name:** Butterfly Girl
**Height:** 6.25
**Status:** Open issue, retired
**Issue Year:** 1982
**Issue Price:** $210
**Last Year:** 1988
**Last Retail Price:** $275
**High Auction Price:** $550
**Low Auction Price:** $275

**Ref. No.:** 1413
**Name:** Illusion
**Height:** 6.25
**Status:** Open issue, active
**Issue Year:** 1982
**Issue Price:** $115
**2003 Retail Price:** $275

**Ref. No.:** 1414
**Name:** Fantasy
**Height:** 6.25
**Status:** Open issue, active
**Issue Year:** 1982
**Issue Price:** $115
**2003 Retail Price:** $275

**Ref. No.:** 1475
**Name:** Wishing on a Star
**Height:** 6.5
**Status:** Open issue, retired
**Issue Year:** 1985
**Issue Price:** $130
**Last Year:** 1988
**Last Retail Price:** $150
**High Auction Price:** $600
**Low Auction Price:** $275

**Ref. No.:** 5826
**Name:** Little Unicorn
**Height:** 6.5
**Status:** Open issue, retired
**Issue Year:** 1991
**Issue Price:** $275
**Last Year:** 1997
**Last Retail Price:** $295

**Ref. No.:** 6758
**Name:** Drifting through
   Dreamland
**Height:** 6.5
**Status:** Open issue, active
**Issue Year:** 2001
**Issue Price:** $370
**2003 Retail Price:** $395

**Ref. No.:** 6786
**Name:** A Visit to Dreamland
**Height:** 6.5
**Status:** Open issue, active
**Issue Year:** 2001
**Issue Price:** $495
**2003 Retail Price:** $495

**Ref. No.:** 6797
**Name:** A Fairy Tale Princess
**Height:** 6.5
**Status:** Open issue, retired
**Issue Year:** 2001
**Issue Price:** $325
**Last Year:** 2002
**Last Retail Price:** $350

**Ref. No.:** 6830
**Name:** Love Letters
**Height:** 6.5
**Status:** Open issue, active
**Issue Year:** 2002
**Issue Price:** $225
**2003 Retail Price:** $225

**Ref. No.:** 6798
**Name:** A Fairy Tale Prince
**Height:** 6.75
**Status:** Open issue, retired
**Issue Year:** 2001
**Issue Price:** $325
**Last Year:** 2002
**Last Retail Price:** $350

**Ref. No.:** 1436
**Name:** Moon Glow
**Height:** 7
**Status:** Open issue, retired
**Issue Year:** 1983
**Issue Price:** $97.50
**Last Year:** 1988
**Last Retail Price:** $125
**High Auction Price:** $500
**Low Auction Price:** $300

*Fantasy*

**Ref. No.:** 1437
**Name:** Moonlight
**Height:** 7
**Status:** Open issue, retired
**Issue Year:** 1983
**Issue Price:** $97.50
**Last Year:** 1988
**Last Retail Price:** $125
**High Auction Price:** $450
**Low Auction Price:** $350

**Ref. No.:** 1476
**Name:** Star Light, Star Bright
**Height:** 7
**Status:** Open issue, retired
**Issue Year:** 1985
**Issue Price:** $130
**Last Year:** 1988
**Last Retail Price:** $150
**High Auction Price:** $400
**Low Auction Price:** $250

**Ref. No.:** 5710
**Name:** Fantasy Friend
**Height:** 7
**Status:** Open issue, retired
**Issue Year:** 1990
**Issue Price:** $420
**Last Year:** 1993
**Last Retail Price:** $495

**Ref. No.:** 126.06
**Name:** Children with Donkey
**Height:** 7.25
**Status:** Very rare
**Issue Year:** 1963
**Issue Price:** Unknown
**Last Year:** Unknown
**Last Retail Price:** Unknown

**Ref. No.:** 5854
**Name:** Floral Fantasy
**Height:** 7.25
**Status:** Open issue, retired
**Issue Year:** 1992
**Issue Price:** $690
**Last Year:** 1995
**Last Retail Price:** $710

**Ref. No.:** 6242
**Name:** Winged Companions
**Height:** 7.25
**Status:** Open issue, retired
**Issue Year:** 1996
**Issue Price:** $270
**Last Year:** 1999
**Last Retail Price:** $270

**Ref. No.:** 1438
**Name:** Full Moon
**Height:** 7.5
**Status:** Open issue, retired
**Issue Year:** 1983
**Issue Price:** $115
**Last Year:** 1988
**Last Retail Price:** $140
**High Auction Price:** $675
**Low Auction Price:** $425

**Ref. No.:** 1477
**Name:** Star Gazing
**Height:** 7.5
**Status:** Open issue, retired
**Issue Year:** 1985
**Issue Price:** $130
**Last Year:** 1988
**Last Retail Price:** $150
**High Auction Price:** $450
**Low Auction Price:** $250

**Ref. No.:** 6311
**Name:** Cupid
**Height:** 7.5
**Status:** Open issue, retired
**Issue Year:** 1996
**Issue Price:** $200
**Last Year:** 2001
**Last Retail Price:** $200

**Ref. No.:** 6644
**Name:** Lakeside Daydream
**Height:** 7.5
**Status:** Open issue, active
**Issue Year:** 2000
**Issue Price:** $495
**2003 Retail Price:** $495
**Comment:** Introduced by select
  dealers in 1999

**Ref. No.:** 1092
**Name:** Satyr with Snail
**Height:** 7.75
**Status:** Very rare
**Issue Year:** 1971
**Issue Price:** $30
**Last Year:** 1975
**Last Retail Price:** Unknown

**Ref. No.:** 5861
**Name:** Fairy Flowers
**Height:** 8
**Status:** Open issue, retired
**Issue Year:** 1992
**Issue Price:** $630
**Last Year:** 1993
**Last Retail Price:** $655

*Fantasy*

**Ref. No.:** 6651
**Name:** Wings Of Fantasy
**Height:** 8
**Status:** Open issue, active
**Issue Year:** 2000
**Issue Price:** $775
**2003 Retail Price:** $795

**Ref. No.:** 1013
**Name:** Centaur Boy
**Height:** 8.25
**Status:** Open issue, retired
**Issue Year:** 1969
**Issue Price:** $45
**Last Year:** 1989
**Last Retail Price:** $215
**High Auction Price:** $575
**Low Auction Price:** $275

**Ref. No.:** 1435
**Name:** Blue Moon
**Height:** 8.5
**Status:** Open issue, retired
**Issue Year:** 1983
**Issue Price:** $97.50
**Last Year:** 1988
**Last Retail Price:** $125
**High Auction Price:** $600
**Low Auction Price:** $250

**Ref. No.:** 5860
**Name:** Fairy Garland
**Height:** 8.5
**Status:** Open issue, retired
**Issue Year:** 1992
**Issue Price:** $630
**Last Year:** 1995
**Last Retail Price:** $650

**Ref. No.:** 5880
**Name:** Playful Unicorn
**Height:** 8.5
**Status:** Open issue, retired
**Issue Year:** 1992
**Issue Price:** $295
**Last Year:** 1998
**Last Retail Price:** $320

**Ref. No.:** 6579
**Name:** Petals Of Peace
**Height:** 8.75
**Status:** Open issue, active
**Issue Year:** 1999
**Issue Price:** $310
**2003 Retail Price:** $350
**Comment:** Introduced by select
    dealers in 1998

**Ref. No.:** 312.13
**Name:** Snowman
**Height:** 9
**Status:** Very rare
**Issue Year:** 1970
**Issue Price:** Unknown
**Last Year:** Unknown
**Last Retail Price:** Unknown

**Ref. No.:** 1093
**Name:** Satyr with Frog
**Height:** 9
**Status:** Very rare
**Issue Year:** 1971
**Issue Price:** $50
**Last Year:** 1975
**Last Retail Price:** Unknown

**Ref. No.:** 4607
**Name:** Cupid
**Height:** 9
**Status:** Open issue, retired
**Issue Year:** 1969
**Issue Price:** $15
**Last Year:** 1980
**Last Retail Price:** $50
**Auction Price:** $200

**Ref. No.:** 5993
**Name:** Unicorn and Friend
**Height:** 9.25
**Status:** Open issue, retired
**Issue Year:** 1993
**Issue Price:** $355
**Last Year:** 1998
**Last Retail Price:** $355

**Ref. No.:** 6596
**Name:** Cupid's Arrow
**Height:** 9.25
**Status:** Open issue, retired
**Issue Year:** 2000
**Issue Price:** $230
**Last Year:** 2002
**Last Retail Price:** $235

**Ref. No.:** 1012
**Name:** Centaur Girl
**Height:** 9.5
**Status:** Open issue, retired
**Issue Year:** 1969
**Issue Price:** $45
**Last Year:** 1989
**Last Retail Price:** $215
**High Auction Price:** $700
**Low Auction Price:** $250

*Fantasy*

**Ref. No.:** 5785
**Name:** Ocean Beauty
**Height:** 10
**Status:** Open issue, active
**Issue Year:** 1991
**Issue Price:** $625
**2003 Retail Price:** $675

**Ref. No.:** 6877
**Name:** In a Magical Garden
**Height:** 10
**Status:** Open issue, active
**Issue Year:** 2002
**Issue Price:** $645
**2003 Retail Price:** $650

**Ref. No.:** 6878
**Name:** Secrets of the Forest
**Height:** 10
**Status:** Open issue, active
**Issue Year:** 2002
**Issue Price:** $645
**2003 Retail Price:** $650

**Ref. No.:** 1006
**Name:** Pan with Cymbals
**Height:** 10.5
**Status:** Open issue, retired
**Issue Year:** 1969
**Issue Price:** $45
**Last Year:** 1975
**Last Retail Price:** $45
**High Auction Price:** $500
**Low Auction Price:** $425

**Ref. No.:** 1007
**Name:** Pan with Pipes
**Height:** 10.5
**Status:** Open issue, retired
**Issue Year:** 1969
**Issue Price:** $45
**Last Year:** 1975
**Last Retail Price:** $45
**High Auction Price:** $450
**Low Auction Price:** $425

**Ref. No.:** 1008
**Name:** Satyr Group
**Height:** 10.5
**Status:** Open issue, retired
**Issue Year:** 1969
**Issue Price:** Unknown
**Last Year:** 1975
**Last Retail Price:** $95
**Auction Price:** $1000

**Ref. No.:** 6007
**Name:** The Goddess and Unicorn
**Height:** 10.75
**Status:** Open issue, active
**Issue Year:** 1993
**Issue Price:** $1675
**2003 Retail Price:** $1675

**Ref. No.:** 4595
**Name:** Fairy
**Height:** 11
**Status:** Open issue, retired
**Issue Year:** 1969
**Issue Price:** $27.50
**Last Year:** 1994
**Last Retail Price:** $140

**Ref. No.:** 6458
**Name:** Fountain of Love
**Height:** 11
**Status:** Open issue, active
**Issue Year:** 1998
**Issue Price:** $395
**2003 Retail Price:** $450

**Ref. No.:** 1130
**Name:** Love of Europe
**Height:** 11.5
**Status:** Very rare
**Issue Year:** 1971
**Issue Price:** $160
**Last Year:** 1972
**Last Retail Price:** Unknown

**Ref. No.:** 1131
**Name:** Faun
**Height:** 11.5
**Status:** Very rare
**Issue Year:** 1971
**Issue Price:** $155
**Last Year:** 1972
**Last Retail Price:** Unknown

**Ref. No.:** 1601
**Name:** Rock Nymph
**Height:** 11.5
**Status:** Open issue, retired
**Issue Year:** 1989
**Issue Price:** $665
**Last Year:** 1995
**Last Retail Price:** $795

*Fantasy*

**Ref. No.:** 6241
**Name:** Allegory of Spring
**Height:** 11.5
**Status:** Open issue, retired
**Issue Year:** 1995
**Issue Price:** $735
**Last Year:** 2000
**Last Retail Price:** $735

**Ref. No.:** 6833
**Name:** Petals of Fantasy
**Height:** 11.5
**Status:** Open issue, active
**Issue Year:** 2002
**Issue Price:** $580
**2003 Retail Price:** $595

**Ref. No.:** 1132
**Name:** Carriage of Bacchus
**Height:** 11.75
**Status:** Very Rare
**Issue Year:** 1971
**Issue Price:** $160
**Last Year:** 1972
**Last Retail Price:** Unknown

**Ref. No.:** 1348
**Name:** Pearl Mermaid
**Height:** 11.75
**Status:** Open issue, retired
**Issue Year:** 1978
**Issue Price:** $225
**Last Year:** 1983
**Last Retail Price:** $245
**Auction Price:** $2000

**Ref. No.:** 241.1
**Name:** Lady with Cupid
**Height:** 12.25
**Status:** Very rare
**Issue Year:** 1958
**Issue Price:** Unknown
**Last Year:** Unknown
**Last Retail Price:** Unknown

**Ref. No.:** 1129
**Name:** Boys Playing with Goat
**Height:** 12.25
**Status:** Very Rare
**Issue Year:** 1971
**Issue Price:** $100
**Last Year:** 1975
**Last Retail Price:** Unknown

**Ref. No.:** 1129.3
**Name:** Boys Playing with Goat
   (White)
**Height:** 12.25
**Status:** Very Rare
**Issue Year:** 1971
**Issue Price:** $75
**Last Year:** 1975
**Last Retail Price:** Unknown

**Ref. No.:** 1602
**Name:** Spring Nymph
**Height:** 12.5
**Status:** Open issue, retired
**Issue Year:** 1989
**Issue Price:** $665
**Last Year:** 1995
**Last Retail Price:** $825

**Ref. No.:** 5068
**Name:** Fairy Queen
**Height:** 12.75
**Status:** Open issue, retired
**Issue Year:** 1980
**Issue Price:** $625
**Last Year:** 1983
**Last Retail Price:** $685
**High Auction Price:** $950
**Low Auction Price:** $900

**Ref. No.:** 1135
**Name:** Diana
**Height:** 13.25
**Status:** Very rare
**Issue Year:** 1971
**Issue Price:** $120
**Last Year:** 1972
**Last Retail Price:** Unknown

**Ref. No.:** 6269
**Name:** Diana, Goddess of
   the Hunt
**Height:** 14
**Status:** Open issue, retired
**Issue Year:** 1996
**Issue Price:** $1550
**Last Year:** 2000
**Last Retail Price:** $1550

**Ref. No.:** 6432
**Name:** Sea of Love
**Height:** 14
**Status:** Open issue, retired
**Issue Year:** 1997
**Issue Price:** $1190
**Last Year:** 2000
**Last Retail Price:** $1290

*Fantasy*

**Ref. No.:** 1136
**Name:** Orpheus
**Height:** 14.5
**Status:** Very rare
**Issue Year:** 1971
**Issue Price:** $135
**Last Year:** 1972
**Last Retail Price:** Unknown

**Ref. No.:** 6578
**Name:** Graceful Tune
**Height:** 14.5
**Status:** Open issue, retired
**Issue Year:** 1999
**Issue Price:** $470
**Last Year:** 2002
**Last Retail Price:** $480
**Comment:** Introduced by select
    dealers in 1998

**Ref. No.:** 6324
**Name:** Princess of Peace
**Height:** 15.75
**Status:** Open issue, retired
**Issue Year:** 1996
**Issue Price:** $830
**Last Year:** 2000
**Last Retail Price:** $830

**Ref. No.:** 1349
**Name:** Mermaids Playing
**Height:** 16
**Status:** Open issue, retired
**Issue Year:** 1978
**Issue Price:** $425
**Last Year:** 1983
**Last Retail Price:** $625
**High Auction Price:** $3000
**Low Auction Price:** $2500

**Ref. No.:** 6397
**Name:** In Neptune's Waves
**Height:** 16
**Status:** Open issue, retired
**Issue Year:** 1997
**Issue Price:** $1030
**Last Year:** 1999
**Last Retail Price:** $1030

**Ref. No.:** 1347
**Name:** Mermaid on Wave
**Height:** 16.5
**Status:** Open issue, retired
**Issue Year:** 1978
**Issue Price:** $260
**Last Year:** 1983
**Last Retail Price:** $282.50
**Auction Price:** $1800

**Ref. No.:** 981.14
**Name:** Allegory to the Peace
**Height:** 19
**Issue Year:** 1969
**Issue Price:** Unknown
**Last Year:** Unknown
**Last Retail Price:** Unknown

**Ref. No.:** 6707
**Name:** Peace And Liberty
**Height:** 19.5
**Status:** Open issue, active
**Issue Year:** 2000
**Issue Price:** $1500
**2003 Retail Price:** $1750

**Ref. No.:** 5819
**Name:** Allegory of Liberty
**Height:** 20.5
**Status:** Open issue, active
**Issue Year:** 1991
**Issue Price:** $1950
**2003 Retail Price:** $2100

*Fantasy*

# *Animals*

**Ref. No.:** 5317
**Name:** Miniature Lamb
**Height:** 1.25
**Status:** Open edition, retired
**Issue Year:** 1985
**Issue Price:** $30
**Last Year:** 1990
**Last Retail Price:** $50

**Ref. No.:** 1045
**Name:** Small Hippopotamus
**Height:** 1.5
**Status:** Very Rare
**Issue Year:** 1969
**Issue Price:** $9.50
**Last Year:** 1970
**Last Retail Price:** Unknown

**Ref. No.:** 5312
**Name:** Miniature Bison, Resting
**Height:** 1.5
**Status:** Open edition, retired
**Issue Year:** 1985
**Issue Price:** $50
**Last Year:** 1990
**Last Retail Price:** $70
**High Auction Price:** $163
**Low Auction Price:** $100

**Ref. No.:** 5314
**Name:** Miniature Deer
**Height:** 2
**Status:** Open edition, retired
**Issue Year:** 1985
**Issue Price:** $40
**Last Year:** 1990
**Last Retail Price:** $60
**Auction Price:** $175

**Ref. No.:** 5435
**Name:** Cougar
**Height:** 2
**Status:** Open edition, retired
**Issue Year:** 1987
**Issue Price:** $65
**Last Year:** 1990
**Last Retail Price:** $80
**High Auction Price:** $450
**Low Auction Price:** $200

**Ref. No.:** 5437
**Name:** Rhino
**Height:** 2
**Status:** Open edition, retired
**Issue Year:** 1987
**Issue Price:** $50
**Last Year:** 1990
**Last Retail Price:** $65
**Auction Price:** $200

**Ref. No.:** 5438
**Name:** Elephant
**Height:** 2
**Status:** Open edition, retired
**Issue Year:** 1987
**Issue Price:** $50
**Last Year:** 1990
**Last Retail Price:** $65

**Ref. No.:** 1044
**Name:** Large Hippopotamus
**Height:** 2.25
**Status:** Very Rare
**Issue Year:** 1969
**Issue Price:** $16.50
**Last Year:** 1970
**Last Retail Price:** Unknown

**Ref. No.:** 5313
**Name:** Miniature Bison,
    Attacking
**Height:** 2.25
**Status:** Open edition, retired
**Issue Year:** 1985
**Issue Price:** $57.50
**Last Year:** 1990
**Last Retail Price:** $75
**High Auction Price:** $225
**Low Auction Price:** $163

**Ref. No.:** 5436
**Name:** Lion
**Height:** 2.25
**Status:** Open edition, retired
**Issue Year:** 1987
**Issue Price:** $50
**Last Year:** 1990
**Last Retail Price:** $65
**High Auction Price:** $300
**Low Auction Price:** $200

**Ref. No.:** 6173
**Name:** A Moment's Rest
**Height:** 2.25
**Status:** Open issue, active
**Issue Year:** 1995
**Issue Price:** Unknown
**2003 Retail Price:** $140

**Ref. No.:** 6703
**Name:** From Nature's Palette
**Height:** 2.5
**Status:** Open issue, active
**Issue Year:** 2000
**Issue Price:** $140
**2003 Retail Price:** $145

*Animals*

**Ref. No.:** 1047
**Name:** Sheep
**Height:** 2.75
**Status:** Very Rare
**Issue Year:** 1969
**Issue Price:** $9
**Last Year:** 1970
**Last Retail Price:** Unknown

**Ref. No.:** 5315
**Name:** Miniature Dromedary
**Height:** 2.75
**Status:** Open edition, retired
**Issue Year:** 1985
**Issue Price:** $45
**Last Year:** 1990
**Last Retail Price:** $65
**Auction Price:** $150

**Ref. No.:** 6702
**Name:** Nature's Observer
**Height:** 2.75
**Status:** Open issue, active
**Issue Year:** 2000
**Issue Price:** $160
**2003 Retail Price:** $165

**Ref. No.:** 1065
**Name:** Fox and Cub
**Height:** 3
**Status:** Open edition, retired
**Issue Year:** 1969
**Issue Price:** $17.50
**Last Year:** 1985
**Last Retail Price:** $87.5
**High Auction Price:** $725
**Low Auction Price:** $250

**Ref. No.:** 1206
**Name:** Bear Seated
**Height:** 3
**Status:** Open edition, retired
**Issue Year:** 1972
**Issue Price:** $16
**Last Year:** 1989
**Last Retail Price:** $60
**Auction Price:** $225

**Ref. No.:** 1209
**Name:** Seated Polar Bear
**Height:** 3
**Status:** Open issue, active
**Issue Year:** 1972
**Issue Price:** $16
**2003 Retail Price:** $75

**Ref. No.:** 5022
**Name:** Painful Lion
**Height:** 3
**Status:** Open edition, retired
**Issue Year:** 1978
**Issue Price:** $95
**Last Year:** 1981
**Last Retail Price:** $125

**Ref. No.:** 5228
**Name:** Playful Piglets
**Height:** 3
**Status:** Open issue, retired
**Issue Year:** 1984
**Issue Price:** $80
**Last Year:** 1998
**Last Retail Price:** $165

**Ref. No.:** 5432
**Name:** Monkey
**Height:** 3
**Status:** Open edition, retired
**Issue Year:** 1987
**Issue Price:** $60
**Last Year:** 1990
**Last Retail Price:** $75
**High Auction Price:** $250
**Low Auction Price:** $150

**Ref. No.:** 6330
**Name:** Refreshing Pause
**Height:** 3
**Status:** Open issue, active
**Issue Year:** 1996
**Issue Price:** $170
**2003 Retail Price:** $175

**Ref. No.:** 6589
**Name:** Morning Calm
**Height:** 3
**Status:** Open issue, retired
**Issue Year:** 1998
**Issue Price:** $130
**Last Year:** 2002
**Last Retail Price:** $135

**Ref. No.:** 1443
**Name:** Bearly Love
**Height:** 3.5
**Status:** Open issue, retired
**Issue Year:** 1983
**Issue Price:** $55
**Last Year:** 1999
**Last Retail Price:** $140

*Animals*

**Ref. No.:** 2037
**Name:** Hedgehog
**Height:** 3.5
**Status:** Open edition, retired
**Issue Year:** 1971
**Issue Price:** $12.50
**Last Year:** 1973
**Last Retail Price:** $15

**Ref. No.:** 5316
**Name:** Miniature Giraffe
**Height:** 3.5
**Status:** Open edition, retired
**Issue Year:** 1985
**Issue Price:** $50
**Last Year:** 1990
**Last Retail Price:** $70
**Auction Price:** $250

**Ref. No.:** 5392
**Name:** Balancing Act
**Height:** 3.5
**Status:** Open edition, retired
**Issue Year:** 1986
**Issue Price:** $35
**Last Year:** 1990
**Last Retail Price:** $50
**High Auction Price:** $175
**Low Auction Price:** $150

**Ref. No.:** 5434
**Name:** Miniature Polar Bear
**Height:** 3.5
**Status:** Open issue, retired
**Issue Year:** 1987
**Issue Price:** $65
**Last Year:** 2000
**Last Retail Price:** $115

**Ref. No.:** 301.13
**Name:** Polar Bear
**Height:** 4
**Status:** Very Rare
**Issue Year:** 1965
**Issue Price:** Unknown
**Last Year:** Unknown
**Last Retail Price:** Unknown

**Ref. No.:** 1046
**Name:** Lamb
**Height:** 4
**Status:** Very Rare
**Issue Year:** 1969
**Issue Price:** $10.50
**Last Year:** 1970
**Last Retail Price:** Unknown
**Auction Price:** $250

**Ref. No.:** 1204
**Name:** Attentive Bear
**Height:** 4
**Status:** Open edition, retired
**Issue Year:** 1972
**Issue Price:** $16
**Last Year:** 1989
**Last Retail Price:** $60
**Auction Price:** $225

**Ref. No.:** 1207
**Name:** Attentive Polar Bear
**Height:** 4
**Status:** Open issue, active
**Issue Year:** 1972
**Issue Price:** $16
**2003 Retail Price:** $75

**Ref. No.:** 1210
**Name:** Round Fish
**Height:** 4
**Status:** Very Rare
**Issue Year:** 1972
**Issue Price:** $35
**Last Year:** 1981
**Last Retail Price:** Unknown
**High Auction Price:** $675
**Low Auction Price:** $550

**Ref. No.:** 6354
**Name:** Attentive Polar Bear with
Flowers
**Height:** 4
**Status:** Open issue, active
**Issue Year:** 1997
**Issue Price:** $100
**2003 Retail Price:** $100

**Ref. No.:** 6356
**Name:** Polar Bear Seated with
Flowers
**Height:** 4
**Status:** Open issue, retired
**Issue Year:** 1997
**Issue Price:** $100
**Last Year:** 2001
**Last Retail Price:** $100

**Ref. No.:** 6460
**Name:** Lucky Strolling
**Height:** 4
**Status:** Open issue, retired
**Issue Year:** 1997
**Issue Price:** $120
**Last Year:** 2001
**Last Retail Price:** $120

*Animals*

**Ref. No.:** 4821
**Name:** Burro
**Height:** 4.25
**Status:** Open edition, retired
**Issue Year:** 1972
**Issue Price:** $24
**Last Year:** 1979
**Last Retail Price:** $45
**Auction Price:** $450

**Ref. No.:** 5433
**Name:** Kangaroo
**Height:** 4.25
**Status:** Open edition, retired
**Issue Year:** 1987
**Issue Price:** $65
**Last Year:** 1990
**Last Retail Price:** $80
**High Auction Price:** $300
**Low Auction Price:** $225

**Ref. No.:** 5673
**Name:** A Quiet Moment
**Height:** 4.25
**Status:** Open issue, retired
**Issue Year:** 1990
**Issue Price:** $450
**Last Year:** 1997
**Last Retail Price:** $520

**Ref. No.:** 300.13
**Name:** Polar Bear
**Height:** 4.5
**Status:** Very Rare
**Issue Year:** 1965
**Issue Price:** Unknown
**Last Year:** Unknown
**Last Retail Price:** Unknown

**Ref. No.:** 328.13
**Name:** Polar Bear
**Height:** 4.5
**Status:** Very Rare
**Issue Year:** 1965
**Issue Price:** Unknown
**Last Year:** Unknown
**Last Retail Price:** Unknown

**Ref. No.:** 6859
**Name:** Pond Dreamer
**Height:** 4.5
**Status:** Open issue, active
**Issue Year:** 2002
**Issue Price:** $195
**2003 Retail Price:** $195

**Ref. No.:** 1203
**Name:** Little Horse Resting
**Height:** 4.75
**Status:** Open edition, retired
**Issue Year:** 1972
**Issue Price:** $40
**Last Year:** 1981
**Last Retail Price:** $82.5
**Auction Price:** $650

**Ref. No.:** 1205
**Name:** Good Bear
**Height:** 4.75
**Status:** Open edition, retired
**Issue Year:** 1972
**Issue Price:** $16
**Last Year:** 1989
**Last Retail Price:** $60
**Auction Price:** $225

**Ref. No.:** 4639
**Name:** Naughty Pony
**Height:** 4.75
**Status:** Open edition, retired
**Issue Year:** 1969
**Issue Price:** $15
**Last Year:** 1972
**Last Retail Price:** $17.50

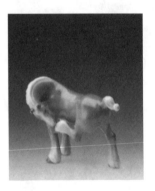

**Ref. No.:** 327.13
**Name:** Gazelle
**Height:** 5
**Status:** Very Rare
**Issue Year:** 1963
**Issue Price:** Unknown
**Last Year:** Unknown
**Last Retail Price:** Unknown

**Ref. No.:** 4524
**Name:** Donkey in Love
**Height:** 5
**Status:** Open edition, retired
**Issue Year:** 1969
**Issue Price:** $15
**Last Year:** 1985
**Last Retail Price:** $82.5
**High Auction Price:** $500
**Low Auction Price:** $325

**Ref. No.:** 4861
**Name:** Horse
**Height:** 5
**Status:** Open edition, retired
**Issue Year:** 1974
**Issue Price:** $55
**Last Year:** 1978
**Last Retail Price:** $85
**Auction Price:** $450

*Animals*

**Ref. No.:** 4863
**Name:** Horse
**Height:** 5
**Status:** Open edition, retired
**Issue Year:** 1974
**Issue Price:** $55
**Last Year:** 1978
**Last Retail Price:** $85
**Auction Price:** $500

**Ref. No.:** 6355
**Name:** Polar Bear Resting with
  Flowers
**Height:** 5
**Status:** Open issue, retired
**Issue Year:** 1997
**Issue Price:** $100
**Last Year:** 2001
**Last Retail Price:** $100

**Ref. No.:** 6410
**Name:** Would You Be Mine?
**Height:** 5
**Status:** Open issue, retired
**Issue Year:** 1997
**Issue Price:** $190
**Last Year:** 2000
**Last Retail Price:** $190

**Ref. No.:** 6462
**Name:** Lucky in Love
**Height:** 5
**Status:** Open issue, active
**Issue Year:** 1997
**Issue Price:** $110
**2003 Retail Price:** $125

**Ref. No.:** 6547
**Name:** Baby Girl Lamb
**Height:** 5
**Status:** Open issue, retired
**Issue Year:** 1998
**Issue Price:** $105
**Last Year:** 2000
**Last Retail Price:** $120

**Ref. No.:** 1208
**Name:** Resting Polar Bear
**Height:** 5.25
**Status:** Open issue, active
**Issue Year:** 1972
**Issue Price:** $16
**2003 Retail Price:** $75

**Ref. No.:** 6860
**Name:** Underwater Calm
**Height:** 5.25
**Status:** Open issue, active
**Issue Year:** 2002
**Issue Price:** $195
**2003 Retail Price:** $195

**Ref. No.:** 5018
**Name:** Painful Monkey
**Height:** 5.5
**Status:** Open edition, retired
**Issue Year:** 1978
**Issue Price:** $135
**Last Year:** 1981
**Last Retail Price:** $175
**Auction Price:** $700

**Ref. No.:** 5020
**Name:** Painful Elephant
**Height:** 5.5
**Status:** Open edition, retired
**Issue Year:** 1978
**Issue Price:** $85
**Last Year:** 1981
**Last Retail Price:** $110

**Ref. No.:** 5318
**Name:** Miniature Seal Family
**Height:** 5.5
**Status:** Open edition, retired
**Issue Year:** 1985
**Issue Price:** $77.50
**Last Year:** 1990
**Last Retail Price:** $110
**High Auction Price:** $275
**Low Auction Price:** $250

**Ref. No.:** 5683
**Name:** Beautiful Burro
**Height:** 5.5
**Status:** Open edition, retired
**Issue Year:** 1990
**Issue Price:** $280
**Last Year:** 1993
**Last Retail Price:** $325

**Ref. No.:** 5672
**Name:** Hi There!
**Height:** 5.75
**Status:** Open issue, retired
**Issue Year:** 1990
**Issue Price:** $450
**Last Year:** 1996
**Last Retail Price:** $520

*Animals*

**Ref. No.:** 56.04
**Name:** Baby Deer and Bunny
**Height:** 6
**Status:** Very Rare
**Issue Year:** 1955
**Issue Price:** Unknown
**Last Year:** Unknown
**Last Retail Price:** Unknown

**Ref. No.:** 5674
**Name:** A Fawn and a Friend
**Height:** 6
**Status:** Open issue, retired
**Issue Year:** 1990
**Issue Price:** $450
**Last Year:** 1996
**Last Retail Price:** $520

**Ref. No.:** 6409
**Name:** A Surprise Visit
**Height:** 6
**Status:** Open issue, retired
**Issue Year:** 1997
**Issue Price:** $190
**Last Year:** 2000
**Last Retail Price:** $190

**Ref. No.:** 6461
**Name:** Lucky's Call
**Height:** 6
**Status:** Open issue, retired
**Issue Year:** 1997
**Issue Price:** $155
**Last Year:** 2001
**Last Retail Price:** $155

**Ref. No.:** 1005
**Name:** Giraffe Group
**Height:** 6.25
**Status:** Open edition, retired
**Issue Year:** 1969
**Issue Price:** $60
**Last Year:** 1970
**Last Retail Price:** $60

**Ref. No.:** 1062
**Name:** Bull with Head Down
**Height:** 6.5
**Status:** Open edition, retired
**Issue Year:** 1969
**Issue Price:** $90
**Last Year:** 1975
**Last Retail Price:** $170

**Ref. No.:** 1064
**Name:** Deer
**Height:** 6.5
**Status:** Open edition, retired
**Issue Year:** 1969
**Issue Price:** $27.50
**Last Year:** 1986
**Last Retail Price:** $112.5
**High Auction Price:** $450
**Low Auction Price:** $275

**Ref. No.:** 4683
**Name:** Calf
**Height:** 6.5
**Status:** Open edition, retired
**Issue Year:** 1970
**Issue Price:** $17.50
**Last Year:** 1972
**Last Retail Price:** $20

**Ref. No.:** 4944
**Name:** Rhinoceros
**Height:** 6.5
**Status:** Open edition, retired
**Issue Year:** 1976
**Issue Price:** $95
**Last Year:** 1978
**Last Retail Price:** $125

**Ref. No.:** 5019
**Name:** Painful Giraffe
**Height:** 6.5
**Status:** Open edition, retired
**Issue Year:** 1978
**Issue Price:** $115
**Last Year:** 1981
**Last Retail Price:** $150

**Ref. No.:** 5545
**Name:** El Toro
**Height:** 6.5
**Status:** Open edition, retired
**Issue Year:** 1989
**Issue Price:** $225
**Last Year:** 1991
**Last Retail Price:** $260

**Ref. No.:** 6745
**Name:** Arctic Family
**Height:** 6.5
**Status:** Open issue, active
**Issue Year:** 2001
**Issue Price:** $175
**2003 Retail Price:** $175

*Animals*

**Ref. No.:** 5023
**Name:** Painful Kangaroo
**Height:** 6.75
**Status:** Open edition, retired
**Issue Year:** 1978
**Issue Price:** $150
**Last Year:** 1981
**Last Retail Price:** $195

**Ref. No.:** 113.06
**Name:** Giraffe With Baby
**Height:** 7
**Status:** Very Rare
**Issue Year:** 1958
**Issue Price:** Unknown
**Last Year:** Unknown
**Last Retail Price:** Unknown

**Ref. No.:** 299.13
**Name:** Polar Bear
**Height:** 7
**Status:** Very Rare
**Issue Year:** 1965
**Issue Price:** Unknown
**Last Year:** Unknown
**Last Retail Price:** Unknown

**Ref. No.:** 1063
**Name:** Bull, with Head Up
**Height:** 7
**Status:** Open edition, retired
**Issue Year:** 1969
**Issue Price:** $90
**Last Year:** 1975
**Last Retail Price:** $125
**Auction Price:** $1500

**Ref. No.:** 4765
**Name:** Maternal Elephant
**Height:** 7
**Status:** Open edition, retired
**Issue Year:** 1971
**Issue Price:** $50
**Last Year:** 1975
**Last Retail Price:** $80

**Ref. No.:** 4862
**Name:** Horse
**Height:** 7
**Status:** Open edition, retired
**Issue Year:** 1974
**Issue Price:** $55
**Last Year:** 1978
**Last Retail Price:** $85

**Ref. No.:** 5302
**Name:** Antelope Drinking
**Height:** 7
**Status:** Open edition, retired
**Issue Year:** 1985
**Issue Price:** $215
**Last Year:** 1988
**Last Retail Price:** $250
**High Auction Price:** $650
**Low Auction Price:** $300

**Ref. No.:** 6470
**Name:** A Swimming Lesson
**Height:** 7
**Status:** Open issue, active
**Issue Year:** 1997
**Issue Price:** $260
**2003 Retail Price:** $295

**Ref. No.:** 6531
**Name:** A New Life
**Height:** 7
**Status:** Open issue, retired
**Issue Year:** 1998
**Issue Price:** $490
**Last Year:** 2000
**Last Retail Price:** $530

**Ref. No.:** 6546
**Name:** Baby Boy Lamb
**Height:** 7
**Status:** Open issue, retired
**Issue Year:** 1998
**Issue Price:** $105
**Last Year:** 2000
**Last Retail Price:** $120

**Ref. No.:** 6573
**Name:** Parading Donkey
**Height:** 7
**Status:** Open issue, retired
**Issue Year:** 1998
**Issue Price:** $220
**Last Year:** 2000
**Last Retail Price:** $275

**Ref. No.:** 5021
**Name:** Painful Bear
**Height:** 7.25
**Status:** Open edition, retired
**Issue Year:** 1978
**Issue Price:** $75
**Last Year:** 1981
**Last Retail Price:** $95

*Animals*

**Ref. No.:** 4945
**Name:** Bison
**Height:** 7.5
**Status:** Open edition, retired
**Issue Year:** 1976
**Issue Price:** $100
**Last Year:** 1978
**Last Retail Price:** $130
**Auction Price:** $3000

**Ref. No.:** 6034
**Name:** Monkey Business
**Height:** 7.75
**Status:** Open edition, retired
**Issue Year:** 1993
**Issue Price:** $785
**Last Year:** 1994
**Last Retail Price:** $745
**Auction Price:** $900

**Ref. No.:** 6456
**Name:** Dance of the Dolphins
**Height:** 8
**Status:** Open issue, retired
**Issue Year:** 1997
**Issue Price:** $315
**Last Year:** 2002
**Last Retail Price:** $385

**Ref. No.:** 5461
**Name:** Koala Love
**Height:** 8.25
**Status:** Open edition, retired
**Issue Year:** 1988
**Issue Price:** $115
**Last Year:** 1993
**Last Retail Price:** $150
**High Auction Price:** $400
**Low Auction Price:** $300

**Ref. No.:** 5544
**Name:** Derby Winner
**Height:** 8.25
**Status:** Open edition, retired
**Issue Year:** 1989
**Issue Price:** $225
**Last Year:** 1991
**Last Retail Price:** $260
**Auction Price:** $350

**Ref. No.:** 4532
**Name:** Watchful Gazelle
**Height:** 8.5
**Status:** Open edition, retired
**Issue Year:** 1969
**Issue Price:** $30
**Last Year:** 1970
**Last Retail Price:** $30

**Ref. No.:** 1134
**Name:** Bull
**Height:** 9
**Status:** Very Rare
**Issue Year:** 1971
**Issue Price:** $130
**Last Year:** 1972
**Last Retail Price:** Unknown
**Auction Price:** $1500

**Ref. No.:** 4562
**Name:** Llama Resting
**Height:** 9
**Status:** Open edition, retired
**Issue Year:** 1969
**Issue Price:** $25
**Last Year:** 1972
**Last Retail Price:** $30

**Ref. No.:** 4774
**Name:** Dormouse
**Height:** 9
**Status:** Open edition, retired
**Issue Year:** 1971
**Issue Price:** $30
**Last Year:** 1983
**Last Retail Price:** $155
**High Auction Price:** $350
**Low Auction Price:** $200

**Ref. No.:** 5001
**Name:** Elk Family
**Height:** 9
**Status:** Open edition, retired
**Issue Year:** 1978
**Issue Price:** $550
**Last Year:** 1981
**Last Retail Price:** $700
**High Auction Price:** $1500
**Low Auction Price:** $900

**Ref. No.:** 277.12
**Name:** Horse
**Height:** 9.5
**Status:** Very Rare
**Issue Year:** 1958
**Issue Price:** Unknown
**Last Year:** Unknown
**Last Retail Price:** Unknown

**Ref. No.:** 356.13
**Name:** Horse and Squirrel
**Height:** 9.5
**Status:** Very Rare
**Issue Year:** 1965
**Issue Price:** Unknown
**Last Year:** Unknown
**Last Retail Price:** Unknown

*Animals*

**Ref. No.:** 4769
**Name:** Ermine
**Height:** 9.5
**Status:** Open edition, retired
**Issue Year:** 1971
**Issue Price:** $25
**Last Year:** 1975
**Last Retail Price:** $40
**Auction Price:** $700

**Ref. No.:** 6899
**Name:** Orca
**Height:** 9.5
**Status:** Open issue, active
**Issue Year:** 2002
**Issue Price:** $450
**2003 Retail Price:** $450

**Ref. No.:** 6436
**Name:** The Dolphins
**Height:** 10
**Status:** Open issue, active
**Issue Year:** 1997
**Issue Price:** $965
**2003 Retail Price:** $1125

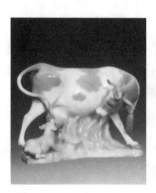

**Ref. No.:** 4640
**Name:** Cow with Pig
**Height:** 10.25
**Status:** Open edition, retired
**Issue Year:** 1969
**Issue Price:** $42.50
**Last Year:** 1981
**Last Retail Price:** $135
**Auction Price:** $800

**Ref. No.:** 1133
**Name:** Horse
**Height:** 10.5
**Status:** Very Rare
**Issue Year:** 1971
**Issue Price:** $115
**Last Year:** 1972
**Last Retail Price:** Unknown
**Auction Price:** $900

**Ref. No.:** 4521
**Name:** Deer Hunt
**Height:** 10.5
**Status:** Open edition, retired
**Issue Year:** 1969
**Issue Price:** $110
**Last Year:** 1970
**Last Retail Price:** $115

**Ref. No.:** 4529
**Name:** Gazelle Jumping
**Height:** 10.5
**Status:** Open edition, retired
**Issue Year:** 1969
**Issue Price:** $45
**Last Year:** 1970
**Last Retail Price:** $50

**Ref. No.:** 4531
**Name:** Gazelle Group
**Height:** 10.5
**Status:** Open edition, retired
**Issue Year:** 1969
**Issue Price:** $85
**Last Year:** 1971
**Last Retail Price:** $105

**Ref. No.:** 4880
**Name:** Pursuit
**Height:** 11
**Status:** Open edition, retired
**Issue Year:** 1974
**Issue Price:** $425
**Last Year:** 1983
**Last Retail Price:** $950

**Ref. No.:** 6873
**Name:** First Steps on the Prairie
**Height:** 11.25
**Status:** Open issue, active
**Issue Year:** 2002
**Issue Price:** $1225
**2003 Retail Price:** $1250

**Ref. No.:** 3511
**Name:** Horse Heads
**Height:** 11.5
**Status:** Open edition, retired
**Issue Year:** 1978
**Issue Price:** $260
**Last Year:** 1990
**Last Retail Price:** $450
**High Auction Price:** $700
**Low Auction Price:** $550

**Ref. No.:** 4530
**Name:** Gazelle Landing
**Height:** 11.5
**Status:** Open edition, retired
**Issue Year:** 1969
**Issue Price:** $45
**Last Year:** 1970
**Last Retail Price:** $50

*Animals*

**Ref. No.:** 4655
**Name:** Horse Group
**Height:** 11.5
**Status:** Open issue, retired
**Issue Year:** 1969
**Issue Price:** $110
**Last Year:** 2000
**Last Retail Price:** $760

**Ref. No.:** 1151
**Name:** Two Elephants
**Height:** 11.75
**Status:** Open issue, retired
**Issue Year:** 1971
**Issue Price:** $45
**Last Year:** 1999
**Last Retail Price:** $440

**Ref. No.:** 6796
**Name:** Majesty of the Seas
**Height:** 12
**Status:** Open issue, active
**Issue Year:** 2001
**Issue Price:** $775
**2003 Retail Price:** $850

**Ref. No.:** 5271
**Name:** Gazelle
**Height:** 13
**Status:** Open edition, retired
**Issue Year:** 1985
**Issue Price:** $205
**Last Year:** 1988
**Last Retail Price:** $250
**High Auction Price:** $550
**Low Auction Price:** $400

**Ref. No.:** 4964
**Name:** Bucks
**Height:** 13.75
**Status:** Open edition, retired
**Issue Year:** 1977
**Issue Price:** $725
**Last Year:** 1981
**Last Retail Price:** $1000

**Ref. No.:** 4561
**Name:** Llama Group
**Height:** 14.25
**Status:** Open edition, retired
**Issue Year:** 1969
**Issue Price:** $55
**Last Year:** 1970
**Last Retail Price:** $60

**Ref. No.:** 1150
**Name:** Elephants Walking
**Height:** 14.5
**Status:** Open issue, active
**Issue Year:** 1971
**Issue Price:** $100
**2003 Retail Price:** $795

**Ref. No.:** 4597
**Name:** Two Horses
**Height:** 14.5
**Status:** Open edition, retired
**Issue Year:** 1969
**Issue Price:** $240
**Last Year:** 1990
**Last Retail Price:** $1200
**High Auction Price:** $1000
**Low Auction Price:** $900

**Ref. No.:** 4764
**Name:** Elephant Family
**Height:** 14.5
**Status:** Open edition, retired
**Issue Year:** 1971
**Issue Price:** $90
**Last Year:** 1975
**Last Retail Price:** $145

**Ref. No.:** 5043
**Name:** Hind and Baby Deer
**Height:** 14.5
**Status:** Open edition, retired
**Issue Year:** 1980
**Issue Price:** $650
**Last Year:** 1981
**Last Retail Price:** $705
**High Auction Price:** $3600
**Low Auction Price:** $2000

**Ref. No.:** 6742
**Name:** Underwater Explorers
**Height:** 14.5
**Status:** Open issue, active
**Issue Year:** 2000
**Issue Price:** $655
**2003 Retail Price:** $675

**Ref. No.:** 1420
**Name:** Born Free
**Height:** 15
**Status:** Open issue, active
**Issue Year:** 1982
**Issue Price:** $1520
**2003 Retail Price:** $3350

*Animals*

**Ref. No.:** 4781
**Name:** Horse
**Height:** 16.5
**Status:** Open edition, retired
**Issue Year:** 1971
**Issue Price:** $150
**Last Year:** 1979
**Last Retail Price:** $350

**Ref. No.:** 1021
**Name:** Horse's Group
**Height:** 17.25
**Status:** Open edition, active
**Issue Year:** 1969
**Issue Price:** $465
**Auction Price:** $1400
**2003 Retail Price:** $2595

**Ref. No.:** 1022
**Name:** Horse's Group, White
**Height:** 17.25
**Status:** Open issue, active
**Issue Year:** 1969
**Issue Price:** $465
**2003 Retail Price:** $2150

**Ref. No.:** 5131
**Name:** Frolicking Stags
**Height:** 18
**Status:** Open edition, retired
**Issue Year:** 1982
**Issue Price:** $1250
**Last Year:** 1985
**Last Retail Price:** $1250

**Ref. No.:** 1567
**Name:** Running Free
**Height:** 19
**Status:** Open issue, retired
**Issue Year:** 1987
**Issue Price:** $1150
**Auction Price:** $1350
**Last Year:** 1998
**Last Retail Price:** $1600

**Ref. No.:** 1566
**Name:** Wild Stallions
**Height:** 20.5
**Status:** Open edition, retired
**Issue Year:** 1987
**Issue Price:** $1100
**Last Year:** 1993
**Last Retail Price:** $1465

**Domestic Animals**

**Ref. No.:** 5309
**Name:** Miniature Cocker Spaniel
**Height:** 1
**Status:** Open edition, retired
**Issue Year:** 1985
**Issue Price:** $35
**Last Year:** 1993
**Last Retail Price:** $70
**Auction Price:** $150

**Ref. No.:** 5310
**Name:** Miniature Cocker Spaniel
**Height:** 1
**Status:** Open edition, retired
**Issue Year:** 1985
**Issue Price:** $35
**Last Year:** 1993
**Last Retail Price:** $70
**Auction Price:** $175

**Ref. No.:** 105.06
**Name:** Dog and Dice
**Height:** 1.5
**Issue Year:** 1956
**Issue Price:** Unknown
**Last Year:** Unknown
**Last Retail Price:** Unknown

**Ref. No.:** 5307
**Name:** Miniature Kitten
**Height:** 1.75
**Status:** Open edition, retired
**Issue Year:** 1985
**Issue Price:** $35
**Last Year:** 1993
**Last Retail Price:** $70
**Auction Price:** $225

**Ref. No.:** 5394
**Name:** Poor Puppy
**Height:** 1.75
**Status:** Open edition, retired
**Issue Year:** 1986
**Issue Price:** $25
**Last Year:** 1990
**Last Retail Price:** $40

**Ref. No.:** 279.12
**Name:** Rabbit Couple
**Height:** 2
**Status:** Very Rare
**Issue Year:** 1962
**Issue Price:** Unknown
**Last Year:** Unknown
**Last Retail Price:** Unknown

*Animals*

**Ref. No.:** 324.13
**Name:** Sleepy Dog
**Height:** 2
**Status:** Very Rare
**Issue Year:** 1976
**Issue Price:** Unknown
**Last Year:** Unknown
**Last Retail Price:** Unknown

**Ref. No.:** 352.13
**Name:** Long Rabbit
**Height:** 2
**Status:** Very Rare
**Issue Year:** 1965
**Issue Price:** Unknown
**Last Year:** Unknown
**Last Retail Price:** Unknown

**Ref. No.:** 5311
**Name:** Miniature Puppies (3)
**Height:** 2
**Status:** Open edition, retired
**Issue Year:** 1985
**Issue Price:** $65
**Last Year:** 1990
**Last Retail Price:** $90
**High Auction Price:** $200
**Low Auction Price:** $175

**Ref. No.:** 5393
**Name:** Curiosity
**Height:** 2
**Status:** Open edition, retired
**Issue Year:** 1986
**Issue Price:** $25
**Last Year:** 1990
**Last Retail Price:** $40
**Auction Price:** $150

**Ref. No.:** 6417
**Name:** Unlikely Friends
**Height:** 2
**Status:** Open issue, active
**Issue Year:** 1997
**Issue Price:** $125
**2003 Retail Price:** $125

**Ref. No.:** 55.04
**Name:** Bunny
**Height:** 2.25
**Status:** Very Rare
**Issue Year:** 1954
**Issue Price:** Unknown
**Last Year:** Unknown
**Last Retail Price:** Unknown

**Ref. No.:** 1072
**Name:** Beagle Puppy
**Height:** 2.25
**Status:** Open edition, retired
**Issue Year:** 1969
**Issue Price:** $16.50
**Last Year:** 1991
**Last Retail Price:** $120

**Ref. No.:** 1260
**Name:** Dalmatian
**Height:** 2.25
**Status:** Open edition, retired
**Issue Year:** 1974
**Issue Price:** $25
**Last Year:** 1981
**Last Retail Price:** $25

**Ref. No.:** 1261
**Name:** Dalmatian
**Height:** 2.25
**Status:** Open edition, retired
**Issue Year:** 1974
**Issue Price:** $25
**Last Year:** 1981
**Last Retail Price:** $25

**Ref. No.:** 5308
**Name:** Miniature Cat
**Height:** 2.25
**Status:** Open edition, retired
**Issue Year:** 1985
**Issue Price:** $35
**Last Year:** 1993
**Last Retail Price:** $70
**Auction Price:** $225
  (sold with 5307)

**Ref. No.:** 5904
**Name:** Sleeping Bunny
**Height:** 2.25
**Status:** Open issue, retired
**Issue Year:** 1992
**Issue Price:** $75
**Last Year:** 1997
**Last Retail Price:** $75

**Ref. No.:** 5349
**Name:** Relaxing
**Height:** 2.5
**Status:** Open edition, retired
**Issue Year:** 1986
**Issue Price:** $47.50
**Last Year:** 1990
**Last Retail Price:** $60
**Auction Price:** $150

*Animals*

**Ref. No.:** 6097
**Name:** Sleeping Bunny with
    Flowers
**Height:** 2.5
**Status:** Open issue, retired
**Issue Year:** 1994
**Issue Price:** $110
**Last Year:** 1997
**Last Retail Price:** $110

**Ref. No.:** 278.12
**Name:** Rabbit Scratching
**Height:** 2.75
**Status:** Very Rare
**Issue Year:** 1962
**Issue Price:** Unknown
**Last Year:** Unknown
**Last Retail Price:** Unknown

**Ref. No.:** 1067
**Name:** Old Dog
**Height:** 2.75
**Status:** Open edition, retired
**Issue Year:** 1969
**Issue Price:** $40
**Last Year:** 1978
**Last Retail Price:** $90
**Auction Price:** $700

**Ref. No.:** 4901
**Name:** Vagabond Dog
**Height:** 2.75
**Status:** Open edition, retired
**Issue Year:** 1974
**Issue Price:** $25
**Last Year:** 1979
**Last Retail Price:** $45

**Ref. No.:** 6666
**Name:** Graceful Landing
**Height:** 2.75
**Status:** Open issue, active
**Issue Year:** 1999
**Issue Price:** $155
**2003 Retail Price:** $165

**Ref. No.:** 106.06
**Name:** Collie
**Height:** 3
**Status:** Very Rare
**Issue Year:** 1956
**Issue Price:** Unknown
**Last Year:** Unknown
**Last Retail Price:** Unknown

**Ref. No.:** 1071
**Name:** Beagle Puppy
**Height:** 3
**Status:** Open edition, retired
**Issue Year:** 1969
**Issue Price:** $16.50
**Last Year:** 1990
**Last Retail Price:** $135
**Auction Price:** $325

**Ref. No.:** 1289
**Name:** Good Puppy
**Height:** 3
**Status:** Open edition, retired
**Issue Year:** 1974
**Issue Price:** $16.60
**Last Year:** 1985
**Last Retail Price:** $42
**High Auction Price:** $275
**Low Auction Price:** $190

**Ref. No.:** 4749
**Name:** Small Dog
**Height:** 3
**Status:** Open edition, retired
**Issue Year:** 1971
**Issue Price:** $5.50
**Last Year:** 1985
**Last Retail Price:** $31.5
**High Auction Price:** $200
**Low Auction Price:** $125

**Ref. No.:** 4772
**Name:** Rabbit Eating
**Height:** 3
**Status:** Open issue, retired
**Issue Year:** 1971
**Issue Price:** $16
**Last Year:** 1998
**Last Retail Price:** $135

**Ref. No.:** 4773
**Name:** Rabbit Eating (Gray)
**Height:** 3
**Status:** Open issue, retired
**Issue Year:** 1971
**Issue Price:** $16
**Last Year:** 1998
**Last Retail Price:** $130

**Ref. No.:** 4917
**Name:** Dog and Butterfly
**Height:** 3
**Status:** Open edition, retired
**Issue Year:** 1974
**Issue Price:** $50
**Last Year:** 1981
**Last Retail Price:** $110

*Animals*

**Ref. No.:** 5236
**Name:** Cat and Mouse
**Height:** 3
**Status:** Open issue, active
**Issue Year:** 1984
**Issue Price:** $55
**2003 Retail Price:** $100

**Ref. No.:** 6212
**Name:** Little Hunter
**Height:** 3.25
**Status:** Open issue, retired
**Issue Year:** 1995
**Issue Price:** $115
**Last Year:** 2000
**Last Retail Price:** $115

**Ref. No.:** 1262
**Name:** Dalmatian
**Height:** 3.5
**Status:** Open edition, retired
**Issue Year:** 1974
**Issue Price:** $25
**Last Year:** 1981
**Last Retail Price:** $25

**Ref. No.:** 1442
**Name:** Kitty Confrontation
**Height:** 3.5
**Status:** Open issue, active
**Issue Year:** 1983
**Issue Price:** $155
**2003 Retail Price:** $295

**Ref. No.:** 4902
**Name:** Moping Dog
**Height:** 3.5
**Status:** Open edition, retired
**Issue Year:** 1974
**Issue Price:** $35
**Last Year:** 1979
**Last Retail Price:** $65

**Ref. No.:** 5114
**Name:** Pet Me!
**Height:** 3.5
**Status:** Open issue, retired
**Issue Year:** 1982
**Issue Price:** $40
**Last Year:** 1999
**Last Retail Price:** $80

**Ref. No.:** 5348
**Name:** On the Scent
**Height:** 3.5
**Status:** Open edition, retired
**Issue Year:** 1986
**Issue Price:** $47.50
**Last Year:** 1990
**Last Retail Price:** $60
**High Auction Price:** $300
**Low Auction Price:** $175

**Ref. No.:** 5350
**Name:** On Guard
**Height:** 3.5
**Status:** Open edition, retired
**Issue Year:** 1986
**Issue Price:** $50
**Last Year:** 1990
**Last Retail Price:** $75
**Auction Price:** $450

**Ref. No.:** 5351
**Name:** Woe is Me
**Height:** 3.5
**Status:** Open edition, retired
**Issue Year:** 1986
**Issue Price:** $45
**Last Year:** 1990
**Last Retail Price:** $70
**Auction Price:** $200

**Ref. No.:** 5888
**Name:** That Tickles!
**Height:** 3.5
**Status:** Open edition, retired
**Issue Year:** 1992
**Issue Price:** $95
**Last Year:** 1995
**Last Retail Price:** $105

**Ref. No.:** 6599
**Name:** Bosom Buddies
**Height:** 3.5
**Status:** Open issue, retired
**Issue Year:** 1999
**Issue Price:** $235
**Last Year:** 2002
**Last Retail Price:** $240

**Ref. No.:** 5906
**Name:** Preening Bunny
**Height:** 3.75
**Status:** Open issue, retired
**Issue Year:** 1992
**Issue Price:** $75
**Last Year:** 1997
**Last Retail Price:** $80

*Animals*

**Ref. No.:** 308.13
**Name:** Hunting Dog
**Height:** 4
**Status:** Very Rare
**Issue Year:** 1963
**Issue Price:** Unknown
**Last Year:** Unknown
**Last Retail Price:** Unknown

**Ref. No.:** 1367
**Name:** Playful Dogs
**Height:** 4
**Status:** Open edition, retired
**Issue Year:** 1978
**Issue Price:** $160
**Last Year:** 1982
**Last Retail Price:** $205

**Ref. No.:** 5110
**Name:** Looking for a Clue
**Height:** 4
**Status:** Open edition, retired
**Issue Year:** 1982
**Issue Price:** $50
**Last Year:** 1985
**Last Retail Price:** $50
**High Auction Price:** $525
**Low Auction Price:** $500

**Ref. No.:** 5112
**Name:** Play with Me!
**Height:** 4
**Status:** Open issue, retired
**Issue Year:** 1982
**Issue Price:** $40
**Last Year:** 2000
**Last Retail Price:** $80

**Ref. No.:** 5356
**Name:** Wolfhound
**Height:** 4
**Status:** Open edition, retired
**Issue Year:** 1986
**Issue Price:** $45
**Last Year:** 1990
**Last Retail Price:** $65
**High Auction Price:** $250
**Low Auction Price:** $200

**Ref. No.:** 6099
**Name:** Preening Bunny with
    Flowers
**Height:** 4
**Status:** Open issue, retired
**Issue Year:** 1994
**Issue Price:** $140
**Last Year:** 1997
**Last Retail Price:** $140

**Ref. No.:** 6337
**Name:** Poodle
**Height:** 4
**Status:** Open issue, retired
**Issue Year:** 1997
**Issue Price:** $150
**Last Year:** 2000
**Last Retail Price:** $150

**Ref. No.:** 6566
**Name:** Secret Spot
**Height:** 4
**Status:** Open issue, active
**Issue Year:** 1998
**Issue Price:** $210
**2003 Retail Price:** $245

**Ref. No.:** 6568
**Name:** Kitten Patrol
**Height:** 4
**Status:** Open issue, retired
**Issue Year:** 1999
**Issue Price:** $180
**Last Year:** 2002
**Last Retail Price:** $185

**Ref. No.:** 6642
**Name:** Little Stowaway
**Height:** 4
**Status:** Open issue, active
**Issue Year:** 2000
**Issue Price:** $155
**2003 Retail Price:** $165
**Comment:** Introduced by select
    dealers in 1999

**Ref. No.:** 1066
**Name:** Basset
**Height:** 4.25
**Status:** Open edition, retired
**Issue Year:** 1969
**Issue Price:** $23.50
**Last Year:** 1981
**Last Retail Price:** $127.5
**High Auction Price:** $600
**Low Auction Price:** $475

**Ref. No.:** 1070
**Name:** Beagle Puppy
**Height:** 4.25
**Status:** Open edition, retired
**Issue Year:** 1969
**Issue Price:** $16.50
**Last Year:** 1991
**Last Retail Price:** $120

*Animals*

**Ref. No.:** 5091
**Name:** Scaredy Cat
**Height:** 4.25
**Status:** Open issue, retired
**Issue Year:** 1980
**Issue Price:** $60
**Last Year:** 1998
**Last Retail Price:** $95

**Ref. No.:** 6098
**Name:** Attentive Bunny with
    Flowers
**Height:** 4.25
**Status:** Open issue, active
**Issue Year:** 1994
**Issue Price:** $140
**2003 Retail Price:** $145

**Ref. No.:** 6210
**Name:** Gentle Surprise
**Height:** 4.25
**Status:** Open issue, active
**Issue Year:** 1995
**Issue Price:** $125
**2003 Retail Price:** $125

**Ref. No.:** 5905
**Name:** Attentive Bunny
**Height:** 4.5
**Status:** Open issue, retired
**Issue Year:** 1992
**Issue Price:** $75
**Last Year:** 1998
**Last Retail Price:** $75

**Ref. No.:** 6567
**Name:** Dreamy Kitten
**Height:** 4.5
**Status:** Open issue, active
**Issue Year:** 1999
**Issue Price:** $250
**2003 Retail Price:** $265

**Ref. No.:** 6574
**Name:** Take Me Home!
**Height:** 4.5
**Status:** Open issue, active
**Issue Year:** 2000
**Issue Price:** $295
**2003 Retail Price:** $295

**Ref. No.:** 6832
**Name:** A Sweet Smell
**Height:** 4.5
**Status:** Open issue, active
**Issue Year:** 2002
**Issue Price:** $195
**2003 Retail Price:** $195

**Ref. No.:** 5111
**Name:** Baffled
**Height:** 4.75
**Status:** Open edition, retired
**Issue Year:** 1982
**Issue Price:** $44
**Last Year:** 1985
**Last Retail Price:** $44
**High Auction Price:** $700
**Low Auction Price:** $400

**Ref. No.:** 6652
**Name:** Kitty Care
**Height:** 4.75
**Status:** Open issue, retired
**Issue Year:** 2000
**Issue Price:** $255
**Last Year:** 2002
**Last Retail Price:** $265

**Ref. No.:** 6665
**Name:** Let's Fly Away
**Height:** 4.75
**Status:** Open issue, active
**Issue Year:** 2000
**Issue Price:** $155
**2003 Retail Price:** $165
**Comment:** Introduced by select
  dealers in 1999

**Ref. No.:** 321.13
**Name:** Bulldog
**Height:** 5
**Status:** Very Rare
**Issue Year:** 1968
**Last Year:** Unknown
**Issue Price:** Unknown
**Last Retail Price:** Unknown

**Ref. No.:** 1282
**Name:** Afghan Hound
**Height:** 5
**Status:** Open edition, retired
**Issue Year:** 1974
**Issue Price:** $45
**Last Year:** 1985
**Last Retail Price:** $87.50
**High Auction Price:** $750
**Low Auction Price:** $350

*Animals*

**Ref. No.:** 1316
**Name:** Dog
**Height:** 5
**Status:** Open edition, retired
**Issue Year:** 1974
**Issue Price:** $45
**Last Year:** 1981
**Last Retail Price:** $100

**Ref. No.:** 1441
**Name:** A Litter of Love
**Height:** 5
**Status:** Open issue, active
**Issue Year:** 1983
**Issue Price:** $385
**2003 Retail Price:** $650

**Ref. No.:** 1444
**Name:** Purr-Fect
**Height:** 5
**Status:** Open issue, active
**Issue Year:** 1983
**Issue Price:** $350
**2003 Retail Price:** $625

**Ref. No.:** 5887
**Name:** Washing Up
**Height:** 5
**Status:** Open edition, retired
**Issue Year:** 1992
**Issue Price:** $95
**Last Year:** 1995
**Last Retail Price:** $95

**Ref. No.:** 6211
**Name:** New Friend
**Height:** 5
**Status:** Open issue, active
**Issue Year:** 1995
**Issue Price:** $120
**2003 Retail Price:** $125

**Ref. No.:** 6398
**Name:** Morning Delivery
**Height:** 5
**Status:** Open issue, retired
**Issue Year:** 1997
**Issue Price:** $160
**Last Year:** 2001
**Last Retail Price:** $160

**Ref. No.:** 6469
**Name:** Our Cozy Home
**Height:** 5
**Status:** Open issue, active
**Issue Year:** 1997
**Issue Price:** $195
**2003 Retail Price:** $225

**Ref. No.:** 5113
**Name:** Cat
**Height:** 5.25
**Status:** Open issue, active
**Issue Year:** 1982
**Issue Price:** $40
**2003 Retail Price:** $95

**Ref. No.:** 6616
**Name:** Kitty Surprise
**Height:** 5.25
**Status:** Open issue, retired
**Issue Year:** 1999
**Issue Price:** $280
**Last Year:** 2001
**Last Retail Price:** $280

**Ref. No.:** 6617
**Name:** Puppy Surprise
**Height:** 5.25
**Status:** Open issue, retired
**Issue Year:** 1999
**Issue Price:** $280
**Last Year:** 2001
**Last Retail Price:** $280

**Ref. No.:** 6618
**Name:** Fawn Surprise
**Height:** 5.25
**Status:** Open issue, retired
**Issue Year:** 1999
**Issue Price:** $280
**Last Year:** 2001
**Last Retail Price:** $280

**Ref. No.:** 6829
**Name:** Unexpected Visit
**Height:** 5.25
**Status:** Open issue, active
**Issue Year:** 2002
**2003 Retail Price:** $195

*Animals*

**Ref. No.:** 1259
**Name:** Poodle
**Height:** 5.5
**Status:** Open edition, retired
**Issue Year:** 1974
**Issue Price:** $27.50
**Last Year:** 1985
**Last Retail Price:** $65
**High Auction Price:** $500
**Low Auction Price:** $375

**Ref. No.:** 4642
**Name:** Dog
**Height:** 5.5
**Status:** Open edition, retired
**Issue Year:** 1969
**Issue Price:** $22.50
**Last Year:** 1981
**Last Retail Price:** $80
**Auction Price:** $700

**Ref. No.:** 5886
**Name:** Hippity Hop
**Height:** 5.5
**Status:** Open edition, retired
**Issue Year:** 1992
**Issue Price:** $95
**Last Year:** 1995
**Last Retail Price:** $95

**Ref. No.:** 5907
**Name:** Sitting Bunny
**Height:** 5.5
**Status:** Open issue, retired
**Issue Year:** 1992
**Issue Price:** $75
**Last Year:** 1998
**Last Retail Price:** $80

**Ref. No.:** 6100
**Name:** Sitting Bunny with
    Flowers
**Height:** 5.5
**Status:** Open issue, active
**Issue Year:** 1994
**Issue Price:** $110
**2003 Retail Price:** $125

**Ref. No.:** 6775
**Name:** A Purr-Fect Fit
**Height:** 5.5
**Status:** Open issue, active
**Issue Year:** 2001
**Issue Price:** $335
**2003 Retail Price:** $350
**Comment:** To be retired as of
    December 31, 2003

**Ref. No.:** 309.13
**Name:** Rabbit Standing
**Height:** 6
**Status:** Very Rare
**Issue Year:** 1965
**Issue Price:** Unknown
**Last Year:** Unknown
**Last Retail Price:** Unknown

**Ref. No.:** 323.13
**Name:** Flirt
**Height:** 6
**Status:** Very Rare
**Issue Year:** 1971
**Issue Price:** Unknown
**Last Year:** Unknown
**Last Retail Price:** Unknown

**Ref. No.:** 1139
**Name:** Dog and Snail
**Height:** 6
**Status:** Open edition, retired
**Issue Year:** 1971
**Issue Price:** $40
**Last Year:** 1981
**Last Retail Price:** $160
**Auction Price:** $450

**Ref. No.:** 1149
**Name:** Dog's Head
**Height:** 6
**Status:** Open edition, retired
**Issue Year:** 1971
**Issue Price:** $27.50
**Last Year:** 1981
**Last Retail Price:** $30
**Auction Price:** $400

**Ref. No.:** 1153
**Name:** Dog Playing Guitar
**Height:** 6
**Status:** Open edition, retired
**Issue Year:** 1971
**Issue Price:** $32.5
**Last Year:** 1978
**Last Retail Price:** $65
**Auction Price:** $350

**Ref. No.:** 1257
**Name:** Mother with Pups
**Height:** 6
**Status:** Open edition, retired
**Issue Year:** 1974
**Issue Price:** $50
**Last Year:** 1981
**Last Retail Price:** $90
**High Auction Price:** $800
**Low Auction Price:** $650

*Animals*

**Ref. No.:** 1258
**Name:** Playing Dogs
**Height:** 6
**Status:** Open edition, retired
**Issue Year:** 1974
**Issue Price:** $47.50
**Last Year:** 1981
**Last Retail Price:** $85
**High Auction Price:** $1100
**Low Auction Price:** $550

**Ref. No.:** 4641
**Name:** Pekingese Sitting
**Height:** 6
**Status:** Open edition, retired
**Issue Year:** 1969
**Issue Price:** $20
**Last Year:** 1985
**Last Retail Price:** $65
**High Auction Price:** $575
**Low Auction Price:** $250

**Ref. No.:** 4643
**Name:** Skye Terrier
**Height:** 6
**Status:** Open edition, retired
**Issue Year:** 1969
**Issue Price:** $15
**Last Year:** 1985
**Last Retail Price:** $50
**High Auction Price:** $700
**Low Auction Price:** $325

**Ref. No.:** 6459
**Name:** Collie with Puppy
**Height:** 6
**Status:** Open issue, retired
**Issue Year:** 1997
**Issue Price:** $350
**Last Year:** 2000
**Last Retail Price:** $355

**Ref. No.:** 6743
**Name:** A Cozy Fit
**Height:** 6
**Status:** Open issue, active
**Issue Year:** 2001
**Issue Price:** $265
**2003 Retail Price:** $275

**Ref. No.:** 5902
**Name:** Easter Bunnies
**Height:** 6.25
**Status:** Open issue, retired
**Issue Year:** 1992
**Issue Price:** $240
**Last Year:** 1996
**Last Retail Price:** $250

**Ref. No.:** 322.13
**Name:** Sad Dog
**Height:** 6.5
**Status:** Very Rare
**Issue Year:** 1971
**Issue Price:** Unknown
**Last Year:** Unknown
**Last Retail Price:** Unknown

**Ref. No.:** 1068
**Name:** Great Dane
**Height:** 6.5
**Status:** Open edition, retired
**Issue Year:** 1969
**Issue Price:** $55
**Last Year:** 1989
**Last Retail Price:** $380
**High Auction Price:** $625
**Low Auction Price:** $600

**Ref. No.:** 5889
**Name:** Snack Time
**Height:** 6.75
**Status:** Open edition, retired
**Issue Year:** 1992
**Issue Price:** $95
**Last Year:** 1995
**Last Retail Price:** $105

**Ref. No.:** 4583
**Name:** Setter
**Height:** 7
**Status:** Open edition, retired
**Issue Year:** 1969
**Issue Price:** $21
**Last Year:** 1981
**Last Retail Price:** $105
**Auction Price:** $650

**Ref. No.:** 1128
**Name:** Dog in the Basket
**Height:** 7.5
**Status:** Open edition, retired
**Issue Year:** 1971
**Issue Price:** $17.50
**Last Year:** 1985
**Last Retail Price:** $92.5
**High Auction Price:** $550
**Low Auction Price:** $300

**Ref. No.:** 1156
**Name:** Dog Playing Bongos
**Height:** 7.5
**Status:** Open edition, retired
**Issue Year:** 1971
**Issue Price:** $32.50
**Last Year:** 1978
**Last Retail Price:** $70
**High Auction Price:** $750
**Low Auction Price:** $400

*Animals*

**Ref. No.:** 4857
**Name:** Papillon Dog
**Height:** 7.5
**Status:** Open edition, retired
**Issue Year:** 1974
**Issue Price:** $40
**Last Year:** 1979
**Last Retail Price:** $65
**Auction Price:** $700

**Ref. No.:** 6688
**Name:** Looking Pretty
**Height:** 7.5
**Status:** Open issue, active
**Issue Year:** 2000
**Issue Price:** $245
**2003 Retail Price:** $250

**Ref. No.:** 1155
**Name:** Dog Singer
**Height:** 7.75
**Status:** Open edition, retired
**Issue Year:** 1971
**Issue Price:** $32.50
**Last Year:** 1978
**Last Retail Price:** $70
**High Auction Price:** $425
**Low Auction Price:** $325

**Ref. No.:** 4731
**Name:** German Shepherd
    with Pup
**Height:** 7.75
**Status:** Open edition, retired
**Issue Year:** 1970
**Issue Price:** $40
**Last Year:** 1975
**Last Retail Price:** $70
**Auction Price:** $850

**Ref. No.:** 1121
**Name:** Pups in a Box
**Height:** 8.5
**Status:** Open edition, retired
**Issue Year:** 1971
**Issue Price:** $33
**Last Year:** 1978
**Last Retail Price:** $115

**Ref. No.:** 1152
**Name:** Dog Playing Guitar
**Height:** 8.5
**Status:** Open edition, retired
**Issue Year:** 1971
**Issue Price:** $32.50
**Last Year:** 1978
**Last Retail Price:** $90
**High Auction Price:** $375
**Low Auction Price:** $240

**Ref. No.:** 1154
**Name:** Dog Playing Bass Fiddle
**Height:** 8.5
**Status:** Open edition, retired
**Issue Year:** 1971
**Issue Price:** $36.50
**Last Year:** 1978
**Last Retail Price:** $85
**High Auction Price:** $500
**Low Auction Price:** $400

**Ref. No.:** 6502
**Name:** Please Come Home!
**Height:** 8.5
**Status:** Open issue, active
**Issue Year:** 1999
**Issue Price:** $695
**2003 Retail Price:** $775
**Comment:** Introduced by select
dealers in 1998

**Ref. No.:** 325.13
**Name:** Poodle
**Height:** 8.75
**Status:** Very Rare
**Issue Year:** 1966
**Issue Price:** Unknown
**Last Year:** Unknown
**Last Retail Price:** Unknown

**Ref. No.:** 6744
**Name:** A Well Heeled Puppy
**Height:** 8.75
**Status:** Open issue, active
**Issue Year:** 2001
**Issue Price:** $345
**2003 Retail Price:** $375

**Ref. No.:** 6557
**Name:** Playful Poodle
**Height:** 9
**Status:** Open issue, retired
**Issue Year:** 1998
**Issue Price:** $530
**Last Year:** 2001
**Last Retail Price:** $530

**Ref. No.:** 6454
**Name:** German Shepherd with
Puppies
**Height:** 9
**Status:** Open issue, retired
**Issue Year:** 1997
**Issue Price:** $475
**Last Year:** 2000
**Last Retail Price:** $510

Animals

**Ref. No.:** 4957
**Name:** Attentive Dogs
**Height:** 9.75
**Status:** Open edition, retired
**Issue Year:** 1977
**Issue Price:** $350
**Last Year:** 1981
**Last Retail Price:** $500

**Ref. No.:** 6522
**Name:** Through The Clouds
**Height:** 10
**Status:** Open issue, retired
**Issue Year:** 1998
**Issue Price:** $440
**Last Year:** 2001
**Last Retail Price:** $450

**Ref. No.:** 6524
**Name:** Up and Away
**Height:** 10
**Status:** Open issue, retired
**Issue Year:** 1998
**Issue Price:** $560
**Last Year:** 2001
**Last Retail Price:** $560

**Ref. No.:** 6455
**Name:** Collie
**Height:** 11
**Status:** Open issue, retired
**Issue Year:** 1997
**Issue Price:** $295
**Last Year:** 2000
**Last Retail Price:** $300

**Ref. No.:** 1069
**Name:** Afghan
**Height:** 11.5
**Status:** Open edition, retired
**Issue Year:** 1969
**Issue Price:** $36
**Last Year:** 1985
**Last Retail Price:** $135
**High Auction Price:** $650
**Low Auction Price:** $525

**Ref. No.:** 5154
**Name:** Egyptian Cat (White)
**Height:** 13
**Status:** Open edition, retired
**Issue Year:** 1982
**Issue Price:** $90
**Last Year:** 1985
**Last Retail Price:** $90

### Birds

**Ref. No.:** 6558
**Name:** Great Dane
**Height:** 19
**Status:** Open issue, retired
**Issue Year:** 1998
**Issue Price:** $890
**Last Year:** 2000
**Last Retail Price:** $935

**Ref. No.:** 4630
**Name:** Chick on the Watch
**Height:** 1
**Status:** Open edition, retired
**Issue Year:** 1969
**Issue Price:** $3.50
**Last Year:** 1972
**Last Retail Price:** $5

**Ref. No.:** 4631
**Name:** Coquettish Chick
**Height:** 1
**Status:** Open edition, retired
**Issue Year:** 1969
**Issue Price:** $3.50
**Last Year:** 1972
**Last Retail Price:** $5

**Ref. No.:** 1599
**Name:** Nesting Crane
**Height:** 2
**Status:** Open issue, retired
**Issue Year:** 1989
**Issue Price:** $95
**Last Year:** 1997
**Last Retail Price:** $115

**Ref. No.:** 4632
**Name:** Sleepy Chick
**Height:** 2
**Status:** Open edition, retired
**Issue Year:** 1969
**Issue Price:** $3.50
**Last Year:** 1972
**Last Retail Price:** $5

**Ref. No.:** 4895
**Name:** Ducklings
**Height:** 2
**Status:** Open issue, active
**Issue Year:** 1974
**Issue Price:** $27.50
**2003 Retail Price:** $95

*Animals*

**Ref. No.:** 1053
**Name:** Bird
**Height:** 2.25
**Status:** Open edition, retired
**Issue Year:** 1969
**Issue Price:** $13
**Last Year:** 1985
**Last Retail Price:** $52
**Auction Price:** $100

**Ref. No.:** 1264
**Name:** Flying Duck
**Height:** 2.75
**Status:** Open issue, retired
**Issue Year:** 1974
**Issue Price:** $20
**Last Retail Price:** $90
**Last Year:** 1998
**Last Retail Price:** $90

**Ref. No.:** 4629
**Name:** Guardian Chick
**Height:** 2.75
**Status:** Open edition, retired
**Issue Year:** 1969
**Issue Price:** $3.50
**Last Year:** 1972
**Last Retail Price:** $5

**Ref. No.:** 1598
**Name:** Fluttering Crane
**Height:** 3
**Status:** Open issue, retired
**Issue Year:** 1989
**Issue Price:** $115
**Last Year:** 1997
**Last Retail Price:** $145

**Ref. No.:** 1600
**Name:** Landing Crane
**Height:** 3
**Status:** Open issue, retired
**Issue Year:** 1989
**Issue Price:** $115
**Last Year:** 1997
**Last Retail Price:** $145

**Ref. No.:** 4551
**Name:** Little Duck
**Height:** 3.75
**Status:** Open issue, retired
**Issue Year:** 1969
**Issue Price:** Unknown
**Last Year:** 2001
**Last Retail Price:** $50

**Ref. No.:** 1056
**Name:** Duck
**Height:** 4
**Status:** Open edition, retired
**Issue Year:** 1969
**Issue Price:** $19
**Last Year:** 1978
**Last Retail Price:** $65
**Auction Price:** $275

**Ref. No.:** 1226
**Name:** Nightingale
**Height:** 4
**Status:** Open edition, retired
**Issue Year:** 1972
**Issue Price:** $30
**Last Year:** 1981
**Last Retail Price:** $120

**Ref. No.:** 1307
**Name:** Little Ducks after Mother
**Height:** 4
**Status:** Open issue, active
**Issue Year:** 1974
**Issue Price:** $47.50
**2003 Retail Price:** $150

**Ref. No.:** 5722
**Name:** Follow Me
**Height:** 4
**Status:** Open issue, active
**Issue Year:** 1990
**Issue Price:** $140
**2003 Retail Price:** $175

**Ref. No.:** 6175
**Name:** White Swan
**Height:** 4
**Status:** Open issue, active
**Issue Year:** 1995
**Issue Price:** $90
**2003 Retail Price:** $95

**Ref. No.:** 6499
**Name:** White Swan with Flowers
**Height:** 4
**Status:** Open issue, active
**Issue Year:** 1998
**Issue Price:** $110
**2003 Retail Price:** $125

*Animals*

**Ref. No.:** 1041
**Name:** Hen
**Height:** 4.25
**Status:** Open edition, retired
**Issue Year:** 1969
**Issue Price:** $13
**Last Year:** 1975
**Last Retail Price:** $13

**Ref. No.:** 1227
**Name:** Ladybird and Nightingale
**Height:** 4.25
**Status:** Open edition, retired
**Issue Year:** 1973
**Issue Price:** $40
**Last Year:** 1981
**Last Retail Price:** $150

**Ref. No.:** 1265
**Name:** Duck Jumping
**Height:** 4.25
**Status:** Open issue, retired
**Issue Year:** 1974
**Issue Price:** $20
**Last Year:** 1998
**Last Retail Price:** $90

**Ref. No.:** 1301
**Name:** Little Bird
**Height:** 4.25
**Status:** Open edition, retired
**Issue Year:** 1974
**Issue Price:** $72.50
**Last Year:** 1983
**Last Retail Price:** $185
**High Auction Price:** $400
**Low Auction Price:** $375

**Ref. No.:** 1439
**Name:** How Do You Do!
**Height:** 4.25
**Status:** Open issue, active
**Issue Year:** 1983
**Issue Price:** $185
**2003 Retail Price:** $295

**Ref. No.:** 4715
**Name:** Mandarin Duck
**Height:** 4.25
**Status:** Open edition, retired
**Issue Year:** 1970
**Issue Price:** $13.50
**Last Year:** 1972
**Last Retail Price:** $15

**Ref. No.:** 5288
**Name:** Mallard Duck
**Height:** 4.25
**Status:** Open edition, retired
**Issue Year:** 1985
**Issue Price:** $310
**Last Year:** 1994
**Last Retail Price:** $520

**Ref. No.:** 4553
**Name:** Little Duck
**Height:** 4.5
**Status:** Open issue, retired
**Issue Year:** 1969
**Issue Price:** Unknown
**Last Year:** 2001
**Last Retail Price:** $50

**Ref. No.:** 6864
**Name:** Sweet Sounds of the
  Morning
**Height:** 4.5
**Status:** Open issue, active
**Issue Year:** 2002
**Issue Price:** $225
**2003 Retail Price:** $225

**Ref. No.:** 1042
**Name:** Hen
**Height:** 4.75
**Status:** Open edition, retired
**Issue Year:** 1969
**Issue Price:** $13
**Last Year:** 1975
**Last Retail Price:** $13

**Ref. No.:** 1169
**Name:** Couple of Doves
**Height:** 4.75
**Status:** Open issue, active
**Issue Year:** 1971
**Issue Price:** $32
**2003 Retail Price:** $175

**Ref. No.:** 1170
**Name:** Kissing Doves
**Height:** 4.75
**Status:** Open issue, retired
**Issue Year:** 1971
**Issue Price:** $25
**Last Year:** 1988
**Auction Price:** $250

*Animals*

**Ref. No.:** 1171
**Name:** Dove Pair
**Height:** 4.75
**Status:** Open edition, retired
**Issue Year:** 1971
**Issue Price:** $25
**Last Year:** 1978
**Last Retail Price:** $110

**Ref. No.:** 1244
**Name:** Fluttering Nightingale
**Height:** 4.75
**Status:** Open edition, retired
**Issue Year:** 1973
**Issue Price:** $44
**Last Year:** 1981
**Last Retail Price:** $142

**Ref. No.:** 1302
**Name:** Blue Creeper
**Height:** 4.75
**Status:** Open edition, retired
**Issue Year:** 1974
**Issue Price:** $110
**Last Year:** 1985
**Last Retail Price:** $227
**Auction Price:** $525

**Ref. No.:** 4552
**Name:** Little Duck
**Height:** 4.75
**Status:** Open issue, retired
**Issue Year:** 1969
**Issue Price:** Unknown
**Last Year:** 2001
**Last Retail Price:** $50

**Ref. No.:** 5421
**Name:** Barn Owl
**Height:** 4.75
**Status:** Open edition, retired
**Issue Year:** 1987
**Issue Price:** $120
**Last Year:** 1990
**Last Retail Price:** $145
**High Auction Price:** $275
**Low Auction Price:** $175

**Ref. No.:** 5422
**Name:** Hawk Owl
**Height:** 4.75
**Status:** Open edition, retired
**Issue Year:** 1987
**Issue Price:** $120
**Last Year:** 1990
**Last Retail Price:** $145
**High Auction Price:** $350
**Low Auction Price:** $275

**Ref. No.:** 329.13
**Name:** Martin
**Height:** 5
**Status:** Very Rare
**Issue Year:** 1968
**Issue Price:** Unknown
**Last Year:** Unknown
**Last Retail Price:** Unknown

**Ref. No.:** 1015
**Name:** Dove
**Height:** 5
**Status:** Open edition, retired
**Issue Year:** 1969
**Issue Price:** $21
**Last Year:** 1994
**Last Retail Price:** $100

**Ref. No.:** 1043
**Name:** Cock
**Height:** 5
**Status:** Open edition, retired
**Issue Year:** 1969
**Issue Price:** $13
**Last Year:** 1975
**Last Retail Price:** $13

**Ref. No.:** 1051
**Name:** Tern
**Height:** 5
**Status:** Open edition, retired
**Issue Year:** 1969
**Issue Price:** $21
**Last Year:** 1978
**Last Retail Price:** $80
**Auction Price:** $500

**Ref. No.:** 1054
**Name:** Bird
**Height:** 5
**Status:** Open edition, retired
**Issue Year:** 1969
**Issue Price:** $14
**Last Year:** 1985
**Last Retail Price:** $75
**Auction Price:** $100

**Ref. No.:** 1057
**Name:** Duck
**Height:** 5
**Status:** Open edition, retired
**Issue Year:** 1969
**Issue Price:** $19.50
**Last Year:** 1978
**Last Retail Price:** $65

*Animals*

**Ref. No.:** 1228
**Name:** Nightingale Pair
**Height:** 5
**Status:** Open edition, retired
**Issue Year:** 1972
**Issue Price:** $80
**Last Year:** 1981
**Last Retail Price:** $240
**Auction Price:** $475

**Ref. No.:** 1263
**Name:** Duck Running
**Height:** 5
**Status:** Open issue, retired
**Issue Year:** 1974
**Issue Price:** $20
**Last Year:** 1998
**Last Retail Price:** $90

**Ref. No.:** 1300
**Name:** Bird and Butterfly
**Height:** 5
**Status:** Open edition, retired
**Issue Year:** 1974
**Issue Price:** $100
**Last Year:** 1985
**Last Retail Price:** $210
**Auction Price:** $950

**Ref. No.:** 1303
**Name:** Bird on Cactus
**Height:** 5
**Status:** Open edition, retired
**Issue Year:** 1974
**Issue Price:** $150
**Last Year:** 1983
**Last Retail Price:** $350
**High Auction Price:** $750
**Low Auction Price:** $500

**Ref. No.:** 4525
**Name:** Turkeys
**Height:** 5
**Status:** Open edition, retired
**Issue Year:** 1969
**Issue Price:** $17.50
**Last Year:** 1972
**Last Retail Price:** $20

**Ref. No.:** 4628
**Name:** Hen with Chicks
**Height:** 5
**Status:** Open edition, retired
**Issue Year:** 1969
**Issue Price:** $20
**Last Year:** 1972
**Last Retail Price:** $25

**Ref. No.:** 5248
**Name:** Penguin
**Height:** 5
**Status:** Open edition, retired
**Issue Year:** 1984
**Issue Price:** $70
**Last Year:** 1988
**Last Retail Price:** $85
**High Auction Price:** $200
**Low Auction Price:** $190

**Ref. No.:** 6289
**Name:** Peaceful Dove
**Height:** 5
**Status:** Open issue, retired
**Issue Year:** 1996
**Issue Price:** $105
**Last Year:** 1999
**Last Retail Price:** $115

**Ref. No.:** 6290
**Name:** Proud Dove
**Height:** 5
**Status:** Open issue, retired
**Issue Year:** 1996
**Issue Price:** $105
**Last Year:** 1999
**Last Retail Price:** $105

**Ref. No.:** 6287
**Name:** Restless Dove
**Height:** 5.25
**Status:** Open issue, retired
**Issue Year:** 1996
**Last Year:** 1998
**Issue Price:** $105
**Last Retail Price:** $105

**Ref. No.:** 4549
**Name:** Geese Group
**Height:** 6
**Status:** Open issue, retired
**Issue Year:** 1969
**Issue Price:** $28.50
**Last Year:** 1996
**Last Retail Price:** $245

**Ref. No.:** 4667
**Name:** Birds
**Height:** 6
**Status:** Open edition, retired
**Issue Year:** 1969
**Issue Price:** $25
**Last Year:** 1985
**Last Retail Price:** $142
**Auction Price:** $200

*Animals*

**Ref. No.:** 4829
**Name:** Swan
**Height:** 6
**Status:** Open edition, retired
**Issue Year:** 1972
**Issue Price:** $16
**Last Year:** 1983
**Last Retail Price:** $75
**High Auction Price:** $500
**Low Auction Price:** $300

**Ref. No.:** 5249
**Name:** Penguin
**Height:** 6
**Status:** Open edition, retired
**Issue Year:** 1984
**Issue Price:** $70
**Last Year:** 1988
**Last Retail Price:** $85
**High Auction Price:** $275
**Low Auction Price:** $175

**Ref. No.:** 5419
**Name:** Great Gray Owl
**Height:** 6
**Status:** Open edition, retired
**Issue Year:** 1987
**Issue Price:** $190
**Last Year:** 1990
**Last Retail Price:** $230
**High Auction Price:** $275
**Low Auction Price:** $175

**Ref. No.:** 5420
**Name:** Horned Owl
**Height:** 6
**Status:** Open edition, retired
**Issue Year:** 1987
**Issue Price:** $150
**Last Year:** 1990
**Last Retail Price:** $180
**High Auction Price:** $225
**Low Auction Price:** $175

**Ref. No.:** 6359
**Name:** Couple of Doves with
Flowers
**Height:** 6
**Status:** Open issue, active
**Issue Year:** 1997
**Issue Price:** $225
**2003 Retail Price:** $225

**Ref. No.:** 6517
**Name:** How Skillful!
**Height:** 6
**Status:** Open issue, active
**Issue Year:** 1998
**Issue Price:** $390
**2003 Retail Price:** $425

**Ref. No.:** 1299
**Name:** Bird in Nest
**Height:** 6.25
**Status:** Open edition, retired
**Issue Year:** 1974
**Issue Price:** $120
**Last Year:** 1985
**Last Retail Price:** $235
**Auction Price:** $950

**Ref. No.:** 5247
**Name:** Penguin
**Height:** 6.5
**Status:** Open edition, retired
**Issue Year:** 1984
**Issue Price:** $70
**Last Year:** 1988
**Last Retail Price:** $85
**High Auction Price:** $325
**Low Auction Price:** $200

**Ref. No.:** 1016
**Name:** Dove
**Height:** 7
**Status:** Open edition, retired
**Issue Year:** 1969
**Issue Price:** $36
**Last Year:** 1995
**Last Retail Price:** $190

**Ref. No.:** 1298
**Name:** Birds Resting
**Height:** 7
**Status:** Open edition, retired
**Issue Year:** 1974
**Issue Price:** $235
**Last Year:** 1985
**Last Retail Price:** $575
**Auction Price:** $1100

**Ref. No.:** 1371
**Name:** Ready to Fly
**Height:** 7
**Status:** Open edition, retired
**Issue Year:** 1978
**Issue Price:** $375
**Last Year:** 1985
**Last Retail Price:** $500

**Ref. No.:** 1612
**Name:** Preening Crane
**Height:** 7
**Status:** Open issue, retired
**Issue Year:** 1989
**Issue Price:** $385
**Last Year:** 1998
**Last Retail Price:** $485

*Animals*

**Ref. No.:** 4589
**Name:** Small Rooster
**Height:** 7
**Status:** Open edition, retired
**Issue Year:** 1969
**Issue Price:** $15
**Last Year:** 1981
**Last Retail Price:** $55

**Ref. No.:** 5231
**Name:** Swan with Wings Spread
**Height:** 7
**Status:** Open issue, active
**Issue Year:** 1984
**Issue Price:** $50
**Auction Price:** $500
**2003 Retail Price:** $150

**Ref. No.:** 1613
**Name:** Bowing Crane
**Height:** 7.75
**Status:** Open issue, retired
**Issue Year:** 1989
**Issue Price:** $385
**Last Year:** 1998
**Last Retail Price:** $485

**Ref. No.:** 5418
**Name:** Short Eared Owl
**Height:** 7.75
**Status:** Open edition, retired
**Issue Year:** 1987
**Issue Price:** $200
**Last Year:** 1990
**Last Retail Price:** $250
**High Auction Price:** $225
**Low Auction Price:** $150

**Ref. No.:** 297.13
**Name:** Ostriches
**Height:** 8
**Status:** Very Rare
**Issue Year:** 1963
**Issue Price:** Unknown
**Last Year:** Unknown
**Last Retail Price:** Unknown

**Ref. No.:** 1369
**Name:** Bird Trio
**Height:** 8
**Status:** Open edition, retired
**Issue Year:** 1978
**Issue Price:** $710
**Last Year:** 1985
**Last Retail Price:** $2500

**Ref. No.:** 1370
**Name:** Birds Singing
**Height:** 8
**Status:** Open edition, retired
**Issue Year:** 1978
**Issue Price:** $510
**Last Year:** 1985
**Last Retail Price:** $660
**Auction Price:** $1250

**Ref. No.:** 4587
**Name:** Rooster
**Height:** 8
**Status:** Open edition, retired
**Issue Year:** 1969
**Issue Price:** $25
**Last Year:** 1979
**Last Retail Price:** $70
**Auction Price:** $450

**Ref. No.:** 4588
**Name:** White Cockerel
**Height:** 8
**Status:** Open edition, retired
**Issue Year:** 1969
**Issue Price:** $17.50
**Last Year:** 1979
**Last Retail Price:** $50

**Ref. No.:** 5230
**Name:** Graceful Swan
**Height:** 8
**Status:** Open issue, retired
**Issue Year:** 1984
**Issue Price:** $35
**Last Year:** 2000
**Last Retail Price:** $115

**Ref. No.:** 6288
**Name:** Taking Flight
**Height:** 8
**Status:** Open issue, retired
**Issue Year:** 1996
**Issue Price:** $150
**Last Year:** 1999
**Last Retail Price:** $165

**Ref. No.:** 82.06
**Name:** Parrot
**Height:** 8.25
**Status:** Very Rare
**Issue Year:** 1956
**Issue Price:** Unknown
**Last Year:** Unknown
**Last Retail Price:** Unknown

*Animals*

**Ref. No.:** 1224
**Name:** Eagle Owl
**Height:** 8.25
**Status:** Open edition, retired
**Issue Year:** 1972
**Issue Price:** $170
**Last Year:** 1978
**Last Retail Price:** $205

**Ref. No.:** 1368
**Name:** Spring Birds
**Height:** 9
**Status:** Open edition, retired
**Issue Year:** 1978
**Issue Price:** $1600
**Last Year:** 1990
**Last Retail Price:** $2500
**Auction Price:** $3200

**Ref. No.:** 6291
**Name:** Love Nest
**Height:** 9
**Status:** Open issue, active
**Issue Year:** 1996
**Issue Price:** $260
**2003 Retail Price:** $290

**Ref. No.:** 338.13
**Name:** Pheasant
**Height:** 10
**Status:** Very Rare
**Issue Year:** 1968
**Issue Price:** Unknown
**Last Year:** Unknown
**Last Retail Price:** Unknown

**Ref. No.:** 1611
**Name:** Courting Cranes
**Height:** 10
**Status:** Open issue, active
**Issue Year:** 1989
**Issue Price:** $565
**2003 Retail Price:** $695

**Ref. No.:** 6591
**Name:** Elegant Trio
**Height:** 10
**Status:** Open issue, retired
**Issue Year:** 1999
**Issue Price:** $675
**Last Year:** 2002
**Last Retail Price:** $675

**Ref. No.:** 330.13
**Name:** Group of Pelicans
**Height:** 10.25
**Status:** Very Rare
**Issue Year:** 1968
**Issue Price:** Unknown
**Last Year:** Unknown
**Last Retail Price:** Unknown

**Ref. No.:** 331.13
**Name:** Pheasant
**Height:** 11
**Status:** Very Rare
**Issue Year:** 1973
**Issue Price:** Unknown
**Last Year:** Unknown
**Last Retail Price:** Unknown

**Ref. No.:** 4550
**Name:** Turtle Dove
**Height:** 11
**Status:** Open issue, retired
**Issue Year:** 1969
**Issue Price:** $47.50
**Last Year:** 1998
**Last Retail Price:** $265

**Ref. No.:** 1009
**Name:** Sea Gull
**Height:** 11.75
**Status:** Open edition, retired
**Issue Year:** 1969
**Issue Price:** $120
**Last Year:** 1970
**Last Retail Price:** $120

**Ref. No.:** 4759
**Name:** Ducks Flapping
**Height:** 11.75
**Status:** Open edition, retired
**Issue Year:** 1971
**Issue Price:** $45
**Last Year:** 1981
**Last Retail Price:** $300

**Ref. No.:** 1614
**Name:** Dancing Crane
**Height:** 12
**Status:** Open issue, retired
**Issue Year:** 1989
**Issue Price:** $385
**Last Year:** 2000
**Last Retail Price:** $485

*Animals*

**Ref. No.:** 337.13
**Name:** Pheasant
**Height:** 13
**Status:** Very Rare
**Issue Year:** 1968
**Issue Price:** Unknown
**Last Year:** Unknown
**Last Retail Price:** Unknown

**Ref. No.:** 6476
**Name:** A Symbol of Pride
**Height:** 13
**Status:** Open issue, retired
**Issue Year:** 1998
**Issue Price:** $695
**Last Year:** 2001
**Last Retail Price:** $740

**Ref. No.:** 6641
**Name:** The Flamingos
**Height:** 13.5
**Status:** Open issue, retired
**Issue Year:** 1999
**Issue Price:** $495
**Last Year:** 2001
**Last Retail Price:** $495

**Ref. No.:** 5691
**Name:** Marshland Mates
**Height:** 13.75
**Status:** Open issue, active
**Issue Year:** 1990
**Issue Price:** $950
**2003 Retail Price:** $1200

**Ref. No.:** 276.12
**Name:** Turtle Doves
**Height:** 17
**Status:** Very Rare
**Issue Year:** 1959
**Issue Price:** Unknown
**Last Year:** Unknown
**Last Retail Price:** Unknown

**Ref. No.:** 1032
**Name:** Crane
**Height:** 17.75
**Status:** Very Rare
**Issue Year:** 1969
**Issue Price:** $80
**Last Year:** 1975
**Last Retail Price:** Unknown

**Ref. No.:** 1456
**Name:** Cranes
**Height:** 19
**Status:** Open issue, active
**Issue Year:** 1983
**Issue Price:** $1000
**2003 Retail Price:** $1990

**Ref. No.:** 1335
**Name:** Doves Group
**Height:** 20.75
**Status:** Open edition, retired
**Issue Year:** 1977
**Issue Price:** $475
**Last Year:** 1990
**Last Retail Price:** $1350
**High Auction Price:** $1700
**Low Auction Price:** $1100

**Ref. No.:** 6433
**Name:** Cranes in Flight with Base
**Height:** 22
**Status:** Open issue, retired
**Issue Year:** 1997
**Issue Price:** $1390
**Last Year:** 2001
**Last Retail Price:** $1460

**Ref. No.:** 5912
**Name:** Swans Take Flight
**Height:** 22.75
**Status:** Open issue, active
**Issue Year:** 1992
**Issue Price:** $2850
**2003 Retail Price:** $2995

**Ref. No.:** 1319
**Name:** Herons
**Height:** 23
**Status:** Open issue, active
**Issue Year:** 1976
**Issue Price:** $1550
**2003 Retail Price:** $2625

*Animals*

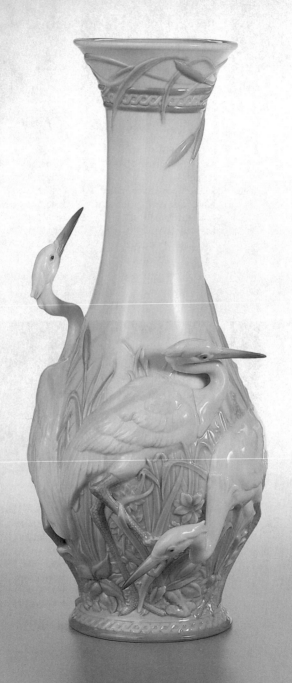

**Vases**

**Ref. No.:** 7502
**Name:** Miniature Vase
**Height:** 2.75
**Status:** Limited edition, sold out
**Issue Year:** 1988
**Issue Price:** Unknown
**Last Year:** 1988
**Comment:** Exclusive to the
   Franklin Mint

**Ref. No.:** 5636
**Name:** Lladró Vase
**Height:** 3
**Status:** Open edition, retired
**Issue Year:** 1989
**Issue Price:** $110
**Last Year:** 1990
**Last Retail Price:** $120

**Ref. No.:** 1692
**Name:** Small Vase
**Height:** 3.25
**Status:** Open edition, retired
**Issue Year:** 1989
**Issue Price:** $65
**Last Year:** 1991
**Last Retail Price:** $75

**Ref. No.:** 5260
**Name:** Vase-Decorated
**Height:** 3.5
**Status:** Open edition, retired
**Issue Year:** 1984
**Issue Price:** $45
**Last Year:** 1990
**Last Retail Price:** $65
**Auction Price:** $125

**Ref. No.:** 5260.3
**Name:** Vase
**Height:** 3.5
**Status:** Open edition, retired
**Issue Year:** 1984
**Issue Price:** $45
**Last Year:** 1988
**Last Retail Price:** $55
**Auction Price:** $100

**Ref. No.:** 5527.4
**Name:** Silver Vase No. 16
**Height:** 3.5
**Status:** Open edition, retired
**Issue Year:** 1988
**Issue Price:** $55
**Last Year:** 1991
**Last Retail Price:** $70

**Ref. No.:** 5527.5
**Name:** Topaz Vase No. 16
**Height:** 3.5
**Status:** Open edition, retired
**Issue Year:** 1988
**Issue Price:** $55
**Last Year:** 1991
**Last Retail Price:** $70

**Ref. No.:** 319.13
**Name:** Vase No. 6
**Height:** 4
**Status:** Very Rare
**Issue Year:** 1958
**Issue Price:** Unknown
**Last Year:** Unknown
**Last Retail Price:** Unknown

**Ref. No.:** 1221.3
**Name:** Little Vase
**Height:** 4
**Status:** Open edition, retired
**Issue Year:** 1972
**Issue Price:** $40
**Last Year:** 1980
**Last Retail Price:** $40

**Ref. No.:** 5257
**Name:** Vase-Decorated
**Height:** 4
**Status:** Open edition, retired
**Issue Year:** 1984
**Issue Price:** $55
**Last Year:** 1990
**Last Retail Price:** $75
**Auction Price:** $475
   (sold with 5256)

**Ref. No.:** 5257.3
**Name:** Vase
**Height:** 4
**Status:** Open edition, retired
**Issue Year:** 1984
**Issue Price:** $55
**Last Year:** 1988
**Last Retail Price:** $70

**Ref. No.:** 5258
**Name:** Vase-Decorated
**Height:** 4
**Status:** Open edition, retired
**Issue Year:** 1984
**Issue Price:** $55
**Last Year:** 1990
**Last Retail Price:** $75
**High Auction Price:** $250
**Low Auction Price:** $175

**Ref. No.:** 5258.3
**Name:** Vase
**Height:** 4
**Status:** Open edition, retired
**Issue Year:** 1984
**Issue Price:** $55
**Last Year:** 1988
**Last Retail Price:** $70

**Ref. No.:** 5568
**Name:** Conical Snail
**Height:** 4
**Status:** Open edition, retired
**Issue Year:** 1989
**Issue Price:** $75
**Last Year:** 1990
**Last Retail Price:** $85

**Ref. No.:** 1222.3
**Name:** Little Vase
**Height:** 4.25
**Status:** Open edition, retired
**Issue Year:** 1972
**Issue Price:** $35
**Last Year:** 1979
**Last Retail Price:** $40
**Auction Price:** $300

**Ref. No.:** 1693
**Name:** Round Vase
**Height:** 4.25
**Status:** Open edition, retired
**Issue Year:** 1989
**Issue Price:** $75
**Last Year:** 1991
**Last Retail Price:** $90

**Ref. No.:** 5259
**Name:** Vase-Decorated
**Height:** 4.25
**Status:** Open edition, retired
**Issue Year:** 1984
**Issue Price:** $65
**Last Year:** 1990
**Last Retail Price:** $90

**Ref. No.:** 5259.3
**Name:** Vase
**Height:** 4.25
**Status:** Open edition, retired
**Issue Year:** 1984
**Issue Price:** $65
**Last Year:** 1988
**Last Retail Price:** $80

**Ref. No.:** 5262
**Name:** Vase-Decorated
**Height:** 4.25
**Status:** Open edition, retired
**Issue Year:** 1984
**Issue Price:** $70
**Last Year:** 1990
**Last Retail Price:** $95
**Auction Price:** $125

**Ref. No.:** 5262.3
**Name:** Vase
**Height:** 4.25
**Status:** Open edition, retired
**Issue Year:** 1984
**Issue Price:** $70
**Last Year:** 1988
**Last Retail Price:** $85

**Ref. No.:** 5526.4
**Name:** Silver Vase No. 14
**Height:** 4.25
**Status:** Open edition, retired
**Issue Year:** 1988
**Issue Price:** $75
**Last Year:** 1991
**Last Retail Price:** $95

**Ref. No.:** 5526.5
**Name:** Topaz Vase No. 15
**Height:** 4.25
**Status:** Open edition, retired
**Issue Year:** 1988
**Issue Price:** $75
**Last Year:** 1991
**Last Retail Price:** $95

**Ref. No.:** 5635
**Name:** Lladró Vase
**Height:** 4.25
**Status:** Open edition, retired
**Issue Year:** 1989
**Issue Price:** $115
**Last Year:** 1990
**Last Retail Price:** $125

**Ref. No.:** 6066
**Name:** Round Blue Jug
**Height:** 4.25
**Status:** Open issue, retired
**Issue Year:** 1993
**Issue Price:** Unknown
**Last Year:** 1996
**Last Retail Price:** $230

**Ref. No.:** 6073
**Name:** Round Green Jug
**Height:** 4.25
**Status:** Open issue, retired
**Issue Year:** 1993
**Issue Price:** Unknown
**Last Year:** 1996
**Last Retail Price:** $200

**Ref. No.:** 6080
**Name:** Violet Round Jug
**Height:** 4.25
**Status:** Open issue, retired
**Issue Year:** 1993
**Issue Price:** Unknown

**Ref. No.:** 5582
**Name:** Small Lily Vase
**Height:** 4.5
**Status:** Open edition, retired
**Issue Year:** 1989
**Issue Price:** $100
**Last Year:** 1990
**Last Retail Price:** $110

**Ref. No.:** 1219.3
**Name:** Little Vase
**Height:** 4.75
**Status:** Open edition, retired
**Issue Year:** 1972
**Issue Price:** $35
**Last Year:** 1979
**Last Retail Price:** $40

**Ref. No.:** 1220.3
**Name:** Little Rose Vase
**Height:** 4.75
**Status:** Open edition, retired
**Issue Year:** 1972
**Issue Price:** $35
**Last Year:** 1979
**Last Retail Price:** $40
**Auction Price:** $250

**Ref. No.:** 5570
**Name:** Octagonal Chinese Vase
**Height:** 4.75
**Status:** Open edition, retired
**Issue Year:** 1989
**Issue Price:** $70
**Last Year:** 1990
**Last Retail Price:** $75

**Ref. No.:** 1691
**Name:** Large Vase
**Height:** 5
**Status:** Open edition, retired
**Issue Year:** 1989
**Issue Price:** $65
**Last Year:** 1991
**Last Retail Price:** $75

**Ref. No.:** 5261
**Name:** Covered Jug_Decorated
**Height:** 5
**Status:** Open edition, retired
**Issue Year:** 1984
**Issue Price:** $70
**Last Year:** 1990
**Last Retail Price:** $95

**Ref. No.:** 5261.3
**Name:** Covered Jug
**Height:** 5
**Status:** Open edition, retired
**Issue Year:** 1984
**Issue Price:** $70
**Last Year:** 1988
**Last Retail Price:** $85

**Ref. No.:** 5521.4
**Name:** Silver Oriental Vase No. 13
**Height:** 5
**Status:** Open edition, retired
**Issue Year:** 1988
**Issue Price:** $65
**Last Year:** 1991
**Last Retail Price:** $85

**Ref. No.:** 5521.5
**Name:** Topaz Vase No. 13
**Height:** 5
**Status:** Open edition, retired
**Issue Year:** 1988
**Issue Price:** $65
**Last Year:** 1991
**Last Retail Price:** $85

**Ref. No.:** 5566
**Name:** Nautilus Vase
**Height:** 5
**Status:** Open edition, retired
**Issue Year:** 1989
**Issue Price:** $110
**Last Year:** 1990
**Last Retail Price:** $120

**Ref. No.:** 5567
**Name:** Double Nautilus Vase
**Height:** 5
**Status:** Open edition, retired
**Issue Year:** 1989
**Issue Price:** $200
**Last Year:** 1990
**Last Retail Price:** $220

**Ref. No.:** 5519.5
**Name:** Red Topaz Vase No. 12
**Height:** 5.25
**Status:** Open edition, retired
**Issue Year:** 1988
**Issue Price:** $70
**Last Year:** 1991
**Last Retail Price:** $90

**Ref. No.:** 5519.4
**Name:** Spring Red-Silver Vase
   No. 12
**Height:** 5.5
**Status:** Open edition, retired
**Issue Year:** 1988
**Issue Price:** $70
**Last Year:** 1991
**Last Retail Price:** $90

**Ref. No.:** 5528.4
**Name:** Silver Vase No. 17
**Height:** 5.5
**Status:** Open edition, retired
**Issue Year:** 1988
**Issue Price:** $70
**Last Year:** 1991
**Last Retail Price:** $90

**Ref. No.:** 5528.5
**Name:** Silver Vase No. 17
**Height:** 5.5
**Status:** Open edition, retired
**Issue Year:** 1988
**Issue Price:** $70
**Last Year:** 1991
**Last Retail Price:** $90

**Ref. No.:** 5536.4
**Name:** Silver Vase No. 25
**Height:** 6
**Status:** Open edition, retired
**Issue Year:** 1988
**Issue Price:** $135
**Last Year:** 1991
**Last Retail Price:** $175

**Ref. No.:** 5536.5
**Name:** Topaz Vase No. 25
**Height:** 6
**Status:** Open edition, retired
**Issue Year:** 1988
**Issue Price:** $135
**Last Year:** 1991
**Last Retail Price:** $175

**Ref. No.:** 4710
**Name:** Small Floral Vase
**Height:** 6.25
**Status:** Open edition, retired
**Issue Year:** 1970
**Issue Price:** $10
**Last Year:** 1975
**Last Retail Price:** $17.50

**Ref. No.:** 5557
**Name:** Wide Octagonal Vase
**Height:** 6.25
**Status:** Open edition, retired
**Issue Year:** 1989
**Issue Price:** $240
**Last Year:** 1990
**Last Retail Price:** $265

**Ref. No.:** 6058
**Name:** Symphony Vase
**Height:** 6.25
**Status:** Open issue, retired
**Issue Year:** 1993
**Issue Price:** Unknown

**Ref. No.:** 6059
**Name:** Prelude Vase
**Height:** 6.25
**Status:** Open issue, retired
**Issue Year:** 1993
**Issue Price:** Unknown

**Ref. No.:** 6060
**Name:** Sonata Vase
**Height:** 6.25
**Status:** Open issue, retired
**Issue Year:** 1993
**Issue Price:** Unknown

**Ref. No.:** 6061
**Name:** Suite Vase
**Height:** 6.25
**Status:** Open issue, retired
**Issue Year:** 1993
**Issue Price:** Unknown
**Last Year:** 1996
**Last Retail Price:** $300

**Ref. No.:** 5562
**Name:** Striped Clover Vase
**Height:** 6.5
**Status:** Open edition, retired
**Issue Year:** 1989
**Issue Price:** $75
**Last Year:** 1990
**Last Retail Price:** $85

**Ref. No.:** 5581
**Name:** Medium Lily Vase
**Height:** 6.5
**Status:** Open edition, retired
**Issue Year:** 1989
**Issue Price:** $135
**Last Year:** 1990
**Last Retail Price:** $150

**Ref. No.:** 5631
**Name:** Lladró Vase
**Height:** 6.5
**Status:** Open edition, retired
**Issue Year:** 1989
**Issue Price:** $150
**Last Year:** 1990
**Last Retail Price:** $165
**Auction Price:** $400

**Ref. No.:** 5633
**Name:** Water Dreamer Vase
**Height:** 6.5
**Status:** Open edition, retired
**Issue Year:** 1989
**Issue Price:** $150
**Last Year:** 1990
**Last Retail Price:** $165
**High Auction Price:** $500
**Low Auction Price:** $350

**Ref. No.:** 5634
**Name:** Water Baby Vase
**Height:** 6.5
**Status:** Open edition, retired
**Issue Year:** 1989
**Issue Price:** $175
**Last Year:** 1990
**Last Retail Price:** $195

**Ref. No.:** 6067
**Name:** Blue Teumosin Vase
**Height:** 6.50
**Status:** Open issue, active
**Issue Year:** 1993
**Issue Price:** Unknown
**2003 Retail Price:** Not sold in
the United States

**Ref. No.:** 6074
**Name:** Green Teumosin Vase
**Height:** 6.50
**Status:** Open issue, active
**Issue Year:** 1993
**Issue Price:** Unknown
**2003 Retail Price:** Not sold in
the United States

**Ref. No.:** 6081
**Name:** Violet Teumosin Vase
**Height:** 6.50
**Status:** Open issue, retired
**Issue Year:** 1993
**Issue Price:** Unknown
**Last Year:** Unknown
**Last Retail Price:** Unknown

**Ref. No.:** 1218.3
**Name:** Miniature Vase
**Height:** 7
**Status:** Open edition, retired
**Issue Year:** 1972
**Issue Price:** $35
**Last Year:** 1979
**Last Retail Price:** $40
**Auction Price:** $175

**Ref. No.:** 1589
**Name:** Ricinus Palm Vase
**Height:** 7
**Status:** Open edition, retired
**Issue Year:** 1988
**Issue Price:** $475
**Last Year:** 1993
**Last Retail Price:** $630

**Ref. No.:** 1593
**Name:** Chrysanthemum Vase
**Height:** 7
**Status:** Open edition, retired
**Issue Year:** 1988
**Issue Price:** $425
**Last Year:** 1991
**Last Retail Price:** $495

**Ref. No.:** 5504.4
**Name:** Silver Vase No. 1
**Height:** 7
**Status:** Open edition, retired
**Issue Year:** 1988
**Issue Price:** $200
**Last Year:** 1991
**Last Retail Price:** $260

**Ref. No.:** 5504.5
**Name:** Topaz Vase No. 1
**Height:** 7
**Status:** Open edition, retired
**Issue Year:** 1988
**Issue Price:** $200
**Last Year:** 1991
**Last Retail Price:** $260

**Ref. No.:** 5510.4
**Name:** Silver 7 Vase No. 24
**Height:** 7
**Status:** Open edition, retired
**Issue Year:** 1988
**Issue Price:** $85
**Last Year:** 1991
**Last Retail Price:** $110

**Ref. No.:** 5510.5
**Name:** Topaz 7 Vase No. 24
**Height:** 7
**Status:** Open edition, retired
**Issue Year:** 1988
**Issue Price:** $85
**Last Year:** 1991
**Last Retail Price:** $110

**Ref. No.:** 5630
**Name:** Lladró Vase
**Height:** 7
**Status:** Open edition, retired
**Issue Year:** 1989
**Issue Price:** $95
**Last Year:** 1990
**Last Retail Price:** $105

**Ref. No.:** 5630.1
**Name:** Lladró Vase
**Height:** 7
**Status:** Open edition, retired
**Issue Year:** 1989
**Issue Price:** $95
**Last Year:** 1990
**Last Retail Price:** $105

**Ref. No.:** 5630.3
**Name:** Lladró Vase
**Height:** 7
**Status:** Open edition, retired
**Issue Year:** 1989
**Issue Price:** $60
**Last Year:** 1990
**Last Retail Price:** $65

**Ref. No.:** 5822
**Name:** Vase No. 4, Verde Oscuro
**Height:** 7
**Status:** Open issue, retired
**Issue Year:** 1991
**Issue Price:** Unknown
**Last Year:** 1994
**Last Retail Price:** Not available in the United States

**Ref. No.:** 57.04
**Name:** Florals Urn
**Height:** 7.5
**Status:** Very Rare
**Issue Year:** 1953
**Issue Price:** Unknown
**Last Year:** Unknown
**Last Retail Price:** Unknown

**Ref. No.:** 58.04
**Name:** Landscape Vase
**Height:** 7.5
**Status:** Very Rare
**Issue Year:** 1953
**Issue Price:** Unknown
**Last Year:** Unknown
**Last Retail Price:** Unknown

**Ref. No.:** 4696
**Name:** Dragon Tibor Jar
**Height:** 7.5
**Status:** Open edition, retired
**Issue Year:** 1970
**Issue Price:** $27.50
**Last Year:** 1975
**Last Retail Price:** $50

**Ref. No.:** 5577
**Name:** Lilac Cuboid Vase
**Height:** 7.5
**Status:** Open edition, retired
**Issue Year:** 1989
**Issue Price:** $175
**Last Year:** 1990
**Last Retail Price:** $195

**Ref. No.:** 5577.1
**Name:** Brown Cuboid Vase
**Height:** 7.5
**Status:** Open edition, retired
**Issue Year:** 1989
**Issue Price:** $125
**Last Year:** 1990
**Last Retail Price:** $135

**Ref. No.:** 5577.3
**Name:** Green Cuboid Vase
**Height:** 7.5
**Status:** Open edition, retired
**Issue Year:** 1989
**Issue Price:** $130
**Last Year:** 1990
**Last Retail Price:** $145

**Ref. No.:** 5577.4
**Name:** Violet Cuboid Vase
**Height:** 7.5
**Status:** Open edition, retired
**Issue Year:** 1989
**Issue Price:** $145
**Last Year:** 1990
**Last Retail Price:** $160

**Ref. No.:** 5561
**Name:** Green Clover Vase
**Height:** 7.75
**Status:** Open edition, retired
**Issue Year:** 1989
**Issue Price:** $130
**Last Year:** 1991
**Last Retail Price:** $155
**Auction Price:** $225

**Ref. No.:** 5561.3
**Name:** Lilac Clover Vase
**Height:** 7.75
**Status:** Open edition, retired
**Issue Year:** 1989
**Issue Price:** $135
**Last Year:** 1991
**Last Retail Price:** $160
**Auction Price:** $300

**Ref. No.:** 5623
**Name:** Green Grecian Dancers
    Vase
**Height:** 7.75
**Status:** Open edition, retired
**Issue Year:** 1989
**Issue Price:** $360
**Last Year:** 1990
**Last Retail Price:** $395

**Ref. No.:** 5623.3
**Name:** White Grecian Dancers
Vase
**Height:** 7.75
**Status:** Open edition, retired
**Issue Year:** 1989
**Issue Price:** $325
**Last Year:** 1990
**Last Retail Price:** $350

**Ref. No.:** 5824
**Name:** Vase No. 2, Verde Oscuro
**Height:** 7.75
**Status:** Open edition, retired
**Issue Year:** 1991
**Issue Price:** Unknown
**Last Year:** 1994
**Last Retail Price:** Not available
in the United States
**Auction Price:** $300

**Ref. No.:** 6389
**Name:** The Bouquet
**Height:** 8
**Status:** Open issue, retired
**Issue Year:** 1997
**Issue Price:** $95
**Last Year:** 1998
**Last Retail Price:** $95

**Ref. No.:** 4723
**Name:** Spring Vase
**Height:** 8.25
**Status:** Open edition, retired
**Issue Year:** 1970
**Issue Price:** $18
**Last Year:** 1975
**Last Retail Price:** $30

**Ref. No.:** 5516.4
**Name:** Slender Silver Vase No. 10
**Height:** 8.25
**Status:** Open edition, retired
**Issue Year:** 1988
**Issue Price:** $160
**Last Year:** 1991
**Last Retail Price:** $205

**Ref. No.:** 5516.5
**Name:** Topaz Vase No. 10
**Height:** 8.25
**Status:** Open edition, retired
**Issue Year:** 1988
**Issue Price:** $160
**Last Year:** 1991
**Last Retail Price:** $205

**Ref. No.:** 5560
**Name:** Wide Tulip Vase
**Height:** 8.25
**Status:** Open edition, retired
**Issue Year:** 1989
**Issue Price:** $110
**Last Year:** 1990
**Last Retail Price:** $120
**Auction Price:** $300

**Ref. No.:** 5622
**Name:** Grecian Court Vase
**Height:** 8.25
**Status:** Open edition, retired
**Issue Year:** 1989
**Issue Price:** $430
**Last Year:** 1990
**Last Retail Price:** $475

**Ref. No.:** 5622.3
**Name:** Small Tree of Life Vase
**Height:** 8.25
**Status:** Open edition, retired
**Issue Year:** 1989
**Issue Price:** $400
**Last Year:** 1990
**Last Retail Price:** $450

**Ref. No.:** 4709
**Name:** Spring Vase
**Height:** 8.5
**Status:** Open edition, retired
**Issue Year:** 1970
**Issue Price:** $16.50
**Last Year:** 1975
**Last Retail Price:** $27.50

**Ref. No.:** 4722
**Name:** Vase
**Height:** 8.5
**Status:** Open edition, retired
**Issue Year:** 1970
**Issue Price:** $20
**Last Year:** 1972
**Last Retail Price:** $25

**Ref. No.:** 4771
**Name:** Spring Vase
**Height:** 8.5
**Status:** Open edition, retired
**Issue Year:** 1971
**Issue Price:** $20
**Last Year:** 1975
**Last Retail Price:** $32.50

**Ref. No.:** 4778
**Name:** Deep Floral Vase
**Height:** 8.5
**Status:** Open edition, retired
**Issue Year:** 1971
**Issue Price:** $20
**Last Year:** 1975
**Last Retail Price:** $32.50

**Ref. No.:** 5509.4
**Name:** Red-Silver Vase No. 6
**Height:** 8.5
**Status:** Open edition, retired
**Issue Year:** 1988
**Issue Price:** $200
**Last Year:** 1991
**Last Retail Price:** $260

**Ref. No.:** 5509.5
**Name:** Red-Topaz Vase No. 6
**Height:** 8.5
**Status:** Open edition, retired
**Issue Year:** 1988
**Issue Price:** $200
**Last Year:** 1991
**Last Retail Price:** $255

**Ref. No.:** 5559
**Name:** Square Vase
**Height:** 8.5
**Status:** Open edition, retired
**Issue Year:** 1989
**Issue Price:** $115
**Last Year:** 1990
**Last Retail Price:** $125

**Ref. No.:** 1122
**Name:** Pastoral Vase
**Height:** 9
**Status:** Very Rare
**Issue Year:** 1971
**Issue Price:** $55
**Last Year:** 1975
**Last Retail Price:** Unknown

**Ref. No.:** 1122.3
**Name:** White Pastoral Vase
**Height:** 9
**Status:** Open edition, retired
**Issue Year:** 1971
**Issue Price:** $35
**Last Year:** 1975
**Last Retail Price:** $55

**Ref. No.:** 5511.4
**Name:** Silver 8 Vase No. 14
**Height:** 9
**Status:** Open edition, retired
**Issue Year:** 1988
**Issue Price:** $125
**Last Year:** 1991
**Last Retail Price:** $160

**Ref. No.:** 5511.5
**Name:** Topaz 8 Vase No. 14
**Height:** 9
**Status:** Open edition, retired
**Issue Year:** 1988
**Issue Price:** $125
**Last Year:** 1991
**Last Retail Price:** $160

**Ref. No.:** 1115
**Name:** Floral Jug
**Height:** 9.5
**Status:** Very Rare
**Issue Year:** 1971
**Issue Price:** $35
**Last Year:** 1979
**Last Retail Price:** Unknown

**Ref. No.:** 1115.3
**Name:** White Floral Jug
**Height:** 9.5
**Status:** Open edition, retired
**Issue Year:** 1971
**Issue Price:** $20
**Last Year:** 1978
**Last Retail Price:** $50

**Ref. No.:** 5507.4
**Name:** Topaz Vase No. 4
**Height:** 9.5
**Status:** Open edition, retired
**Issue Year:** 1988
**Issue Price:** $155
**Last Year:** 1991
**Last Retail Price:** $200

**Ref. No.:** 5507.5
**Name:** Topaz Vase No. 4
**Height:** 9.5
**Status:** Open edition, retired
**Issue Year:** 1988
**Issue Price:** $155
**Last Year:** 1991
**Last Retail Price:** $200

**Ref. No.:** 5531.4
**Name:** Silver Vase No. 20
**Height:** 9.5
**Status:** Open edition, retired
**Issue Year:** 1988
**Issue Price:** $135
**Last Year:** 1991
**Last Retail Price:** $175

**Ref. No.:** 5531.5
**Name:** Topaz Vase No. 20
**Height:** 9.5
**Status:** Open edition, retired
**Issue Year:** 1988
**Issue Price:** $135
**Last Year:** 1991
**Last Retail Price:** $175

**Ref. No.:** 5563
**Name:** Blue Basket Vase
**Height:** 9.5
**Status:** Open edition, retired
**Issue Year:** 1989
**Issue Price:** $190
**Last Year:** 1990
**Last Retail Price:** $210

**Ref. No.:** 5563.3
**Name:** White Basket Vase
**Height:** 9.5
**Status:** Open edition, retired
**Issue Year:** 1989
**Issue Price:** $190
**Last Year:** 1990
**Last Retail Price:** $210

**Ref. No.:** 4690
**Name:** Yellow Dragon Vase
**Height:** 9.75
**Status:** Open edition, retired
**Issue Year:** 1970
**Issue Price:** $35
**Last Year:** 1981
**Last Retail Price:** $137.5
**High Auction Price:** $700
**Low Auction Price:** $550

**Ref. No.:** 4690.3
**Name:** Jug Decorated
**Height:** 9.75
**Status:** Open edition, retired
**Issue Year:** 1970
**Issue Price:** $350
**Last Year:** 1981
**Last Retail Price:** $192.50

**Ref. No.:** 4691
**Name:** Flower Vase
**Height:** 9.75
**Status:** Open edition, retired
**Issue Year:** 1970
**Issue Price:** $36.50
**Last Year:** 1981
**Last Retail Price:** $160
**Auction Price:** $350

**Ref. No.:** 4691.3
**Name:** White Flower Vase
**Height:** 9.75
**Status:** Open edition, retired
**Issue Year:** 1970
**Issue Price:** $40
**Last Year:** 1981
**Last Retail Price:** $230

**Ref. No.:** 4697
**Name:** White Vase
**Height:** 9.75
**Status:** Open edition, retired
**Issue Year:** 1970
**Issue Price:** $13.50
**Last Year:** 1975
**Last Retail Price:** $22.50

**Ref. No.:** 5556.3
**Name:** Red Octagonal Flower
Vase
**Height:** 10
**Status:** Open edition, retired
**Issue Year:** 1989
**Issue Price:** $225
**Last Year:** 1990
**Last Retail Price:** $250

**Ref. No.:** 1119
**Name:** Mermaid Vase
**Height:** 10.25
**Status:** Open edition, retired
**Issue Year:** 1971
**Issue Price:** $60
**Last Year:** 1972
**Last Retail Price:** $65

**Ref. No.:** 1592
**Name:** Ricinus Palm Vase
**Height:** 10.25
**Status:** Open edition, retired
**Issue Year:** 1988
**Issue Price:** $395
**Last Year:** 1993
**Last Retail Price:** $550

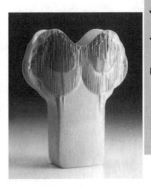

**Ref. No.:** 1596
**Name:** Chrysanthemum Vase
**Height:** 10.25
**Status:** Open edition, retired
**Issue Year:** 1988
**Issue Price:** $395
**Last Year:** 1991
**Last Retail Price:** $495

**Ref. No.:** 1623
**Name:** Lladró Vase
**Height:** 10.25
**Status:** Open edition, retired
**Issue Year:** 1989
**Issue Price:** $360
**Last Year:** 1990
**Last Retail Price:** $395

**Ref. No.:** 1623.1
**Name:** Lladró Vase
**Height:** 10.25
**Status:** Open edition, retired
**Issue Year:** 1989
**Issue Price:** $215
**Last Year:** 1990
**Last Retail Price:** $2235

**Ref. No.:** 1623.3
**Name:** Lladró Vase
**Height:** 10.25
**Status:** Open edition, retired
**Issue Year:** 1989
**Issue Price:** $100
**Last Year:** 1990
**Last Retail Price:** $110

**Ref. No.:** 5533.4
**Name:** Silver Vase No. 22
**Height:** 10.25
**Status:** Open edition, retired
**Issue Year:** 1988
**Issue Price:** $140
**Last Year:** 1991
**Last Retail Price:** $180

**Ref. No.:** 5533.5
**Name:** Topaz Vase No. 22
**Height:** 10.25
**Status:** Open edition, retired
**Issue Year:** 1988
**Issue Price:** $140
**Last Year:** 1991
**Last Retail Price:** $180

**Ref. No.:** 5558
**Name:** Slender Octagonal Vase
**Height:** 10.25
**Status:** Open edition, retired
**Issue Year:** 1989
**Issue Price:** $260
**Last Year:** 1990
**Last Retail Price:** $285

**Ref. No.:** 5564
**Name:** Sparrow Vase
**Height:** 10.25
**Status:** Open edition, retired
**Issue Year:** 1989
**Issue Price:** $190
**Last Year:** 1991
**Last Retail Price:** $225

**Ref. No.:** 5565
**Name:** Fantasy Dragon Vase
**Height:** 10.25
**Status:** Open edition, retired
**Issue Year:** 1989
**Issue Price:** $185
**Last Year:** 1991
**Last Retail Price:** $220

**Ref. No.:** 5569
**Name:** Lily Vase
**Height:** 10.25
**Status:** Open edition, retired
**Issue Year:** 1989
**Issue Price:** $215
**Last Year:** 1990
**Last Retail Price:** $235

**Ref. No.:** 5580
**Name:** Large Lily Vase
**Height:** 10.25
**Status:** Open edition, retired
**Issue Year:** 1989
**Issue Price:** $165
**Last Year:** 1990
**Last Retail Price:** $180

**Ref. No.:** 5823
**Name:** Vase No.3 Verde Oscuro
**Height:** 10.25
**Status:** Open issue, retired
**Issue Year:** 1991
**Issue Price:** Unknown
**Last Year:** 1994
**Last Retail Price:** Not available
in the United States

**Ref. No.:** 51.04
**Name:** The Bouquet Urn
**Height:** 10.5
**Status:** Very Rare
**Issue Year:** 1953
**Issue Price:** Unknown
**Last Year:** Unknown
**Last Retail Price:** Unknown

**Ref. No.:** 316.13
**Name:** Vase No. 3
**Height:** 10.5
**Status:** Very Rare
**Issue Year:** 1958
**Issue Price:** Unknown
**Last Year:** Unknown
**Last Retail Price:** Unknown

**Ref. No.:** 5508.4
**Name:** Topaz Vase No. 5
**Height:** 10.5
**Status:** Open edition, retired
**Issue Year:** 1988
**Issue Price:** $150
**Last Year:** 1991
**Last Retail Price:** $195

**Ref. No.:** 5508.5
**Name:** Topaz Vase No. 5
**Height:** 10.5
**Status:** Open edition, retired
**Issue Year:** 1988
**Issue Price:** $150
**Last Year:** 1991
**Last Retail Price:** $195
**Auction Price:** $250

**Ref. No.:** 45.03
**Name:** Landscape Urn
**Height:** 10.75
**Status:** Very Rare
**Issue Year:** 1953
**Issue Price:** Unknown
**Last Year:** Unknown
**Last Retail Price:** Unknown

**Ref. No.:** 1687
**Name:** Small Poppy Vase
**Height:** 11
**Status:** Open edition, retired
**Issue Year:** 1989
**Issue Price:** $250
**Last Year:** 1991
**Last Retail Price:** $300

**Ref. No.:** 4770
**Name:** Don Quixote Vase
**Height:** 11
**Status:** Open edition, retired
**Issue Year:** 1971
**Issue Price:** $25
**Last Year:** 1975
**Last Retail Price:** $40

**Ref. No.:** 5534.4
**Name:** Silver Vase No. 23
**Height:** 11
**Status:** Open edition, retired
**Issue Year:** 1988
**Issue Price:** $170
**Last Year:** 1991
**Last Retail Price:** $220

**Ref. No.:** 5534.5
**Name:** Topaz Vase No. 23
**Height:** 11
**Status:** Open edition, retired
**Issue Year:** 1988
**Issue Price:** $170
**Last Year:** 1991
**Last Retail Price:** $220

**Ref. No.:** 5624
**Name:** Poseidon Vase
**Height:** 11
**Status:** Open edition, retired
**Issue Year:** 1989
**Issue Price:** $575
**Last Year:** 1990
**Last Retail Price:** $625

**Ref. No.:** 315.13
**Name:** Vase No. 2
**Height:** 11.25
**Status:** Very Rare
**Issue Year:** 1958
**Issue Price:** Unknown
**Last Year:** Unknown
**Last Retail Price:** Unknown

**Ref. No.:** 1112
**Name:** Mermaid
**Height:** 11.25
**Status:** Open edition, retired
**Issue Year:** 1971
**Issue Price:** $55
**Last Year:** 1972
**Last Retail Price:** $60

**Ref. No.:** 1588
**Name:** Fantasy Vase
**Height:** 11.5
**Status:** Open edition, retired
**Issue Year:** 1988
**Issue Price:** $695
**Last Year:** 1993
**Last Retail Price:** $945

**Ref. No.:** 1590
**Name:** Ricinus Palm Vase
**Height:** 11.5
**Status:** Open edition, retired
**Issue Year:** 1988
**Issue Price:** $650
**Last Year:** 1993
**Last Retail Price:** $865

**Ref. No.:** 1594
**Name:** Chrysanthemum Vase
**Height:** 11.5
**Status:** Open edition, retired
**Issue Year:** 1988
**Issue Price:** $495
**Last Year:** 1991
**Last Retail Price:** $595

**Ref. No.:** 4721
**Name:** Vase
**Height:** 11.5
**Status:** Open edition, retired
**Issue Year:** 1970
**Issue Price:** $27.50
**Last Year:** 1975
**Last Retail Price:** $50

**Ref. No.:** 5571.3
**Name:** Red Vase with Handles
**Height:** 11.5
**Status:** Open edition, retired
**Issue Year:** 1989
**Issue Price:** $215
**Last Year:** 1990
**Last Retail Price:** $235

**Ref. No.:** 5578
**Name:** Brown Compact Vase
**Height:** 11.5
**Status:** Open edition, retired
**Issue Year:** 1989
**Issue Price:** $175
**Last Year:** 1990
**Last Retail Price:** $195

**Ref. No.:** 5578.1
**Name:** Brown Compact Vase
**Height:** 11.5
**Status:** Open edition, retired
**Issue Year:** 1989
**Issue Price:** $130
**Last Year:** 1990
**Last Retail Price:** $145

**Ref. No.:** 5578.3
**Name:** Green Compact Vase
**Height:** 11.5
**Status:** Open edition, retired
**Issue Year:** 1989
**Issue Price:** $135
**Last Year:** 1990
**Last Retail Price:** $150

**Ref. No.:** 5578.4
**Name:** Violet Compact Vase
**Height:** 11.5
**Status:** Open edition, retired
**Issue Year:** 1989
**Issue Price:** $150
**Last Year:** 1990
**Last Retail Price:** $165

**Ref. No.:** 5621
**Name:** Large Tree of Life Vase
**Height:** 11.5
**Status:** Open edition, retired
**Issue Year:** 1989
**Issue Price:** $270
**Last Year:** 1990
**Last Retail Price:** $295

**Ref. No.:** 5621.3
**Name:** Large White Tree of Life
Vase
**Height:** 11.5
**Status:** Open edition, retired
**Issue Year:** 1989
**Issue Price:** $250
**Last Year:** 1990
**Last Retail Price:** $275

**Ref. No.:** 59.04
**Name:** The Lovers
**Height:** 11.75
**Status:** Very Rare
**Issue Year:** 1955
**Issue Price:** Unknown
**Last Year:** Unknown
**Last Retail Price:** Unknown

**Ref. No.:** 1583
**Name:** Crocus Vase
**Height:** 11.75
**Status:** Open edition, retired
**Issue Year:** 1988
**Issue Price:** $475
**Last Year:** 1993
**Last Retail Price:** $630

**Ref. No.:** 1584
**Name:** Poppies Vase
**Height:** 11.75
**Status:** Open edition, retired
**Issue Year:** 1988
**Issue Price:** $575
**Last Year:** 1993
**Last Retail Price:** $785

**Ref. No.:** 1586
**Name:** Trumpet Flower Vase
**Height:** 11.75
**Status:** Open edition, retired
**Issue Year:** 1988
**Issue Price:** $525
**Last Year:** 1993
**Last Retail Price:** $735

**Ref. No.:** 5512.4
**Name:** Silver Spring Vase No. 9
**Height:** 11.75
**Status:** Open edition, retired
**Issue Year:** 1988
**Issue Price:** $265
**Last Year:** 1991
**Last Retail Price:** $345

**Ref. No.:** 5512.5
**Name:** Topaz Vase No. 9
**Height:** 11.75
**Status:** Open edition, retired
**Issue Year:** 1988
**Issue Price:** $265
**Last Year:** 1991
**Last Retail Price:** $345

**Ref. No.:** 5620
**Name:** Grecian Vase I
**Height:** 11.75
**Status:** Open edition, retired
**Issue Year:** 1989
**Issue Price:** $240
**Last Year:** 1990
**Last Retail Price:** $275

**Ref. No.:** 5620.3
**Name:** Grecian Vase II
**Height:** 11.75
**Status:** Open edition, retired
**Issue Year:** 1989
**Issue Price:** $225
**Last Year:** 1990
**Last Retail Price:** $265

**Ref. No.:** 6880
**Name:** Herons' Realm Covered
 Vase
**Height:** 12
**Status:** Open issue, active
**Issue Year:** 2002
**Issue Price:** $425
**2003 Retail Price:** $425

**Ref. No.:** 5505.4
**Name:** Silver Vase No. 2
**Height:** 12.25
**Status:** Open edition, retired
**Issue Year:** 1988
**Issue Price:** $150
**Last Year:** 1991
**Last Retail Price:** $195

**Ref. No.:** 5505.5
**Name:** Topaz Vase No. 2
**Height:** 12.25
**Status:** Open edition, retired
**Issue Year:** 1988
**Issue Price:** $150
**Last Year:** 1991
**Last Retail Price:** $195

**Ref. No.:** 5506.4
**Name:** Silver Turia Vase No. 3
**Height:** 12.25
**Status:** Open edition, retired
**Issue Year:** 1988
**Issue Price:** $155
**Last Year:** 1991
**Last Retail Price:** $200
**Auction Price:** $350

**Ref. No.:** 5506.5
**Name:** Topaz Vase No. 3
**Height:** 12.25
**Status:** Open edition, retired
**Issue Year:** 1988
**Issue Price:** $155
**Last Year:** 1991
**Last Retail Price:** $200

**Ref. No.:** 63.04
**Name:** Urn
**Height:** 12.5
**Status:** Very Rare
**Issue Year:** 1955
**Issue Price:** Unknown
**Last Year:** Unknown
**Last Retail Price:** Unknown

**Ref. No.:** 314.13
**Name:** Vase No. 1
**Height:** 12.5
**Status:** Very Rare
**Issue Year:** 1958
**Issue Price:** Unknown
**Last Year:** Unknown
**Last Retail Price:** Unknown

**Ref. No.:** 1585
**Name:** Lily Candy Vase
**Height:** 12.5
**Status:** Open edition, retired
**Issue Year:** 1988
**Issue Price:** $295
**Last Year:** 1991
**Last Retail Price:** $350

**Ref. No.:** 5556
**Name:** Octagonal Flower Vase
**Height:** 12.5
**Status:** Open edition, retired
**Issue Year:** 1989
**Issue Price:** $275
**Last Year:** 1990
**Last Retail Price:** $300

**Ref. No.:** 62.04
**Name:** Urn
**Height:** 12.75
**Status:** Very Rare
**Issue Year:** 1955
**Issue Price:** Unknown
**Last Year:** Unknown
**Last Retail Price:** Unknown

**Ref. No.:** 2047
**Name:** Jug
**Height:** 13
**Status:** Open edition, retired
**Issue Year:** 1971
**Issue Price:** $40
**Last Year:** 1975
**Last Retail Price:** $65

**Ref. No.:** 52.04
**Name:** Flowers Urn
**Height:** 13.25
**Status:** Very Rare
**Issue Year:** 1953
**Issue Price:** Unknown
**Last Year:** Unknown
**Last Retail Price:** Unknown

**Ref. No.:** 1587
**Name:** Gladiolus Vase
**Height:** 13.25
**Status:** Open issue, retired
**Issue Year:** 1988
**Issue Price:** $350
**Last Year:** 1998
**Last Retail Price:** $700

**Ref. No.:** 1688
**Name:** Large Poppy Vase
**Height:** 13.25
**Status:** Open edition, retired
**Issue Year:** 1989
**Issue Price:** $265
**Last Year:** 1991
**Last Retail Price:** $315

**Ref. No.:** 2050
**Name:** Coral Vase
**Height:** 13.25
**Status:** Open edition, retired
**Issue Year:** 1973
**Issue Price:** $180
**Last Year:** 1979
**Last Retail Price:** $265
**Auction Price:** $600

**Ref. No.:** 5825
**Name:** Vase No. 1, Verde Oscuro
**Height:** 13.25
**Status:** Open issue, retired
**Issue Year:** 1991
**Issue Price:** Unknown
**Last Year:** 1994
**Last Retail Price:** Not available
in the United States

**Ref. No.:** 1591
**Name:** Ricinus Palm Vase
**Height:** 13.5
**Status:** Open edition, retired
**Issue Year:** 1988
**Issue Price:** $575
**Last Year:** 1993
**Last Retail Price:** $785

**Ref. No.:** 1595
**Name:** Chrysanthemum Vase
**Height:** 13.5
**Status:** Open edition, retired
**Issue Year:** 1988
**Issue Price:** $495
**Last Year:** 1991
**Last Retail Price:** $595

**Ref. No.:** 6881
**Name:** Herons' Realm Vase
**Height:** 14
**Status:** Open issue, active
**Issue Year:** 2002
**Issue Price:** $690
**2003 Retail Price:** $695

**Ref. No.:** 5529.4
**Name:** Silver Vase No. 18
**Height:** 14.25
**Status:** Open edition, retired
**Issue Year:** 1988
**Issue Price:** $235
**Last Year:** 1991
**Last Retail Price:** $300

**Ref. No.:** 5529.5
**Name:** Topaz Vase No. 18
**Height:** 14.25
**Status:** Open edition, retired
**Issue Year:** 1988
**Issue Price:** $235
**Last Year:** 1991
**Last Retail Price:** $300

**Ref. No.:** 61.04
**Name:** Urn
**Height:** 14.5
**Status:** Very Rare
**Issue Year:** 1953
**Issue Price:** Unknown
**Last Year:** Unknown
**Last Retail Price:** Unknown

**Ref. No.:** 5532.4
**Name:** Silver Vase No. 21
**Height:** 15.5
**Status:** Open edition, retired
**Issue Year:** 1988
**Issue Price:** $165
**Last Year:** 1991
**Last Retail Price:** $215

**Ref. No.:** 5532.5
**Name:** Topaz Vase No. 21
**Height:** 15.5
**Status:** Open edition, retired
**Issue Year:** 1988
**Issue Price:** $165
**Last Year:** 1991
**Last Retail Price:** $215

**Ref. No.:** 60.04
**Name:** Urn
**Height:** 15.75
**Status:** Very Rare
**Issue Year:** 1950
**Issue Price:** Unknown
**Last Year:** Unknown
**Last Retail Price:** Unknown

**Ref. No.:** 1619
**Name:** Bird Vase
**Height:** 16
**Status:** Limited edition, retired
**Edition Size:** 300
**Issue Year:** 1989
**Issue Price:** $3125
**Last Retail Price:** $3995
**Last Year:** 1998
**Last Retail Price:** $3995

**Ref. No.:** 1690
**Name:** Chinese Vase
**Height:** 16
**Status:** Open edition, retired
**Issue Year:** 1989
**Issue Price:** $345
**Last Year:** 1991
**Last Retail Price:** $410

**Ref. No.:** 4818
**Name:** Red Sunflower Jar
**Height:** 16
**Status:** Open edition, retired
**Issue Year:** 1972
**Issue Price:** $45
**Last Year:** 1975
**Last Retail Price:** $70

**Ref. No.:** 4819
**Name:** Brown Sunflower Jar
**Height:** 16
**Status:** Open edition, retired
**Issue Year:** 1972
**Issue Price:** $45
**Last Year:** 1975
**Last Retail Price:** $70

**Ref. No.:** 1140
**Name:** Floral Group (two vases)
**Height:** 16.5
**Status:** Very Rare
**Issue Year:** 1971
**Issue Price:** Unknown
**Last Year:** 1972
**Last Retail Price:** Unknown

**Ref. No.:** 4742
**Name:** Octagonal Jar
**Height:** 16.5
**Status:** Open edition, retired
**Issue Year:** 1971
**Issue Price:** $120
**Last Year:** 1973
**Last Retail Price:** $150

**Ref. No.:** 4846
**Name:** Mandarin Vase
**Height:** 16.5
**Status:** Open edition, retired
**Issue Year:** 1973
**Issue Price:** $215
**Last Year:** 1981
**Last Retail Price:** $660

**Ref. No.:** 5016
**Name:** Mandarin Vase
**Height:** 16.5
**Status:** Open edition, retired
**Issue Year:** 1978
**Issue Price:** $450
**Last Year:** 1981
**Last Retail Price:** $580

**Ref. No.:** 4743
**Name:** Pink Octagonal Jar
**Height:** 17
**Status:** Open edition, retired
**Issue Year:** 1971
**Issue Price:** $45
**Last Year:** 1973
**Last Retail Price:** $55

**Ref. No.:** 4744
**Name:** Blue Octagonal Jar
**Height:** 17
**Status:** Open edition, retired
**Issue Year:** 1971
**Issue Price:** $45
**Last Year:** 1972
**Last Retail Price:** $50

**Ref. No.:** 4745
**Name:** Green Octagonal Jar
**Height:** 17
**Status:** Open edition, retired
**Issue Year:** 1971
**Issue Price:** $45
**Last Year:** 1973
**Last Retail Price:** $55

**Ref. No.:** 5524.4
**Name:** Topaz 14 Vase No. 47
**Height:** 17
**Status:** Open edition, retired
**Issue Year:** 1988
**Issue Price:** $400
**Last Year:** 1991
**Last Retail Price:** $515

**Ref. No.:** 5524.5
**Name:** Topaz 14 Vase No. 47
**Height:** 17
**Status:** Open edition, retired
**Issue Year:** 1988
**Issue Price:** $400
**Last Year:** 1991
**Last Retail Price:** $515

**Ref. No.:** 5530.4
**Name:** Silver Vase No. 19
**Height:** 17
**Status:** Open edition, retired
**Issue Year:** 1988
**Issue Price:** $235
**Last Year:** 1991
**Last Retail Price:** $300

**Ref. No.:** 5530.5
**Name:** Topaz Vase No. 19
**Height:** 17
**Status:** Open edition, retired
**Issue Year:** 1988
**Issue Price:** $235
**Last Year:** 1991
**Last Retail Price:** $300

**Ref. No.:** 1120.3
**Name:** Dragon Vase
**Height:** 17.25
**Status:** Open edition, retired
**Issue Year:** 1971
**Issue Price:** $65
**Last Year:** 1974
**Last Retail Price:** $95

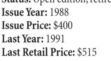

**Ref. No.:** 317.13
**Name:** Vase No. 4
**Height:** 17.75
**Status:** Very Rare
**Issue Year:** 1958
**Issue Price:** Unknown
**Last Year:** Unknown
**Last Retail Price:** Unknown

**Ref. No.:** 1536
**Name:** Japanese Vase
**Height:** 17.75
**Status:** Limited edition, sold out
**Edition Size:** 750
**Issue Year:** 1988
**Issue Price:** $2600
**Last Year:** 1990
**Last Retail Price:** $3000
**High Auction Price:** $3750
**Low Auction Price:** $3250

**Ref. No.:** 1581
**Name:** Lilies Vase
**Height:** 17.75
**Status:** Open edition, retired
**Issue Year:** 1988
**Issue Price:** $525
**Last Year:** 1991
**Last Retail Price:** $650

**Ref. No.:** 1217
**Name:** Pekinese Vase
**Height:** 18.5
**Status:** Open edition, retired
**Issue Year:** 1972
**Issue Price:** $450
**Last Year:** 1981
**Last Retail Price:** $600

**Ref. No.:** 5571
**Name:** Vase with Handles
**Height:** 18.5
**Status:** Open edition, retired
**Issue Year:** 1989
**Issue Price:** $550
**Last Year:** 1990
**Last Retail Price:** $600

**Ref. No.:** 6030
**Name:** Maidenhead Vase
**Height:** 18.5
**Status:** Open edition, retired
**Issue Year:** 1993
**Issue Price:** $1350
**Last Year:** 1995
**Last Retail Price:** $1350

**Ref. No.:** 1363
**Name:** Peking Vase
**Height:** 19
**Status:** Open edition, retired
**Issue Year:** 1978
**Issue Price:** $540
**Last Year:** 1991
**Last Retail Price:** $1285
**Auction Price:** $550

**Ref. No.:** 1364
**Name:** Peking Vase
**Height:** 19
**Status:** Open edition, retired
**Issue Year:** 1978
**Issue Price:** $900
**Last Year:** 1991
**Last Retail Price:** $1600
**High Auction Price:** $950
**Low Auction Price:** $900

**Ref. No.:** 1365
**Name:** Birds and Flowers Peking
  Vase
**Height:** 19
**Status:** Open edition, retired
**Issue Year:** 1978
**Issue Price:** $900
**Last Year:** 1991
**Last Retail Price:** $1950

**Ref. No.:** 4741
**Name:** Classic Floral Vase
**Height:** 19
**Status:** Open edition, retired
**Issue Year:** 1971
**Issue Price:** $100
**Last Year:** 1979
**Last Retail Price:** $260

**Ref. No.:** 4752
**Name:** Blue Peonies Cylindrical
  Vase
**Height:** 19
**Status:** Open edition, retired
**Issue Year:** 1971
**Issue Price:** $50
**Last Year:** 1979
**Last Retail Price:** $230
**Auction Price:** $475

**Ref. No.:** 4753
**Name:** Green Peonies Cylindrical
  Vase
**Height:** 19
**Status:** Open edition, retired
**Issue Year:** 1971
**Issue Price:** $50
**Last Year:** 1979
**Last Retail Price:** $230

**Ref. No.:** 4754
**Name:** Peach Pink Cylindrical
    Vase
**Height:** 19
**Status:** Open edition, retired
**Issue Year:** 1971
**Issue Price:** $55
**Last Year:** 1979
**Last Retail Price:** $275

**Ref. No.:** 4832
**Name:** Vase
**Height:** 19
**Status:** Open edition, retired
**Issue Year:** 1972
**Issue Price:** $85
**Last Year:** 1981
**Last Retail Price:** $520
**Auction Price:** $600

**Ref. No.:** 4845
**Name:** Peking Vase with Butterfly
**Height:** 19
**Status:** Open edition, retired
**Issue Year:** 1973
**Issue Price:** $150
**Last Year:** 1981
**Last Retail Price:** $455

**Ref. No.:** 1137
**Name:** Paradise Vase
**Height:** 19.25
**Status:** Limited edition, sold out
**Issue Year:** 1971
**Issue Price:** $335
**Last Year:** 1972
**Last Retail Price:** $355

**Ref. No.:** 1138
**Name:** Rooster Vase
**Height:** 19.25
**Status:** Limited edition, sold out
**Issue Year:** 1971
**Issue Price:** $335
**Last Year:** 1972
**Last Retail Price:** $355
**High Auction Price:** $1000
**Low Auction Price:** $900

**Ref. No.:** 1191
**Name:** Floral Vase
**Height:** 19.25
**Status:** Limited edition, sold out
**Edition Size:** 150
**Issue Year:** 1972
**Issue Price:** $465
**Last Year:** 1982
**Last Retail Price:** $1900

**Ref. No.:** 1192
**Name:** Red Magno Vase
**Height:** 19.25
**Status:** Limited edition, sold out
**Edition Size:** 150
**Issue Year:** 1972
**Issue Price:** $535
**Last Year:** 1982
**Last Retail Price:** $2750

**Ref. No.:** 1198
**Name:** Blue Empire Vase
**Height:** 19.25
**Status:** Very Rare
**Issue Year:** 1972
**Issue Price:** $300
**Last Year:** 1975
**Last Retail Price:** Unknown

**Ref. No.:** 1199
**Name:** Blue Empire Vase
**Height:** 19.25
**Status:** Limited edition, sold out
**Edition Size:** 300
**Issue Year:** 1972
**Issue Price:** $610
**Last Year:** 1982
**Last Retail Price:** $2750

**Ref. No.:** 1582
**Name:** Pansy Vase
**Height:** 19.25
**Status:** Open issue, retired
**Issue Year:** 1988
**Issue Price:** $775
**Last Year:** 1998
**Last Retail Price:** $1500

**Ref. No.:** 5535.4
**Name:** Silver Vase No. 24
**Height:** 19.25
**Status:** Open edition, retired
**Issue Year:** 1988
**Issue Price:** $345
**Last Year:** 1991
**Last Retail Price:** $450

**Ref. No.:** 5535.5
**Name:** Topaz Vase No. 24
**Height:** 19.25
**Status:** Open edition, retired
**Issue Year:** 1988
**Issue Price:** $345
**Last Year:** 1991
**Last Retail Price:** $445

*Functional*

**Ref. No.:** 5918
**Name:** Fanciful Flight Vase
**Height:** 19.25
**Status:** Limited edition, sold out
**Edition Size:** 300
**Issue Year:** 1992
**Issue Price:** $4000
**Last Year:** 2001
**Last Retail Price:** $4800

**Ref. No.:** 1193
**Name:** Empire Vase
**Height:** 19.75
**Status:** Very Rare
**Issue Year:** 1972
**Issue Price:** $300
**Last Year:** 1975
**Last Retail Price:** Unknown

**Ref. No.:** 1197
**Name:** Floral Vase
**Height:** 19.75
**Status:** Limited edition, sold out
**Edition Size:** 150
**Issue Year:** 1972
**Issue Price:** $445
**Last Year:** 1982
**Last Retail Price:** $2000

**Ref. No.:** 1116
**Name:** Green Dragon Vase
**Height:** 20
**Status:** Open edition, retired
**Issue Year:** 1971
**Issue Price:** $90
**Last Year:** 1973
**Last Retail Price:** $90

**Ref. No.:** 1116.3
**Name:** Blue-White Dragon Vase
**Height:** 20
**Status:** Open edition, retired
**Issue Year:** 1971
**Issue Price:** $90
**Last Year:** 1973
**Last Retail Price:** $115

**Ref. No.:** 1141
**Name:** Green Imperial Vase
**Height:** 20
**Status:** Very Rare
**Issue Year:** 1971
**Issue Price:** $60
**Last Year:** 1972
**Last Retail Price:** Unknown

**Ref. No.:** 1142
**Name:** Yellow Imperial Jug
**Height:** 20
**Status:** Very Rare
**Issue Year:** 1971
**Issue Price:** $60
**Last Year:** 1972
**Last Retail Price:** Unknown

**Ref. No.:** 1143
**Name:** Red Imperial Jug
**Height:** 20
**Status:** Very Rare
**Issue Year:** 1971
**Issue Price:** $70
**Last Year:** 1972
**Last Retail Price:** Unknown

**Ref. No.:** 1190
**Name:** Paradise Bird Vase
**Height:** 20
**Status:** Open edition, retired
**Issue Year:** 1972
**Issue Price:** $340
**Last Year:** 1975
**Last Retail Price:** $520

**Ref. No.:** 1118
**Name:** Floral Vase
**Height:** 20.5
**Status:** Open edition, retired
**Issue Year:** 1971
**Issue Price:** $160
**Last Year:** 1972
**Last Retail Price:** $170

**Ref. No.:** 1617
**Name:** Swallow Vase
**Height:** 20.5
**Status:** Limited edition, sold out
**Edition Size:** 300
**Issue Year:** 1989
**Issue Price:** $2300
**Last Year:** 1998
**Last Retail Price:** $3075

**Ref. No.:** 1620
**Name:** Peacock Vase
**Height:** 20.5
**Status:** Limited edition, sold out
**Edition Size:** 300
**Issue Year:** 1989
**Issue Price:** $2450
**Last Year:** 1998
**Last Retail Price:** $3150

*Functional*

**Ref. No.:** 1621
**Name:** Pheasants and Mums Vase
**Height:** 20.5
**Status:** Limited edition, sold out
**Edition Size:** 300
**Issue Year:** 1989
**Issue Price:** $2575
**Last Year:** 1998
**Last Retail Price:** $3300

**Ref. No.:** 4740
**Name:** Cylindrical Floral Vase
**Height:** 20.5
**Status:** Open edition, retired
**Issue Year:** 1971
**Issue Price:** $130
**Last Year:** 1979
**Last Retail Price:** $335

**Ref. No.:** 1760
**Name:** Oriental Bird Vase No. 1
**Height:** 20.75
**Status:** Limited edition, active
**Edition Size:** 300
**Issue Year:** 1992
**Issue Price:** $6700
**2003 Retail Price:** $7000

**Ref. No.:** 1761
**Name:** Oriental Bird Vase No. 2
**Height:** 20.75
**Status:** Limited edition, active
**Edition Size:** 300
**Issue Year:** 1992
**Issue Price:** $6700
**2003 Retail Price:** $7000

**Ref. No.:** 5517.4
**Name:** Silver Vase No. 11
**Height:** 20.75
**Status:** Open edition, retired
**Issue Year:** 1988
**Issue Price:** $425
**Last Year:** 1991
**Last Retail Price:** $550

**Ref. No.:** 5517.5
**Name:** Topaz Vase No. 11
**Height:** 20.75
**Status:** Open edition, retired
**Issue Year:** 1988
**Issue Price:** $425
**Last Year:** 1991
**Last Retail Price:** $550

**Ref. No.:** 5916
**Name:** Oriental Peonies Vase
No. 1
**Height:** 20.75
**Status:** Limited edition, sold out
**Edition Size:** 300
**Issue Year:** 1992
**Issue Price:** $6700
**Last Year:** 2001
**Last Retail Price:** $8000

**Ref. No.:** 5917
**Name:** Oriental Peonies Vase
No. 2
**Height:** 20.75
**Status:** Limited edition, sold out
**Edition Size:** 300
**Issue Year:** 1992
**Issue Price:** $6700
**Last Year:** 2001
**Last Retail Price:** $8000

**Ref. No.:** 318.13
**Name:** Vase No. 5
**Height:** 21.25
**Status:** Very Rare
**Issue Year:** 1958
**Issue Price:** Unknown
**Last Year:** Unknown
**Last Retail Price:** Unknown

**Ref. No.:** 1618
**Name:** Rose Garden Vase
**Height:** 21.25
**Status:** Limited edition, sold out
**Edition Size:** 300
**Issue Year:** 1989
**Issue Price:** $2750
**Last Year:** 2000
**Last Retail Price:** $4800

**Ref. No.:** 1117
**Name:** Floral Vase
**Height:** 24.5
**Status:** Open edition, retired
**Issue Year:** 1971
**Issue Price:** $210
**Last Year:** 1972
**Last Retail Price:** $225

**Ref. No.:** 1200
**Name:** Peacocks Floral Vase
**Height:** 28.75
**Status:** Limited edition, sold out
**Edition Size:** 150
**Issue Year:** 1972
**Issue Price:** $1285
**Last Year:** 1978
**Last Retail Price:** $2200
**Auction Price:** $2350

**Lamps**

**Ref. No.:** 1362
**Name:** Pheasant Vase
**Height:** 29.25
**Status:** Limited edition, sold out
**Edition Size:** 750
**Issue Year:** 1978
**Issue Price:** $4100
**Last Year:** 1987
**Last Retail Price:** $8500

**Ref. No.:** 320.13
**Name:** Vase No. 7
**Height:** 39
**Status:** Very Rare
**Issue Year:** 1958
**Issue Price:** Unknown
**Last Year:** Unknown
**Last Retail Price:** Unknown

**Ref. No.:** 4785
**Name:** Lamp with Blue Fluting
**Height:** 9.25
**Status:** Open edition, retired
**Issue Year:** 1971
**Issue Price:** $35
**Last Year:** 1973
**Last Retail Price:** $45

**Ref. No.:** 4543
**Name:** Angel with Flute
**Height:** 10
**Status:** Open edition, retired
**Issue Year:** 1969
**Issue Price:** $25
**Last Year:** 1975
**Last Retail Price:** $45

**Ref. No.:** 4544
**Name:** Chinese Angel
**Height:** 10
**Status:** Open edition, retired
**Issue Year:** 1969
**Issue Price:** $25
**Last Year:** 1970
**Last Retail Price:** $25

**Ref. No.:** 4545
**Name:** Black Angel
**Height:** 10
**Status:** Open edition, retired
**Issue Year:** 1969
**Issue Price:** $25
**Last Year:** 1975
**Last Retail Price:** $45

**Ref. No.:** 4546
**Name:** Thinking Angel
**Height:** 10
**Status:** Open edition, retired
**Issue Year:** 1969
**Issue Price:** $25
**Last Year:** 1976
**Last Retail Price:** $45

**Ref. No.:** 4547
**Name:** Praying Angel
**Height:** 10
**Status:** Open edition, retired
**Issue Year:** 1969
**Issue Price:** $25
**Last Year:** 1975
**Last Retail Price:** $45

**Ref. No.:** 4574
**Name:** Fairy
**Height:** 10
**Status:** Open edition, retired
**Issue Year:** 1969
**Issue Price:** $30
**Last Year:** 1972
**Last Retail Price:** $35

**Ref. No.:** 88.06
**Name:** Young Flutist
**Height:** 10.25
**Status:** Very Rare
**Issue Year:** 1956
**Issue Price:** Unknown
**Last Year:** Unknown
**Last Retail Price:** Unknown

**Ref. No.:** 4573
**Name:** Duck's Group
**Height:** 10.25
**Status:** Open edition, retired
**Issue Year:** 1969
**Issue Price:** $30
**Last Year:** 1972
**Last Retail Price:** $35

**Ref. No.:** 76.05
**Name:** Hunting
**Height:** 10.50
**Status:** Very rare
**Issue Year:** 1957
**Issue Price:** Unknown
**Last Year:** Unknown
**Last Retail Price:** Unknown

**Ref. No.:** 355.13
**Name:** Giraffe
**Height:** 11
**Status:** Very Rare
**Issue Year:** 1960
**Issue Price:** Unknown
**Last Year:** Unknown
**Last Retail Price:** Unknown

**Ref. No.:** 2011
**Name:** Horse Head
**Height:** 11
**Status:** Open edition, retired
**Issue Year:** 1970
**Issue Price:** $20
**Last Year:** 1982
**Last Retail Price:** $65

**Ref. No.:** 4578
**Name:** New Shepherdess
**Height:** 11
**Status:** Open edition, retired
**Issue Year:** 1969
**Issue Price:** $45
**Last Year:** 1976
**Last Retail Price:** $95

**Ref. No.:** 4579
**Name:** New Shepherd
**Height:** 11
**Status:** Open edition, retired
**Issue Year:** 1969
**Issue Price:** $45
**Last Year:** 1976
**Last Retail Price:** $190

**Ref. No.:** 4702
**Name:** Horse Head
**Height:** 11
**Status:** Open edition, retired
**Issue Year:** 1970
**Issue Price:** $30
**Last Year:** 1972
**Last Retail Price:** $35

**Ref. No.:** 5575
**Name:** Lilac Round Cuboid
**Height:** 11
**Status:** Open edition, retired
**Issue Year:** 1989
**Issue Price:** $335
**Last Year:** 1990
**Last Retail Price:** $365

**Ref. No.:** 5575.1
**Name:** Brown Round Cuboid
**Height:** 11
**Status:** Open edition, retired
**Issue Year:** 1989
**Issue Price:** $250
**Last Year:** 1990
**Last Retail Price:** $275

**Ref. No.:** 5575.3
**Name:** Green Round Cuboid
**Height:** 11
**Status:** Open edition, retired
**Issue Year:** 1989
**Issue Price:** $265
**Last Year:** 1990
**Last Retail Price:** $290

**Ref. No.:** 5575.4
**Name:** Violet Round Cuboid
**Height:** 11
**Status:** Open edition, retired
**Issue Year:** 1989
**Issue Price:** $300
**Last Year:** 1990
**Last Retail Price:** $330

**Ref. No.:** 307.13
**Name:** Fawns
**Height:** 11.25
**Status:** Very Rare
**Issue Year:** 1969
**Issue Price:** Unknown
**Last Year:** Unknown
**Last Retail Price:** Unknown

**Ref. No.:** 365.13
**Name:** Young Shepherd
**Height:** 11.50
**Status:** Very rare
**Issue Year:** 1965
**Issue Price:** Unknown
**Last Year:** Unknown
**Last Retail Price:** Unknown

**Ref. No.:** 366.13
**Name:** Young Shepherdess
**Height:** 11.50
**Status:** Very rare
**Issue Year:** 1965
**Issue Price:** Unknown
**Last Year:** Unknown
**Last Retail Price:** Unknown

**Ref. No.:** 86.06
**Name:** The Hunter
**Height:** 11.75
**Status:** Very Rare
**Issue Year:** 1956
**Issue Price:** Unknown
**Last Year:** Unknown
**Last Retail Price:** Unknown

**Ref. No.:** 87.06
**Name:** Girl with Flower Basket
**Height:** 11.75
**Status:** Very Rare
**Issue Year:** 1956
**Issue Price:** Unknown
**Last Year:** Unknown
**Last Retail Price:** Unknown

**Ref. No.:** 4704
**Name:** Minuet Florelia
**Height:** 12.25
**Status:** Open edition, retired
**Issue Year:** 1970
**Issue Price:** $18.50
**Last Year:** 1979
**Last Retail Price:** $50

**Ref. No.:** 4793
**Name:** Blue Pomal
**Height:** 12.25
**Status:** Open edition, retired
**Issue Year:** 1972
**Issue Price:** $30
**Last Year:** 1979
**Last Retail Price:** $75

**Ref. No.:** 4794
**Name:** Grey Lamp
**Height:** 12.25
**Status:** Open edition, retired
**Issue Year:** 1972
**Issue Price:** $30
**Last Year:** 1975
**Last Retail Price:** $45

**Ref. No.:** 4795
**Name:** White Lamp
**Height:** 12.25
**Status:** Open edition, retired
**Issue Year:** 1972
**Issue Price:** $27.50
**Last Year:** 1979
**Last Retail Price:** $65

**Ref. No.:** 4507
**Name:** Girl
**Height:** 13
**Status:** Open edition, retired
**Issue Year:** 1969
**Issue Price:** $55
**Last Year:** 1985
**Last Retail Price:** $240
**High Auction Price:** $750
**Low Auction Price:** $350

**Ref. No.:** 4508
**Name:** Boy
**Height:** 13
**Status:** Open edition, retired
**Issue Year:** 1969
**Issue Price:** $55
**Last Year:** 1985
**Last Retail Price:** $240
**High Auction Price:** $750
**Low Auction Price:** $350

**Ref. No.:** 4711
**Name:** Girl with Dove
**Height:** 13
**Status:** Open edition, retired
**Issue Year:** 1970
**Issue Price:** $27.50
**Last Year:** 1985
**Last Retail Price:** $180

**Ref. No.:** 4712
**Name:** Shepherd
**Height:** 13
**Status:** Open edition, retired
**Issue Year:** 1970
**Issue Price:** $35
**Last Year:** 1985
**Last Retail Price:** $125
**Auction Price:** $350

**Ref. No.:** 350.13
**Name:** Gazelle
**Height:** 13.25
**Status:** Very Rare
**Issue Year:** 1961
**Issue Price:** Unknown
**Last Year:** Unknown
**Last Retail Price:** Unknown

**Ref. No.:** 4775
**Name:** Lantern
**Height:** 13.25
**Status:** Open edition, retired
**Issue Year:** 1971
**Issue Price:** $22.50
**Last Year:** 1973
**Last Retail Price:** $27

**Ref. No.:** 4776
**Name:** Opal Blue
**Height:** 13.25
**Status:** Open edition, retired
**Issue Year:** 1971
**Issue Price:** $20
**Last Year:** 1975
**Last Retail Price:** $32

**Ref. No.:** 4777
**Name:** Opal Green
**Height:** 13.25
**Status:** Open edition, retired
**Issue Year:** 1971
**Issue Price:** $20
**Last Year:** 1975
**Last Retail Price:** $32

**Ref. No.:** 5574
**Name:** Blue Memphis
**Height:** 13.25
**Status:** Open edition, retired
**Issue Year:** 1989
**Issue Price:** $250
**Last Year:** 1990
**Last Retail Price:** $275

**Ref. No.:** 5574.3
**Name:** Green Memphis
**Height:** 13.25
**Status:** Open edition, retired
**Issue Year:** 1989
**Issue Price:** $285
**Last Year:** 1990
**Last Retail Price:** $315

**Ref. No.:** 354.13
**Name:** Gazelle
**Height:** 13.75
**Status:** Very Rare
**Issue Year:** 1960
**Issue Price:** Unknown
**Last Year:** Unknown
**Last Retail Price:** Unknown

**Ref. No.:** 4555
**Name:** Shepherd with Girl
**Height:** 13.75
**Status:** Open edition, retired
**Issue Year:** 1969
**Issue Price:** $75
**Last Year:** 1970
**Last Retail Price:** $80

**Ref. No.:** 4526
**Name:** Colombine
**Height:** 14
**Status:** Open edition, retired
**Issue Year:** 1969
**Issue Price:** $75
**Last Year:** 1985
**Last Retail Price:** $310
**Auction Price:** $525

**Ref. No.:** 4527
**Name:** Violinist
**Height:** 14
**Status:** Open edition, retired
**Issue Year:** 1969
**Issue Price:** $75
**Last Year:** 1985
**Last Retail Price:** $325
**Auction Price:** $375

**Ref. No.:** 303.13
**Name:** Cone Lamp
**Height:** 14.25
**Status:** Very Rare
**Issue Year:** 1958
**Issue Price:** Unknown
**Last Year:** Unknown
**Last Retail Price:** Unknown

**Ref. No.:** 351.13
**Name:** Horse
**Height:** 15
**Status:** Very Rare
**Issue Year:** 1965
**Issue Price:** Unknown
**Last Year:** Unknown
**Last Retail Price:** Unknown

**Ref. No.:** 2006
**Name:** Water Carrier Girl
**Height:** 15
**Status:** Open edition, retired
**Issue Year:** 1970
**Issue Price:** $30
**Last Year:** 1975
**Last Retail Price:** $50

**Ref. No.:** 4528
**Name:** Ballet
**Height:** 15
**Status:** Open edition, retired
**Issue Year:** 1969
**Issue Price:** $120
**Last Year:** 1985
**Last Retail Price:** $475
**High Auction Price:** $950
**Low Auction Price:** $475

**Ref. No.:** 4703
**Name:** Spring Posey
**Height:** 15
**Status:** Open edition, retired
**Issue Year:** 1970
**Issue Price:** $30
**Last Year:** 1979
**Last Retail Price:** $80

**Ref. No.:** 4727
**Name:** Shepherd with Kid
**Height:** 15
**Status:** Open edition, retired
**Issue Year:** 1970
**Issue Price:** $25
**Last Year:** 1975
**Last Retail Price:** $45

**Ref. No.:** 4728
**Name:** Shepherdess with Lamb
**Height:** 15
**Status:** Open edition, retired
**Issue Year:** 1970
**Issue Price:** $25
**Last Year:** 1975
**Last Retail Price:** $45

**Ref. No.:** 4786
**Name:** Excelsior Brown
**Height:** 15
**Status:** Open edition, retired
**Issue Year:** 1971
**Issue Price:** $45
**Last Year:** 1973
**Last Retail Price:** $55

**Ref. No.:** 4787
**Name:** Rialto Beige
**Height:** 15
**Status:** Open edition, retired
**Issue Year:** 1972
**Issue Price:** $50
**Last Year:** 1979
**Last Retail Price:** $120

**Ref. No.:** 4788
**Name:** Rialto Green
**Height:** 15
**Status:** Open edition, retired
**Issue Year:** 1972
**Issue Price:** $35
**Last Year:** 1979
**Last Retail Price:** $85

**Ref. No.:** 4789
**Name:** Rialto White
**Height:** 15
**Status:** Open edition, retired
**Issue Year:** 1972
**Issue Price:** $30
**Last Year:** 1979
**Last Retail Price:** $75

**Ref. No.:** 5576
**Name:** Lilac Compact Vase
**Height:** 15
**Status:** Open edition, retired
**Issue Year:** 1989
**Issue Price:** $325
**Last Year:** 1990
**Last Retail Price:** $355

**Ref. No.:** 5576.1
**Name:** Brown Compact Vase
**Height:** 15
**Status:** Open edition, retired
**Issue Year:** 1989
**Issue Price:** $275
**Last Year:** 1990
**Last Retail Price:** $300

**Ref. No.:** 5576.3
**Name:** Green Compact Vase
**Height:** 15
**Status:** Open edition, retired
**Issue Year:** 1989
**Issue Price:** $285
**Last Year:** 1990
**Last Retail Price:** $315

**Ref. No.:** 5576.4
**Name:** Violet Compact Vase
**Height:** 15
**Status:** Open edition, retired
**Issue Year:** 1989
**Issue Price:** $325
**Last Year:** 1990
**Last Retail Price:** $355

**Ref. No.:** 245.1
**Name:** Harlequin and Ballerina
**Height:** 15.25
**Status:** Very Rare
**Issue Year:** 1961
**Issue Price:** Unknown
**Last Year:** Unknown
**Last Retail Price:** Unknown

**Ref. No.:** 4705
**Name:** Pisa
**Height:** 15.75
**Status:** Open edition, retired
**Issue Year:** 1970
**Issue Price:** $30
**Last Year:** 1973
**Last Retail Price:** $40

**Ref. No.:** 4790
**Name:** Pomal Brown
**Height:** 15.75
**Status:** Open edition, retired
**Issue Year:** 1972
**Issue Price:** $45
**Last Year:** 1979
**Last Retail Price:** $110
**High Auction Price:** $325
**Low Auction Price:** $225

**Ref. No.:** 4791
**Name:** Pomal Grey
**Height:** 15.75
**Status:** Open edition, retired
**Issue Year:** 1972
**Issue Price:** $30
**Last Year:** 1975
**Last Retail Price:** $45

**Ref. No.:** 4792
**Name:** Pomal White
**Height:** 15.75
**Status:** Open edition, retired
**Issue Year:** 1972
**Issue Price:** $30
**Last Year:** 1979
**Last Retail Price:** $75
**Auction Price:** $300

**Ref. No.:** 4820
**Name:** Woman from Guadalupe
**Height:** 15.75
**Status:** Open edition, retired
**Issue Year:** 1972
**Issue Price:** $80
**Last Year:** 1973
**Last Retail Price:** $95

**Ref. No.:** 5572.3
**Name:** Red Vase with Handles
   Lamp
**Height:** 15.75
**Status:** Open edition, retired
**Issue Year:** 1989
**Issue Price:** $325
**Last Year:** 1990
**Last Retail Price:** $360

**Ref. No.:** 5632
**Name:** Lladró Lamp
**Height:** 15.75
**Status:** Open edition, retired
**Issue Year:** 1989
**Issue Price:** $225
**Last Year:** 1990
**Last Retail Price:** $250

**Ref. No.:** 5632.3
**Name:** Lladró Lamp
**Height:** 15.75
**Status:** Open edition, retired
**Issue Year:** 1989
**Issue Price:** $195
**Last Year:** 1990
**Last Retail Price:** $215

**Ref. No.:** 1689
**Name:** Lladró
**Height:** 16
**Status:** Open edition, retired
**Issue Year:** 1989
**Issue Price:** $210
**Last Year:** 1990
**Last Retail Price:** $230

**Ref. No.:** 4681
**Name:** Turtle Dove
**Height:** 16
**Status:** Open edition, retired
**Issue Year:** 1969
**Issue Price:** $22.50
**Last Year:** 1970
**Last Retail Price:** $25

**Ref. No.:** 4782
**Name:** Blue Full Moon
**Height:** 16
**Status:** Open edition, retired
**Issue Year:** 1971
**Issue Price:** $60
**Last Year:** 1975
**Last Retail Price:** $100

**Ref. No.:** 4783
**Name:** Grey Full Moon
**Height:** 16
**Status:** Open edition, retired
**Issue Year:** 1971
**Issue Price:** $40
**Last Year:** 1973
**Last Retail Price:** $50

**Ref. No.:** 4784
**Name:** Brown Full Moon
**Height:** 16
**Status:** Open edition, retired
**Issue Year:** 1971
**Issue Price:** $40
**Last Year:** 1975
**Last Retail Price:** $65

**Ref. No.:** 5579
**Name:** Lily Vase
**Height:** 16
**Status:** Open edition, retired
**Issue Year:** 1989
**Issue Price:** $340
**Last Year:** 1990
**Last Retail Price:** $375

**Ref. No.:** 6598
**Name:** The Enchanted Forest
**Height:** 16
**Status:** Open issue, retired
**Issue Year:** 1999
**Issue Price:** $440
**Last Year:** 2001
**Last Retail Price:** $440

**Ref. No.:** 6611
**Name:** A Flight Of Fantasy
**Height:** 16.5
**Status:** Open issue, retired
**Issue Year:** 1999
**Issue Price:** $490
**Last Year:** 2001
**Last Retail Price:** $490

**Ref. No.:** 1607
**Name:** Nymph Lamp with Base
**Height:** 17
**Status:** Open issue, retired
**Issue Year:** 1989
**Issue Price:** $1750
**Last Year:** 2000
**Last Retail Price:** $1795

**Ref. No.:** 4625
**Name:** From the Mountains
**Height:** 17
**Status:** Open edition, retired
**Issue Year:** 1969
**Issue Price:** $60
**Last Year:** 1972
**Last Retail Price:** $70

**Ref. No.:** 4633
**Name:** Girl with Mandolin
**Height:** 17
**Status:** Open edition, retired
**Issue Year:** 1969
**Issue Price:** $100
**Last Year:** 1985
**Last Retail Price:** $375
**Auction Price:** $475

**Ref. No.:** 4634
**Name:** Boy with Violin
**Height:** 17
**Status:** Open edition, retired
**Issue Year:** 1969
**Issue Price:** $100
**Last Year:** 1985
**Last Retail Price:** $330
**High Auction Price:** $550
**Low Auction Price:** $400

**Ref. No.:** 4592
**Name:** Horse Rearing
**Height:** 17.25
**Status:** Open edition, retired
**Issue Year:** 1969
**Issue Price:** $60
**Last Year:** 1972
**Last Retail Price:** $70

**Ref. No.:** 4593
**Name:** Horse Bucking
**Height:** 17.25
**Status:** Open edition, retired
**Issue Year:** 1969
**Issue Price:** $60
**Last Year:** 1972
**Last Retail Price:** $70
**Auction Price:** $400

**Ref. No.:** 5573
**Name:** Square Vase
**Height:** 17.25
**Status:** Open edition, retired
**Issue Year:** 1989
**Issue Price:** $310
**Last Year:** 1990
**Last Retail Price:** $340

**Ref. No.:** 4624
**Name:** Afternoon Snack
**Height:** 17.75
**Status:** Open edition, retired
**Issue Year:** 1969
**Issue Price:** $60
**Last Year:** 1972
**Last Retail Price:** $70

**Ref. No.:** 4706
**Name:** Lamp
**Height:** 18
**Status:** Open edition, retired
**Issue Year:** 1970
**Issue Price:** $35
**Last Year:** 1979
**Last Retail Price:** $95

**Ref. No.:** 4751
**Name:** Minerva
**Height:** 18
**Status:** Open edition, retired
**Issue Year:** 1971
**Issue Price:** $35
**Last Year:** 1979
**Last Retail Price:** $90
**Auction Price:** $350

**Ref. No.:** 1616
**Name:** Carousel
**Height:** 19
**Status:** Open edition, retired
**Issue Year:** 1989
**Issue Price:** $1700
**Last Year:** 1991
**Last Retail Price:** $2000
**Auction Price:** $1250

**Ref. No.:** 4746
**Name:** Octagonal Jar, Pink
**Height:** 19
**Status:** Open edition, retired
**Issue Year:** 1971
**Issue Price:** $45
**Last Year:** 1973
**Last Retail Price:** $55

**Ref. No.:** 4747
**Name:** Octagonal Jar, Blue
**Height:** 19
**Status:** Open edition, retired
**Issue Year:** 1971
**Issue Price:** $45
**Last Year:** 1972
**Last Retail Price:** $45

**Ref. No.:** 4748
**Name:** Octagonal Jar, Green
**Height:** 19
**Status:** Open edition, retired
**Issue Year:** 1971
**Issue Price:** $45
**Last Year:** 1973
**Last Retail Price:** $55

**Ref. No.:** 1622
**Name:** Birds and Peonies
**Height:** 19.75
**Status:** Limited edition, sold out
**Edition Size:** 300
**Issue Year:** 1989
**Issue Price:** $3000
**Last Year:** 1998
**Last Retail Price:** $3750

**Ref. No.:** 2111
**Name:** Elephant
**Height:** 19.75
**Status:** Open edition, retired
**Issue Year:** 1978
**Issue Price:** $685
**Last Year:** 1985
**Last Retail Price:** $935

**Ref. No.:** 4707
**Name:** Olympia
**Height:** 20
**Status:** Open edition, retired
**Issue Year:** 1970
**Issue Price:** $45
**Last Year:** 1979
**Last Retail Price:** $125

**Ref. No.:** 4708
**Name:** Dragons Jug
**Height:** 20
**Status:** Open edition, retired
**Issue Year:** 1970
**Issue Price:** $70
**Last Year:** 1980
**Last Retail Price:** $220

**Ref. No.:** 4708.3
**Name:** Dragons Jug, White
**Height:** 20
**Status:** Open edition, retired
**Issue Year:** 1970
**Issue Price:** $70
**Last Year:** 1981
**Last Retail Price:** $235

**Ref. No.:** 6762
**Name:** Underwater Explorer
   (Lamp)
**Height:** 20
**Status:** Open issue, retired
**Issue Year:** 2001
**Issue Price:** $445
**Last Year:** 2002
**Last Retail Price:** $475

**Ref. No.:** 360.13
**Name:** Student
**Height:** 20.5
**Status:** Open issue, retired
**Issue Year:** 1967
**Issue Price:** Unknown
**Last Year:** Unknown
**Last Retail Price:** Unknown

**Ref. No.:** 5241
**Name:** Ballet Theme
**Height:** 22
**Status:** Open edition, retired
**Issue Year:** 1984
**Issue Price:** $565
**Last Year:** 1991
**Last Retail Price:** $900
**High Auction Price:** $1250
**Low Auction Price:** $1100

**Ref. No.:** 5242
**Name:** Ballet Theme
**Height:** 22
**Status:** Open edition, retired
**Issue Year:** 1984
**Issue Price:** $490
**Last Year:** 1991
**Last Retail Price:** $785
**High Auction Price:** $1200
**Low Auction Price:** $800

**Ref. No.:** 246.1
**Name:** Ghost Tree
**Height:** 22.25
**Status:** Open issue, retired
**Issue Year:** 1967
**Issue Price:** Unknown
**Last Year:** Unknown
**Last Retail Price:** Unknown

**Ref. No.:** 6508
**Name:** Pierrot's Proposal (Lamp)
**Height:** 23
**Status:** Open issue, retired
**Issue Year:** 1998
**Issue Price:** $1350
**Last Year:** 2001
**Last Retail Price:** $1600

**Ref. No.:** 5572
**Name:** Vase with Handles
**Height:** 23.25
**Status:** Open edition, retired
**Issue Year:** 1989
**Issue Price:** $650
**Last Year:** 1990
**Last Retail Price:** $715

**Clocks**

**Ref. No.:** 1124
**Name:** La Tarantella
**Height:** 24
**Status:** Very Rare
**Issue Year:** 1971
**Issue Price:** $575
**Last Year:** 1989
**Last Retail Price:** Unknown
**High Auction Price:** $2250
**Low Auction Price:** $1500

**Ref. No.:** 2446
**Name:** Loving Words (Lamp)
**Height:** 31.5
**Status:** Open issue, active
**Issue Year:** 2002
**Issue Price:** $2180
**2003 Retail Price:** $2180
**Comment:** Gres

**Ref. No.:** 5653
**Name:** Avila Clock
**Height:** 2.75
**Status:** Open issue, retired
**Issue Year:** 1989
**Issue Price:** $125
**Last Year:** 1995
**Last Retail Price:** $135

**Ref. No.:** 5652
**Name:** Marbella Clock
**Height:** 3
**Status:** Open issue, retired
**Issue Year:** 1989
**Issue Price:** $125
**Last Year:** 1994
**Last Retail Price:** $135
**Auction Price:** $175

**Ref. No.:** 5655.3
**Name:** Diamond Clock
**Height:** 3
**Status:** Open issue, retired
**Issue Year:** 1990
**Issue Price:** $100

**Ref. No.:** 5925
**Name:** Diamond Clock
**Height:** 3
**Status:** Open issue, retired
**Issue Year:** 1990
**Last Year:** 1996
**Last Retail Price:** $140

**Ref. No.:** 5654.3
**Name:** Floral Clock
**Height:** 3.25
**Status:** Open issue, retired
**Issue Year:** 1990
**Issue Price:** $100
**Last Year:** 1994
**Last Retail Price:** $135

**Ref. No.:** 5924
**Name:** Floral Quartz Clock
**Height:** 3.25
**Status:** Open issue, retired
**Issue Year:** 1990
**Issue Price:** Unknown
**Last Year:** 1994
**Last Retail Price:** $135

**Ref. No.:** 6068
**Name:** Blue Clock
**Height:** 4.75
**Status:** Open issue, retired
**Issue Year:** 1993
**Issue Price:** Unknown
**Last Year:** 1996
**Last Retail Price:** $430

**Ref. No.:** 6075
**Name:** Green Clock
**Height:** 4.75
**Status:** Open issue, retired
**Issue Year:** 1993
**Issue Price:** Unknown

**Ref. No.:** 6082
**Name:** Violet Clock
**Height:** 4.75
**Status:** Open issue, retired
**Issue Year:** 1993
**Issue Price:** Unknown
**Last Year:** 1996
**Last Retail Price:** $435

**Ref. No.:** 5654
**Name:** Valencia Clock
**Height:** 5
**Status:** Open issue, retired
**Issue Year:** 1989
**Issue Price:** $175
**Last Year:** 1994
**Last Retail Price:** $195

**Ref. No.:** 5970
**Name:** Bow Clock
**Height:** 5
**Status:** Open issue, retired
**Issue Year:** 1993
**Issue Price:** $270
**Last Year:** 2000
**Last Retail Price:** $245

**Ref. No.:** 5653.1
**Name:** Garland Clock
**Height:** 5.75
**Status:** Open issue, retired
**Issue Year:** 1990
**Issue Price:** $160
**Last Year:** 1995
**Last Retail Price:** $195

**Ref. No.:** 5655
**Name:** Segovia Clock
**Height:** 5.75
**Status:** Open issue, retired
**Issue Year:** 1989
**Issue Price:** $175
**Last Year:** 1996
**Last Retail Price:** $215

**Ref. No.:** 5926
**Name:** Garland Clock
**Height:** 5.75
**Status:** Open issue, retired
**Issue Year:** 1990
**Issue Price:** Unknown
**Last Year:** 1995
**Last Retail Price:** $195

**Ref. No.:** 5776
**Name:** Two Sisters Clock
**Height:** 6
**Status:** Open issue, retired
**Issue Year:** 1991
**Issue Price:** $400
**Last Year:** 2002
**Last Retail Price:** $465

**Ref. No.:** 7541
**Name:** Moongate Clock
**Height:** 6
**Status:** Open issue, active
**Issue Year:** 1994
**Issue Price:** Unknown
**Comment:** Sold exclusively
   in Bermuda

**Ref. No.:** 5777
**Name:** Swan Clock
**Height:** 7.25
**Status:** Open issue, retired
**Issue Year:** 1991
**Issue Price:** $425
**Last Year:** 2002
**Last Retail Price:** $565

**Ref. No.:** 5778
**Name:** Pierrot Clock
**Height:** 8
**Status:** Open issue, retired
**Issue Year:** 1991
**Issue Price:** $400
**Last Year:** 2001
**Last Retail Price:** $475

**Ref. No.:** 5992
**Name:** Time For Love
**Height:** 9.75
**Status:** Open issue, retired
**Issue Year:** 1993
**Issue Price:** $800
**Last Year:** 2001
**Last Retail Price:** $760

**Candle Holders**

**Ref. No.:** 5973
**Name:** Angelic Time
**Height:** 11
**Status:** Open issue, active
**Issue Year:** 1993
**Issue Price:** $1100
**2003 Retail Price:** $1050

**Ref. No.:** 1781
**Name:** Allegory of Time
**Height:** 19.75
**Status:** Limited edition, sold out
**Edition Size:** 5000
**Issue Year:** 1994
**Issue Price:** Unknown
**Last Year:** 1998
**Last Retail Price:** $1290

**Ref. No.:** 5629
**Name:** Lladró Candleholder
**Height:** 4.75
**Status:** Open issue, retired
**Issue Year:** 1989
**Issue Price:** $55
**Last Year:** 1990
**Last Retail Price:** $60

**Ref. No.:** 5627
**Name:** Lladró Candleholder
**Height:** 5
**Status:** Open issue, retired
**Issue Year:** 1989
**Issue Price:** $55
**Last Year:** 1990
**Last Retail Price:** $60

**Ref. No.:** 6706
**Name:** Menorah
**Height:** 5.5
**Status:** Open issue, active
**Issue Year:** 2000
**Issue Price:** $325
**2003 Retail Price:** $325

**Ref. No.:** 5625
**Name:** Lladró Candleholder
**Height:** 6
**Status:** Open issue, retired
**Issue Year:** 1989
**Issue Price:** $105
**Last Year:** 1990
**Last Retail Price:** $110

**Ref. No.:** 5628
**Name:** Lladró Candleholder
**Height:** 6
**Status:** Open issue, retired
**Issue Year:** 1989
**Issue Price:** $80
**Last Year:** 1990
**Last Retail Price:** $85
**Auction Price:** $175

**Ref. No.:** 5626
**Name:** Lladró Candleholder
**Height:** 7.25
**Status:** Open issue, retired
**Issue Year:** 1989
**Issue Price:** $90
**Last Year:** 1990
**Last Retail Price:** $95

**Ref. No.:** 6883
**Name:** Herons' Realm
Candleholder (crouching)
**Height:** 8.75
**Status:** Open issue, active
**Issue Year:** 2002
**Issue Price:** $295
**2003 Retail Price:** $295

*Functional*

**Ref. No.:** 1110
**Name:** Mermaid Candleholder
**Height:** 9
**Status:** Open issue, retired
**Issue Year:** 1971
**Issue Price:** $20
**Last Year:** 1972
**Last Retail Price:** $20

**Ref. No.:** 6882
**Name:** Herons' Realm
   Candleholder (standing)
**Height:** 9.25
**Status:** Open issue, active
**Issue Year:** 2002
**Issue Price:** $295
**2003 Retail Price:** $295

**Ref. No.:** 5227
**Name:** Female Candelabra
**Height:** 10
**Status:** Open issue, retired
**Issue Year:** 1984
**Issue Price:** $660
**Last Year:** 1985
**Last Retail Price:** $660
**High Auction Price:** $800
**Low Auction Price:** $650

**Ref. No.:** 5226
**Name:** Male Candelabra
**Height:** 10.25
**Status:** Open issue, retired
**Issue Year:** 1984
**Issue Price:** $660
**Last Year:** 1985
**Last Retail Price:** $660
**High Auction Price:** $800
**Low Auction Price:** $650

**Ref. No.:** 5949
**Name:** Angel with Lyre
   Candleholder
**Height:** 11.75
**Status:** Open issue, retired
**Issue Year:** 1993
**Issue Price:** $295
**Last Year:** 1997
**Last Retail Price:** $315

**Ref. No.:** 5950
**Name:** Angel with Tambourine
   Candleholder
**Height:** 11.75
**Status:** Open issue, retired
**Issue Year:** 1993
**Issue Price:** $295
**Last Year:** 1997
**Last Retail Price:** $315

**Ref. No.:** 6586
**Name:** Angelic Light
**Height:** 13
**Status:** Open issue, sold out
**Issue Year:** 1998
**Issue Price:** $198
**Last Year:** 2001
**Last Retail Price:** $250

**Ref. No.:** 6619
**Name:** Holiday Light
**Height:** 13.25
**Status:** Open issue, sold out
**Issue Year:** 1999
**Issue Price:** $225
**Last Year:** 2001
**Last Retail Price:** $250

**Ref. No.:** 5225
**Name:** Oriental Candelabra
**Height:** 17.25
**Status:** Open issue, retired
**Issue Year:** 1984
**Issue Price:** $685
**Last Year:** 1985
**Last Retail Price:** $685

**Murals and Plaques**

**Ref. No.:** 7116
**Name:** Small Lladró Plaque
**Height:** 2
**Status:** Open issue, active

**Ref. No.:** 7506
**Name:** Carlos I Imperial Plaque
**Height:** 4
**Status:** Open issue, active
**Issue Year:** 1989
**Issue Price:** Unknown
**Comment:** Exclusive to Pedro
   Domeq, S.A.

**Ref. No.:** 7601
**Name:** Lladró Society Plaque
**Height:** 4
**Status:** Limited edition, sold out
**Issue Year:** 1985
**Issue Price:** $35
**Last Year:** 1998
**Auction Price:** $75
**Comment:** Charter membership
   year (1985)

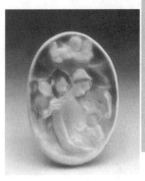

**Ref. No.:** 5808
**Name:** New World Medallion
**Height:** 6
**Status:** Limited edition, sold out
**Edition Size:** 5000
**Issue Year:** 1991
**Issue Price:** $200
**Last Year:** 1994
**Last Retail Price:** $215
**Auction Price:** $150

**Ref. No.:** 229.09
**Name:** Nativity
**Height:** 6.25
**Status:** Very rare
**Issue Year:** 1961
**Issue Price:** Unknown
**Last Year:** Unknown
**Last Retail Price:** Unknown

**Ref. No.:** 334.13
**Name:** Nativity Plaque
**Height:** 7
**Status:** Very rare
**Issue Year:** 1970
**Issue Price:** Unknown
**Last Year:** Unknown
**Last Retail Price:** Unknown

**Ref. No.:** 5965
**Name:** The Clipper Ship
**Height:** 10.75
**Status:** Open issue, retired
**Issue Year:** 1993
**Issue Price:** $240
**Last Year:** 1996
**Last Retail Price:** $250

**Ref. No.:** 5281
**Name:** Nativity bas relief
**Height:** 11
**Status:** Open issue, retired
**Issue Year:** 1985
**Issue Price:** $210
**Last Year:** 1988
**Last Retail Price:** $230
**High Auction Price:** $450
**Low Auction Price:** $275

**Ref. No.:** 6247
**Name:** Challenge
**Height:** 15
**Status:** Open issue, retired
**Issue Year:** 1995
**Issue Price:** $350
**Last Year:** 1996
**Last Retail Price:** $350

**Ref. No.:** 43.03
**Name:** Gametime
**Height:** 15.75
**Status:** Very rare
**Issue Year:** 1948
**Issue Price:** Unknown
**Last Year:** Unknown
**Last Retail Price:** Unknown
**Comment:** Personally created by Jose Lladró

**Ref. No.:** 2092
**Name:** Holy Virgin
**Height:** 16
**Status:** Open issue, retired
**Issue Year:** 1978
**Issue Price:** $200
**Last Year:** 1981
**Last Retail Price:** $260

**Ref. No.:** 2012
**Name:** Mounted Harlequin
**Height:** 21
**Status:** Open issue, retired
**Issue Year:** 1970
**Issue Price:** $200
**Last Year:** 1981
**Last Retail Price:** $210

Plates

**Ref. No.:** 2054
**Name:** Mounted Ballerina
**Height:** 25.25
**Status:** Open issue, retired
**Issue Year:** 1974
**Issue Price:** $350
**Last Year:** 1981
**Last Retail Price:** $780

**Ref. No.:** 1268
**Name:** Virgin Mural
**Height:** 33.75
**Status:** Very rare
**Issue Year:** 1974
**Issue Price:** $915
**Last Year:** 1981
**Last Retail Price:** Unknown

**Ref. No.:** 7501
**Name:** Miniature Plate
**Height:** 3.25
**Status:** Limited edition, sold out
**Issue Year:** 1990
**Issue Price:** Unknown
**Last Year:** 1990
**Last Retail Price:** Unknown
**Comment:** Exclusive to the Franklin Mint

**Ref. No.:** 5998
**Name:** Looking Out
**Height:** 3.75
**Status:** Open issue, retired
**Issue Year:** 1993
**Issue Price:** $38
**Last Year:** 1998
**Last Retail Price:** $38

**Ref. No.:** 5964
**Name:** Great Voyage
**Height:** 4
**Status:** Open issue, retired
**Issue Year:** 1993
**Issue Price:** $50
**Last Year:** 1994
**Last Retail Price:** $50

**Ref. No.:** 5999
**Name:** Swinging
**Height:** 4
**Status:** Open issue, retired
**Issue Year:** 1993
**Issue Price:** $38
**Last Year:** 1998
**Last Retail Price:** $38

**Ref. No.:** 6000
**Name:** Duck
**Height:** 4
**Status:** Open issue, retired
**Issue Year:** 1993
**Issue Price:** $38
**Last Year:** 1998
**Last Retail Price:** $38

**Ref. No.:** 6158
**Name:** Friends
**Height:** 4
**Status:** Open issue, retired
**Issue Year:** 1994
**Issue Price:** $32
**Last Year:** 1998
**Last Retail Price:** $32

**Ref. No.:** 6159
**Name:** Apple Picking
**Height:** 4
**Status:** Open issue, retired
**Issue Year:** 1994
**Issue Price:** $32
**Last Year:** 1998
**Last Retail Price:** $32

**Ref. No.:** 6160
**Name:** Turtledove
**Height:** 4
**Status:** Open issue, retired
**Issue Year:** 1994
**Issue Price:** $32
**Last Year:** 1998
**Last Retail Price:** $60

**Ref. No.:** 6161
**Name:** Flamingo
**Height:** 4
**Status:** Open issue, retired
**Issue Year:** 1994
**Issue Price:** $32
**Last Year:** 1998
**Last Retail Price:** $32

**Ref. No.:** 6162
**Name:** Resting
**Height:** 4
**Status:** Open issue, retired
**Issue Year:** 1994
**Issue Price:** $32
**Last Year:** 1998
**Last Retail Price:** $32

**Ref. No.:** 6184
**Name:** Christmas Melodies Plate
**Height:** 4
**Status:** Limited edition, sold out
**Issue Year:** 1994
**Issue Price:** Unknown
**Last Year:** 1994
**Last Retail Price:** $30

**Ref. No.:** 12.02
**Name:** Surprised Cat
**Height:** 7
**Status:** Very rare
**Issue Year:** 1943
**Issue Price:** Unknown
**Last Year:** Unknown
**Last Retail Price:** Unknown
**Comment:** Personally painted
by José Lladró

**Ref. No.:** 44.03
**Name:** Man's Portrait
**Height:** 7
**Status:** Very rare
**Issue Year:** 1949
**Issue Price:** Unknown
**Last Year:** Unknown
**Last Retail Price:** Unknown
**Comment:** Personally painted
by José Lladró

**Ref. No.:** 7006
**Name:** Christmas Caroling
**Height:** 8
**Status:** Limited edition, sold out
**Issue Year:** 1971
**Issue Price:** $35
**Last Year:** 1971
**Last Retail Price:** $27
**High Auction Price:** $300
**Low Auction Price:** $65

**Ref. No.:** 7007
**Name:** Birds and Chicks
**Height:** 8
**Status:** Limited edition, sold out
**Issue Year:** 1972
**Issue Price:** $70
**Last Year:**1972
**Last Retail Price:** $27
**High Auction Price:** $250
**Low Auction Price:** $65

**Ref. No.:** 7008
**Name:** Christmas Carolers
**Height:** 8
**Status:** Limited edition, sold out
**Issue Year:** 1972
**Issue Price:** $70
**Last Year:** 1972
**Last Retail Price:** $35
**High Auction Price:** $225
**Low Auction Price:** $65

**Ref. No.:** 7009
**Name:** Mother and Children
**Height:** 8
**Status:** Limited edition, sold out
**Issue Year:** 1973
**Issue Price:** $70
**Last Year:**1973
**Last Retail Price:** $35
**Auction Price:** $65

**Ref. No.:** 7010
**Name:** Boy and Girl at Christmas
**Height:** 8
**Status:** Limited edition, sold out
**Issue Year:** 1973
**Issue Price:** $35
**Last Year:** 1973
**Last Retail Price:** $45
**High Auction Price:** $200
**Low Auction Price:** $65

**Ref. No.:** 7011
**Name:** Nursing Mother
**Height:** 8
**Status:** Limited edition, sold out
**Issue Year:** 1974
**Issue Price:** $75
**Last Year:**1974
**Last Retail Price:** $45
**Auction Price:** $65

**Ref. No.:** 7012
**Name:** Christmas Carolers
**Height:** 8
**Status:** Limited edition, sold out
**Issue Year:** 1974
**Issue Price:** $75
**Last Year:** 1974
**Last Retail Price:** $55
**Auction Price:** $65

**Ref. No.:** 7013
**Name:** Mother and Child
**Height:** 8
**Status:** Limited edition, sold out
**Issue Year:** 1975
**Issue Price:** $85
**Last Year:**1975
**Last Retail Price:** $60
**Auction Price:** $65

**Ref. No.:** 7014
**Name:** Christmas Cherubs
**Height:** 8
**Status:** Limited edition, sold out
**Issue Year:** 1975
**Issue Price:** $85
**Last Year:** 1975
**Last Retail Price:** $60
**Auction Price:** $65

**Ref. No.:** 7015
**Name:** Tender Vigil
**Height:** 8
**Status:** Limited edition, sold out
**Issue Year:** 1976
**Issue Price:** $65
**Last Year:**1976
**Last Retail Price:** $60
**Auction Price:** $65

**Ref. No.:** 7016
**Name:** Christ Child
**Height:** 8
**Status:** Limited edition, sold out
**Issue Year:** 1976
**Issue Price:** $65
**Last Year:** 1976
**Last Retail Price:** $60
**Auction Price:** $65

**Ref. No.:** 7021
**Name:** Mother and Daughter
**Height:** 8
**Status:** Limited edition, sold out
**Issue Year:** 1977
**Issue Price:** $65
**Last Year:**1977
**Last Retail Price:** $67
**Auction Price:** $65

**Ref. No.:** 7022
**Name:** Nativity
**Height:** 8
**Status:** Limited edition, sold out
**Issue Year:** 1977
**Issue Price:** $65
**Last Year:** 1977
**Last Retail Price:** $70
**Auction Price:** $65

**Ref. No.:** 7023
**Name:** Mother's Day Plate
**Height:** 8
**Status:** Limited edition, sold out
**Issue Year:** 1980
**Issue Price:** $45
**Last Year:**1980
**Last Retail Price:** $65
**High Auction Price:** $175
**Low Auction Price:** $65

**Ref. No.:** 7024
**Name:** 1980 Christmas Plate
**Height:** 8
**Status:** Limited edition, sold out
**Issue Year:** 1980
**Issue Price:** $45
**Last Year:** 1980
**Last Retail Price:** $90
**High Auction Price:** $75
**Low Auction Price:** $65

**Ref. No.:** 7025
**Name:** Mothers Day Plate - 1971
**Height:** 8
**Status:** Limited edition, sold out
**Issue Year:** 1971
**Issue Price:** $50
**Last Year:**1971
**Last Retail Price:** $25
**Auction Price:** $65

**Ref. No.:** 7105
**Name:** New Arrival
**Height:** 8
**Status:** Limited edition, sold out
**Issue Year:** 1978
**Issue Price:** $65
**Last Year:**1978
**Last Retail Price:** $80
**Auction Price:** $65

**Ref. No.:** 7106
**Name:** Christmas Caroling Child
**Height:** 8
**Status:** Limited edition, sold out
**Issue Year:** 1978
**Issue Price:** $65
**Last Year:** 1978
**Last Retail Price:** $80
**Auction Price:** $65

**Ref. No.:** 7107
**Name:** Off to School
**Height:** 8
**Status:** Limited edition, sold out
**Issue Year:** 1979
**Issue Price:** $55
**Last Year:** 1979
**Last Retail Price:** $90
**Auction Price:** $65

**Ref. No.:** 7108
**Name:** Christmas Snow Dance
**Height:** 8
**Status:** Limited edition, sold out
**Issue Year:** 1979
**Issue Price:** $55
**Last Year:** 1979
**Last Retail Price:** $90
**Auction Price:** $65

**Ref. No.:** 2.01
**Name:** Village
**Height:** 9
**Status:** Very rare
**Issue Year:** 1942
**Issue Price:** Unknown
**Last Year:** Unknown
**Last Retail Price:** Unknown
**Comment:** Personally painted
by José Lladró

**Ref. No.:** 18.02
**Name:** The Round Plate
**Height:** 9
**Status:** Very rare
**Issue Year:** 1946
**Issue Price:** Unknown
**Last Year:** Unknown
**Last Retail Price:** Unknown
**Comment:** Personally painted
by José Lladró

**Ref. No.:** 42.03
**Name:** Young Man's Portrait
**Height:** 9
**Status:** Very rare
**Issue Year:** 1948
**Issue Price:** Unknown
**Last Year:** Unknown
**Last Retail Price:** Unknown
**Comment:** Personally painted
by José Lladró

**Ref. No.:** 11.02
**Name:** Old Salts
**Height:** 10.25
**Status:** Very rare
**Issue Year:** 1944
**Issue Price:** Unknown
**Last Year:** Unknown
**Last Retail Price:** Unknown
**Comment:** Personally painted
by José Lladró

**Ref. No.:** 13.02
**Name:** Waiting
**Height:** 11
**Status:** Very rare
**Issue Year:** 1943
**Issue Price:** Unknown
**Last Year:** Unknown
**Last Retail Price:** Unknown
**Comment:** Personally painted
    by José Lladró

**Ref. No.:** 21.02
**Name:** Boy's Portrait
**Height:** 13
**Status:** Very rare
**Issue Year:** 1943
**Issue Price:** Unknown
**Last Year:** Unknown
**Last Retail Price:** Unknown
**Comment:** Personally painted
    by José Lladró

**Ref. No.:** 15.02
**Name:** Waiting for Daddy
**Height:** 13.25
**Status:** Very rare
**Issue Year:** 1945
**Issue Price:** Unknown
**Last Year:** Unknown
**Last Retail Price:** Unknown
**Comment:** Personally painted
    by José Lladró

**Ref. No.:** 41.03
**Name:** Serenade
**Height:** 13.25
**Status:** Very rare
**Issue Year:** 1949
**Issue Price:** Unknown
**Last Year:** Unknown
**Last Retail Price:** Unknown
**Comment:** Personally painted
    by José Lladró

**Ref. No.:** 31.02
**Name:** Horse and Dogs Plate
**Height:** 13.75
**Status:** Very rare
**Issue Year:** 1944
**Issue Price:** Unknown
**Last Year:** Unknown
**Last Retail Price:** Unknown
**Comment:** Personally painted
    by José Lladró

**Ref. No.:** 27.02
**Name:** Don Quixote
**Height:** 15
**Status:** Very rare
**Issue Year:** 1949
**Issue Price:** Unknown
**Last Year:** Unknown
**Last Retail Price:** Unknown
**Comment:** Personally painted
    by José Lladró

**Cups**

Ref. No.: 6042
Name: Playful Pals Cup and
Saucer
Height: 2.25
Status: Open issue, retired
Issue Year: 1994
Issue Price: $175
Last Year: 2000
Last Retail Price: $175

Ref. No.: 6043
Name: Doves Cup and Saucer
Height: 2.25
Status: Open issue, retired
Issue Year: 1994
Issue Price: $160
Last Year: 2000
Last Retail Price: $160

Ref. No.: 6044
Name: Kittens Cup and Saucer
Height: 2.25
Status: Open issue, retired
Issue Year: 1994
Issue Price: $175
Last Year: 2000
Last Retail Price: $175

Ref. No.: 6045
Name: Ducklings Cup and Saucer
Height: 2.25
Status: Open issue, retired
Issue Year: 1994
Issue Price: $160
Last Year: 2000
Last Retail Price: $160

Ref. No.: 6046
Name: Cautious Friends Cup and
Saucer
Height: 2.25
Status: Open issue, retired
Issue Year: 1994
Issue Price: $175
Last Year: 2000
Last Retail Price: $175

Ref. No.: 6047
Name: Springtime Pals Cup and
Saucer
Height: 2.25
Status: Open issue, retired
Issue Year: 1994
Issue Price: $175
Last Year: 2000
Last Retail Price: $175

**Ref. No.:** 6048
**Name:** Orchid Cup and Saucer
**Height:** 2.25
**Status:** Open issue, retired
**Issue Year:** 1994
**Issue Price:** $145
**Last Year:** 1999
**Last Retail Price:** $145

**Ref. No.:** 6049
**Name:** Pansy Cup and Saucer
**Height:** 2.25
**Status:** Open issue, retired
**Issue Year:** 1994
**Issue Price:** $145
**Last Year:** 1999
**Last Retail Price:** $145

**Ref. No.:** 6050
**Name:** Rose Cup and Saucer
**Height:** 2.25
**Status:** Open issue, retired
**Issue Year:** 1994
**Issue Price:** $145
**Last Year:** 1999
**Last Retail Price:** $145

**Ref. No.:** 6051
**Name:** Blue Bell Cup and Saucer
**Height:** 2.25
**Status:** Open issue, retired
**Issue Year:** 1994
**Issue Price:** $145
**Last Year:** 1999
**Last Retail Price:** $145

**Ref. No.:** 6052
**Name:** Calla Lily Cup and Saucer
**Height:** 2.25
**Status:** Open issue, retired
**Issue Year:** 1994
**Issue Price:** $145
**Last Year:** 1999
**Last Retail Price:** $145

**Ref. No.:** 6053
**Name:** Daisy Cup and Saucer
**Height:** 2.25
**Status:** Open issue, retired
**Issue Year:** 1994
**Issue Price:** $145
**Last Year:** 1999
**Last Retail Price:** $145

**Bowls, Centerpieces and Dishes**

**Ref. No.:** 5263
**Name:** Chalice - Decorated
**Height:** 3.25
**Status:** Open issue, retired
**Issue Year:** 1984
**Issue Price:** $45
**Last Year:**1990
**Last Retail Price:** $65
**Auction Price:** $125

**Ref. No.:** 5263.3
**Name:** Chalice
**Height:** 3.25
**Status:** Open issue, retired
**Issue Year:** 1984
**Issue Price:** $45
**Last Year:**1988
**Last Retail Price:** $55

**Ref. No.:** 53.04
**Name:** Bon-bon Dish
**Height:** 2
**Status:** Very rare
**Issue Year:** 1952
**Issue Price:** Unknown
**Last Year:** Unknown
**Last Retail Price:** Unknown

**Ref. No.:** 5265
**Name:** Centerpiece, Decorated
**Height:** 2
**Status:** Open edition, retired
**Issue Year:** 1984
**Issue Price:** $50
**Last Year:** 1990
**Last Retail Price:** $70

**Ref. No.:** 5265.3
**Name:** Centerpiece
**Height:** 2
**Status:** Open edition, retired
**Issue Year:** 1984
**Issue Price:** $50
**Last Year:** 1988
**Last Retail Price:** $60

**Ref. No.:** 5268
**Name:** Centerpiece, Decorated
**Height:** 2
**Status:** Open edition, retired
**Issue Year:** 1984
**Issue Price:** $60
**Last Year:** 1990
**Last Retail Price:** $80
**Auction Price:** $150

**Ref. No.:** 5268.3
**Name:** Centerpiece
**Height:** 2
**Status:** Open edition, retired
**Issue Year:** 1984
**Issue Price:** $60
**Last Year:** 1988
**Last Retail Price:** $75

**Ref. No.:** 6064
**Name:** Blue Arabia Centerpiece
**Height:** 2.25
**Status:** Open issue, retired
**Issue Year:** 1993
**Issue Price:** Unknown
**Last Year:** 1996
**Last Retail Price:** $300

**Ref. No.:** 6071
**Name:** Green Arabia Centerpiece
**Height:** 2.25
**Status:** Open issue, retired
**Issue Year:** 1993
**Issue Price:** Unknown
**Last Year:** 1996
**Last Retail Price:** $310

**Ref. No.:** 6078
**Name:** Violet Arabia Centerpiece
**Height:** 2.25
**Status:** Open issue, retired
**Issue Year:** 1993
**Issue Price:** Unknown
**Last Year:** 1996
**Last Retail Price:** $290

**Ref. No.:** 6065
**Name:** Blue Ararat Centerpiece
**Height:** 3.25
**Status:** Open issue, retired
**Issue Year:** 1993
**Issue Price:** Unknown

**Ref. No.:** 6072
**Name:** Green Ararat Centerpiece
**Height:** 3.25
**Status:** Open issue, retired
**Issue Year:** 1993
**Issue Price:** Unknown

**Ref. No.:** 6079
**Name:** Violet Ararat Centerpiece
**Height:** 3.25
**Status:** Open issue, retired
**Issue Year:** 1993
**Issue Price:** Unknown

**Ref. No.:** 4737
**Name:** Fruit Bowl
**Height:** 4
**Status:** Open edition, retired
**Issue Year:** 1970
**Issue Price:** $15
**Last Year:** 1972
**Last Retail Price:** $15

**Ref. No.:** 4737.3
**Name:** Fruit Bowl
**Height:** 4
**Status:** Open edition, retired
**Issue Year:** 1970
**Issue Price:** $12
**Last Year:** 1972
**Last Retail Price:** $15

**Ref. No.:** 4796
**Name:** Damask Green
Centerpiece
**Height:** 4
**Status:** Open edition, retired
**Issue Year:** 1972
**Issue Price:** $25
**Last Year:** 1973
**Last Retail Price:** $30

**Ref. No.:** 4797
**Name:** Damask Grey Centerpiece
**Height:** 4
**Status:** Open edition, retired
**Issue Year:** 1972
**Issue Price:** $25
**Last Year:** 1973
**Last Retail Price:** $30

**Ref. No.:** 1168
**Name:** Bowl with Flowers
**Height:** 4.75
**Status:** Very rare
**Issue Year:** 1971
**Issue Price:** $22.50
**Last Year:** 1979
**Last Retail Price:** Not available

**Ref. No.:** 1168.3
**Name:** Bowl with White Flowers
**Height:** 4.75
**Status:** Very rare
**Issue Year:** 1971
**Issue Price:** $12.50
**Last Year:** 1978
**Last Retail Price:** Unknown

**Ref. No.:** 4736
**Name:** Star Centerpiece
**Height:** 5
**Status:** Open edition, retired
**Issue Year:** 1970
**Issue Price:** $35
**Last Year:** 1972
**Last Retail Price:** $40

**Ref. No.:** 4736.3
**Name:** Star Centerpiece
**Height:** 5
**Status:** Open edition, retired
**Issue Year:** 1970
**Issue Price:** $30
**Last Year:** 1972
**Last Retail Price:** $35

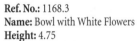

**Ref. No.:** 4724
**Name:** Star Centerpiece
**Height:** 5.5
**Status:** Open edition, retired
**Issue Year:** 1970
**Issue Price:** $40
**Last Year:** 1972
**Last Retail Price:** $45

**Ref. No.:** 4724.3
**Name:** Star Centerpiece, White
**Height:** 5.5
**Status:** Open edition, retired
**Issue Year:** 1970
**Issue Price:** $35
**Last Year:** 1972
**Last Retail Price:** $40

**Ref. No.:** 1113
**Name:** Mermaid Centerpiece
**Height:** 6
**Status:** Open edition, retired
**Issue Year:** 1971
**Issue Price:** $135
**Last Year:** 1972
**Last Retail Price:** $145

**Ref. No.:** 1079
**Name:** Boy with Lyre
**Height:** 6.5
**Status:** Very rare
**Issue Year:** 1969
**Issue Price:** $20
**Last Year:** 1970
**Last Retail Price:** Unknown

**Ref. No.:** 1080
**Name:** Girl with Watering Can
**Height:** 6.5
**Status:** Very rare
**Issue Year:** 1969
**Issue Price:** $20
**Last Year:** 1970
**Last Retail Price:** Unknown

**Ref. No.:** 4733
**Name:** Butterfly Centerpiece
**Height:** 7
**Status:** Open edition, retired
**Issue Year:** 1970
**Issue Price:** $40
**Last Year:** 1973
**Last Retail Price:** $55

**Ref. No.:** 4766
**Name:** Decorative Peacock
**Height:** 7
**Status:** Open edition, retired
**Issue Year:** 1971
**Issue Price:** $27.50
**Last Year:** 1973
**Last Retail Price:** $35

**Ref. No.:** 4766.3
**Name:** Decorative Peacock
**Height:** 7
**Status:** Open edition, retired
**Issue Year:** 1971
**Issue Price:** $27.50
**Last Year:** 1973
**Last Retail Price:** $35

**Ref. No.:** 4767
**Name:** Royal Peacock
**Height:** 7
**Status:** Open edition, retired
**Issue Year:** 1971
**Issue Price:** $13.50
**Last Year:** 1978
**Last Retail Price:** $35

**Ref. No.:** 4692
**Name:** Decorative Dove
**Height:** 7.50
**Status:** Open edition, retired
**Issue Year:** 1970
**Issue Price:** $17.50
**Last Year:** 1973
**Last Retail Price:** $25

**Ref. No.:** 1114
**Name:** Pastoral Bowl
**Height:** 8.50
**Status:** Open edition, retired
**Issue Year:** 1971
**Issue Price:** $85
**Last Year:** 1975
**Last Retail Price:** $140

**Ref. No.:** 1114.3
**Name:** Pastoral Bowl, White
**Height:** 8.50
**Status:** Open edition, retired
**Issue Year:** 1971
**Issue Price:** $60
**Last Year:** 1975
**Last Retail Price:** $100

**Ref. No.:** 4695
**Name:** Mandarin Duck
**Height:** 8.50
**Status:** Open edition, retired
**Issue Year:** 1970
**Issue Price:** $13.50
**Last Year:** 1975
**Last Retail Price:** $25
**High Auction Price:** $425
**Low Auction Price:** $250

**Ref. No.:** 1111
**Name:** Little Mermaid Bowl
**Height:** 9.50
**Status:** Open edition, retired
**Issue Year:** 1971
**Issue Price:** $35
**Last Year:** 1972
**Last Retail Price:** $35

**Ref. No.:** 4693
**Name:** Decorative Pheasant
**Height:** 9.75
**Status:** Open edition, retired
**Issue Year:** 1970
**Issue Price:** $20
**Last Year:** 1973
**Last Retail Price:** $25

**Ref. No.:** 4694
**Name:** Fish Centerpiece
**Height:** 9.75
**Status:** Open edition, retired
**Issue Year:** 1970
**Issue Price:** $35
**Last Year:** 1974
**Last Retail Price:** $55
**Auction Price:** $425

**Ref. No.:** 4694.3
**Name:** Fish Centerpiece
**Height:** 9.75
**Status:** Open edition, retired
**Issue Year:** 1970
**Issue Price:** $35
**Last Year:** 1974
**Last Retail Price:** $55

**Ref. No.:** 30.02
**Name:** Centerpiece
**Height:** 11.25
**Status:** Very rare
**Issue Year:** 1949
**Issue Price:** Unknown
**Last Year:** Unknown
**Last Retail Price:** Unknown
**Comment:** Designed and made
by Jose Lladró

**Ref. No.:** 4734
**Name:** Star Cup, 30 cm.
**Height:** 11.75
**Status:** Open edition, retired
**Issue Year:** 1970
**Issue Price:** $50
**Last Year:** 1972
**Last Retail Price:** $55

**Ref. No.:** 4734.3
**Name:** Star Cup, 30 cm.
**Height:** 11.75
**Status:** Open edition, retired
**Issue Year:** 1970
**Issue Price:** $40
**Last Year:** 1972
**Last Retail Price:** $45

**Ref. No.:** 4735
**Name:** Star Cup, 26 cm.
**Height:** 12.25
**Status:** Open edition, retired
**Issue Year:** 1970
**Issue Price:** $45
**Last Year:** 1972
**Last Retail Price:** $50

**Ref. No.:** 4735.3
**Name:** Star Cup, 26 cm.
**Height:** 12.25
**Status:** Open edition, retired
**Issue Year:** 1970
**Issue Price:** $35
**Last Year:** 1972
**Last Retail Price:** $40

**Ref. No.:** 4738
**Name:** Star Two-level Fruit Bowl
**Height:** 12.5
**Status:** Open edition, retired
**Issue Year:** 1970
**Issue Price:** $85
**Last Year:** 1972
**Last Retail Price:** $95

**Ref. No.:** 4738.3
**Name:** Star Two-level Fruit Bowl
**Height:** 12.5
**Status:** Open edition, retired
**Issue Year:** 1970
**Issue Price:** $65
**Last Year:** 1972
**Last Retail Price:** $75

**Spoons**

**Ref. No.:** 4739
**Name:** Star Three-level Fruit
  Bowl
**Height:** 18.5
**Status:** Open edition, retired
**Issue Year:** 1970
**Issue Price:** $100
**Last Year:** 1972
**Last Retail Price:** $ 115

**Ref. No.:** 4739.3
**Name:** Star Three-level Fruit
  Bowl
**Height:** 18.5
**Status:** Open edition, retired
**Issue Year:** 1970
**Issue Price:** $85
**Last Year:** 1972
**Last Retail Price:** $95

**Ref. No.:** 1548
**Name:** Light Blue Lladró Spoon
**Height:** 6
**Status:** Open issue, retired
**Issue Year:** 1987
**Issue Price:** $70
**Last Year:** 1991
**Last Retail Price:** $100

**Ref. No.:** 1548.1
**Name:** Dark Blue Lladró Spoon
**Height:** 6
**Status:** Open issue, retired
**Issue Year:** 1987
**Issue Price:** $70
**Last Year:** 1991
**Last Retail Price:** $100

**Ref. No.:** 1548.3
**Name:** White Lladró Spoon
**Height:** 6
**Status:** Open issue, retired
**Issue Year:** 1987
**Last Year:** 1991
**Issue Price:** $70
**Last Retail Price:** $100
**Auction Price:** $150

**Ref. No.:** 1548.4
**Name:** Brown Lladró Spoon
**Height:** 6
**Status:** Open issue, retired
**Issue Year:** 1987
**Issue Price:** $70
**Last Year:** 1991
**Last Retail Price:** $100

**Capricho**

**Ref. No.:** 5639
**Name:** Beige Lily Spoon
**Height:** 6
**Status:** Open issue, retired
**Issue Year:** 1989
**Issue Price:** $150
**Last Year:** 1991
**Last Retail Price:** $175

**Ref. No.:** 5639.3
**Name:** Blue Lily Spoon
**Height:** 6
**Status:** Open issue, retired
**Issue Year:** 1989
**Issue Price:** $150
**Last Year:** 1991
**Last Retail Price:** $175

**Ref. No.:** 1560
**Name:** Plain Hat
**Height:** .75
**Status:** Open issue, retired
**Issue Year:** 1987
**Issue Price:** $35
**Last Year:** 1991

**Ref. No.:** 1561
**Name:** White Hat with Blue
　Ribbon
**Height:** 1
**Status:** Open issue, retired
**Issue Year:** 1987
**Issue Price:** $40
**Last Year:** 1991
**Last Retail Price:** $55

**Ref. No.:** 1561.3
**Name:** Pink Hat with White
　Ribbon
**Height:** 1
**Status:** Open issue, retired
**Issue Year:** 1987
**Issue Price:** $40
**Last Year:** 1991
**Last Retail Price:** $55

**Ref. No.:** 1562
**Name:** Medium Broad Brimmed
　White Hat
**Height:** 1
**Status:** Open issue, retired
**Issue Year:** 1987
**Issue Price:** $80
**Last Year:** 1991
**Last Retail Price:** $110

**Ref. No.:** 1562.3
**Name:** Medium Broad Brimmed
　Pink Hat
**Height:** 1
**Status:** Open issue, retired
**Issue Year:** 1987
**Issue Price:** $80
**Last Year:** 1991
**Last Retail Price:** $110

**Ref. No.:** 1563
**Name:** Small Broad Brimmed
　Blue Hat
**Height:** 1
**Status:** Open issue, retired
**Issue Year:** 1987
**Issue Price:** $45
**Last Year:** 1991
**Last Retail Price:** $65

**Ref. No.:** 1563.3
**Name:** Small Broad Brimmed
　Pink Hat
**Height:** 1
**Status:** Open issue, retired
**Issue Year:** 1987
**Issue Price:** $45
**Last Year:** 1991
**Last Retail Price:** $65

**Ref. No.:** 1564
**Name:** Small Pink Hat with
  Ridges
**Height:** 1
**Status:** Open issue, retired
**Issue Year:** 1987
**Issue Price:** $45
**Last Year:** 1991
**Last Retail Price:** $70

**Ref. No.:** 1564.3
**Name:** Small Blue Hat with
  Ridges
**Height:** 1
**Status:** Open issue, retired
**Issue Year:** 1987
**Issue Price:** $45
**Last Year:** 1991
**Last Retail Price:** $70

**Ref. No.:** 1565
**Name:** Feathered Pink Hat
**Height:** 1
**Status:** Open issue, retired
**Issue Year:** 1987
**Issue Price:** $30
**Last Year:** 1991
**Last Retail Price:** $45

**Ref. No.:** 1565.3
**Name:** Feathered Blue Hat
**Height:** 1
**Status:** Open issue, retired
**Issue Year:** 1987
**Issue Price:** $30
**Last Year:** 1991
**Last Retail Price:** $45

**Ref. No.:** 1677
**Name:** Black and White Butterfly
  No. 5
**Height:** 1
**Status:** Open issue, retired
**Issue Year:** 1989
**Issue Price:** $100
**Last Year:** 1991
**Last Retail Price:** $120

**Ref. No.:** 1680
**Name:** Small Pink Butterfly No. 8
**Height:** 1
**Status:** Open issue, retired
**Issue Year:** 1989
**Issue Price:** $72.50
**Last Year:** 1991
**Last Retail Price:** $85
**Auction Price:** $150

**Ref. No.:** 1679
**Name:** Pink and Blue Butterfly
No. 7
**Height:** 1.29
**Status:** Open issue, retired
**Issue Year:** 1989
**Issue Price:** $80
**Last Year:** 1991
**Last Retail Price:** $95

**Ref. No.:** 1569
**Name:** Soft Lace Hat
**Height:** 2
**Status:** Open issue, retired
**Issue Year:** 1987
**Issue Price:** $45
**Last Year:** 1991
**Last Retail Price:** $75

**Ref. No.:** 1676
**Name:** Pink and White Butterfly
No. 4
**Height:** 2
**Status:** Open issue, retired
**Issue Year:** 1989
**Issue Price:** $100
**Last Year:** 1991
**Last Retail Price:** $120

**Ref. No.:** 1570
**Name:** Closed Hat with Blue
Ribbon
**Height:** 2.25
**Status:** Open issue, retired
**Issue Year:** 1987
**Issue Price:** $45
**Last Year:** 1991
**Last Retail Price:** $75

**Ref. No.:** 1571
**Name:** Flying Pink and Blue Hat
**Height:** 2.25
**Status:** Open issue, retired
**Issue Year:** 1987
**Issue Price:** $65
**Last Year:** 1991
**Last Retail Price:** $80

**Ref. No.:** 1675
**Name:** Black Butterfly No. 3
**Height:** 2.25
**Status:** Open issue, retired
**Issue Year:** 1989
**Issue Price:** $120
**Last Year:** 1991
**Last Retail Price:** $140

**Ref. No.:** 1556
**Name:** Oval Basket with Pink
 Trim
**Height:** 2.75
**Status:** Open issue, retired
**Issue Year:** 1987
**Issue Price:** $60
**Last Year:** 1991
**Last Retail Price:** $110

**Ref. No.:** 1556.3
**Name:** Oval Basket with Blue
 Trim
**Height:** 2.75
**Status:** Open issue, retired
**Issue Year:** 1987
**Issue Price:** $60
**Last Year:** 1991
**Last Retail Price:** $110

**Ref. No.:** 1685
**Name:** Great Butterfly No. 13
**Height:** 2.75
**Status:** Open issue, retired
**Issue Year:** 1989
**Issue Price:** $150
**Last Year:** 1991
**Last Retail Price:** $175

**Ref. No.:** 1686
**Name:** Queen Butterfly No. 14
**Height:** 2.75
**Status:** Open issue, retired
**Issue Year:** 1989
**Issue Price:** $125
**Last Year:** 1991
**Last Retail Price:** $150

**Ref. No.:** 1558
**Name:** Small Basket with Pink
 Lace
**Height:** 3
**Status:** Open issue, retired
**Issue Year:** 1987
**Issue Price:** $60
**Last Year:** 1991
**Last Retail Price:** $110

**Ref. No.:** 1558.3
**Name:** Small Basket with Blue
 Lace
**Height:** 3
**Status:** Open issue, retired
**Issue Year:** 1987
**Issue Price:** $60
**Last Year:** 1991
**Last Retail Price:** $110

**Ref. No.:** 1673
**Name:** Lacy Butterfly No. 1
**Height:** 3
**Status:** Open issue, retired
**Issue Year:** 1989
**Issue Price:** $95
**Last Year:** 1991
**Last Retail Price:** $110

**Ref. No.:** 1678
**Name:** Large Pink Butterfly No. 6
**Height:** 3
**Status:** Open issue, retired
**Issue Year:** 1989
**Issue Price:** $100
**Last Year:** 1991
**Last Retail Price:** $120

**Ref. No.:** 1683
**Name:** Spotted Butterfly No. 11
**Height:** 3
**Status:** Open issue, retired
**Issue Year:** 1989
**Issue Price:** $175
**Last Year:** 1991
**Last Retail Price:** $210

**Ref. No.:** 1684
**Name:** Leopard Butterfly No. 12
**Height:** 3
**Status:** Open issue, retired
**Issue Year:** 1989
**Issue Price:** $165
**Last Year:** 1991
**Last Retail Price:** $195

**Ref. No.:** 1674
**Name:** Beautiful Butterfly No. 2
**Height:** 3.25
**Status:** Open issue, retired
**Issue Year:** 1989
**Issue Price:** $100
**Last Year:** 1991
**Last Retail Price:** $120

**Ref. No.:** 1557
**Name:** Small Round Basket
with Pink Trim
**Height:** 3.75
**Status:** Open issue, retired
**Issue Year:** 1987
**Issue Price:** $60
**Last Year:** 1991
**Last Retail Price:** $110

**Ref. No.:** 1557.3
**Name:** Small Round Basket with
Blue Trim
**Height:** 3.75
**Status:** Open issue, retired
**Issue Year:** 1987
**Issue Price:** $60
**Last Year:** 1991
**Last Retail Price:** $110

**Ref. No.:** 1681
**Name:** Blue Butterfly No. 9
**Height:** 4
**Status:** Open issue, retired
**Issue Year:** 1989
**Issue Price:** $185
**Last Year:** 1991
**Last Retail Price:** $220

**Ref. No.:** 1682
**Name:** Pretty Butterfly No. 10
**Height:** 4
**Status:** Open issue, retired
**Issue Year:** 1989
**Issue Price:** $185
**Last Year:** 1991
**Last Retail Price:** $220

**Ref. No.:** 1666
**Name:** Romantic Lady with Veil
**Height:** 6
**Status:** Open edition, retired
**Issue Year:** 1989
**Issue Price:** $420
**Last Year:** 1993
**Last Retail Price:** $520

**Ref. No.:** 1539
**Name:** Small Bust With Veil
**Height:** 8.25
**Status:** Open issue, retired
**Issue Year:** 1988
**Issue Price:** $225
**Last Year:** 2001
**Last Retail Price:** $750

**Ref. No.:** 1667
**Name:** Lavender Lady
**Height:** 9
**Status:** Open edition, retired
**Issue Year:** 1989
**Issue Price:** $385
**Last Year:** 1991
**Last Retail Price:** $450

**Ref. No.:** 1668
**Name:** White Lady
**Height:** 9
**Status:** Open edition, retired
**Issue Year:** 1989
**Issue Price:** $340
**Last Year:** 1991
**Last Retail Price:** $400

**Ref. No.:** 1546
**Name:** Violet Fan with Base
**Height:** 9.75
**Status:** Open issue, retired
**Issue Year:** 1987
**Issue Price:** $650
**Last Year:** 1987
**Last Retail Price:** $675

**Ref. No.:** 1546.3
**Name:** White Fan with Base
**Height:** 9.75
**Status:** Open issue, retired
**Issue Year:** 1987
**Issue Price:** $650
**Last Year:** 1987
**Last Retail Price:** $675

**Ref. No.:** 1003
**Name:** Girl's Head
**Height:** 10
**Status:** Open edition, retired
**Issue Year:** 1969
**Issue Price:** $150
**Last Year:** 1985
**Last Retail Price:** $385
**Auction Price:** $400

**Ref. No.:** 1003.3
**Name:** Girl's Head (White)
**Height:** 10
**Status:** Open edition, retired
**Issue Year:** 1984
**Issue Price:** $392.50
**Last Year:** 1985
**Last Retail Price:** $395
**Auction Price:** $500

**Ref. No.:** 5801
**Name:** Charm
**Height:** 10
**Status:** Limited edition, sold out
**Edition Size:** 500
**Issue Year:** 1991
**Issue Price:** $650
**Last Year:** 1993
**Last Retail Price:** $725

**Ref. No.:** 1538
**Name:** Bust with Black Veil
**Height:** 13.25
**Status:** Open issue, active
**Issue Year:** 1988
**Issue Price:** $650
**2003 Retail Price:** $1390

**Ref. No.:** 5927
**Name:** White Bust with Veil
  with base
**Height:** 13.75
**Status:** Open issue, active
**Issue Year:** 1988
**Issue Price:** Unknown
**2003 Retail Price:** $1250
**Comment:** To be retired or sold
  out as of December 31, 2003

**Ref. No.:** 1712
**Name:** Lady With Mantilla
**Height:** 14.25
**Status:** Open edition, retired
**Issue Year:** 1989
**Issue Price:** $575
**Last Year:** 1991
**Last Retail Price:** $685

**Bells**

**Ref. No.:** 5954
**Name:** Sounds of Winter
**Height:** 4
**Status:** Open issue, retired
**Issue Year:** 1993
**Issue Price:** $150
**Last Year:** 2001
**Last Retail Price:** $150

**Ref. No.:** 5955
**Name:** Sounds of Fall
**Height:** 4
**Status:** Open issue, retired
**Issue Year:** 1993
**Issue Price:** $150
**Last Year:** 2001
**Last Retail Price:** $150

**Ref. No.:** 6176
**Name:** Communion Bell
**Height:** 4.25
**Status:** Open issue, retired
**Issue Year:** 1995
**Issue Price:** $85
**Last Year:** 2001
**Last Retail Price:** $85

*Functional*

**Ref. No.:** 5264
**Name:** Bell - Decorated
**Height:** 4.75
**Status:** Open issue, retired
**Issue Year:** 1984
**Issue Price:** $50
**Last Year:** 1990
**Last Retail Price:** $70

**Ref. No.:** 5264.3
**Name:** Bell
**Height:** 4.75
**Status:** Open issue, retired
**Issue Year:** 1984
**Issue Price:** $50
**Last Year:** 1988
**Last Retail Price:** $60

**Ref. No.:** 5953
**Name:** Sounds of Summer
**Height:** 4.75
**Status:** Open issue, retired
**Issue Year:** 1993
**Issue Price:** $150
**Last Year:** 2001
**Last Retail Price:** $150

**Ref. No.:** 5956
**Name:** Sounds of Spring
**Height:** 4.75
**Status:** Open issue, retired
**Issue Year:** 1993
**Issue Price:** $150
**Last Year:** 2001
**Last Retail Price:** $150

**Ref. No.:** 6416
**Name:** It's a Girl!
**Height:** 7
**Status:** Open issue, active
**Issue Year:** 1997
**Issue Price:** $125
**2003 Retail Price:** $130

**Ref. No.:** 6473
**Name:** Sounds of Peace
**Height:** 7
**Status:** Open issue, active
**Issue Year:** 1998
**Issue Price:** $98
**2003 Retail Price:** $120

**Ref. No.:** 7542
**Name:** 1994 Eternal Love Bell
**Height:** 7.25
**Status:** Limited edition, sold out
**Issue Year:** 1994
**Issue Price:** $95
**Last Year:** 1994
**Last Retail Price:** $95

**Ref. No.:** 6331
**Name:** Bridal Bell
**Height:** 8
**Status:** Open issue, active
**Issue Year:** 1996
**Issue Price:** $155
**2003 Retail Price:** $155

**Ref. No.:** 6415
**Name:** It's a Boy!
**Height:** 8
**Status:** Open issue, active
**Issue Year:** 1997
**Issue Price:** $125
**2003 Retail Price:** $130

**Boxes**

**Ref. No.:** 6200
**Name:** Bridal Bell
**Height:** 8.25
**Status:** Open issue, retired
**Issue Year:** 1995
**Issue Price:** $125
**Last Year:** 2001
**Last Retail Price:** $125

**Ref. No.:** 6474
**Name:** Sounds of Love
**Height:** 9
**Status:** Open issue, active
**Issue Year:** 1998
**Issue Price:** $98
**2003 Retail Price:** $120

**Ref. No.:** 5266
**Name:** Heart Box, decorated
**Height:** 1
**Status:** Open issue, retired
**Issue Year:** 1984
**Issue Price:** $37.50
**Last Year:** 1990
**Last Retail Price:** $55

**Ref. No.:** 5266.3
**Name:** Heart Box, white
**Height:** 1
**Status:** Open issue, retired
**Issue Year:** 1984
**Issue Price:** $37.50
**Last Year:** 1988
**Last Retail Price:** $45

**Ref. No.:** 5267
**Name:** Oval Box, decorated
**Height:** 1
**Status:** Open issue, retired
**Issue Year:** 1984
**Issue Price:** $40
**Last Year:** 1990
**Last Retail Price:** $60

**Ref. No.:** 5267.3
**Name:** Oval Box, white
**Height:** 1
**Status:** Open issue, retired
**Issue Year:** 1984
**Issue Price:** $40
**Last Year:** 1988
**Last Retail Price:** $50

**Ref. No.:** 6056
**Name:** Crown Box
**Height:** 2.25
**Status:** Open issue, retired
**Issue Year:** 1993
**Issue Price:** Unknown
**Last Year:** 1996
**Last Retail Price:** $360

**Ref. No.:** 6057
**Name:** Pineapple Box
**Height:** 2.50
**Status:** Open issue, retired
**Issue Year:** 1993
**Issue Price:** Unknown
**Last Year:** 1996
**Last Retail Price:** $350

**Ref. No.:** 6062
**Name:** Blue Kublay Sweet Box
**Height:** 3.25
**Status:** Open issue, retired
**Issue Year:** 1993
**Issue Price:** Unknown
**Last Year:** 1996
**Last Retail Price:** $280

**Ref. No.:** 6069
**Name:** Green Kublay Sweet Box
**Height:** 3.75
**Status:** Open issue, retired
**Issue Year:** 1993
**Issue Price:** Unknown
**Last Year:** 1996
**Last Retail Price:** $265

**Ref. No.:** 6076
**Name:** Violet Kublay Sweet Box
**Height:** 3.75
**Status:** Open issue, retired
**Issue Year:** 1993
**Issue Price:** Unknown
**Last Year:** 1996
**Last Retail Price:** $310

**Ref. No.:** 6391
**Name:** The Encounter
**Height:** 4
**Status:** Open issue, retired
**Issue Year:** 1997
**Issue Price:** $150
**Last Year:** 1998
**Last Retail Price:** $150

**Ref. No.:** 6054
**Name:** Queen Sweet Box
**Height:** 4.25
**Status:** Open issue, retired
**Issue Year:** 1993
**Issue Price:** Unknown
**Last Year:** 1996
**Last Retail Price:** $450

**Ref. No.:** 6055
**Name:** Aladdin Sweet Box
**Height:** 4.25
**Status:** Open issue, retired
**Issue Year:** 1993
**Issue Price:** Unknown
**Last Year:** 1996
**Last Retail Price:** $460

**Ref. No.:** 6063
**Name:** Blue Heart Sweet Box
**Height:** 4.50
**Status:** Open issue, retired
**Issue Year:** 1993
**Issue Price:** Unknown
**Last Year:** 1996

**Ref. No.:** 6070
**Name:** Green Heart Sweet Box
**Height:** 4.50
**Status:** Open issue, retired
**Issue Year:** 1993
**Issue Price:** Unknown

**Ref. No.:** 6077
**Name:** Violet Heart Sweet Box
**Height:** 4.50
**Status:** Open issue, retired
**Issue Year:** 1993
**Issue Price:** Unknown

**Ref. No.:** 6392
**Name:** The Kiss
**Height:** 6
**Status:** Open issue, retired
**Issue Year:** 1997
**Issue Price:** $150
**Last Year:** 1998
**Last Retail Price:** $150

### Bookends

**Ref. No.:** 2010
**Name:** Horse's Head Bookends
**Height:** 9
**Status:** Open issue, retired
**Issue Year:** 1970
**Issue Price:** $12.50
**Last Year:** 1981
**Last Retail Price:** $40
**Auction Price:** $450

**Ref. No.:** 4661
**Name:** Horse Head Bookend
**Height:** 10.25
**Status:** Open issue, retired
**Issue Year:** 1969
**Issue Price:** $16.50
**Last Year:** 1972
**Last Retail Price:** $20

**Ref. No.:** 4626
**Name:** Velazquez Bookend
**Height:** 12
**Status:** Open issue, retired
**Issue Year:** 1969
**Issue Price:** $90
**Last Year:** 1975
**Last Retail Price:** $90

## Paperweights

**Ref. No.:** 4627
**Name:** Columbus Bookend
**Height:** 12.25
**Status:** Open issue, retired
**Issue Year:** 1969
**Issue Price:** $90
**Last Year:** 1975
**Last Retail Price:** $90

**Ref. No.:** 7551
**Name:** 16th Century Globe
 Paperweight
**Height:** 3
**Status:** Open issue, active
**Issue Year:** 1995
**Issue Price:** $105
**2003 Retail Price:** $120

**Ref. No.:** 5945
**Name:** Olympic Ball
**Height:** 3
**Status:** Limited edition, sold out
**Issue Year:** 1992
**Issue Price:** $60
**Last Year:** 1993
**Last Retail Price:** $60
**Auction Price:** $75

## Flowers

**Ref. No.:** 6138
**Name:** Globe Paperweight
**Height:** 4.75
**Status:** Open issue, retired
**Issue Year:** 1994
**Issue Price:** $95
**Last Year:** 1996
**Last Retail Price:** $95

**Ref. No.:** 1291
**Name:** Flower Basket No. 1
**Height:** 1
**Status:** Open edition, retired
**Issue Year:** 1974
**Issue Price:** $70
**Last Year:** 1983
**Last Retail Price:** $155

**Ref. No.:** 1296
**Name:** Flower Basket No. 6
**Height:** 1
**Status:** Open edition, retired
**Issue Year:** 1974
**Issue Price:** $145
**Last Year:** 1983
**Last Retail Price:** $150

**Ref. No.:** 1097
**Name:** Medium Rose in Case
**Height:** 1.25
**Status:** Open edition, retired
**Issue Year:** 1969
**Issue Price:** $18
**Last Year:** 1978
**Last Retail Price:** $50

**Ref. No.:** 1097.3
**Name:** Medium Rose in Case
**Height:** 1.25
**Status:** Open edition, retired
**Issue Year:** 1969
**Issue Price:** $18
**Last Year:** 1978
**Last Retail Price:** $50

**Ref. No.:** 1098
**Name:** Medium Rose on Plaque
**Height:** 1.25
**Status:** Open edition, retired
**Issue Year:** 1969
**Issue Price:** $35
**Last Year:** 1975
**Last Retail Price:** $65

**Ref. No.:** 1098.3
**Name:** Medium Rose on Plaque
**Height:** 1.25
**Status:** Open edition, retired
**Issue Year:** 1969
**Issue Price:** $35
**Last Year:** 1975
**Last Retail Price:** $65

**Ref. No.:** 1095
**Name:** Big Rose in Case
**Height:** 1.5
**Status:** Open edition, retired
**Issue Year:** 1969
**Issue Price:** $22.50
**Last Year:** 1979
**Last Retail Price:** $65

**Ref. No.:** 1095.3
**Name:** Big Rose in Case
**Height:** 1.5
**Status:** Open edition, retired
**Issue Year:** 1969
**Issue Price:** $22.50
**Last Year:** 1979
**Last Retail Price:** $65

**Ref. No.:** 1096
**Name:** Big Rose on Plaque
**Height:** 1.5
**Status:** Open edition, retired
**Issue Year:** 1969
**Issue Price:** $32.50
**Last Year:** 1975
**Last Retail Price:** $60

**Ref. No.:** 1096.3
**Name:** Big Rose on Plaque
**Height:** 1.5
**Status:** Open edition, retired
**Issue Year:** 1969
**Issue Price:** $27.50
**Last Year:** 1979
**Last Retail Price:** $80

**Ref. No.:** 1099
**Name:** Small Rose in Case
**Height:** 1.5
**Status:** Open edition, retired
**Issue Year:** 1969
**Issue Price:** $17.50
**Last Year:** 1979
**Last Retail Price:** $50

**Ref. No.:** 1099.3
**Name:** Small Rose in Case
**Height:** 1.5
**Status:** Open edition, retired
**Issue Year:** 1969
**Issue Price:** $17.50
**Last Year:** 1979
**Last Retail Price:** $50

**Ref. No.:** 1100
**Name:** Small Rose on Plaque
**Height:** 1.5
**Status:** Open edition, retired
**Issue Year:** 1969
**Issue Price:** $35
**Last Year:** 1975
**Last Retail Price:** $65

**Ref. No.:** 1100.3
**Name:** Small Rose and Plaque
**Height:** 1.5
**Status:** Open edition, retired
**Issue Year:** 1969
**Issue Price:** $35
**Last Year:** 1975
**Last Retail Price:** $65

**Ref. No.:** 1101
**Name:** Two Roses in Case
**Height:** 1.5
**Status:** Very Rare
**Issue Year:** 1969
**Issue Price:** $30
**Last Year:** 1979
**Last Retail Price:** Unknown

**Ref. No.:** 1101.3
**Name:** Two Roses in Case
**Height:** 1.5
**Status:** Open edition, retired
**Issue Year:** 1969
**Issue Price:** $30
**Last Year:** 1979
**Last Retail Price:** $85

**Ref. No.:** 1102
**Name:** Two Roses and Plaque
**Height:** 1.5
**Status:** Open edition, retired
**Issue Year:** 1969
**Issue Price:** $42.50
**Last Year:** 1975
**Last Retail Price:** $42

**Ref. No.:** 1102.3
**Name:** Two Roses on Plaque
**Height:** 1.5
**Status:** Open edition, retired
**Issue Year:** 1969
**Issue Price:** $45
**Last Year:** 1975
**Last Retail Price:** $80

**Ref. No.:** 5179
**Name:** Three Pink Roses
**Height:** 1.5
**Status:** Open edition, retired
**Issue Year:** 1984
**Issue Price:** $70
**Last Year:** 1990
**Last Retail Price:** $110

**Ref. No.:** 5179.3
**Name:** Three Pink Roses
**Height:** 1.5
**Status:** Open edition, retired
**Issue Year:** 1984
**Issue Price:** $67.50
**Last Year:** 1988
**Last Retail Price:** $80

**Ref. No.:** 5180
**Name:** Dahlia with Base
**Height:** 1.5
**Status:** Open edition, retired
**Issue Year:** 1984
**Issue Price:** $65
**Last Year:** 1990
**Last Retail Price:** $95

**Ref. No.:** 5180.3
**Name:** Dahlia
**Height:** 1.5
**Status:** Open edition, retired
**Issue Year:** 1984
**Issue Price:** $62.50
**Last Year:** 1988
**Last Retail Price:** $75

**Ref. No.:** 5181
**Name:** Japanese Camellia
**Height:** 1.5
**Status:** Open edition, retired
**Issue Year:** 1984
**Issue Price:** $70
**Last Year:** 1990
**Last Retail Price:** $90

**Ref. No.:** 5181.3
**Name:** Japanese Camellia
**Height:** 1.5
**Status:** Open edition, retired
**Issue Year:** 1984
**Issue Price:** $60
**Last Year:** 1988
**Last Retail Price:** $70

**Ref. No.:** 5182
**Name:** White Peony with Base
**Height:** 1.5
**Status:** Open edition, retired
**Issue Year:** 1984
**Issue Price:** $85
**Last Year:** 1990
**Last Retail Price:** $125

**Ref. No.:** 5182.3
**Name:** White Peony
**Height:** 1.5
**Status:** Open edition, retired
**Issue Year:** 1984
**Issue Price:** $85
**Last Year:** 1988
**Last Retail Price:** $95

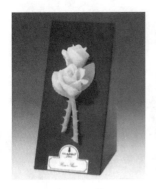

**Ref. No.:** 5183
**Name:** Two Yellow Roses
**Height:** 1.5
**Status:** Open edition, retired
**Issue Year:** 1984
**Issue Price:** $57.50
**Last Year:** 1990
**Last Retail Price:** $85

**Ref. No.:** 5183.3
**Name:** Two Yellow Roses
**Height:** 1.5
**Status:** Open edition, retired
**Issue Year:** 1984
**Issue Price:** $57.50
**Last Year:** 1988
**Last Retail Price:** $65

**Ref. No.:** 5184
**Name:** White Carnation
**Height:** 1.5
**Status:** Open edition, retired
**Issue Year:** 1984
**Issue Price:** $67.50
**Last Year:** 1990
**Last Retail Price:** $100

**Ref. No.:** 5184.3
**Name:** White Carnation
**Height:** 1.5
**Status:** Open edition, retired
**Issue Year:** 1984
**Issue Price:** $65
**Last Year:** 1988
**Last Retail Price:** $75

**Ref. No.:** 5185
**Name:** Lactiflora Peony
**Height:** 1.5
**Status:** Open edition, retired
**Issue Year:** 1984
**Issue Price:** $67.50
**Last Year:** 1990
**Last Retail Price:** $100

**Ref. No.:** 5185.3
**Name:** Lactiflora Peony
**Height:** 1.5
**Status:** Open edition, retired
**Issue Year:** 1984
**Issue Price:** $65
**Last Year:** 1988
**Last Retail Price:** $75

**Ref. No.:** 5186
**Name:** Yellow Begonia
**Height:** 1.5
**Status:** Open edition, retired
**Issue Year:** 1984
**Issue Price:** $67.50
**Last Year:** 1990
**Last Retail Price:** $100

**Ref. No.:** 5186.3
**Name:** Yellow Begonia
**Height:** 1.5
**Status:** Open edition, retired
**Issue Year:** 1984
**Issue Price:** $65
**Last Year:** 1988
**Last Retail Price:** $75

**Ref. No.:** 5187
**Name:** Rhododendron
**Height:** 1.5
**Status:** Open edition, retired
**Issue Year:** 1984
**Issue Price:** $67.50
**Last Year:** 1990
**Last Retail Price:** $100

**Ref. No.:** 5187.3
**Name:** Rhododendron
**Height:** 1.5
**Status:** Open edition, retired
**Issue Year:** 1984
**Issue Price:** $65
**Last Year:** 1988
**Last Retail Price:** $75

**Ref. No.:** 5188
**Name:** Miniature Begonia
**Height:** 1.5
**Status:** Open edition, retired
**Issue Year:** 1984
**Issue Price:** $85
**Last Year:** 1990
**Last Retail Price:** $120

**Ref. No.:** 5188.3
**Name:** Miniature Begonia
**Height:** 1.5
**Status:** Open edition, retired
**Issue Year:** 1984
**Issue Price:** $80
**Last Year:** 1988
**Last Retail Price:** $90
**Auction Price:** $275

**Ref. No.:** 5189
**Name:** Chrysanthemum
**Height:** 1.5
**Status:** Open edition, retired
**Issue Year:** 1984
**Issue Price:** $105
**Last Year:** 1990
**Last Retail Price:** $150

**Ref. No.:** 5189.3
**Name:** Chrysanthemum
**Height:** 1.5
**Status:** Open edition, retired
**Issue Year:** 1984
**Issue Price:** $100
**Last Year:** 1988
**Last Retail Price:** $110

**Ref. No.:** 5190
**Name:** California Poppy
**Height:** 1.5
**Status:** Open edition, retired
**Issue Year:** 1984
**Issue Price:** $100
**Last Year:** 1990
**Last Retail Price:** $180

**Ref. No.:** 5190.3
**Name:** California Poppy
**Height:** 1.5
**Status:** Open edition, retired
**Issue Year:** 1984
**Issue Price:** $97.50
**Last Year:** 1988
**Last Retail Price:** $110

**Ref. No.:** 1273
**Name:** Rose
**Height:** 2
**Status:** Very Rare
**Issue Year:** 1974
**Issue Price:** $25
**Last Year:** 1983
**Last Retail Price:** Unknown

**Ref. No.:** 1292
**Name:** Flower Basket No. 2
**Height:** 2
**Status:** Open edition, retired
**Issue Year:** 1974
**Issue Price:** $85
**Last Year:** 1983
**Last Retail Price:** $190

**Ref. No.:** 1293
**Name:** Flower Basket No. 3
**Height:** 2
**Status:** Open edition, retired
**Issue Year:** 1974
**Issue Price:** $225
**Last Year:** 1983
**Last Retail Price:** $230

**Ref. No.:** 1294
**Name:** Flower Basket No. 4A
**Height:** 2
**Status:** Open edition, retired
**Issue Year:** 1974
**Issue Price:** $125
**Last Year:** 1983
**Last Retail Price:** $275

**Ref. No.:** 1295
**Name:** Flower Basket No. 4B
**Height:** 2
**Status:** Open edition, retired
**Issue Year:** 1974
**Issue Price:** $110
**Last Year:** 1983
**Last Retail Price:** $250

**Ref. No.:** 1549
**Name:** Square Handkerchief
  with Flowers
**Height:** 2
**Status:** Open edition, retired
**Issue Year:** 1988
**Issue Price:** $180
**Last Year:** 1991
**Last Retail Price:** $250

**Ref. No.:** 1550
**Name:** Round Handkerchief
  with Flowers
**Height:** 2
**Status:** Open edition, retired
**Issue Year:** 1987
**Issue Price:** $170
**Last Year:** 1991
**Last Retail Price:** $225

**Ref. No.:** 1559
**Name:** Small Pink Flower Basket
**Height:** 2
**Status:** Open edition, retired
**Issue Year:** 1987
**Issue Price:** $90
**Last Year:** 1991
**Last Retail Price:** $110

**Ref. No.:** 1559.3
**Name:** Small Blue Flower Basket
**Height:** 2
**Status:** Open edition, retired
**Issue Year:** 1987
**Issue Price:** $90
**Last Year:** 1991
**Last Retail Price:** $110

**Ref. No.:** 1552
**Name:** Small Brown Flower
    Basket
**Height:** 2.75
**Status:** Open edition, retired
**Issue Year:** 1987
**Issue Price:** $115
**Last Year:** 1991
**Last Retail Price:** $270

**Ref. No.:** 1552.1
**Name:** Small Brown Flower
    Basket
**Height:** 2.75
**Status:** Open edition, retired
**Issue Year:** 1987
**Issue Price:** $160
**Last Year:** 1991
**Last Retail Price:** $280

**Ref. No.:** 1552.3
**Name:** Small Gray Flower Basket
**Height:** 2.75
**Status:** Open edition, retired
**Issue Year:** 1987
**Issue Price:** $115
**Last Year:** 1991
**Last Retail Price:** $270

**Ref. No.:** 1554
**Name:** Small Brown Flower
    Basket
**Height:** 2.75
**Status:** Open edition, retired
**Issue Year:** 1987
**Issue Price:** $110
**Last Year:** 1991
**Last Retail Price:** $225

**Ref. No.:** 1554.1
**Name:** Small Brown Flower
    Basket
**Height:** 2.75
**Status:** Open edition, retired
**Issue Year:** 1987
**Issue Price:** $130
**Last Year:** 1991
**Last Retail Price:** $235

**Ref. No.:** 1554.3
**Name:** Small Green Flower
    Basket
**Height:** 2.75
**Status:** Open edition, retired
**Issue Year:** 1987
**Issue Price:** $110
**Last Year:** 1991
**Last Retail Price:** $225

**Ref. No.:** 1555
**Name:** Pink Flower Basket
**Height:** 2.75
**Status:** Open edition, retired
**Issue Year:** 1987
**Issue Price:** $140
**Last Year:** 1991
**Last Retail Price:** $210

**Ref. No.:** 1573
**Name:** Small Flower Basket
    with Lace
**Height:** 3
**Status:** Open edition, retired
**Issue Year:** 1987
**Issue Price:** $115
**Last Year:** 1991
**Last Retail Price:** $175

**Ref. No.:** 1573.3
**Name:** Small Flower Basket
    with Lace
**Height:** 3
**Status:** Open edition, retired
**Issue Year:** 1987
**Issue Price:** $115
**Last Year:** 1991
**Last Retail Price:** $175

**Ref. No.:** 1577
**Name:** Basket with Handkerchief
    and Rose
**Height:** 3
**Status:** Open edition, retired
**Issue Year:** 1987
**Issue Price:** $275
**Last Year:** 1991
**Last Retail Price:** $650

**Ref. No.:** 1795
**Name:** Natural Beauty
**Height:** 3
**Status:** Limited edition, active
**Edition Size:** 500
**Issue Year:** 1994
**Issue Price:** $650
**2003 Retail Price:** $650

**Ref. No.:** 7580
**Name:** A Basket of Blossoms
**Height:** 3
**Status:** Open issue, retired
**Issue Year:** 1998
**Issue Price:** $100
**Last Year:** 1998
**Last Retail Price:** $100
**Comment:** Lladró Events
Exclusive

**Ref. No.:** 7577
**Name:** A Basket for You
**Height:** 3.25
**Status:** Open issue, retired
**Issue Year:** 1997
**Last Year:** 1997
**Last Retail Price:** $100
**Comment:** Lladró Events
Exclusive

**Ref. No.:** 7583
**Name:** Only for You
**Height:** 3.25
**Status:** Open issue, retired
**Issue Year:** 1999
**Issue Price:** $100
**Last Year:** 1999
**Last Retail Price:** $100
**Comment:** Lladró Events
Exclusive

**Ref. No.:** 1574
**Name:** Small Round Flower
Basket
**Height:** 3.75
**Status:** Open edition, retired
**Issue Year:** 1987
**Issue Price:** $140
**Last Year:** 1991
**Last Retail Price:** $195

**Ref. No.:** 1574.3
**Name:** Small Round Flower
Basket
**Height:** 3.75
**Status:** Open edition, retired
**Issue Year:** 1987
**Issue Price:** $140
**Last Year:** 1991
**Last Retail Price:** $195

**Ref. No.:** 1073
**Name:** Basket of Roses
**Height:** 4
**Status:** Open edition, retired
**Issue Year:** 1969
**Issue Price:** $65
**Last Year:** 1981
**Last Retail Price:** $65

**Ref. No.:** 1073.3
**Name:** Basket of Roses, White
**Height:** 4
**Status:** Open issue, retired
**Issue Year:** 1969
**Issue Price:** $55
**Last Year:** 1981
**Last Retail Price:** Unknown

**Ref. No.:** 1545
**Name:** Basket of Dahlias
**Height:** 4
**Status:** Open edition, retired
**Issue Year:** 1988
**Issue Price:** $375
**Last Year:** 1991
**Last Retail Price:** $695

**Ref. No.:** 1553
**Name:** Small Brown Flower
  Basket
**Height:** 4
**Status:** Open edition, retired
**Issue Year:** 1987
**Issue Price:** $115
**Last Year:** 1991
**Last Retail Price:** $280

**Ref. No.:** 1553.1
**Name:** Small Brown Flower
  Basket
**Height:** 4
**Status:** Open edition, retired
**Issue Year:** 1987
**Issue Price:** $160
**Last Year:** 1991
**Last Retail Price:** $290

**Ref. No.:** 1553.3
**Name:** Small Gray Flower Basket
**Height:** 4
**Status:** Open edition, retired
**Issue Year:** 1987
**Issue Price:** $115
**Last Year:** 1991
**Last Retail Price:** $280
**Auction Price:** $350

**Ref. No.:** 1625
**Name:** Yellow Oval Basket
**Height:** 4
**Status:** Open edition, retired
**Issue Year:** 1989
**Issue Price:** $445
**Last Year:** 1991
**Last Retail Price:** $525

**Ref. No.:** 1626
**Name:** Blue Oval Basket
**Height:** 4
**Status:** Open edition, retired
**Issue Year:** 1989
**Issue Price:** $445
**Last Year:** 1991
**Last Retail Price:** $525

**Ref. No.:** 1630
**Name:** Fall Basket
**Height:** 4
**Status:** Open edition, retired
**Issue Year:** 1989
**Issue Price:** $535
**Last Year:** 1991
**Last Retail Price:** $630

**Ref. No.:** 7511
**Name:** Basket of Roses
**Height:** 4
**Status:** Open issue, active
**Issue Year:** 1991
**Last Retail Price:** Not available in the US
**Comment:** Exclusive to Banco de Santander

**Ref. No.:** 1221
**Name:** Little Jug with Flowers
**Height:** 4.25
**Status:** Open edition, retired
**Issue Year:** 1972
**Issue Price:** Unknown
**Last Year:** 1980
**Last Retail Price:** $40

**Ref. No.:** 1572
**Name:** Flowers Chest
**Height:** 4.25
**Status:** Open issue, retired
**Issue Year:** 1987
**Issue Price:** $550
**Last Year:** 2001
**Last Retail Price:** $1200

**Ref. No.:** 1627
**Name:** Spring Shower Basket
**Height:** 4.25
**Status:** Open edition, retired
**Issue Year:** 1989
**Issue Price:** $675
**Last Year:** 1991
**Last Retail Price:** $800

**Ref. No.:** 1628
**Name:** May Flower Basket
**Height:** 4.25
**Status:** Open edition, retired
**Issue Year:** 1989
**Issue Price:** $485
**Last Year:** 1991
**Last Retail Price:** $575

**Ref. No.:** 1633
**Name:** Rust Wild Flower Vase
**Height:** 4.75
**Status:** Open edition, retired
**Issue Year:** 1989
**Issue Price:** $300
**Last Year:** 1991
**Last Retail Price:** $350

**Ref. No.:** 1551
**Name:** Small Vase with Iris
**Height:** 5
**Status:** Open edition, retired
**Issue Year:** 1987
**Issue Price:** $110
**Last Year:** 1991
**Last Retail Price:** $130
**Auction Price:** $450

**Ref. No.:** 1634
**Name:** Blue Wild Flower Vase
**Height:** 5
**Status:** Open edition, retired
**Issue Year:** 1989
**Issue Price:** $275
**Last Year:** 1991
**Last Retail Price:** $325

**Ref. No.:** 1792
**Name:** Fluvial Cup with Roses
**Height:** 5.5
**Status:** Limited edition, sold out
**Edition Size:** 500
**Issue Year:** 1994
**Issue Price:** $1150
**Last Year:** 1998
**Last Retail Price:** $1150

**Ref. No.:** 1542
**Name:** Iris Arrangement
**Height:** 6
**Status:** Open edition, retired
**Issue Year:** 1988
**Issue Price:** $800
**Last Year:** 1990
**Last Retail Price:** $500

**Ref. No.:** 1629
**Name:** Spring Basket
**Height:** 6
**Status:** Open edition, retired
**Issue Year:** 1989
**Issue Price:** $550
**Last Year:** 1991
**Last Retail Price:** $640

**Ref. No.:** 1219
**Name:** Miniature Flower Vase
**Height:** 6.25
**Status:** Open edition, retired
**Issue Year:** 1972
**Issue Price:** $40
**Last Year:** 1979
**Last Retail Price:** $40

**Ref. No.:** 1543
**Name:** Basket of Margaritas
**Height:** 6.25
**Status:** Open edition, retired
**Issue Year:** 1988
**Issue Price:** $450
**Last Year:** 1991
**Last Retail Price:** $900
**Auction Price:** $800

**Ref. No.:** 1575
**Name:** Flat Flower Basket
**Height:** 6.25
**Status:** Open edition, retired
**Issue Year:** 1987
**Issue Price:** $450
**Last Year:** 1991
**Last Retail Price:** $750
**Auction Price:** $275

**Ref. No.:** 1576
**Name:** Flat Basket with Violets
**Height:** 6.25
**Status:** Open edition, retired
**Issue Year:** 1987
**Issue Price:** $375
**Last Year:** 1991
**Last Retail Price:** $650
**Auction Price:** $550

**Ref. No.:** 1790
**Name:** Neoclassic Colored Cup
**Height:** 6.25
**Status:** Limited edition, sold out
**Edition Size:** 500
**Issue Year:** 1994
**Issue Price:** $1370
**Last Year:** 2001
**Last Retail Price:** $1400

**Ref. No.:** 1791
**Name:** Bisque Neoclassic Cup
**Height:** 6.25
**Status:** Limited edition, sold out
**Edition Size:** 500
**Issue Year:** 1994
**Issue Price:** $1250
**Last Year:** 1998
**Last Retail Price:** $1300

**Ref. No.:** 1793
**Name:** Fluvial Cup with Branch
**Height:** 6.25
**Status:** Limited edition, sold out
**Edition Size:** 500
**Issue Year:** 1994
**Issue Price:** $1590
**Last Year:** 2000
**Last Retail Price:** $1590

**Ref. No.:** 1794
**Name:** Fluvial Cup with Waterlily
**Height:** 6.25
**Status:** Limited edition, sold out
**Edition Size:** 500
**Issue Year:** 1994
**Issue Price:** $1350
**Last Year:** 1998
**Last Retail Price:** $1350

**Ref. No.:** 1218
**Name:** Blue Flower Vase
**Height:** 7
**Status:** Open edition, retired
**Issue Year:** 1972
**Issue Price:** $40
**Last Year:** 1979
**Last Retail Price:** $40

**Ref. No.:** 1222
**Name:** Little Flower Jug
**Height:** 7
**Status:** Open edition, retired
**Issue Year:** 1972
**Issue Price:** $40
**Last Year:** 1979
**Last Retail Price:** $40

**Ref. No.:** 1544
**Name:** Basket of Roses
**Height:** 7
**Status:** Open edition, retired
**Issue Year:** 1988
**Issue Price:** $400
**Last Year:** 1991
**Last Retail Price:** $650
**Auction Price:** $600

**Ref. No.:** 1631
**Name:** Spring Blossom
**Height:** 7
**Status:** Open edition, retired
**Issue Year:** 1989
**Issue Price:** $550
**Last Year:** 1991
**Last Retail Price:** $640

**Ref. No.:** 1632
**Name:** Violet Vase
**Height:** 7
**Status:** Open edition, retired
**Issue Year:** 1989
**Issue Price:** $445
**Last Year:** 1991
**Last Retail Price:** $525

**Ref. No.:** 1789
**Name:** Large Neoclassic Cup
**Height:** 7
**Status:** Limited edition, sold out
**Edition Size:** 300
**Issue Year:** 1994
**Issue Price:** $2695
**Last Year:** 1998
**Last Retail Price:** $2695

**Ref. No.:** 1220
**Name:** Little Jug Rose with
Flowers
**Height:** 7.5
**Status:** Open edition, retired
**Issue Year:** 1972
**Issue Price:** $40
**Last Year:** 1979
**Last Retail Price:** $40

**Ref. No.:** 1786
**Name:** Blue Romantic Vase
**Height:** 8
**Status:** Limited edition, active
**Edition Size:** 300
**Issue Year:** 1994
**Issue Price:** $2250
**2003 Retail Price:** $2250

**Ref. No.:** 1787
**Name:** White Romantic Vase
**Height:** 9
**Status:** Limited edition, sold out
**Edition Size:** 300
**Issue Year:** 1994
**Issue Price:** $2590
**Last Retail Price:** $2598

**Ref. No.:** 1830
**Name:** Woodland Treasure
**Height:** 9
**Status:** Limited edition, sold out
**Edition Size:** 300
**Issue Year:** 1998
**Issue Price:** $690
**Last Year:** 2000
**Last Retail Price:** $825

**Ref. No.:** 1831
**Name:** The Poetry of Flowers
**Height:** 9
**Status:** Limited edition, sold out
**Edition Size:** 300
**Issue Year:** 1998
**Issue Price:** $830
**Last Year:** 2000
**Last Retail Price:** $950

**Ref. No.:** 6523
**Name:** Flying High
**Height:** 10
**Status:** Open issue, retired
**Issue Year:** 1998
**Issue Price:** $635
**Last Year:** 2000
**Last Retail Price:** $635

**Ref. No.:** 1541
**Name:** Orchid Arrangement
**Height:** 10.25
**Status:** Open edition, retired
**Issue Year:** 1988
**Issue Price:** $500
**Last Year:** 1990
**Last Retail Price:** $500
**Auction Price:** $1700

**Ref. No.:** 1827
**Name:** A Touch of Holland
**Height:** 11
**Status:** Limited edition, sold out
**Edition Size:** 300
**Issue Year:** 1998
**Issue Price:** $1650
**Last Year:** 2000
**Last Retail Price:** $1750

**Ref. No.:** 1829
**Name:** Flowers of The Sea
**Height:** 11
**Status:** Limited edition, sold out
**Edition Size:** 300
**Issue Year:** 1998
**Issue Price:** $895
**Last Year:** 2000
**Last Retail Price:** $1050

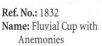

**Ref. No.:** 1832
**Name:** Fluvial Cup with Anemonies
**Height:** 11
**Status:** Limited edition, sold out
**Edition Size:** 150
**Issue Year:** 1998
**Issue Price:** $1850
**Last Year:** 2001
**Last Retail Price:** $1950

**Ref. No.:** 4717
**Name:** Bellflowers Bouquet
**Height:** 13.75
**Status:** Very rare
**Issue Year:** 1970
**Issue Price:** $10
**Last Year:** 1972
**Last Retail Price:** Unknown

**Ref. No.:** 1828
**Name:** Flowers of The Marsh
**Height:** 14
**Status:** Limited edition, sold out
**Edition Size:** 300
**Issue Year:** 1998
**Issue Price:** $1750
**Last Year:** 2000
**Last Retail Price:** $1850

**Ref. No.:** 1184
**Name:** Anemonas Bunch
**Height:** 15
**Status:** Limited edition, sold out
**Edition Size:** 200
**Issue Year:** 1971
**Issue Price:** $400
**Last Year:** 1978
**Last Retail Price:** $950

**Ref. No.:** 1185
**Name:** Floral
**Height:** 15
**Status:** Limited edition, sold out
**Edition Size:** 200
**Issue Year:** 1971
**Issue Price:** $475
**Last Year:** 1974
**Last Retail Price:** $325

**Ref. No.:** 1833
**Name:** Neoclassic Cup with Lilies
**Height:** 15
**Status:** Limited edition, active
**Edition Size:** 150
**Issue Year:** 1998
**Issue Price:** $2750
**2003 Retail Price:** $2850

## Eggs

**Ref. No.:** 1186
**Name:** Branch with Buds
**Height:** 15.75
**Status:** Limited edition, sold out
**Edition Size:** 200
**Issue Year:** 1971
**Issue Price:** $575
**Last Year:** 1976
**Last Retail Price:** $750

**Ref. No.:** 6083
**Name:** 1993 Limited Edition Egg
**Height:** 4
**Status:** Limited edition, sold out
**Issue Year:** 1993
**Issue Price:** $145
**Last Year:** 1993
**Last Retail Price:** $145
**High Auction Price:** $500
**Low Auction Price:** $250

**Ref. No.:** 7532
**Name:** 1994 Limited Edition Egg
**Height:** 4
**Status:** Limited edition, sold out
**Issue Year:** 1994
**Issue Price:** $150
**Last Year:** 1994
**Last Retail Price:** $150
**High Auction Price:** $275
**Low Auction Price:** $175

**Ref. No.:** 7548
**Name:** 1995 Limited Edition Egg
**Height:** 4
**Status:** Limited edition, sold out
**Issue Year:** 1995
**Issue Price:** $150
**Last Year:** 1995
**Last Retail Price:** $150

**Ref. No.:** 7550
**Name:** 1996 Limited Edition Egg
**Height:** 4
**Status:** Limited edition, sold out
**Issue Year:** 1996
**Issue Price:** $155
**Last Year:** 1996
**Last Retail Price:** $155

**Ref. No.:** 7552
**Name:** 1997 Limited Edition Egg
**Height:** 4
**Status:** Limited edition, sold out
**Issue Year:** 1997
**Issue Price:** $155
**Last Year:** 1997
**Last Retail Price:** $155

**Ref. No.:** 6292
**Name:** Spring Egg
**Height:** 5
**Status:** Open issue, retired
**Issue Year:** 1996
**Issue Price:** $365
**Last Year:** 2001
**Last Retail Price:** $365

**Ref. No.:** 6293
**Name:** Summer Egg
**Height:** 5
**Status:** Open issue, retired
**Issue Year:** 1997
**Issue Price:** $365
**Last Year:** 2001
**Last Retail Price:** $365

**Ref. No.:** 6294
**Name:** Autumn Egg
**Height:** 5
**Status:** Open issue, retired
**Issue Year:** 1998
**Issue Price:** $365
**Last Year:** 2001
**Last Retail Price:** $365

**Ref. No.:** 6590
**Name:** Garden Stroll—
  1998 Limited Edition Egg
**Height:** 5
**Status:** Open issue, retired
**Issue Year:** 1998
**Issue Price:** $150
**Last Year:** 1998
**Last Retail Price:** $150

**Ref. No.:** 6295
**Name:** Winter Egg
**Height:** 5.25
**Status:** Open issue, retired
**Issue Year:** 1999
**Issue Price:** $365
**Last Year:** 2001
**Last Retail Price:** $365

**Ref. No.:** 6698
**Name:** Parisian Afternoon –
  2000 Egg
**Height:** 5.25
**Status:** Open issue, sold out
**Issue Year:** 2000
**Last Year:** 2000
**Last Retail Price:** $150

**Portraits**

Ref. No.: 29.02
Name: Nobleman
Height: 3.75
Status: Very rare
Issue Year: 1949
Issue Price: Unknown
Last Year: Unknown
Last Retail Price: Unknown
Comment: Personally painted
   by José Lladró

Ref. No.: 26.02
Name: Portrait of an Artist
Height: 4
Status: Very rare
Issue Year: 1948
Issue Price: Unknown
Last Year: Unknown
Last Retail Price: Unknown
Comment: Personally painted
   by Juan Lladró

Ref. No.: 24.02
Name: Lover
Height: 4.25
Status: Very rare
Issue Year: 1948
Issue Price: Unknown
Last Year: Unknown
Last Retail Price: Unknown
Comment: Personally painted
   by Juan Lladró

Ref. No.: 23.02
Name: Jesus
Height: 5
Status: Very rare
Issue Year: 1949
Issue Price: Unknown
Last Year: Unknown
Last Retail Price: Unknown
Comment: Personally painted
   by Juan Lladró

Ref. No.: 19.02
Name: The Square Plate
Height: 7
Status: Very rare
Issue Year: 1946
Issue Price: Unknown
Last Year: Unknown
Last Retail Price: Unknown
Comment: Personally painted
   by Juan Lladró

Ref. No.: 20.02
Name: Flower Vase
Height: 7
Status: Very rare
Issue Year: 1947
Issue Price: Unknown
Last Year: Unknown
Last Retail Price: Unknown
Comment: Personally painted
   by José Lladró

**Ref. No.:** 22.02
**Name:** Lady's Portrait
**Height:** 7
**Status:** Very rare
**Issue Year:** 1947
**Issue Price:** Unknown
**Last Year:** Unknown
**Last Retail Price:** Unknown
**Comment:** Personally painted
by José Lladró

**Ref. No.:** 25.02
**Name:** Tenderness
**Height:** 7
**Status:** Very rare
**Issue Year:** 1946
**Issue Price:** Unknown
**Last Year:** Unknown
**Last Retail Price:** Unknown
**Comment:** Personally painted
by Juan Lladró

**Ref. No.:** 16.02
**Name:** The Umbrella
**Height:** 7.25
**Status:** Very rare
**Issue Year:** 1946
**Issue Price:** Unknown
**Last Year:** Unknown
**Last Retail Price:** Unknown
**Comment:** Personally painted
by Juan Lladró

**Ref. No.:** 17.02
**Name:** The Portrait
**Height:** 7.25
**Status:** Very rare
**Issue Year:** 1946
**Issue Price:** Unknown
**Last Year:** Unknown
**Last Retail Price:** Unknown
**Comment:** Personally painted
by Juan Lladró

**Ref. No.:** 28.02
**Name:** Old Man
**Height:** 7.25
**Status:** Very rare
**Issue Year:** 1949
**Issue Price:** Unknown
**Last Year:** Unknown
**Last Retail Price:** Unknown
**Comment:** Personally painted
by José Lladró

**Ref. No.:** 1.01
**Name:** Contemplation
**Height:** 8.25
**Status:** Very rare
**Issue Year:** 1944
**Issue Price:** Unknown
**Last Year:** Unknown
**Last Retail Price:** Unknown
**Comment:** Personally painted
by José Lladró

**Ref. No.:** 14.02
**Name:** Returning Home
**Height:** 9
**Status:** Very rare
**Issue Year:** 1945
**Issue Price:** Unknown
**Last Year:** Unknown
**Last Retail Price:** Unknown
**Comment:** Personally painted
by Juan Lladró

**Ref. No.:** 5.01
**Name:** Advice to Sancho
**Height:** 9.75
**Status:** Very rare
**Issue Year:** 1944
**Issue Price:** Unknown
**Last Year:** Unknown
**Last Retail Price:** Unknown
**Comment:** Personally painted
by Juan Lladró

**Ref. No.:** 3.01
**Name:** Fantasy
**Height:** 11
**Status:** Very rare
**Issue Year:** 1941
**Issue Price:** Unknown
**Last Year:** Unknown
**Last Retail Price:** Unknown
**Comment:** Personally painted
by Juan Lladró

## Masks

**Ref. No.:** 4.01
**Name:** Acrobats
**Height:** 11
**Status:** Very rare
**Issue Year:** 1944
**Issue Price:** Unknown
**Last Year:** Unknown
**Last Retail Price:** Unknown
**Comment:** Personally painted
by Juan Lladró

**Ref. No.:** 1642
**Name:** Bat Mask No. 8
**Height:** 4.25
**Status:** Open issue, retired
**Issue Year:** 1989
**Issue Price:** $690
**Last Year:** 1991
**Last Retail Price:** $810

**Ref. No.:** 1644
**Name:** Cat Eyes Mask No. 10
**Height:** 4.25
**Status:** Open issue, retired
**Issue Year:** 1989
**Issue Price:** $465
**Last Year:** 1991
**Last Retail Price:** $550

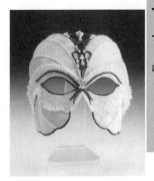

**Ref. No.:** 1645
**Name:** Snow Queen Mask No. 11
**Height:** 4.25
**Status:** Open issue, retired
**Issue Year:** 1989
**Issue Price:** $390
**Last Year:** 1991
**Last Retail Price:** $460
**Auction Price:** $450

**Ref. No.:** 1643
**Name:** Bird of Paradise Mask
No. 9
**Height:** 4.75
**Status:** Open issue, retired
**Issue Year:** 1989
**Issue Price:** $490
**Last Year:** 1991
**Last Retail Price:** $575

**Ref. No.:** 1637
**Name:** Princess Mask No. 3
**Height:** 5
**Status:** Open issue, retired
**Issue Year:** 1989
**Issue Price:** $400
**Last Year:** 1991
**Last Retail Price:** $470
**Auction Price:** $500

**Ref. No.:** 1638
**Name:** Celebration Mask No. 4
**Height:** 5
**Status:** Open issue, retired
**Issue Year:** 1989
**Issue Price:** $700
**Last Year:** 1991
**Last Retail Price:** $825

**Ref. No.:** 1639
**Name:** Magician's Mask No. 5
**Height:** 5
**Status:** Open issue, retired
**Issue Year:** 1989
**Issue Price:** $660
**Last Year:** 1991
**Last Retail Price:** $775

**Ref. No.:** 1641
**Name:** Kaleidoscope Mask No. 7
**Height:** 5
**Status:** Open issue, retired
**Issue Year:** 1989
**Issue Price:** $725
**Last Year:** 1991
**Last Retail Price:** $850

**Ref. No.:** 1636
**Name:** Flower Queen Mask No. 2
**Height:** 6
**Status:** Open issue, retired
**Issue Year:** 1989
**Issue Price:** $660
**Last Year:** 1991
**Last Retail Price:** $775

**Ref. No.:** 1640
**Name:** Fire Dancer Mask No. 6
**Height:** 6
**Status:** Open issue, retired
**Issue Year:** 1989
**Issue Price:** $530
**Last Year:** 1991
**Last Retail Price:** $625

**Ref. No.:** 1635
**Name:** Pansy Mask No. 1
**Height:** 7
**Status:** Open issue, retired
**Issue Year:** 1989
**Issue Price:** $975
**Last Year:** 1991
**Last Retail Price:** $1150

## Crosses

**Ref. No.:** 1651
**Name:** Roses Cross No. 3
**Height:** 2
**Status:** Open issue, retired
**Issue Year:** 1989
**Issue Price:** $200
**Last Year:** 1991
**Last Retail Price:** $220-270

**Ref. No.:** 1655
**Name:** Romantic Cross No. 7
**Height:** 2
**Status:** Open issue, retired
**Issue Year:** 1989
**Issue Price:** $115
**Last Year:** 1991
**Last Retail Price:** $135

**Ref. No.:** 1656
**Name:** Ornate Cross No. 8
**Height:** 2
**Status:** Open issue, retired
**Issue Year:** 1989
**Issue Price:** $125
**Last Year:** 1991
**Last Retail Price:** $150

**Ref. No.:** 1657
**Name:** Renaissance Cross No. 9
**Height:** 2
**Status:** Open issue, retired
**Issue Year:** 1989
**Issue Price:** $115
**Last Year:** 1991
**Last Retail Price:** $135

**Ref. No.:** 1658
**Name:** Simplicity Cross No. 10
**Height:** 2
**Status:** Open issue, retired
**Issue Year:** 1989
**Issue Price:** $155
**Last Year:** 1991
**Last Retail Price:** $170-195

**Ref. No.:** 1659
**Name:** Cross of Lilies No. 11
**Height:** 2
**Status:** Open issue, retired
**Issue Year:** 1989
**Issue Price:** $185
**Last Year:** 1991
**Last Retail Price:** $215

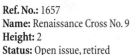

**Ref. No.:** 1660
**Name:** Cross of Diamonds No. 12
**Height:** 2
**Status:** Open issue, retired
**Issue Year:** 1989
**Issue Price:** $135
**Last Year:** 1991
**Last Retail Price:** $160

**Ref. No.:** 1646
**Name:** Violet Rosary
**Height:** 2.25
**Status:** Open issue, retired
**Issue Year:** 1989
**Issue Price:** $325
**Last Year:** 1991
**Last Retail Price:** $375

**Ref. No.:** 1647
**Name:** White Rosary
**Height:** 2.25
**Status:** Open issue, retired
**Issue Year:** 1989
**Issue Price:** $290
**Last Year:** 1991
**Last Retail Price:** $340

**Ref. No.:** 1648
**Name:** Gray Rosary
**Height:** 2.25
**Status:** Open issue, retired
**Issue Year:** 1989
**Issue Price:** $300
**Last Year:** 1991
**Last Retail Price:** $350

**Ref. No.:** 1654
**Name:** Cross of Hearts No. 6
**Height:** 2.25
**Status:** Open issue, retired
**Issue Year:** 1989
**Issue Price:** $220
**Last Year:** 1991
**Last Retail Price:** $260

**Ref. No.:** 1649
**Name:** Floral Cross No. 1
**Height:** 2.75
**Status:** Open issue, retired
**Issue Year:** 1989
**Issue Price:** $300
**Last Year:** 1991
**Last Retail Price:** $350

**Ref. No.:** 1650
**Name:** Floral Cross No. 2
**Height:** 2.75
**Status:** Open issue, retired
**Issue Year:** 1989
**Issue Price:** $230
**Last Year:** 1991
**Last Retail Price:** $270

**Ref. No.:** 1652
**Name:** Medieval Cross No. 4
**Height:** 2.75
**Status:** Open issue, retired
**Issue Year:** 1989
**Issue Price:** $250
**Last Year:** 1991
**Last Retail Price:** $295

**Ref. No.:** 1653
**Name:** Baroque Cross No. 5
**Height:** 2.75
**Status:** Open issue, retired
**Issue Year:** 1989
**Issue Price:** $215
**Last Year:** 1991
**Last Retail Price:** $250

## Other Functional

**Ref. No.:** 7500
**Name:** Lladró Thimble
**Height:** 1
**Status:** Limited edition, sold out
**Issue Year:** 1983
**Last Year:** 1983
**Last Retail Price:** Unknown
**Comment:** Exclusive to the
  Franklin Mint

**Ref. No.:** 1540
**Name:** Pink Ballet Slippers
**Height:** 3
**Status:** Open issue, retired
**Issue Year:** 1988
**Issue Price:** $275
**Last Year:** 1991
**Last Retail Price:** $375

**Ref. No.:** 1540.3
**Name:** White Ballet Slippers
**Height:** 3
**Status:** Open issue, retired
**Issue Year:** 1988
**Issue Price:** $275
**Last Year:** 1991
**Last Retail Price:** $375

**Ref. No.:** 5613
**Name:** Sealore Pipe
**Height:** 3
**Status:** Open issue, retired
**Issue Year:** 1989
**Issue Price:** $125
**Last Year:** 1993
**Last Retail Price:** $160
**High Auction Price:** $325
**Low Auction Price:** $225

**Ref. No.:** 7519
**Name:** Liquor 43 Brooch
**Height:** 3
**Status:** Open issue, active
**Issue Year:** 1993
**Issue Price:** Unknown
**2003 Retail Price:** Unknown
**Comment:** Exclusive to Diego
  Zamora, S.A. (Offered with
  Liquor 43 Bottle)

**Ref. No.:** 5967
**Name:** Discovery Mug - 1992
**Height:** 3.75
**Status:** Limited edition, sold out
**Issue Year:** 1992
**Issue Price:** $90
**Last Year:** 1992
**Last Retail Price:** $90
**Auction Price:** $150

**Ref. No.:** 6040
**Name:** Creamer
**Height:** 3.75
**Status:** Open issue, retired
**Issue Year:** 1994
**Issue Price:** $270
**Last Year:** 2000
**Last Retail Price:** $270

**Ref. No.:** 6041
**Name:** Sugar
**Height:** 5
**Status:** Open issue, retired
**Issue Year:** 1994
**Issue Price:** $335
**Last Year:** 2000
**Last Retail Price:** $335

**Ref. No.:** 6776
**Name:** Stepping Into Spring
**Height:** 5.25
**Status:** Open issue, retired
**Issue Year:** 2001
**Issue Price:** $295
**Last Year:** 2001
**Last Retail Price:** $295
**Comment:** 2001 Exclusive to
selected dealers

**Ref. No.:** 5243
**Name:** Happy Day Spanish
**Height:** 5.5
**Status:** Open issue, retired
**Issue Year:** 1984
**Issue Price:** $185
**Last Year:** 1986
**Last Retail Price:** $200
**Auction Price:** $325

**Ref. No.:** 5244
**Name:** Best Wishes
**Height:** 5.5
**Status:** Open issue, retired
**Issue Year:** 1984
**Issue Price:** $185
**Last Year:** 1986
**Last Retail Price:** $185
**High Auction Price:** $325
**Low Auction Price:** $250

**Ref. No.:** 5245
**Name:** A Thought for Today
**Height:** 5.5
**Status:** Open issue, retired
**Issue Year:** 1984
**Issue Price:** $180
**Last Year:** 1986
**Last Retail Price:** $180
**High Auction Price:** $325
**Low Auction Price:** $175

**Ref. No.:** 6678
**Name:** Dreidel With Dove
**Height:** 5.5
**Status:** Open issue, active
**Issue Year:** 2000
**Issue Price:** $95
**2003 Retail Price:** $100

**Ref. No.:** 6679
**Name:** Dreidel
**Height:** 5.5
**Status:** Open issue, active
**Issue Year:** 2000
**Issue Price:** $115
**2003 Retail Price:** $125

**Ref. No.:** 333.13
**Name:** Renaissance Boot
**Height:** 6.25
**Status:** Very rare
**Issue Year:** 1972
**Issue Price:** Unknown
**Last Year:** Unknown
**Last Retail Price:** Unknown
**Auction Price:** $750

**Ref. No.:** 332.13
**Name:** Boot
**Height:** 7
**Status:** Very rare
**Issue Year:** 1972
**Last Year:** Unknown
**Last Retail Price:** Unknown
**Auction Price:** $800

**Ref. No.:** 4725
**Name:** Toiletry Set
**Height:** 7
**Status:** Open issue, retired
**Issue Year:** 1970
**Issue Price:** $30
**Last Year:** 1972
**Last Retail Price:** $35

**Ref. No.:** 4833
**Name:** Chess Set and Board
**Height:** 7.75
**Status:** Open issue, retired
**Issue Year:** 1972
**Issue Price:** $410
**Last Year:** 1985
**Last Retail Price:** $1325
**Auction Price:** $2750

**Ref. No.:** 4833.3
**Name:** Chess Pieces Only
**Height:** 7.75
**Status:** Open issue, retired
**Issue Year:** 1972
**Issue Price:** $300
**Last Year:** 1985
**Last Retail Price:** $600
**High Auction Price:** $2500
**Low Auction Price:** $2200

**Ref. No.:** 6039
**Name:** Beverage Server
**Height:** 8
**Status:** Open issue, retired
**Issue Year:** 1994
**Issue Price:** $520
**Last Year:** 2000
**Last Retail Price:** $520

**Ref. No.:** 6554
**Name:** Treasures Of The Heart
**Height:** 8
**Status:** Open issue, retired
**Issue Year:** 1999
**Issue Price:** $215
**Last Year:** 2001
**Last Retail Price:** $215

**Ref. No.:** 6555
**Name:** Springtime Scent
**Height:** 8
**Status:** Open issue, retired
**Issue Year:** 1999
**Issue Price:** $255
**Last Year:** 2001
**Last Retail Price:** $255

**Ref. No.:** 5133
**Name:** Fifa Trophy
**Height:** 9
**Status:** Open issue, retired
**Issue Year:** 1982
**Issue Price:** $250
**Last Year:** 1983
**Last Retail Price:** $250
**High Auction Price:** $650
**Low Auction Price:** $500

**Ref. No.:** 7505
**Name:** Carlos I Liquor Bottle
**Height:** 9.25
**Status:** Open issue, active
**Issue Year:** 1993
**Issue Price:** Unknown
**2003 Retail Price:** Unknown
**Comment:** Exclusive to Pedro
   Domeq, S.A

**Ref. No.:** 7516
**Name:** Liquor 43 Bottle
**Height:** 9.50
**Status:** Limited Edition, active
**Edition Size:** 8000
**Issue Year:** 1993
**Issue Price:** Unknown
**2003 Retail Price:** Unknown
**Comment:** Exclusive to Diego
   Zamora, S.A.

**Ref. No.:** 6006
**Name:** Oriental Colonnade
**Height:** 19.25
**Status:** Open issue, retired
**Issue Year:** 1993
**Issue Price:** $1950
**Last Year:** 1995
**Last Retail Price:** $1875

**Ref. No.:** 6333
**Name:** Medieval Chess Set
**Height:** 20
**Status:** Open issue, active
**Issue Year:** 1996
**Issue Price:** $2120
**2003 Retail Price:** $2250
**Comment:** Board (Ref. No.
   8036) @ $145

# *Special Collections*

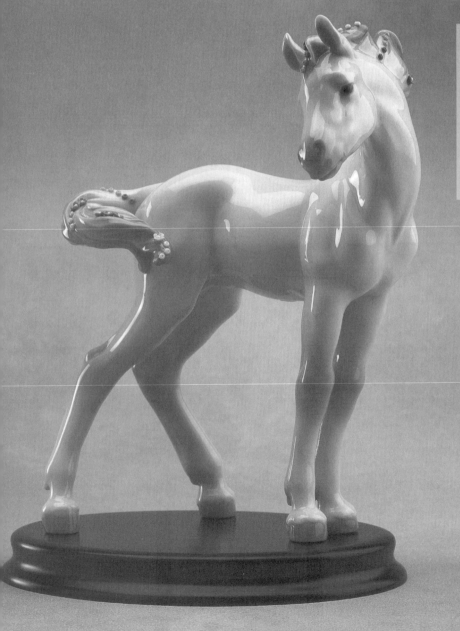

## Days of the Week

**Ref. No.:** 6012
**Name:** Monday's Child (Girl)
**Height:** 4.75
**Status:** Open issue, retired
**Issue Year:** 1993
**Issue Price:** $295
**Last Year:** 1997
**Last Retail Price:** $290

**Ref. No.:** 6011
**Name:** Monday's Child (Boy)
**Height:** 5.5
**Status:** Open issue, retired
**Issue Year:** 1993
**Issue Price:** $280
**Last Year:** 1997
**Last Retail Price:** $285

**Ref. No.:** 6020
**Name:** Friday's Child (Girl)
**Height:** 5.75
**Status:** Open issue, retired
**Issue Year:** 1993
**Issue Price:** $260
**Last Year:** 1997
**Last Retail Price:** $250

**Ref. No.:** 6024
**Name:** Sunday's Child (Girl)
**Height:** 6.25
**Status:** Open issue, retired
**Issue Year:** 1993
**Issue Price:** $260
**Last Year:** 1997
**Last Retail Price:** $250

**Ref. No.:** 6014
**Name:** Tuesday's Child (Girl)
**Height:** 6.5
**Status:** Open issue, retired
**Issue Year:** 1993
**Issue Price:** $280
**Last Year:** 1998
**Last Retail Price:** $285

**Ref. No.:** 6018
**Name:** Thursday's Child (Girl)
**Height:** 7.25
**Status:** Open issue, retired
**Issue Year:** 1993
**Issue Price:** $280
**Last Year:** 1997
**Last Retail Price:** $285

**Ref. No.:** 6013
**Name:** Tuesday's Child (Boy)
**Height:** 7.5
**Status:** Open issue, retired
**Issue Year:** 1993
**Issue Price:** $260
**Last Year:** 1997
**Last Retail Price:** $250

**Ref. No.:** 6017
**Name:** Thursday's Child (Boy)
**Height:** 7.5
**Status:** Open issue, retired
**Issue Year:** 1993
**Issue Price:** $260
**Last Year:** 1997
**Last Retail Price:** $250

**Ref. No.:** 6019
**Name:** Friday's Child (Boy)
**Height:** 7.5
**Status:** Open issue, retired
**Issue Year:** 1993
**Issue Price:** $260
**Last Year:** 1997
**Last Retail Price:** $250

**Ref. No.:** 6022
**Name:** Saturday's Child (Girl)
**Height:** 7.5
**Status:** Open issue, retired
**Issue Year:** 1993
**Issue Price:** $280
**Last Year:** 1997
**Last Retail Price:** $285

**Ref. No.:** 6015
**Name:** Wednesday's Child (Boy)
**Height:** 7.75
**Status:** Open issue, retired
**Issue Year:** 1993
**Issue Price:** $280
**Last Year:** 1997
**Last Retail Price:** $285

**Ref. No.:** 6016
**Name:** Wednesday's Child (Girl)
**Height:** 7.75
**Status:** Open issue, retired
**Issue Year:** 1993
**Issue Price:** $280
**Last Year:** 1997
**Last Retail Price:** $285

**Zodiac**

**Ref. No.:** 6021
**Name:** Saturday's Child (Boy)
**Height:** 8.25
**Status:** Open issue, retired
**Issue Year:** 1993
**Issue Price:** $245
**Last Year:** 1997
**Last Retail Price:** $285

**Ref. No.:** 6023
**Name:** Sunday's Child (Boy)
**Height:** 8.25
**Status:** Open issue, retired
**Issue Year:** 1993
**Issue Price:** $260
**Last Year:** 1997
**Last Retail Price:** $250

**Ref. No.:** 6221
**Name:** Aries
**Height:** 8.5
**Status:** Open edition, retired
**Issue Year:** 1995
**Issue Price:** $198
**Last Year:** 1997
**Last Retail Price:** $210

**Ref. No.:** 6222
**Name:** Capricorn
**Height:** 9
**Status:** Open issue, retired
**Issue Year:** 1995
**Issue Price:** $198
**Last Year:** 1997
**Last Retail Price:** $210

**Ref. No.:** 6217
**Name:** Sagittarius
**Height:** 9.25
**Status:** Open edition, retired
**Issue Year:** 1995
**Issue Price:** $198
**Last Year:** 1997
**Last Retail Price:** $210

**Ref. No.:** 6224
**Name:** Cancer
**Height:** 9.5
**Status:** Open issue, retired
**Issue Year:** 1995
**Issue Price:** $198
**Last Year:** 1997
**Last Retail Price:** $210

**Ref. No.:** 6219
**Name:** Gemini
**Height:** 9.75
**Status:** Open edition, retired
**Issue Year:** 1995
**Issue Price:** $198
**Last Year:** 1997
**Last Retail Price:** $210

**Ref. No.:** 6214
**Name:** Leo
**Height:** 10.25
**Status:** Open issue, retired
**Issue Year:** 1995
**Issue Price:** $198
**Last Year:** 1997
**Last Retail Price:** $210

**Ref. No.:** 6216
**Name:** Aquarius
**Height:** 10.5
**Status:** Open issue, retired
**Issue Year:** 1995
**Issue Price:** $198
**Last Year:** 1997
**Last Retail Price:** $210

**Ref. No.:** 6218
**Name:** Taurus
**Height:** 10.5
**Status:** Open issue, retired
**Issue Year:** 1995
**Issue Price:** $198
**Last Year:** 1997
**Last Retail Price:** $210

**Ref. No.:** 6223
**Name:** Pisces
**Height:** 10.75
**Status:** Open edition, retired
**Issue Year:** 1995
**Issue Price:** $198
**Last Year:** 1997
**Last Retail Price:** $210

**Ref. No.:** 6225
**Name:** Scorpio
**Height:** 11
**Status:** Open issue, retired
**Issue Year:** 1995
**Issue Price:** $198
**Last Year:** 1997
**Last Retail Price:** $210

**Four Seasons**

**Ref. No.:** 6215
**Name:** Virgo
**Height:** 11.75
**Status:** Open issue, retired
**Issue Year:** 1995
**Issue Price:** $198
**Last Year:** 1997
**Last Retail Price:** $210

**Ref. No.:** 6220
**Name:** Libra
**Height:** 12.25
**Status:** Open edition, retired
**Issue Year:** 1995
**Issue Price:** $198
**Last Year:** 1997
**Last Retail Price:** $210

**Ref. No.:** 7613
**Name:** Spring Bell
**Height:** 3
**Status:** Limited edition, sold out
**Issue Year:** 1991
**Issue Price:** $35
**Last Year:** 1991
**Last Retail Price:** $35

**Ref. No.:** 7614
**Name:** Summer Bell
**Height:** 3
**Status:** Limited edition, sold out
**Issue Year:** 1992
**Issue Price:** $35
**Last Year:** 1992
**Last Retail Price:** $35

**Ref. No.:** 7615
**Name:** Autumn Bell
**Height:** 3
**Status:** Limited edition, sold out
**Issue Year:** 1993
**Issue Price:** $35
**Last Year:** 1993
**Last Retail Price:** $35

**Ref. No.:** 7616
**Name:** Winter Bell
**Height:** 3
**Status:** Limited edition, sold out
**Issue Year:** 1994
**Issue Price:** $35
**Last Year:** 1994
**Last Retail Price:** $35

**Dinosaurs**

Ref. No.: 7543
Name: "Spike" dinosaur
Height: 3
Status: Open issue, retired
Issue Year: 1994
Issue Price: $95
Last Year: 1997
Last Retail Price: $105

Ref. No.: 7545
Name: "Rocky" dinosaur
Height: 3.75
Status: Open issue, retired
Issue Year: 1994
Issue Price: $110
Last Year: 1997
Last Retail Price: $120

Ref. No.: 7547
Name: "Rex" dinosaur
Height: 4.75
Status: Open issue, retired
Issue Year: 1994
Issue Price: $125
Last Year: 1997
Last Retail Price: $140

**Disney**

Ref. No.: 7544
Name: "Brutus" dinosaur
Height: 7.25
Status: Open issue, retired
Issue Year: 1994
Issue Price: $125
Last Year: 1997
Last Retail Price: $140

Ref. No.: 7546
Name: "Stretch" dinosaur
Height: 7.5
Status: Open issue, retired
Issue Year: 1994
Issue Price: $125
Last Year: 1997
Last Retail Price: $140

Ref. No.: 7534
Name: Dopey
Height: 5
Status: Open issue, retired
Issue Year: 1995
Issue Price: $175
Last Year: 1997
Last Retail Price: $175
Comment: Distributed
    exclusively through Disney

**Ref. No.:** 7539
**Name:** Sleepy
**Height:** 5.75
**Status:** Open issue, retired
**Issue Year:** 1994
**Issue Price:** $175
**Last Year:** 1997
**Last Retail Price:** $175
**Comment:** Distributed
exclusively through Disney

**Ref. No.:** 7535
**Name:** Sneezy
**Height:** 6
**Status:** Open issue, retired
**Issue Year:** 1994
**Issue Price:** $175
**Last Year:** 1997
**Last Retail Price:** $175
**Comment:** Distributed
exclusively through Disney

**Ref. No.:** 7536
**Name:** Bashful
**Height:** 6
**Status:** Open issue, retired
**Issue Year:** 1994
**Issue Price:** $175
**Last Year:** 1997
**Last Retail Price:** $175
**Comment:** Distributed
exclusively through Disney

**Ref. No.:** 7537
**Name:** Happy
**Height:** 6
**Status:** Open issue, retired
**Issue Year:** 1994
**Issue Price:** $195
**Last Year:** 1997
**Last Retail Price:** $195
**Comment:** Distributed
exclusively through Disney

**Ref. No.:** 7538
**Name:** Grumpy
**Height:** 6
**Status:** Open issue, retired
**Issue Year:** 1994
**Issue Price:** $175
**Last Year:** 1997
**Last Retail Price:** $175
**Comment:** Distributed
exclusively through Disney

**Ref. No.:** 7533
**Name:** Doc
**Height:** 6.25
**Status:** Open issue, retired
**Issue Year:** 1994
**Issue Price:** $195
**Last Year:** 1997
**Last Retail Price:** $195
**Comment:** Distributed
exclusively through Disney

**Ref. No.:** 7518
**Name:** Tinkerbell
**Height:** 7
**Status:** Limited edition, sold out
**Edition Size:**1500
**Issue Year:** 1992
**Issue Price:** $350
**Last Year:** 1992
**Last Retail Price:** $350
**High Auction Price:** $3800
**Low Auction Price:** $2600

**Ref. No.:** 7553
**Name:** Cinderella and Her
    Fairy Godmother
**Height:** 8
**Status:** Limited edition, sold out
**Edition Size:**2500
**Issue Year:** 1994
**Issue Price:** $875
**Last Year:** 1995
**Last Retail Price:** $875

**Ref. No.:** 7529
**Name:** Peter Pan
**Height:** 9
**Status:** Limited edition, sold out
**Edition Size:**2000
**Issue Year:** 1993
**Issue Price:** $400
**Last Year:** 1993
**Last Retail Price:** $400
**High Auction Price:** $3400
**Low Auction Price:** $1750

**Ref. No.:** 7555
**Name:** Snow White
**Height:** 9
**Status:** Open issue, retired
**Issue Year:** 1994
**Issue Price:** $295
**Last Year:** 1997
**Last Retail Price:** $295
**Comment:** Distributed
    exclusively through Disney

**Ref. No.:** 7558
**Name:** Snow White's Wishing
    Well
**Height:** 12
**Status:** Open issue, retired
**Issue Year:** 1995
**Issue Price:** $1500
**Last Year:** 1997
**Last Retail Price:** $1500
**Comment:** Distributed
    exclusively through Disney

**Ref. No.:** 7560
**Name:** Sleeping Beauty's Dance
**Height:** 12.50
**Status:** Limited edition, sold out
**Issue Year:** 1995
**Issue Price:** $1280
**Last Year:** 1995
**Last Retail Price:** $1280
**Auction Price:** $2500

**Norman Rockwell**

**Ref. No.:** 1406
**Name:** Love Letter
**Height:** 7.5
**Status:** Limited edition, sold out
**Edition Size:** 5000
**Issue Year:** 1982
**Issue Price:** $650
**Last Retail Price:** $650
**Auction Price:** $1000

**Ref. No.:** 1411
**Name:** Daydreamer
**Height:** 8
**Status:** Limited edition, sold out
**Edition Size:** 5000
**Issue Year:** 1982
**Issue Price:** $450
**Last Retail Price:** $475
**Auction Price:** $1400

**Ref. No.:** 1410
**Name:** Springtime of '27
**Height:** 8.75
**Status:** Limited edition, sold out
**Edition Size:** 5000
**Issue Year:** 1982
**Issue Price:** $450
**Last Retail Price:** $450
**Auction Price:** $2400

**Ref. No.:** 1405
**Name:** Court Jester
**Height:** 9.25
**Status:** Limited edition, sold out
**Edition Size:** 5000
**Issue Year:** 1982
**Issue Price:** $600
**Last Retail Price:** $650
**Auction Price:** $1700

**Ref. No.:** 1407
**Name:** Summer Stock
**Height:** 9.75
**Status:** Limited edition, sold out
**Edition Size:** 5000
**Issue Year:** 1982
**Issue Price:** $750
**Last Retail Price:** $750
**Auction Price:** $700

**Ref. No.:** 1408
**Name:** Practice Makes Perfect
**Height:** 10.5
**Status:** Limited edition, sold out
**Edition Size:** 5000
**Issue Year:** 1982
**Issue Price:** $725
**Last Retail Price:** $800
**Auction Price:** $800

## Inspiration Millenium Collection

**Ref. No.:** 1409
**Name:** Young Love
**Height:** 11.75
**Status:** Limited edition, sold out
**Edition Size:** 5000
**Issue Year:** 1982
**Issue Price:** $450
**Last Retail Price:** $450
**Auction Price:** $1000

**Ref. No.:** 6696
**Name:** Father Time
**Height:** 11
**Status:** Open issue, sold out
**Issue Year:** 1999
**Issue Price:** $420
**Last Year:** 2000
**Last Retail Price:** $420

**Ref. No.:** 6570
**Name:** New Horizons
**Height:** 15
**Status:** Open issue, sold out
**Issue Year:** 1999
**Issue Price:** $560
**Last Year:** 2000
**Last Retail Price:** $560

**Ref. No.:** 6569
**Name:** The Milky Way
**Height:** 16
**Status:** Open issue, sold out
**Issue Year:** 1998
**Issue Price:** $685
**Last Year:** 2000
**Last Retail Price:** $750

**Ref. No.:** 6571
**Name:** Rebirth
**Height:** 16.75
**Status:** Open issue, sold out
**Issue Year:** 2000
**Last Year:** 2000
**Last Retail Price:** $1270

**Ref. No.:** 1859
**Name:** Father Sun
**Height:** 18.75
**Status:** Limited edition, sold out
**Edition Size:** 500
**Issue Year:** 2000
**Last Year:** 2002
**Last Retail Price:** $1750

*Special Collections*

## Inspiration Gaudí Collection

**Ref. No.:** 1861
**Name:** Mother Earth
**Height:** 30
**Status:** Limited edition, active
**Edition Size:** 500
**Issue Year:** 2000
**Issue Price:** $975
**2003 Retail Price:** $5450
**Comment:** To be retired or sold
  out as of December 31, 2003

**Ref. No.:** 6660
**Name:** Gaudí Lady
**Height:** 18.5
**Status:** Limited edition, active
**Edition Size:** 1500
**Issue Year:** 2000
**Issue Price:** $2465
**2003 Retail Price:** $2500

**Ref. No.:** 6661
**Name:** Parque Guell
**Height:** 7.5
**Status:** Open issue, active
**Issue Year:** 2000
**Issue Price:** $690
**2003 Retail Price:** $690

**Ref. No.:** 6662
**Name:** Garden In Barcelona
**Height:** 4.75
**Status:** Open issue, active
**Issue Year:** 2000
**Issue Price:** $345
**2003 Retail Price:** $350

**Ref. No.:** 6663
**Name:** In Barcelona
**Height:** 4.75
**Status:** Open issue, active
**Issue Year:** 2000
**Issue Price:** $275
**2003 Retail Price:** $275

**Ref. No.:** 6664
**Name:** Modernism
**Height:** 5.25
**Status:** Open issue, active
**Issue Year:** 2000
**Issue Price:** $255
**2003 Retail Price:** $275

**Reflections Of Love Collection**

**Ref. No.:** 6600
**Name:** Bud Vase
**Height:** 6.5
**Status:** Open issue, retired
**Issue Year:** 2000
**Issue Price:** $125
**Last Year:** 2001
**Last Retail Price:** $125
**Comment:** Introduced by select dealers in 1999

**Ref. No.:** 6601
**Name:** Clock
**Height:** 5.25
**Status:** Open issue, retired
**Issue Year:** 2000
**Issue Price:** $190
**Last Year:** 2001
**Last Retail Price:** $190
**Comment:** Introduced by select dealers in 1999

**Ref. No.:** 6602
**Name:** Box
**Height:** 4
**Status:** Open issue, retired
**Issue Year:** 2000
**Issue Price:** $125
**Last Year:** 2001
**Last Retail Price:** $130
**Comment:** Introduced by select dealers in 1999

**Chinese Zodiac Collection**

**Ref. No.:** 6603
**Name:** Frame
**Height:** 10.75
**Status:** Open issue, retired
**Issue Year:** 2000
**Issue Price:** $290
**Last Year:** 2001
**Last Retail Price:** $300
**Comment:** Introduced by select dealers in 1999

**Ref. No.:** 6624
**Name:** Bouquet Of Love
**Height:** 2
**Status:** Open issue, retired
**Issue Year:** 2000
**Issue Price:** $145
**Last Year:** 2002
**Last Retail Price:** $160
**Comment:** Introduced by select dealers in 1999

**Ref. No.:** 6715
**Name:** The Dragon
**Height:** 5.5
**Status:** Active
**Issue Year:** 2000
**Issue Price:** $395
**2003 Retail Price:** $395
**Comment:** Chinese Zodiac Collection

**Mariposa Collection**

**Ref. No.:** 6780
**Name:** The Snake
**Height:** 7.5
**Status:** Open issue, active
**Issue Year:** 2001
**Issue Price:** $320
**2003 Retail Price:** $325
**Comment:** Chinese Zodiac
Collection

**Ref. No.:** 6827
**Name:** The Horse
**Height:** 9.25
**Status:** Open issue, active
**Issue Year:** 2002
**2003 Retail Price:** $395
**Comment:** Chinese Zodiac
Collection

**Ref. No.:** 7200
**Name:** Spring Frog (Mariposa
Collection)
**Height:** N/A
**Status:** Open issue, active
**Issue Year:** 2001
**Issue Price:** $165
**Comment:** Gump's by Mail
Exclusive

**Gift Boxes**

**Ref. No.:** 7202
**Name:** Spring Butterfly
(Mariposa Collection)
**Height:** N/A
**Status:** Open issue, active
**Issue Year:** 2001
**Issue Price:** $140
**Comment:** Gump's by Mail
Exclusive

**Ref. No.:** 7207
**Name:** Decorative Platter
(Mariposa Collection)
**Height:** N/A
**Status:** Open issue, active
**Issue Year:** 2001
**Issue Price:** $450
**Comment:** Gump's by Mail
Exclusive

**Ref. No.:** 7801
**Name:** Summer Pond
**Status:** Open issue, active
**Issue Year:** 2002
**Issue Price:** $310
**2003 Retail Price:** $310
**Comment:** Includes From
Nature's Palette (2.5 x 3.5)
& Nature's Observer
(2.75 x 2.75)

**Ref. No.:** 7802
**Name:** Sea Legend
**Status:** Open issue, active
**Issue Year:** 2002
**Issue Price:** $460
**2003 Retail Price:** $460
**Comment:** Includes Illusion
(7.5 x 5.25) & Pond Dreamer
(4.5 x 4.5)

**Ref. No.:** 7803
**Name:** Ancient Orient
**Status:** Open issue, active
**Issue Year:** 2002
**Issue Price:** $220
**2003 Retail Price:** $220
**Comment:** Includes Tall Chinese
(8 x 3.25) & Short Chinese
(6.75 x 4.5)

**Ref. No.:** 7800
**Name:** Heavenly Friends
**Status:** Open issue, active
**Issue Year:** 2002
**Issue Price:** $190
**2003 Retail Price:** $190
**Comment:** Includes Angel
Praying (5.25 x 3.25)
& Angel Thinking (4 x 4)

# Nudes & Sculptures

**Ref. No.:** 5981
**Name:** The Past (Black)
**Height:** 7
**Status:** Open edition, retired
**Issue Year:** 1993
**Issue Price:** $325
**Last Year:** 1995
**Last Retail Price:** $310

**Ref. No.:** 5982
**Name:** The Past (Sand)
**Height:** 7
**Status:** Open edition, retired
**Issue Year:** 1993
**Issue Price:** $325
**Last Year:** 1995
**Last Retail Price:** $310

**Ref. No.:** 5983
**Name:** Beauty (White)
**Height:** 7
**Status:** Open edition, retired
**Issue Year:** 1993
**Issue Price:** $325
**Last Year:** 1995
**Last Retail Price:** $310

**Ref. No.:** 5985
**Name:** Beauty (Sand)
**Height:** 7
**Status:** Open edition, retired
**Issue Year:** 1993
**Issue Price:** $325
**Last Year:** 1995
**Last Retail Price:** $310

**Ref. No.:** 5980
**Name:** The Past (White)
**Height:** 7.5
**Status:** Open edition, retired
**Issue Year:** 1993
**Issue Price:** $325
**Last Year:** 1995
**Last Retail Price:** $310

**Ref. No.:** 5984
**Name:** Beauty (Black)
**Height:** 7.5
**Status:** Open edition, retired
**Issue Year:** 1993
**Issue Price:** $325
**Last Year:** 1995
**Last Retail Price:** $310

**Ref. No.:** 5977
**Name:** Revelation (White)
**Height:** 8
**Status:** Open edition, retired
**Issue Year:** 1993
**Issue Price:** $325
**Last Year:** 1995
**Last Retail Price:** $310

**Ref. No.:** 5978
**Name:** Revelation (Black)
**Height:** 8
**Status:** Open edition, retired
**Issue Year:** 1993
**Issue Price:** $325
**Last Year:** 1995
**Last Retail Price:** $310

**Ref. No.:** 5979
**Name:** Revelation (Sand)
**Height:** 8
**Status:** Open edition, retired
**Issue Year:** 1993
**Issue Price:** $325
**Last Year:** 1995
**Last Retail Price:** $310

**Ref. No.:** 3025
**Name:** Resting Nude
**Height:** 8.5
**Status:** Limited edition, sold out
**Edition Size:** 200
**Issue Year:** 1991
**Issue Price:** $650
**Last Year:** 1992
**Last Retail Price:** $650
**High Auction Price:** $1000
**Low Auction Price:** $650

**Ref. No.:** 3549
**Name:** Reposing
**Height:** 9
**Status:** Limited edition, sold out
**Edition Size:** 300
**Issue Year:** 1983
**Issue Price:** $425
**Last Year:** 1984
**Last Retail Price:** $425

**Ref. No.:** 217.08
**Name:** Nude With Dolphin
**Height:** 9.5
**Status:** Very rare
**Issue Year:** 1958
**Issue Price:** Unknown
**Last Year:** Unknown
**Last Retail Price:** Unknown

*Nudes & Sculptures*

**Ref. No.:** 3547
**Name:** Reclining Nude
**Height:** 9.75
**Status:** Limited edition, sold out
**Edition Size:** 75
**Issue Year:** 1983
**Issue Price:** $650
**Last Year:** 1983
**Last Retail Price:** $650

**Ref. No.:** 3000
**Name:** Dawn
**Height:** 10.5
**Status:** Limited edition, sold out
**Edition Size:** 300
**Issue Year:** 1983
**Issue Price:** $325
**Last Year:** 1985
**Last Retail Price:** $525

**Ref. No.:** 3536
**Name:** Relaxation
**Height:** 10.5
**Status:** Limited edition, sold out
**Edition Size:** 100
**Issue Year:** 1983
**Issue Price:** $525
**Last Year:** 1983
**Last Retail Price:** $525

**Ref. No.:** 3022
**Name:** Daydreaming
**Height:** 11.75
**Status:** Limited edition, sold out
**Edition Size:** 500
**Issue Year:** 1990
**Issue Price:** $600
**Last Year:** 2001
**Last Retail Price:** $775

**Ref. No.:** 2091
**Name:** Woman with Baby
**Height:** 12
**Status:** Open issue, retired
**Issue Year:** 1978
**Issue Price:** $125
**Last Year:** 1981
**Last Retail Price:** $160

**Ref. No.:** 4512
**Name:** Nude
**Height:** 12
**Status:** Open edition, retired
**Issue Year:** 1969
**Issue Price:** $44
**Last Year:** 1985
**Last Retail Price:** $125
**High Auction Price:** $1200
**Low Auction Price:** $225

**Ref. No.:** 4512.3
**Name:** Torso in White
**Height:** 12
**Status:** Open edition, retired
**Issue Year:** 1983
**Issue Price:** $100
**Last Year:** 1985
**Last Retail Price:** $100
**High Auction Price:** $375
**Low Auction Price:** $175

**Ref. No.:** 3539
**Name:** Daintiness
**Height:** 12.25
**Status:** Limited edition, sold out
**Edition Size:** 100
**Issue Year:** 1983
**Issue Price:** $1000
**Last Year:** 1983
**Last Retail Price:** $1000

**Ref. No.:** 3533
**Name:** Observer
**Height:** 13.25
**Status:** Limited edition, sold out
**Edition Size:** 115
**Issue Year:** 1983
**Issue Price:** $900
**Last Year:** 1993
**Last Retail Price:** $1650

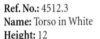

**Ref. No.:** 3534
**Name:** In The Distance
**Height:** 13.25
**Status:** Limited edition, sold out
**Edition Size:** 75
**Issue Year:** 1983
**Issue Price:** $525
**Last Year:** 1983
**Last Retail Price:** $525
**Auction Price:** $750

**Ref. No.:** 3528
**Name:** Wrestling
**Height:** 14.5
**Status:** Limited edition, sold out
**Edition Size:** 50
**Issue Year:** 1983
**Issue Price:** $950
**Last Year:** 1983
**Last Retail Price:** $950

**Ref. No.:** 3031
**Name:** Resting
**Height:** 14.5
**Status:** Limited edition, sold out
**Edition Size:** 300
**Issue Year:** 1995
**Issue Price:** $995
**Last Year:** 1998
**Last Retail Price:** $995

*Nudes & Sculptures*

**Ref. No.:** 3544
**Name:** Reflections
**Height:** 15
**Status:** Limited edition, sold out
**Edition Size:** 75
**Issue Year:** 1983
**Issue Price:** $650
**Last Year:** 1995
**Last Retail Price:** $1050
**Auction Price:** $500

**Ref. No.:** 3530
**Name:** Anxiety
**Height:** 15.5
**Status:** Limited edition, sold out
**Edition Size:** 125
**Issue Year:** 1983
**Issue Price:** $1075
**Last Year:** 1993
**Last Retail Price:** $1875

**Ref. No.:** 3020
**Name:** Demureness
**Height:** 15.5
**Status:** Limited edition, sold out
**Edition Size:** 300
**Issue Year:** 1989
**Issue Price:** $525
**Last Year:** 1993
**Last Retail Price:** $525

**Ref. No.:** 3030
**Name:** Nude Kneeling
**Height:** 15.75
**Status:** Limited edition, sold out
**Edition Size:** 300
**Issue Year:** 1995
**Issue Price:** $975
**Last Year:** 1998
**Last Retail Price:** $975

**Ref. No.:** 336.13
**Name:** Nude
**Height:** 16
**Status:** Very rare
**Issue Year:** 1972
**Issue Price:** Unknown
**Last Year:** Unknown
**Last Retail Price:** Unknown

**Ref. No.:** 2243
**Name:** Flight of Fancy
**Height:** 16.25
**Status:** Limited edition, sold out
**Edition Size:** 300
**Issue Year:** 1993
**Issue Price:** $1400
**Last Year:** 1994
**Last Retail Price:** $1400

**Ref. No.:** 3535
**Name:** Slave
**Height:** 16.25
**Status:** Limited edition, sold out
**Edition Size:** 50
**Issue Year:** 1983
**Issue Price:** $950
**Last Year:** 1983
**Last Retail Price:** $950

**Ref. No.:** 2181
**Name:** Bathing Nymph
**Height:** 16.5
**Status:** Open edition, retired
**Issue Year:** 1988
**Issue Price:** $560
**Last Year:** 2001
**Last Retail Price:** $815

**Ref. No.:** 2244
**Name:** The Awakening
**Height:** 17
**Status:** Limited edition, sold out
**Edition Size:** 300
**Issue Year:** 1993
**Issue Price:** $1200
**Last Year:** 2000
**Last Retail Price:** $1200

**Ref. No.:** 3532
**Name:** Plentitude
**Height:** 17.25
**Status:** Limited edition, sold out
**Edition Size:** 50
**Issue Year:** 1983
**Issue Price:** $1000
**Last Year:** 1983
**Last Retail Price:** $1000

**Ref. No.:** 3542
**Name:** Yoga
**Height:** 17.25
**Status:** Limited edition, sold out
**Edition Size:** 125
**Issue Year:** 1983
**Last Year:** 1983
**Issue Price:** $650
**Last Retail Price:** $650

**Ref. No.:** 2079
**Name:** Nude with Rose
**Height:** 18
**Status:** Open issue, retired
**Issue Year:** 1978
**Issue Price:** $210
**Last Year:** 1979
**Last Retail Price:** $210

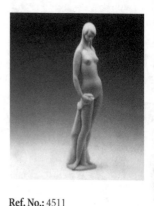

**Ref. No.:** 3503
**Name:** Nude with Dove
**Height:** 18
**Status:** Limited edition, sold out
**Edition Size:** 1500
**Issue Year:** 1978
**Issue Price:** $500
**Last Year:** 1981
**Last Retail Price:** $630

**Ref. No.:** 3579
**Name:** Sweet Enchantment
**Height:** 18
**Status:** Limited edition, sold out
**Edition Size:** 300
**Issue Year:** 1999
**Issue Price:** $890
**Last Year:** 2000
**Last Retail Price:** $890

**Ref. No.:** 4511
**Name:** Nude
**Height:** 18
**Status:** Open issue, retired
**Issue Year:** 1969
**Issue Price:** $115
**Last Year:** 1985
**Last Retail Price:** $180
**High Auction Price:** $1050
**Low Auction Price:** $700

**Ref. No.:** 4511.3
**Name:** Nude in White
**Height:** 18
**Status:** Open issue, retired
**Issue Year:** 1983
**Issue Price:** $150
**Last Year:** 1985
**Last Retail Price:** $150

**Ref. No.:** 2182
**Name:** Daydreamer
**Height:** 18.5
**Status:** Open edition, active
**Issue Year:** 1988
**Issue Price:** $560
**2003 Retail Price:** $795

**Ref. No.:** 3517
**Name:** Nude With Rose
**Height:** 18.5
**Status:** Open edition, active
**Issue Year:** 1978
**Issue Price:** $225
**2003 Retail Price:** $795

**Ref. No.:** 3517.3
**Name:** Nude with Rose
**Height:** 18.5
**Status:** Open issue, retired
**Issue Year:** 1978
**Issue Price:** $215
**Last Year:** 1985
**Last Retail Price:** $335

**Ref. No.:** 3550
**Name:** Boxer
**Height:** 19
**Status:** Limited edition, sold out
**Edition Size:** 300
**Issue Year:** 1983
**Issue Price:** $850
**Last Year:** 1993
**Last Retail Price:** $1450
**Auction Price:** $1250

**Ref. No.:** 3541
**Name:** Tranquility
**Height:** 19
**Status:** Limited edition, sold out
**Edition Size:** 75
**Issue Year:** 1983
**Issue Price:** $1000
**Last Year:** 1983
**Last Retail Price:** $1000

**Ref. No.:** 3014
**Name:** The Nymph
**Height:** 19.25
**Status:** Limited edition, sold out
**Edition Size:** 250
**Issue Year:** 1987
**Issue Price:** $1000
**Last Year:** 1995
**Last Retail Price:** $1450

**Ref. No.:** 3548
**Name:** Serenity
**Height:** 19.25
**Status:** Limited edition, sold out
**Edition Size:** 300
**Issue Year:** 1983
**Issue Price:** $925
**Last Year:** 1993
**Last Retail Price:** $1550

**Ref. No.:** 6249
**Name:** Delphica with Base
**Height:** 19.5
**Status:** Open issue, retired
**Issue Year:** 1996
**Issue Price:** $1200
**Last Year:** 2001
**Last Retail Price:** $1200

*Nudes & Sculptures*

**Ref. No.:** 3537
**Name:** Dreaming
**Height:** 19.75
**Status:** Limited edition, sold out
**Edition Size:** 250
**Issue Year:** 1983
**Issue Price:** $475
**Last Year:** 1983
**Last Retail Price:** $475

**Ref. No.:** 3559
**Name:** Peace Offering
**Height:** 19.75
**Status:** Open issue, active
**Issue Year:** 1985
**Issue Price:** $397.50
**2003 Retail Price:** $875

**Ref. No.:** 2180
**Name:** Dreams of Peace
**Height:** 20
**Status:** Open issue, retired
**Issue Year:** 1988
**Issue Price:** $880
**Last Year:** 2001
**Last Retail Price:** $1450

**Ref. No.:** 3028
**Name:** Modesty
**Height:** 20
**Status:** Limited edition, sold out
**Edition Size:** 300
**Issue Year:** 1994
**Issue Price:** $1295
**Last Year:** 2001
**Last Retail Price:** $1295

**Ref. No.:** 3013
**Name:** Youthful Innocence
**Height:** 20
**Status:** Limited edition, sold out
**Edition Size:** 500
**Issue Year:** 1987
**Issue Price:** $1300
**Last Year:** 1998
**Last Retail Price:** $2300

**Ref. No.:** 3529
**Name:** Companionship
**Height:** 20.5
**Status:** Limited edition, sold out
**Edition Size:** 65
**Issue Year:** 1983
**Issue Price:** $1000
**Last Year:** 1995
**Last Retail Price:** $2135

**Ref. No.:** 3527
**Name:** Togetherness
**Height:** 20.5
**Status:** Limited edition, sold out
**Edition Size:** 75
**Issue Year:** 1982
**Issue Price:** $375
**Last Year:** 1987
**Last Retail Price:** $1100
**Auction Price:** $900

**Ref. No.:** 3016
**Name:** Passion
**Height:** 20.5
**Status:** Limited edition, sold out
**Edition Size:** 750
**Issue Year:** 1988
**Issue Price:** $865
**Last Year:** 1997
**Last Retail Price:** $1250

**Ref. No.:** 3027
**Name:** Ebony
**Height:** 20.75
**Status:** Limited edition, sold out
**Edition Size:** 300
**Issue Year:** 1994
**Issue Price:** $1295
**Last Year:** 1998
**Last Retail Price:** $1295

**Ref. No.:** 3034
**Name:** Subtle Moonlight
**Height:** 20.75
**Status:** Limited edition, sold out
**Edition Size:** 500
**Issue Year:** 2002
**Issue Price:** $1550
**Last Year:** 2003
**Last Retail Price:** $1550

**Ref. No.:** 3002
**Name:** Waiting
**Height:** 21.5
**Status:** Limited edition, sold out
**Edition Size:** 125
**Issue Year:** 1983
**Issue Price:** $1550
**Last Year:** 1983
**Last Retail Price:** $1550

**Ref. No.:** 3546
**Name:** African Woman
**Height:** 22
**Status:** Limited edition, sold out
**Edition Size:** 50
**Issue Year:** 1983
**Issue Price:** $1300
**Last Year:** 1983
**Last Retail Price:** $1300

*Nudes & Sculptures*

**Ref. No.:** 3545
**Name:** Adoration
**Height:** 23.25
**Status:** Limited edition, sold out
**Edition Size:** 150
**Issue Year:** 1983
**Issue Price:** $1050
**Last Year:** 1983
**Last Retail Price:** $1050

**Ref. No.:** 3551
**Name:** Bather
**Height:** 23.25
**Status:** Limited edition, sold out
**Edition Size:** 300
**Issue Year:** 1983
**Issue Price:** $975
**Last Year:** 1983
**Last Retail Price:** $975

**Ref. No.:** 1461
**Name:** Youthful Beauty
**Height:** 23.5
**Status:** Limited edition, sold out
**Edition Size:** 5000
**Issue Year:** 1985
**Issue Price:** $750
**Last Year:** 2001
**Last Retail Price:** $1200

**Ref. No.:** 2128
**Name:** Venus
**Height:** 23.5
**Status:** Open issue, active
**Issue Year:** 1983
**Issue Price:** $650
**2003 Retail Price:** $1350

**Ref. No.:** 3012
**Name:** Classic Beauty
**Height:** 23.5
**Status:** Limited edition, sold out
**Edition Size:** 500
**Issue Year:** 1987
**Issue Price:** $1300
**Last Year:** 2001
**Last Retail Price:** $1900

**Ref. No.:** 3538
**Name:** Youth
**Height:** 23.5
**Status:** Limited edition, sold out
**Edition Size:** 250
**Issue Year:** 1983
**Issue Price:** $525.50
**Last Year:** 1983
**Last Retail Price:** $525
**High Auction Price:** $1200
**Low Auction Price:** $550

**Ref. No.:** 3017
**Name:** Muse
**Height:** 24.5
**Status:** Limited edition, sold out
**Edition Size:** 300
**Issue Year:** 1988
**Issue Price:** $650
**Last Year:** 1993
**Last Retail Price:** $875

**Ref. No.:** 3019
**Name:** True Affection
**Height:** 24.75
**Status:** Limited edition, sold out
**Edition Size:** 300
**Issue Year:** 1988
**Issue Price:** $750
**Last Year:** 1997
**Last Retail Price:** $1100

**Ref. No.:** 3531
**Name:** Victory
**Height:** 25.25
**Status:** Limited edition, sold out
**Edition Size:** 90
**Issue Year:** 1983
**Issue Price:** $1500
**Last Year:** 1983
**Last Retail Price:** $1500

**Ref. No.:** 3026
**Name:** Unadorned Beauty
**Height:** 25.5
**Status:** Limited edition, sold out
**Edition Size:** 200
**Issue Year:** 1991
**Issue Price:** $1700
**Last Year:** 1997
**Last Retail Price:** $1855

**Ref. No.:** 3029
**Name:** Danae
**Height:** 25.5
**Status:** Limited edition, sold out
**Edition Size:** 300
**Issue Year:** 1994
**Issue Price:** $2880
**Last Year:** 2001
**Last Retail Price:** $3900

**Ref. No.:** 3003
**Name:** Indolence
**Height:** 26
**Status:** Limited edition, sold out
**Edition Size:** 150
**Issue Year:** 1983
**Issue Price:** $1465
**Last Year:** 1983
**Last Retail Price:** $1465
**Auction Price:** $1000

*Nudes & Sculptures*

**Ref. No.:** 3005
**Name:** Venus in the Bath
**Height:** 28.25
**Status:** Limited edition, sold out
**Issue Year:** 1983
**Issue Price:** $1175
**Last Year:** 1983
**Last Retail Price:** $1800
**Auction Price:** $750

**Ref. No.:** 3558
**Name:** Innocence
**Height:** 28.25
**Status:** Open issue, retired
**Issue Year:** 1984
**Issue Price:** $960
**Last Year:** 1991
**Last Retail Price:** $1650
**Auction Price:** $800

**Ref. No.:** 3558.3
**Name:** Innocence
**Height:** 28.25
**Status:** Open issue, retired
**Issue Year:** 1984
**Issue Price:** $960
**Last Year:** 1987
**Last Retail Price:** $1075

**Ref. No.:** 3502
**Name:** Native
**Height:** 28.75
**Status:** Open edition, active
**Issue Year:** 1978
**Issue Price:** $700
**2003 Retail Price:** $2450

**Ref. No.:** 4948
**Name:** "Tawny" Nude
**Height:** 31
**Status:** Open edition, retired
**Issue Year:** 1976
**Issue Price:** $600
**Last Year:** 1979
**Last Retail Price:** $600

**Ref. No.:** 3540
**Name:** Pose
**Height:** 31.75
**Status:** Limited edition, sold out
**Edition Size:** 100
**Issue Year:** 1983
**Issue Price:** $1250
**Last Year:** 1983
**Last Retail Price:** $1250

**Ref. No.:** 3015
**Name:** Dignity
**Height:** 33
**Status:** Limited edition, sold out
**Edition Size:** 150
**Issue Year:** 1987
**Issue Price:** $1400
**Last Year:** 1997
**Last Retail Price:** $2185

**Ref. No.:** 3543
**Name:** Demure
**Height:** 33
**Status:** Limited edition, sold out
**Edition Size:** 100
**Issue Year:** 1983
**Issue Price:** $1250
**Last Year:** 1983
**Last Retail Price:** $1250

*Nudes & Sculptures*

**Ref. No.:** 2277
**Name:** Baby Jesus
**Height:** 2.25
**Status:** Open issue, active
**Issue Year:** 1994
**Issue Price:** $85
**2003 Retail Price:** $85

**Ref. No.:** 2281
**Name:** Ox
**Height:** 2.5
**Status:** Open issue, active
**Issue Year:** 1994
**Issue Price:** $185
**2003 Retail Price:** $185

**Ref. No.:** 2449
**Name:** Winged Dreams
**Height:** 2.75
**Status:** Open issue, active
**Issue Year:** 2002
**Issue Price:** $145
**2003 Retail Price:** $150

**Ref. No.:** 2168
**Name:** Julio
**Height:** 3.5
**Status:** Open issue, retired
**Issue Year:** 1987
**Issue Price:** $120
**Last Year:** 1993
**Last Retail Price:** $170
**Auction Price:** $225

**Ref. No.:** 2185
**Name:** Devoted Reader
**Height:** 3.5
**Status:** Open issue, retired
**Issue Year:** 1989
**Issue Price:** $125
**Last Year:** 1994
**Last Retail Price:** $160

**Ref. No.:** 2276
**Name:** Mary
**Height:** 3.5
**Status:** Open edition, active
**Issue Year:** 1994
**Issue Price:** $175
**2003 Retail Price:** $175

**Ref. No.:** 2318
**Name:** Taking Time
**Height:** 3.75
**Status:** Open issue, retired
**Issue Year:** 1995
**Issue Price:** $185
**Last Year:** 1998
**Last Retail Price:** $185

**Ref. No.:** 2282
**Name:** Donkey
**Height:** 4.75
**Status:** Open issue, active
**Issue Year:** 1994
**Issue Price:** $185
**2003 Retail Price:** $185

**Ref. No.:** 2451
**Name:** Winged Delight
**Height:** 4.75
**Status:** Open issue, active
**Issue Year:** 2002
**Issue Price:** $195
**2003 Retail Price:** $195

**Ref. No.:** 2048
**Name:** Gazelle Resting
**Height:** 5
**Status:** Open edition, retired
**Issue Year:** 1971
**Issue Price:** $65
**Last Year:** 1979
**Last Retail Price:** $165

**Ref. No.:** 2088
**Name:** Small Partridge
**Height:** 5
**Status:** Open edition, retired
**Issue Year:** 1978
**Issue Price:** $45
**Last Year:** 1981
**Last Retail Price:** $60
**Auction Price:** $225

**Ref. No.:** 2125
**Name:** Lost In Thought
**Height:** 5
**Status:** Open issue, retired
**Issue Year:** 1981
**Issue Price:** $105
**Last Year:** 1990
**Last Retail Price:** $270
**Auction Price:** $300

*Gres*

**Ref. No.:** 2273
**Name:** Bashful Bather
**Height:** 5
**Status:** Open issue, retired
**Issue Year:** 1994
**Issue Price:** $210
**Last Year:** 2001
**Last Retail Price:** $220

**Ref. No.:** 2321
**Name:** All Tuckered Out
**Height:** 5
**Status:** Open issue, retired
**Issue Year:** 1995
**Issue Price:** $275
**Last Year:** 2001
**Last Retail Price:** $275

**Ref. No.:** 2322
**Name:** Naptime
**Height:** 5
**Status:** Open issue, retired
**Issue Year:** 1995
**Issue Price:** $275
**Last Year:** 2001
**Last Retail Price:** $275

**Ref. No.:** 2383
**Name:** Pacific Jewel
**Height:** 5
**Status:** Open issue, active
**Issue Year:** 1998
**Issue Price:** $170
**2003 Retail Price:** $195

**Ref. No.:** 2292
**Name:** World of Fantasy
**Height:** 5.25
**Status:** Open issue, retired
**Issue Year:** 1994
**Issue Price:** $325
**Last Year:** 1997
**Last Retail Price:** $335

**Ref. No.:** 2450
**Name:** Winged Tenderness
**Height:** 5.25
**Status:** Active
**Issue Year:** 2002
**Issue Price:** $195
**2003 Retail Price:** $195

**Ref. No.:** 2166
**Name:** Paco
**Height:** 5.5
**Status:** Open issue, retired
**Issue Year:** 1987
**Issue Price:** $120
**Last Year:** 1993
**Last Retail Price:** $170

**Ref. No.:** 2269
**Name:** Eskimo Boy with Pet
**Height:** 5.5
**Status:** Open issue, retired
**Issue Year:** 1994
**Issue Price:** $130
**Last Year:** 2001
**Last Retail Price:** $145

**Ref. No.:** 2283
**Name:** Lost Lamb
**Height:** 5.5
**Status:** Open issue, active
**Issue Year:** 1994
**Issue Price:** $140
**2003 Retail Price:** $145

**Ref. No.:** 2317
**Name:** Talk To Me
**Height:** 5.5
**Status:** Open issue, retired
**Issue Year:** 1995
**Issue Price:** $185
**Last Year:** 1998
**Last Retail Price:** $185

**Ref. No.:** 2414
**Name:** Beauty
**Height:** 5.5
**Status:** Open issue, active
**Issue Year:** 2000
**Issue Price:** $250
**2003 Retail Price:** $275

**Ref. No.:** 2184
**Name:** Angel and Friend
**Height:** 5.75
**Status:** Open issue, retired
**Issue Year:** 1989
**Issue Price:** $150
**Last Year:** 1994
**Last Retail Price:** $185

*Gres*

**Ref. No.:** 2313
**Name:** Who's the Fairest?
**Height:** 5.75
**Status:** Open issue, retired
**Issue Year:** 1995
**Issue Price:** $230
**Last Year:** 1998
**Last Retail Price:** $230

**Ref. No.:** 2041
**Name:** Girl's Head
**Height:** 6
**Status:** Open issue, retired
**Issue Year:** 1971
**Issue Price:** $35
**Last Year:** 1975
**Last Retail Price:** $55

**Ref. No.:** 2147
**Name:** Alida
**Height:** 6
**Status:** Open issue, retired
**Issue Year:** 1984
**Issue Price:** $100
**Last Year:** 1994
**Last Retail Price:** $170

**Ref. No.:** 2161
**Name:** Fruit Vendor
**Height:** 6
**Status:** Open issue, retired
**Issue Year:** 1985
**Issue Price:** $120
**Last Year:** 1994
**Last Retail Price:** $230

**Ref. No.:** 2162
**Name:** Fish Vendor
**Height:** 6
**Status:** Open issue, retired
**Issue Year:** 1985
**Issue Price:** $110
**Last Year:** 1994
**Last Retail Price:** $205

**Ref. No.:** 2214
**Name:** Seaside Angel
**Height:** 6
**Status:** Open issue, active
**Issue Year:** 1991
**Issue Price:** $150
**2003 Retail Price:** $175

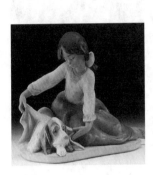

**Ref. No.:** 2287
**Name:** Dog's Best Friend
**Height:** 6
**Status:** Open issue, retired
**Issue Year:** 1994
**Issue Price:** $310
**Last Year:** 2000
**Last Retail Price:** $310

**Ref. No.:** 2319
**Name:** A Lesson Shared
**Height:** 6
**Status:** Open issue, retired
**Issue Year:** 1995
**Issue Price:** $215
**Last Year:** 1997
**Last Retail Price:** $2150

**Ref. No.:** 2413
**Name:** Grace
**Height:** 6
**Status:** Open issue, active
**Issue Year:** 2000
**Issue Price:** $250
**2003 Retail Price:** $275

**Ref. No.:** 2415
**Name:** Youth
**Height:** 6
**Status:** Open issue, active
**Issue Year:** 2000
**Issue Price:** $245
**2003 Retail Price:** $275
**Comment:** To be retired as of December 31, 2003

**Ref. No.:** 2001
**Name:** Cat
**Height:** 6.25
**Status:** Open issue, retired
**Issue Year:** 1970
**Issue Price:** $27.50
**Last Year:** 1975
**Last Retail Price:** $42.50

**Ref. No.:** 2020
**Name:** Little Eagle Owl
**Height:** 6.25
**Status:** Open issue, retired
**Issue Year:** 1971
**Issue Price:** $15
**Last Year:** 1985
**Last Retail Price:** $62
**High Auction Price:** $750
**Low Auction Price:** $425

Gres

**Ref. No.:** 2144
**Name:** Leticia
**Height:** 6.25
**Status:** Open issue, retired
**Issue Year:** 1984
**Issue Price:** $100
**Last Year:** 1995
**Last Retail Price:** $190

**Ref. No.:** 2145
**Name:** Gabriela
**Height:** 6.25
**Status:** Open issue, retired
**Issue Year:** 1984
**Issue Price:** $100
**Last Year:** 1994
**Last Retail Price:** $170
**Auction Price:** $250

**Ref. No.:** 2146
**Name:** Desiree
**Height:** 6.25
**Status:** Open issue, retired
**Issue Year:** 1984
**Issue Price:** $100
**Last Year:** 1995
**Last Retail Price:** $190

**Ref. No.:** 2157
**Name:** Eskimo Girl with
    Cold Feet
**Height:** 6.25
**Status:** Open issue, active
**Issue Year:** 1985
**Issue Price:** $140
**2003 Retail Price:** $300

**Ref. No.:** 2158
**Name:** Pensive Eskimo Girl
**Height:** 6.25
**Status:** Open issue, active
**Issue Year:** 1985
**Issue Price:** $100
**2003 Retail Price:** $225

**Ref. No.:** 2160
**Name:** Flower Vendor
**Height:** 6.25
**Status:** Open issue, retired
**Issue Year:** 1985
**Issue Price:** $110
**Last Year:** 1995
**Last Retail Price:** $215

**Ref. No.:** 2167
**Name:** Fernando
**Height:** 6.25
**Status:** Open issue, retired
**Issue Year:** 1987
**Issue Price:** $120
**Last Year:** 1993
**Last Retail Price:** $170
**Auction Price:** $200

**Ref. No.:** 2262
**Name:** Latest Addition
**Height:** 6.25
**Status:** Open issue, retired
**Issue Year:** 1989
**Issue Price:** Unknown
**Last Year:** 1998
**Last Retail Price:** $495

**Ref. No.:** 2057
**Name:** Short Chinese
**Height:** 6.5
**Status:** Open issue, active
**Issue Year:** 1974
**Issue Price:** $30
**2003 Retail Price:** $120

**Ref. No.:** 2159
**Name:** Pensive Eskimo Boy
**Height:** 6.5
**Status:** Open issue, active
**Issue Year:** 1985
**Issue Price:** $100
**2003 Retail Price:** $225

**Ref. No.:** 2165
**Name:** Chiquita
**Height:** 6.5
**Status:** Open issue, retired
**Issue Year:** 1987
**Issue Price:** $120
**Last Year:** 1993
**Last Retail Price:** $170

**Ref. No.:** 2183
**Name:** Wakeup Kitty
**Height:** 6.5
**Status:** Open issue, retired
**Issue Year:** 1989
**Issue Price:** $225
**Last Year:** 1993
**Last Retail Price:** $285

*Gres*

**Ref. No.:** 2270
**Name:** Eskimo Riders
**Height:** 6.5
**Status:** Open issue, retired
**Issue Year:** 1994
**Issue Price:** $275
**Last Year:** 2001
**Last Retail Price:** $280

**Ref. No.:** 2346
**Name:** Feeding the Ducks
**Height:** 6.5
**Status:** Open issue, retired
**Issue Year:** 1996
**Issue Price:** $305
**Last Year:** 1999
**Last Retail Price:** $305

**Ref. No.:** 2210
**Name:** Lazy Day
**Height:** 6.75
**Status:** Open issue, active
**Issue Year:** 1991
**Issue Price:** $240
**2003 Retail Price:** $275

**Ref. No.:** 2261
**Name:** Little Sister
**Height:** 6.75
**Status:** Open issue, retired
**Issue Year:** 1994
**Issue Price:** $265
**Last Year:** 2001
**Last Retail Price:** $280

**Ref. No.:** 2272
**Name:** My Best Friend
**Height:** 6.75
**Status:** Open issue, retired
**Issue Year:** 1994
**Issue Price:** $240
**Last Year:** 1998
**Last Retail Price:** $240

**Ref. No.:** 2274
**Name:** May Flowers
**Height:** 6.75
**Status:** Open issue, retired
**Issue Year:** 1994
**Issue Price:** $195
**Last Year:** 1998
**Last Retail Price:** $195

**Ref. No.:** 2036
**Name:** Decorative Hen
**Height:** 7
**Status:** Open issue, retired
**Issue Year:** 1971
**Issue Price:** $25
**Last Year:** 1973
**Last Retail Price:** $30

**Ref. No.:** 2042
**Name:** Girl's Head
**Height:** 7
**Status:** Open edition, retired
**Issue Year:** 1971
**Issue Price:** $32.50
**Last Year:** 1975
**Last Retail Price:** $55

**Ref. No.:** 2067
**Name:** Dogs Bust
**Height:** 7
**Status:** Open edition, retired
**Issue Year:** 1977
**Issue Price:** $280
**Last Year:** 1979
**Last Retail Price:** $325
**High Auction Price:** $950
**Low Auction Price:** $800

**Ref. No.:** 2140
**Name:** Pepita with Hat
**Height:** 7
**Status:** Open edition, active
**Issue Year:** 1984
**Issue Price:** $97.50
**2003 Retail Price:** $250

**Ref. No.:** 2152
**Name:** Chinese Girl
**Height:** 7
**Status:** Open issue, retired
**Issue Year:** 1985
**Issue Price:** $90
**Last Year:** 1990
**Last Retail Price:** $130

**Ref. No.:** 2205
**Name:** Prayerful Stitch
**Height:** 7
**Status:** Open issue, retired
**Issue Year:** 1990
**Issue Price:** $160
**Last Year:** 1994
**Last Retail Price:** $190
**Auction Price:** $225

*Gres*

**Ref. No.:** 2260
**Name:** Arctic Friends
**Height:** 7
**Status:** Open issue, retired
**Issue Year:** 1994
**Issue Price:** $380
**Last Year:** 1996
**Last Retail Price:** $380

**Ref. No.:** 2266
**Name:** Little Friskies
**Height:** 7
**Status:** Open issue, retired
**Issue Year:** 1994
**Issue Price:** $250
**Last Year:** 1997
**Last Retail Price:** $260

**Ref. No.:** 2195
**Name:** Heavenly Sounds
**Height:** 7.25
**Status:** Open issue, retired
**Issue Year:** 1990
**Issue Price:** $170
**Last Year:** 1993
**Last Retail Price:** $195

**Ref. No.:** 2238
**Name:** Learning Together
**Height:** 7.25
**Status:** Open issue, retired
**Issue Year:** 1993
**Issue Price:** $500
**Last Year:** 1997
**Last Retail Price:** $500

**Ref. No.:** 2331
**Name:** Little Peasant Girl, Blue
**Height:** 7.25
**Status:** Open issue, active
**Issue Year:** 1996
**Issue Price:** $155
**2003 Retail Price:** $175

**Ref. No.:** 2332
**Name:** Little Peasant Girl, Pink
**Height:** 7.25
**Status:** Open issue, active
**Issue Year:** 1996
**Issue Price:** $155
**2003 Retail Price:** $175

**Ref. No.:** 2035.3
**Name:** Virgin of Orange
(reduced)
**Height:** 7.5
**Status:** Open issue, retired
**Issue Year:** 1971
**Issue Price:** $115
**Last Year:** 1973
**Last Retail Price:** $145

**Ref. No.:** 2141
**Name:** Pedro with Jug
**Height:** 7.5
**Status:** Open issue, active
**Issue Year:** 1984
**Issue Price:** $100
**2003 Retail Price:** $250

**Ref. No.:** 2153
**Name:** Chinese Boy
**Height:** 7.5
**Status:** Open issue, retired
**Issue Year:** 1985
**Issue Price:** $90
**Last Year:** 1990
**Last Retail Price:** $130

**Ref. No.:** 2156
**Name:** Arctic Winter
**Height:** 7.5
**Status:** Open edition, active
**Issue Year:** 1985
**Issue Price:** $75
**2003 Retail Price:** $150

**Ref. No.:** 2194
**Name:** Heavenly Strings
**Height:** 7.5
**Status:** Open issue, retired
**Issue Year:** 1990
**Issue Price:** $170
**Last Year:** 1993
**Last Retail Price:** $195

**Ref. No.:** 2200
**Name:** A Big Hug
**Height:** 7.5
**Status:** Open issue, retired
**Issue Year:** 1990
**Issue Price:** $250
**Auction Price:** $300
**Last Year:** 1997
**Last Retail Price:** $310

*Gres*

**Ref. No.:** 2209
**Name:** Long Day
**Height:** 7.5
**Status:** Open issue, active
**Issue Year:** 1991
**Issue Price:** $295
**2003 Retail Price:** $350

**Ref. No.:** 2289
**Name:** Dressing the Baby
**Height:** 7.5
**Status:** Open issue, retired
**Issue Year:** 1994
**Issue Price:** $325
**Last Year:** 1997
**Last Retail Price:** $325

**Ref. No.:** 2306
**Name:** Hurry Now
**Height:** 7.5
**Status:** Open issue, retired
**Issue Year:** 1995
**Issue Price:** $310
**Last Year:** 2000
**Last Retail Price:** $310

**Ref. No.:** 2351
**Name:** Fishing with Gramps
**Height:** 7.5
**Status:** Open issue, retired
**Issue Year:** 1996
**Issue Price:** $1025
**Last Year:** 2001
**Last Retail Price:** $1025

**Ref. No.:** 2399
**Name:** Little Brave Resting
**Height:** 7.5
**Status:** Open issue, retired
**Issue Year:** 1999
**Issue Price:** $325
**Last Year:** 2001
**Last Retail Price:** $325

**Ref. No.:** 2441
**Name:** A Sweet Gesture
**Height:** 7.5
**Status:** Active
**Issue Year:** 2002
**Issue Price:** $475
**2003 Retail Price:** $475

**Ref. No.:** 2045
**Name:** Setter's Head
**Height:** 7.75
**Status:** Open edition, retired
**Issue Year:** 1971
**Issue Price:** $42.50
**Last Year:** 1981
**Last Retail Price:** $125
**High Auction Price:** $550
**Low Auction Price:** $425

**Ref. No.:** 2056
**Name:** Tall Chinese
**Height:** 7.75
**Status:** Open issue, active
**Issue Year:** 1974
**Issue Price:** $35
**2003 Retail Price:** $120

**Ref. No.:** 2191
**Name:** Forest Born
**Height:** 7.75
**Status:** Open edition, retired
**Issue Year:** 1990
**Issue Price:** $230
**Last Year:** 1991
**Last Retail Price:** $250
**High Auction Price:** $675
**Low Auction Price:** $350

Gres

**Ref. No.:** 2196
**Name:** Heavenly Solo
**Height:** 7.75
**Status:** Open issue, retired
**Issue Year:** 1990
**Issue Price:** $170
**Last Year:** 1993
**Last Retail Price:** $195

**Ref. No.:** 2226
**Name:** Boy's Best Friend
**Height:** 7.75
**Status:** Open issue, active
**Issue Year:** 1992
**Issue Price:** $390
**2003 Retail Price:** $425

**Ref. No.:** 2251
**Name:** Noella
**Height:** 7.75
**Status:** Open edition, active
**Issue Year:** 1993
**Issue Price:** $405
**2003 Retail Price:** $450

**Ref. No.:** 2259
**Name:** Little Fisherman
**Height:** 7.75
**Status:** Open issue, retired
**Issue Year:** 1994
**Issue Price:** $330
**Last Year:** 1999
**Last Retail Price:** $330

**Ref. No.:** 2305
**Name:** Fragrant Bouquet
**Height:** 7.75
**Status:** Open edition, retired
**Issue Year:** 1995
**Issue Price:** $330
**Last Year:** 2001
**Last Retail Price:** $330

**Ref. No.:** 2093
**Name:** Girl Waiting
**Height:** 8
**Status:** Open issue, retired
**Issue Year:** 1978
**Issue Price:** $90
**Last Year:** 1995
**Last Retail Price:** $185

**Ref. No.:** 2228
**Name:** Snowy Sunday
**Height:** 8
**Status:** Open issue, active
**Issue Year:** 1992
**Issue Price:** $550
**2003 Retail Price:** $625

**Ref. No.:** 2310
**Name:** Chit Chat
**Height:** 8
**Status:** Open issue, retired
**Issue Year:** 1995
**Issue Price:** $270
**Last Year:** 1998
**Last Retail Price:** $270

**Ref. No.:** 2382
**Name:** Island Beauty
**Height:** 8
**Status:** Open issue, active
**Issue Year:** 1998
**Issue Price:** $180
**2003 Retail Price:** $195

**Ref. No.:** 2076
**Name:** Lonely
**Height:** 8.25
**Status:** Open issue, retired
**Issue Year:** 1978
**Issue Price:** $72.50
**Last Year:** 1999
**Last Retail Price:** $185

**Ref. No.:** 2089
**Name:** Girl In Rocking Chair
**Height:** 8.25
**Status:** Open issue, retired
**Issue Year:** 1978
**Issue Price:** $235
**Last Year:** 1981
**Last Retail Price:** $275
**High Auction Price:** $400
**Low Auction Price:** $375

**Ref. No.:** 2094
**Name:** Tenderness
**Height:** 8.25
**Status:** Open issue, retired
**Issue Year:** 1978
**Issue Price:** $100
**Last Year:** 2000
**Last Retail Price:** $205

**Ref. No.:** 2155
**Name:** Dozing
**Height:** 8.25
**Status:** Open issue, retired
**Issue Year:** 1985
**Issue Price:** $110
**Last Year:** 1990
**Last Retail Price:** $150
**Auction Price:** $275

**Ref. No.:** 2169
**Name:** Repose
**Height:** 8.25
**Status:** Open issue, active
**Issue Year:** 1987
**Issue Price:** $135
**2003 Retail Price:** $225

**Ref. No.:** 2203
**Name:** Afternoon Chores
**Height:** 8.25
**Status:** Open issue, retired
**Issue Year:** 1990
**Issue Price:** $150
**Last Year:** 1994
**Last Retail Price:** $185
**Auction Price:** $250

*Gres*

**Ref. No.:** 2213
**Name:** Nature's Friend
**Height:** 8.25
**Status:** Open issue, retired
**Issue Year:** 1991
**Issue Price:** $390
**Last Year:** 1993
**Last Retail Price:** $420

**Ref. No.:** 2232
**Name:** Poor Little Bear
**Height:** 8.25
**Status:** Open issue, active
**Issue Year:** 1992
**Issue Price:** $250
**2003 Retail Price:** $275

**Ref. No.:** 2268
**Name:** Playful Kittens
**Height:** 8.25
**Status:** Open issue, retired
**Issue Year:** 1994
**Issue Price:** $285
**Last Year:** 1998
**Last Retail Price:** $300

**Ref. No.:** 2271
**Name:** The Wanderer
**Height:** 8.25
**Status:** Open issue, retired
**Issue Year:** 1994
**Issue Price:** $245
**Last Year:** 1998
**Last Retail Price:** $245

**Ref. No.:** 2307
**Name:** Happy Birthday
**Height:** 8.25
**Status:** Open edition, retired
**Issue Year:** 1994
**Issue Price:** Unknown
**Last Year:** 1997
**Last Retail Price:** $150

**Ref. No.:** 2308
**Name:** Let's Make Up
**Height:** 8.25
**Status:** Open issue, retired
**Issue Year:** 1994
**Issue Price:** Unknown
**Last Year:** 1998
**Last Retail Price:** $265

**Ref. No.:** 2311
**Name:** Good Night
**Height:** 8.25
**Status:** Open issue, retired
**Issue Year:** 1995
**Issue Price:** Unknown
**Last Year:** 1998
**Last Retail Price:** $280

**Ref. No.:** 2333
**Name:** Little Peasant Girl, White
**Height:** 8.25
**Status:** Open issue, active
**Issue Year:** 1996
**Issue Price:** $155
**2003 Retail Price:** $175

**Ref. No.:** 2347
**Name:** Meditation (Blue)
**Height:** 8.25
**Status:** Open edition, retired
**Issue Year:** 1996
**Issue Price:** $145
**Last Year:** 1999
**Last Retail Price:** $145

**Ref. No.:** 2066
**Name:** Monkey Love
**Height:** 8.5
**Status:** Open edition, retired
**Issue Year:** 1977
**Issue Price:** $160
**Last Year:** 1979
**Last Retail Price:** $175
**Auction Price:** $700

**Ref. No.:** 2164
**Name:** My Lost Lamb
**Height:** 8.5
**Status:** Open issue, retired
**Issue Year:** 1987
**Issue Price:** $120
**Last Year:** 1999
**Last Retail Price:** $175

**Ref. No.:** 2186
**Name:** The Greatest Love
**Height:** 8.5
**Status:** Open issue, retired
**Issue Year:** 1989
**Issue Price:** $235
**Last Year:** 1997
**Last Retail Price:** $320

**Ref. No.:** 2197
**Name:** Heavenly Song
**Height:** 8.5
**Status:** Open issue, retired
**Issue Year:** 1990
**Issue Price:** $170
**Last Year:** 1993
**Last Retail Price:** $185

**Ref. No.:** 2201
**Name:** Our Daily Bread
**Height:** 8.5
**Status:** Open issue, retired
**Issue Year:** 1990
**Issue Price:** $150
**Last Year:** 1994
**Last Retail Price:** $185
**Auction Price:** $300

**Ref. No.:** 2223
**Name:** New Lamb
**Height:** 8.5
**Status:** Open issue, retired
**Issue Year:** 1992
**Issue Price:** $365
**Last Year:** 1999
**Last Retail Price:** $385

**Ref. No.:** 2254
**Name:** Step Aside
**Height:** 8.5
**Status:** Open issue, active
**Issue Year:** 1993
**Issue Price:** $280
**2003 Retail Price:** $295

**Ref. No.:** 2264
**Name:** Madonna Head
**Height:** 8.5
**Status:** Open issue, retired
**Issue Year:** 1994
**Issue Price:** $210
**Last Year:** 2000
**Last Retail Price:** $220

**Ref. No.:** 2284
**Name:** Shepherd Boy
**Height:** 8.5
**Status:** Open issue, active
**Issue Year:** 1994
**Issue Price:** $260
**2003 Retail Price:** $295

**Ref. No.:** 2303
**Name:** Not So Fast
**Height:** 8.5
**Status:** Open issue, retired
**Issue Year:** 1995
**Issue Price:** $350
**Last Year:** 1997
**Last Retail Price:** $350

**Ref. No.:** 2320
**Name:** Cat Nap
**Height:** 8.5
**Status:** Open issue, retired
**Issue Year:** 1995
**Issue Price:** $265
**Last Year:** 1999
**Last Retail Price:** $265

**Ref. No.:** 2344
**Name:** Oration
**Height:** 8.5
**Status:** Open issue, active
**Issue Year:** 1996
**Issue Price:** $295
**2003 Retail Price:** $295

**Ref. No.:** 2419
**Name:** Keep Me Warm
**Height:** 8.5
**Status:** Open issue, active
**Issue Year:** 2001
**Issue Price:** $175
**2003 Retail Price:** $195

**Ref. No.:** 2420
**Name:** Hug Me Tight
**Height:** 8.5
**Status:** Open issue, active
**Issue Year:** 2001
**Issue Price:** $175
**2003 Retail Price:** $195

**Ref. No.:** 2421
**Name:** Snuggle Bunny
**Height:** 8.5
**Status:** Open issue, active
**Issue Year:** 2001
**Issue Price:** $175
**2003 Retail Price:** $195

*Gres*

**Ref. No.:** 2178
**Name:** Harvest Helpers
**Height:** 8.75
**Status:** Open issue, active
**Issue Year:** 1988
**Issue Price:** $190
**2003 Retail Price:** $295

**Ref. No.:** 2204
**Name:** Farmyard Grace
**Height:** 8.75
**Status:** Open issue, retired
**Issue Year:** 1990
**Issue Price:** $180
**Last Year:** 1993
**Last Retail Price:** $210
**Auction Price:** $325

**Ref. No.:** 2215
**Name:** Friends in Flight
**Height:** 8.75
**Status:** Open issue, active
**Issue Year:** 1991
**Issue Price:** $165
**2003 Retail Price:** $195

**Ref. No.:** 2216
**Name:** Laundry Day
**Height:** 8.75
**Status:** Open issue, active
**Issue Year:** 1991
**Issue Price:** $350
**2003 Retail Price:** $400

**Ref. No.:** 2225
**Name:** Friendly Sparrow
**Height:** 8.75
**Status:** Open issue, retired
**Issue Year:** 1992
**Issue Price:** $295
**Last Year:** 2002
**Last Retail Price:** $325

**Ref. No.:** 2275
**Name:** Saint Joseph
**Height:** 8.75
**Status:** Open issue, active
**Issue Year:** 1994
**Issue Price:** $270
**2003 Retail Price:** $275

**Ref. No.:** 2288
**Name:** Carefree
**Height:** 8.75
**Status:** Open issue, retired
**Issue Year:** 1994
**Issue Price:** $325
**Last Year:** 1998
**Last Retail Price:** $325

**Ref. No.:** 2327
**Name:** Sad Sax
**Height:** 8.75
**Status:** Open issue, retired
**Issue Year:** 1995
**Issue Price:** $225
**Last Year:** 2001
**Last Retail Price:** $225

**Ref. No.:** 2328
**Name:** Circus Sam
**Height:** 8.75
**Status:** Open issue, retired
**Issue Year:** 1995
**Issue Price:** $225
**Last Year:** 2001
**Last Retail Price:** $225

**Ref. No.:** 3513
**Name:** A Wintry Day
**Height:** 8.75
**Status:** Open issue, retired
**Issue Year:** 1978
**Issue Price:** $525
**Last Year:** 1988
**Last Retail Price:** $575
**High Auction Price:** $1000
**Low Auction Price:** $700

**Ref. No.:** 2087
**Name:** Big Partridge
**Height:** 9
**Status:** Open edition, retired
**Issue Year:** 1978
**Issue Price:** $85
**Last Year:** 1981
**Last Retail Price:** $110

**Ref. No.:** 2097
**Name:** Eskimo Playing
**Height:** 9
**Status:** Open issue, active
**Issue Year:** 1978
**Issue Price:** $225
**2003 Retail Price:** $475

*Gres*

**Ref. No.:** 2202
**Name:** A Helping Hand
**Height:** 9
**Status:** Open issue, retired
**Issue Year:** 1990
**Issue Price:** $150
**Last Year:** 1993
**Last Retail Price:** $185

**Ref. No.:** 2206
**Name:** Sisterly Love
**Height:** 9
**Status:** Open issue, retired
**Issue Year:** 1990
**Issue Price:** $300
**Last Year:** 2002
**Last Retail Price:** $375

**Ref. No.:** 2207
**Name:** What a Day
**Height:** 9
**Status:** Open issue, retired
**Issue Year:** 1990
**Issue Price:** $550
**Last Year:** 2002
**Last Retail Price:** $640

**Ref. No.:** 2278
**Name:** King Melchior
**Height:** 9
**Status:** Open issue, active
**Issue Year:** 1994
**Issue Price:** $290
**2003 Retail Price:** $295

**Ref. No.:** 2352
**Name:** Under My Spell
**Height:** 9
**Status:** Open issue, retired
**Issue Year:** 1996
**Issue Price:** $225
**Last Year:** 1998
**Last Retail Price:** $225

**Ref. No.:** 2361
**Name:** Cold Weather
Companions
**Height:** 9
**Status:** Open issue, active
**Issue Year:** 1997
**Issue Price:** $380
**2003 Retail Price:** $395

**Ref. No.:** 4946
**Name:** Senorita
**Height:** 9
**Status:** Open edition, retired
**Issue Year:** 1976
**Issue Price:** $130
**Last Year:** 1985
**Last Retail Price:** $172
**Auction Price:** $400

**Ref. No.:** 2095
**Name:** Duck Pulling Pigtail
**Height:** 9.25
**Status:** Open issue, retired
**Issue Year:** 1978
**Issue Price:** $110
**Last Year:** 1997
**Last Retail Price:** $275

**Ref. No.:** 2253
**Name:** Noisy Friend
**Height:** 9.25
**Status:** Open issue, retired
**Issue Year:** 1993
**Issue Price:** $280
**Last Year:** 1998
**Last Retail Price:** $280

**Ref. No.:** 2431
**Name:** A Simple Gift
**Height:** 9.25
**Status:** Open issue, active
**Issue Year:** 2001
**Issue Price:** $250
**2003 Retail Price:** $275

**Ref. No.:** 2077
**Name:** The Rain in Spain
**Height:** 9.5
**Status:** Open issue, retired
**Issue Year:** 1978
**Issue Price:** $195
**Last Year:** 1990
**Last Retail Price:** $330
**High Auction Price:** $550
**Low Auction Price:** $475

**Ref. No.:** 2098
**Name:** Girls Collecting Wheat
**Height:** 9.5
**Status:** Open issue, retired
**Issue Year:** 1978
**Issue Price:** $250
**Last Year:** 1981
**Last Retail Price:** $247.5
**High Auction Price:** $650
**Low Auction Price:** $500

*Gres*

**Ref. No.:** 2163
**Name:** Mountain Shepherd
**Height:** 9.5
**Status:** Open issue, retired
**Issue Year:** 1987
**Issue Price:** $135
**Last Year:** 1999
**Last Retail Price:** $235

**Ref. No.:** 2170
**Name:** Spanish Dancer
**Height:** 9.5
**Status:** Open issue, active
**Issue Year:** 1987
**Issue Price:** $225
**2003 Retail Price:** $425

**Ref. No.:** 2171
**Name:** Island Girl
**Height:** 9.5
**Status:** Open issue, retired
**Issue Year:** 1987
**Issue Price:** $150
**Last Year:** 1990
**Last Retail Price:** $170
**Auction Price:** $375

**Ref. No.:** 2175
**Name:** Andean Country Girl
**Height:** 9.5
**Status:** Open issue, retired
**Issue Year:** 1987
**Issue Price:** $230
**Last Year:** 1990
**Last Retail Price:** $250
**Auction Price:** $325

**Ref. No.:** 2279
**Name:** King Gaspar
**Height:** 9.5
**Status:** Open issue, active
**Issue Year:** 1994
**Issue Price:** $290
**2003 Retail Price:** $295

**Ref. No.:** 2286
**Name:** Barnyard Scene
**Height:** 9.5
**Status:** Open issue, retired
**Issue Year:** 1994
**Issue Price:** $260
**Last Year:** 1997
**Last Retail Price:** $270

**Ref. No.:** 2298
**Name:** Hindu Children
**Height:** 9.5
**Status:** Open issue, retired
**Issue Year:** 1995
**Issue Price:** $450
**Last Year:** 2000
**Last Retail Price:** $450

**Ref. No.:** 2334
**Name:** Asian Melody
**Height:** 9.5
**Status:** Open issue, retired
**Issue Year:** 1996
**Issue Price:** $690
**Last Year:** 1998
**Last Retail Price:** $690

**Ref. No.:** 2397
**Name:** Little Chief
**Height:** 9.5
**Status:** Open issue, retired
**Issue Year:** 1999
**Issue Price:** $325
**Last Year:** 2001
**Last Retail Price:** $325

**Ref. No.:** 2432
**Name:** A Farmyard Friend
**Height:** 9.5
**Status:** Open issue, active
**Issue Year:** 2001
**Issue Price:** $200
**2003 Retail Price:** $225
**Comment:** To be retired as of
December 31, 2003

**Ref. No.:** 2096
**Name:** Nosey Puppy
**Height:** 9.75
**Status:** Open issue, retired
**Issue Year:** 1978
**Issue Price:** $190
**Last Year:** 1993
**Last Retail Price:** $410
**Auction Price:** $400

**Ref. No.:** 2113
**Name:** My Little Duckling
**Height:** 9.75
**Status:** Open issue, retired
**Issue Year:** 1980
**Issue Price:** $240
**Last Year:** 1993
**Last Retail Price:** $295

*Gres*

**Ref. No.:** 2124
**Name:** Donkey with Saddle Pack
**Height:** 9.75
**Status:** Open issue, retired
**Issue Year:** 1980
**Issue Price:** $325
**Last Year:** 1983
**Last Retail Price:** $355
**Auction Price:** $850

**Ref. No.:** 2179
**Name:** Sharing the Harvest
**Height:** 9.75
**Status:** Open issue, retired
**Issue Year:** 1988
**Issue Price:** $190
**Last Year:** 2001
**Last Retail Price:** $280

**Ref. No.:** 2237
**Name:** The Old Fishing Hole
**Height:** 9.75
**Status:** Open issue, active
**Issue Year:** 1993
**Issue Price:** $625
**2003 Retail Price:** $640

**Ref. No.:** 2290
**Name:** Surprise
**Height:** 9.75
**Status:** Open issue, retired
**Issue Year:** 1994
**Issue Price:** $335
**Last Year:** 2000
**Last Retail Price:** $335

**Ref. No.:** 2304
**Name:** Love In Bloom
**Height:** 9.75
**Status:** Open issue, retired
**Issue Year:** 1995
**Issue Price:** $420
**Last Year:** 2002
**Last Retail Price:** $420

**Ref. No.:** 2312
**Name:** Goose Trying To Eat
**Height:** 9.75
**Status:** Open issue, retired
**Issue Year:** 1995
**Issue Price:** $325
**Last Year:** 1997
**Last Retail Price:** $325

**Ref. No.:** 2316
**Name:** Closing Scene
**Height:** 9.75
**Status:** Open issue, retired
**Issue Year:** 1995
**Issue Price:** $560
**Last Year:** 1998
**Last Retail Price:** $560

**Ref. No.:** 1106
**Name:** Byzantine Head
**Height:** 10
**Status:** Very Rare
**Issue Year:** 1971
**Issue Price:** $105
**Last Year:** 1975
**Last Retail Price:** Unknown

**Ref. No.:** 2222
**Name:** Tender Moment
**Height:** 10
**Status:** Open issue, retired
**Issue Year:** 1992
**Issue Price:** $400
**Last Year:** 1999
**Last Retail Price:** $450

**Ref. No.:** 2349
**Name:** Sleigh Ride
**Height:** 10
**Status:** Open issue, retired
**Issue Year:** 1996
**Issue Price:** $1520
**Last Year:** 1998
**Last Retail Price:** $1520

**Ref. No.:** 2350
**Name:** Pensive Clown
**Height:** 10
**Status:** Open issue, retired
**Issue Year:** 1996
**Issue Price:** $680
**Last Year:** 1999
**Last Retail Price:** $680

**Ref. No.:** 2385
**Name:** Tropical Flower
**Height:** 10
**Status:** Open issue, active
**Issue Year:** 1998
**Issue Price:** $190
**2003 Retail Price:** $195

Gres

**Ref. No.:** 2392
**Name:** My Memories
**Height:** 10
**Status:** Open issue, retired
**Issue Year:** 1998
**Issue Price:** $345
**Last Year:** 2002
**Last Retail Price:** $400

**Ref. No.:** 2007
**Name:** Eskimo Boy
**Height:** 10.25
**Status:** Open issue, retired
**Issue Year:** 1970
**Issue Price:** $30
**Last Year:** 1990
**Last Retail Price:** $145
**High Auction Price:** $275
**Low Auction Price:** $200

**Ref. No.:** 2007.3
**Name:** Eskimo Boy
**Height:** 10.25
**Status:** Open issue, retired
**Issue Year:** 1970
**Issue Price:** $27.50
**Last Year:** 1990
**Last Retail Price:** $240
**Auction Price:** $175

**Ref. No.:** 2019
**Name:** Owl
**Height:** 10.25
**Status:** Open edition, retired
**Issue Year:** 1971
**Issue Price:** $27.50
**Last Year:** 1973
**Last Retail Price:** $35

**Ref. No.:** 2172
**Name:** Island Beauty
**Height:** 10.25
**Status:** Open issue, retired
**Issue Year:** 1987
**Issue Price:** $150
**Last Year:** 1990
**Last Retail Price:** $170

**Ref. No.:** 2173
**Name:** Ahoy There
**Height:** 10.25
**Status:** Open issue, active
**Issue Year:** 1987
**Issue Price:** $225
**2003 Retail Price:** $350

**Ref. No.:** 2118
**Name:** Schoolmates
**Height:** 10.5
**Status:** Open issue, retired
**Issue Year:** 1980
**Issue Price:** $525
**Last Year:** 1981
**Last Retail Price:** $525
**High Auction Price:** $650
**Low Auction Price:** $500

**Ref. No.:** 2154
**Name:** Hawaiian Flower Vendor
**Height:** 10.5
**Status:** Open issue, retired
**Issue Year:** 1985
**Issue Price:** $245
**Last Year:** 2000
**Last Retail Price:** $510

**Ref. No.:** 2192
**Name:** King of the Forest
**Height:** 10.5
**Status:** Open issue, retired
**Issue Year:** 1990
**Issue Price:** $290
**Last Year:** 1992
**Last Retail Price:** $310
**High Auction Price:** $475
**Low Auction Price:** $375

**Ref. No.:** 2295
**Name:** Peaceful Rest
**Height:** 10.5
**Status:** Open issue, retired
**Issue Year:** 1995
**Issue Price:** $390
**Last Year:** 1998
**Last Retail Price:** $390

**Ref. No.:** 2336
**Name:** Young Water Girl
**Height:** 10.5
**Status:** Open issue, active
**Issue Year:** 1996
**Issue Price:** $315
**2003 Retail Price:** $325

**Ref. No.:** 2345
**Name:** Bedtime Story
**Height:** 10.5
**Status:** Open issue, retired
**Issue Year:** 1996
**Issue Price:** $360
**Last Year:** 1999
**Last Retail Price:** $360

Gres

**Ref. No.:** 2348
**Name:** Prayerful Moment (Blue)
**Height:** 10.5
**Status:** Open edition, retired
**Issue Year:** 1996
**Issue Price:** $145
**Last Year:** 1999
**Last Retail Price:** $145

**Ref. No.:** 2405
**Name:** Midday
**Height:** 10.5
**Status:** Open issue, active
**Issue Year:** 1999
**Issue Price:** $535
**2003 Retail Price:** $550

**Ref. No.:** 3514
**Name:** Pensive Woman with Bird
**Height:** 10.5
**Status:** Open issue, active
**Issue Year:** 1978
**Issue Price:** $500
**2003 Retail Price:** $1050

**Ref. No.:** 2217
**Name:** Gentle Play
**Height:** 10.75
**Status:** Open issue, retired
**Issue Year:** 1991
**Issue Price:** $380
**Last Year:** 1993
**Last Retail Price:** $415

**Ref. No.:** 2236
**Name:** Frosty Outing
**Height:** 10.75
**Status:** Open issue, retired
**Issue Year:** 1993
**Issue Price:** $375
**Last Year:** 1997
**Last Retail Price:** $410

**Ref. No.:** 2398
**Name:** Conversing with Nature
**Height:** 10.75
**Status:** Open issue, retired
**Issue Year:** 1999
**Issue Price:** $370
**Last Year:** 2001
**Last Retail Price:** $370

**Ref. No.:** 1326
**Name:** Comforting Her Friend
**Height:** 11
**Status:** Open issue, retired
**Issue Year:** 1976
**Issue Price:** $195
**Last Year:** 1981
**Last Retail Price:** $210

**Ref. No.:** 2002
**Name:** Gothic King
**Height:** 11
**Status:** Open issue, retired
**Issue Year:** 1970
**Issue Price:** $25
**Last Year:** 1975
**Last Retail Price:** $45
**High Auction Price:** $400
**Low Auction Price:** $300

**Ref. No.:** 2003
**Name:** Gothic Queen
**Height:** 11
**Status:** Open issue, retired
**Issue Year:** 1970
**Issue Price:** $25
**Last Year:** 1975
**Last Retail Price:** $45

**Ref. No.:** 2014
**Name:** Girl Water Carrier
**Height:** 11
**Status:** Open edition, retired
**Issue Year:** 1970
**Issue Price:** $325
**Last Year:** 1975
**Last Retail Price:** $325

**Ref. No.:** 2086
**Name:** The Little Kiss
**Height:** 11
**Status:** Open issue, retired
**Issue Year:** 1978
**Issue Price:** $180
**Last Year:** 1985
**Last Retail Price:** $245

**Ref. No.:** 2127
**Name:** Indian Chief
**Height:** 11
**Status:** Open edition, retired
**Issue Year:** 1983
**Issue Price:** $525
**Last Year:** 1988
**Last Retail Price:** $600
**Auction Price:** $500

Gres

**Ref. No.:** 2242
**Name:** Away to School
**Height:** 11
**Status:** Open issue, active
**Issue Year:** 1993
**Issue Price:** $465
**2003 Retail Price:** $475

**Ref. No.:** 2330
**Name:** The Shepherdess
**Height:** 11
**Status:** Open issue, retired
**Issue Year:** 1996
**Issue Price:** $410
**Last Year:** 1999
**Last Retail Price:** $410

**Ref. No.:** 2335
**Name:** Young Fisherman
**Height:** 11
**Status:** Open issue, retired
**Issue Year:** 1996
**Issue Price:** $225
**Last Year:** 2001
**Last Retail Price:** $225

**Ref. No.:** 2353
**Name:** Shot On Goal
**Height:** 11
**Status:** Open issue, retired
**Issue Year:** 1996
**Issue Price:** $935
**Last Year:** 1998
**Last Retail Price:** $935

**Ref. No.:** 2354
**Name:** Waiting for Spring
**Height:** 11
**Status:** Open issue, retired
**Issue Year:** 1997
**Issue Price:** $385
**Last Year:** 2000
**Last Retail Price:** $400

**Ref. No.:** 2358
**Name:** I'm Sleepy
**Height:** 11
**Status:** Open issue, retired
**Issue Year:** 1997
**Issue Price:** $360
**Last Year:** 2000
**Last Retail Price:** $360

**Ref. No.:** 2388
**Name:** Ready To Go
**Height:** 11
**Status:** Open issue, active
**Issue Year:** 1998
**Issue Price:** $350
**2003 Retail Price:** $375

**Ref. No.:** 3526
**Name:** Watching the Dove
**Height:** 11
**Status:** Open issue, active
**Issue Year:** 1982
**Issue Price:** $265
**2003 Retail Price:** $650

**Ref. No.:** 2219
**Name:** Underfoot
**Height:** 11.25
**Status:** Open issue, retired
**Issue Year:** 1992
**Issue Price:** $360
**Last Year:** 2001
**Last Retail Price:** $425

**Ref. No.:** 2234
**Name:** Playful Push
**Height:** 11.25
**Status:** Open issue, retired
**Issue Year:** 1992
**Issue Price:** $850
**Last Year:** 2000
**Last Retail Price:** $875

**Ref. No.:** 2302
**Name:** Twilight Years
**Height:** 11.25
**Status:** Open issue, retired
**Issue Year:** 1995
**Issue Price:** $385
**Last Year:** 1997
**Last Retail Price:** $385

**Ref. No.:** 2418
**Name:** Meditative Moment
**Height:** 11.25
**Status:** Open issue, active
**Issue Year:** 2001
**Issue Price:** $680
**2003 Retail Price:** $695

Gres

**Ref. No.:** 2436
**Name:** Spirit of the Earth
**Height:** 11.25
**Status:** Open issue, active
**Issue Year:** 2002
**Issue Price:** $565
**2003 Retail Price:** $575

**Ref. No.:** 2438
**Name:** Strings of the Heart
**Height:** 11.25
**Status:** Open issue, active
**Issue Year:** 2002
**Issue Price:** $1155
**2003 Retail Price:** $1195

**Ref. No.:** 2000
**Name:** Monkeys
**Height:** 11.5
**Status:** Open edition, retired
**Issue Year:** 1970
**Issue Price:** $35
**Last Year:** 1975
**Last Retail Price:** $47.50

**Ref. No.:** 2008
**Name:** Eskimo Girl/White Decor
**Height:** 11.5
**Status:** Open edition, active
**Issue Year:** 1970
**Issue Price:** $27.50
**2003 Retail Price:** $295

**Ref. No.:** 2008.1
**Name:** Eskimo Girl
**Height:** 11.5
**Status:** Open issue, retired
**Issue Year:** 1970
**Issue Price:** $30
**Last Year:** 1990
**Last Retail Price:** $145
**High Auction Price:** $275
**Low Auction Price:** $200

**Ref. No.:** 2052
**Name:** Magistrates
**Height:** 11.5
**Status:** Open issue, retired
**Issue Year:** 1974
**Issue Price:** $135
**Last Year:** 1981
**Last Retail Price:** $300
**High Auction Price:** $1650
**Low Auction Price:** $950

**Ref. No.:** 2151
**Name:** A Bird on Hand
**Height:** 11.5
**Status:** Open issue, retired
**Issue Year:** 1985
**Issue Price:** $117.50
**Last Year:** 1999
**Last Retail Price:** $280

**Ref. No.:** 2174
**Name:** Andean Flute Player
**Height:** 11.5
**Status:** Open issue, retired
**Issue Year:** 1987
**Issue Price:** $250
**Last Year:** 1990
**Last Retail Price:** $275
**High Auction Price:** $750
**Low Auction Price:** $350

**Ref. No.:** 2212
**Name:** Patrol Leader
**Height:** 11.5
**Status:** Open issue, retired
**Issue Year:** 1991
**Issue Price:** $390
**Last Year:** 1993
**Last Retail Price:** $420

**Ref. No.:** 2265
**Name:** Quixote Standing Up
**Height:** 11.5
**Status:** Open issue, active
**Issue Year:** 1994
**Issue Price:** $225
**2003 Retail Price:** $250

**Ref. No.:** 2267
**Name:** Dancer
**Height:** 11.5
**Status:** Open edition, retired
**Issue Year:** 1994
**Issue Price:** $220
**Last Year:** 2001
**Last Retail Price:** $240

**Ref. No.:** 2401
**Name:** Little Shepherd
**Height:** 11.5
**Status:** Open issue, retired
**Issue Year:** 1999
**Issue Price:** $275
**Last Year:** 2000
**Last Retail Price:** $275

Gres

**Ref. No.:** 2434
**Name:** Spirit of the Wind
**Height:** 11.5
**Status:** Open issue, active
**Issue Year:** 2002
**Issue Price:** $740
**2003 Retail Price:** $750

**Ref. No.:** 2301
**Name:** Empress
**Height:** 11.75
**Status:** Open edition, retired
**Issue Year:** 1995
**Issue Price:** $795
**Last Year:** 1999
**Last Retail Price:** $795

**Ref. No.:** 2324
**Name:** A Basket of Fun
**Height:** 11.75
**Status:** Open issue, retired
**Issue Year:** 1995
**Issue Price:** $320
**Last Year:** 2001
**Last Retail Price:** $320

**Ref. No.:** 2329
**Name:** Daily Chores
**Height:** 11.75
**Status:** Open issue, retired
**Issue Year:** 1995
**Issue Price:** $345
**Last Year:** 1999
**Last Retail Price:** $345

**Ref. No.:** 2116
**Name:** Divers with Chicken
**Height:** 12
**Status:** Open edition, retired
**Issue Year:** 1980
**Issue Price:** $1250
**Last Year:** 1985
**Last Retail Price:** $1435
**Auction Price:** $800

**Ref. No.:** 2134
**Name:** Nautical Watch
**Height:** 12
**Status:** Open edition, retired
**Issue Year:** 1984
**Issue Price:** $450
**Last Year:** 1988
**Last Retail Price:** $525
**Auction Price:** $800

**Ref. No.:** 2220
**Name:** Free Spirit
**Height:** 12
**Status:** Open issue, retired
**Issue Year:** 1992
**Issue Price:** $235
**Last Year:** 1994
**Last Retail Price:** $245

**Ref. No.:** 2221
**Name:** Spring Beauty
**Height:** 12
**Status:** Open issue, retired
**Issue Year:** 1992
**Issue Price:** $285
**Last Year:** 1994
**Last Retail Price:** $295

**Ref. No.:** 2227
**Name:** Arctic Allies
**Height:** 12
**Status:** Open issue, active
**Issue Year:** 1992
**Issue Price:** $585
**2003 Retail Price:** $625

**Ref. No.:** 2239
**Name:** Valencian Courtship
**Height:** 12
**Status:** Open issue, active
**Issue Year:** 1993
**Issue Price:** $880
**2003 Retail Price:** $895

**Ref. No.:** 2356
**Name:** Country Joy
**Height:** 12
**Status:** Open issue, retired
**Issue Year:** 1997
**Issue Price:** $310
**Last Year:** 1999
**Last Retail Price:** $315

**Ref. No.:** 2376
**Name:** Empress
**Height:** 12
**Status:** Open issue, retired
**Issue Year:** 1998
**Issue Price:** $735
**Last Year:** 2000
**Last Retail Price:** $750

Gres

**Ref. No.:** 2389
**Name:** Time To Go
**Height:** 12
**Status:** Open issue, active
**Issue Year:** 1998
**Issue Price:** $330
**2003 Retail Price:** $375

**Ref. No.:** 2391
**Name:** Loyal Companion
**Height:** 12
**Status:** Open issue, active
**Issue Year:** 1998
**Issue Price:** $400
**2003 Retail Price:** $495

**Ref. No.:** 2025
**Name:** Oriental Dancer
**Height:** 12.25
**Status:** Open issue, retired
**Issue Year:** 1971
**Issue Price:** $45
**Last Year:** 1975
**Last Retail Price:** $75

**Ref. No.:** 2109
**Name:** Laundress and
    Water Carrier
**Height:** 12.25
**Status:** Open edition, retired
**Issue Year:** 1978
**Issue Price:** $325
**Last Year:** 1983
**Last Retail Price:** $425
**High Auction Price:** $550
**Low Auction Price:** $450

**Ref. No.:** 2115
**Name:** Mother's Kiss
**Height:** 12.25
**Status:** Open issue, retired
**Issue Year:** 1980
**Issue Price:** $575
**Last Year:** 1981
**Last Retail Price:** $575
**High Auction Price:** $700
**Low Auction Price:** $450

**Ref. No.:** 2198
**Name:** A King is Born
**Height:** 12.25
**Status:** Open issue, retired
**Issue Year:** 1990
**Issue Price:** $750
**Last Year:** 2001
**Last Retail Price:** $895

**Ref. No.:** 2199
**Name:** Devoted Friends
**Height:** 12.25
**Status:** Open edition, retired
**Issue Year:** 1990
**Issue Price:** $700
**Last Year:** 1995
**Last Retail Price:** $895

**Ref. No.:** 2246
**Name:** Lion Tamer
**Height:** 12.25
**Status:** Open issue, retired
**Issue Year:** 1993
**Issue Price:** $375
**Last Year:** 1995
**Last Retail Price:** $375

**Ref. No.:** 2325
**Name:** Spring Splendor
**Height:** 12.25
**Status:** Open edition, retired
**Issue Year:** 1995
**Issue Price:** $460
**Last Year:** 2001
**Last Retail Price:** $460

**Ref. No.:** 2338
**Name:** Sultan's Dream
**Height:** 12.25
**Status:** Open issue, retired
**Issue Year:** 1996
**Issue Price:** $700
**Last Year:** 2002
**Last Retail Price:** $700

**Ref. No.:** 2189
**Name:** Mother's Pride
**Height:** 12.5
**Status:** Open issue, retired
**Issue Year:** 1990
**Issue Price:** $300
**Last Year:** 1999
**Last Retail Price:** $375

**Ref. No.:** 2208
**Name:** Let's Rest
**Height:** 12.5
**Status:** Open issue, retired
**Issue Year:** 1990
**Issue Price:** $550
**Last Year:** 2002
**Last Retail Price:** $665

Gres

**Ref. No.:** 2230
**Name:** Mary's Child
**Height:** 12.5
**Status:** Open issue, retired
**Issue Year:** 1992
**Issue Price:** $525
**Last Year:** 1994
**Last Retail Price:** $550

**Ref. No.:** 2280
**Name:** King Balthasar
**Height:** 12.5
**Status:** Open issue, active
**Issue Year:** 1994
**Issue Price:** $290
**2003 Retail Price:** $295

**Ref. No.:** 2299
**Name:** Poetic Moment
**Height:** 12.5
**Status:** Open edition, active
**Issue Year:** 1995
**Issue Price:** $465
**2003 Retail Price:** $475

**Ref. No.:** 2314
**Name:** Breezy Afternoon
**Height:** 12.5
**Status:** Open edition, retired
**Issue Year:** 1995
**Issue Price:** $220
**Last Year:** 1998
**Last Retail Price:** $220

**Ref. No.:** 2404
**Name:** Sunset
**Height:** 12.5
**Status:** Open issue, retired
**Issue Year:** 1999
**Issue Price:** $440
**Last Year:** 2002
**Last Retail Price:** $440

**Ref. No.:** 2417
**Name:** Young Mary
**Height:** 12.5
**Status:** Open issue, retired
**Issue Year:** 2000
**Issue Price:** $340
**Last Year:** 2002
**Last Retail Price:** $345

**Ref. No.:** 2427
**Name:** A Morning Walk
**Height:** 12.5
**Status:** Open issue, active
**Issue Year:** 2001
**Issue Price:** $285
**2003 Retail Price:** $325

**Ref. No.:** 2428
**Name:** An Apron Full of Joy
**Height:** 12.5
**Status:** Open issue, active
**Issue Year:** 2001
**Issue Price:** $380
**2003 Retail Price:** $425
**Comment:** To be retired as of
December 31, 2003

**Ref. No.:** 2114
**Name:** A Father's Kiss
**Height:** 12.75
**Status:** Open issue, retired
**Issue Year:** 1980
**Issue Price:** $575
**Last Year:** 1981
**Last Retail Price:** $575
**High Auction Price:** $575
**Low Auction Price:** $425

**Ref. No.:** 2117
**Name:** Divers
**Height:** 12.75
**Status:** Open edition, retired
**Issue Year:** 1980
**Issue Price:** $925
**Last Year:** 1985
**Last Retail Price:** $1650
**Auction Price:** $1000

**Ref. No.:** 2291
**Name:** The Holy Teacher
**Height:** 12.75
**Status:** Open issue, active
**Issue Year:** 1994
**Issue Price:** $375
**2003 Retail Price:** $375

**Ref. No.:** 2410
**Name:** Poetic Interlude
**Height:** 12.75
**Status:** Open issue, active
**Issue Year:** 2000
**Issue Price:** $460
**2003 Retail Price:** $475

*Gres*

**Ref. No.:** 2440
**Name:** A Child's Present
**Height:** 12.75
**Status:** Open issue, active
**Issue Year:** 2002
**Issue Price:** $760
**2003 Retail Price:** $775

**Ref. No.:** 2445
**Name:** Tropical Wonders
**Height:** 12.75
**Status:** Open issue, active
**Issue Year:** 2002
**Issue Price:** $715
**2003 Retail Price:** $725

**Ref. No.:** 2038.3 (Reduced)
**Name:** Eskimo Boy and Girl
**Height:** 13
**Status:** Open issue, retired
**Issue Year:** 1971
**Issue Price:** $70
**Last Year:** 1994
**Last Retail Price:** $455

**Ref. No.:** 2060
**Name:** Monk
**Height:** 13
**Status:** Open issue, retired
**Issue Year:** 1977
**Issue Price:** $60
**Last Year:** 1998
**Last Retail Price:** $155

**Ref. No.:** 2120
**Name:** Girl from Majorca
**Height:** 13
**Status:** Open issue, retired
**Issue Year:** 1978
**Issue Price:** $250
**Last Year:** 1982
**Last Retail Price:** $325

**Ref. No.:** 2130
**Name:** Egyptian Cat
**Height:** 13
**Status:** Open edition, retired
**Issue Year:** 1983
**Issue Price:** $75
**Last Year:** 1985
**Last Retail Price:** $75

**Ref. No.:** 2187
**Name:** Jealous Friend
**Height:** 13
**Status:** Open issue, retired
**Issue Year:** 1989
**Issue Price:** $275
**Last Year:** 1995
**Last Retail Price:** $365

**Ref. No.:** 2190
**Name:** To The Well
**Height:** 13
**Status:** Open edition, retired
**Issue Year:** 1990
**Issue Price:** $255
**Last Year:** 2001
**Last Retail Price:** $295

**Ref. No.:** 2263
**Name:** Mother and Child
**Height:** 13
**Status:** Open issue, retired
**Issue Year:** 1994
**Issue Price:** $285
**Last Year:** 1997
**Last Retail Price:** $285

**Ref. No.:** 2360
**Name:** Hunting Butterflies
**Height:** 13
**Status:** Open issue, retired
**Issue Year:** 1997
**Issue Price:** $465
**Last Year:** 2000
**Last Retail Price:** $465

**Ref. No.:** 2368
**Name:** Colombina
**Height:** 13
**Status:** Open issue, retired
**Issue Year:** 1997
**Issue Price:** $585
**Last Year:** 1999
**Last Retail Price:** $585

**Ref. No.:** 2380
**Name:** A Comforting Friend
**Height:** 13
**Status:** Open issue, active
**Issue Year:** 1998
**Issue Price:** $330
**2003 Retail Price:** $375

*Gres*

**Ref. No.:** 2108
**Name:** Fisherman
**Height:** 13.25
**Status:** Open edition, retired
**Issue Year:** 1978
**Issue Price:** $500
**Last Year:** 1985
**Last Retail Price:** $630
**High Auction Price:** $1050
**Low Auction Price:** $550

**Ref. No.:** 2233
**Name:** Guess What I Have?
**Height:** 13.25
**Status:** Open issue, retired
**Issue Year:** 1992
**Issue Price:** $340
**Last Year:** 2001
**Last Retail Price:** $375

**Ref. No.:** 2235
**Name:** Adoring Mother
**Height:** 13.25
**Status:** Open issue, retired
**Issue Year:** 1993
**Issue Price:** $405
**Last Year:** 1999
**Last Retail Price:** $440

**Ref. No.:** 2256
**Name:** Solitude
**Height:** 13.25
**Status:** Open issue, retired
**Issue Year:** 1994
**Issue Price:** $435
**Last Year:** 1998
**Last Retail Price:** $445

**Ref. No.:** 2257
**Name:** Constant Companions
**Height:** 13.25
**Status:** Open issue, retired
**Issue Year:** 1994
**Issue Price:** $625
**Last Year:** 1997
**Last Retail Price:** $625

**Ref. No.:** 2258
**Name:** Family Love
**Height:** 13.25
**Status:** Open issue, retired
**Issue Year:** 1994
**Issue Price:** $485
**Last Year:** 2000
**Last Retail Price:** $485

**Ref. No.:** 2408
**Name:** Deep In Thought
**Height:** 13.25
**Status:** Open issue, retired
**Issue Year:** 2000
**Issue Price:** $1325
**Last Year:** 2002
**Last Retail Price:** $1350

**Ref. No.:** 2218
**Name:** Costumed Couple
**Height:** 13.5
**Status:** Open issue, retired
**Issue Year:** 1991
**Issue Price:** $680
**Last Year:** 1993
**Last Retail Price:** $750
**Auction Price:** $600

**Ref. No.:** 2240
**Name:** Winged Love
**Height:** 13.5
**Status:** Open issue, retired
**Issue Year:** 1993
**Issue Price:** $300
**Last Year:** 1995
**Last Retail Price:** $310

**Ref. No.:** 2285
**Name:** Musical Muse
**Height:** 13.5
**Status:** Open edition, retired
**Issue Year:** 1994
**Issue Price:** $465
**Last Year:** 1997
**Last Retail Price:** $465

**Ref. No.:** 2411
**Name:** In The Country
**Height:** 13.5
**Status:** Open issue, retired
**Issue Year:** 2000
**Issue Price:** $525
**Last Year:** 2002
**Last Retail Price:** $525

**Ref. No.:** 2423
**Name:** After Class
**Height:** 13.5
**Status:** Open issue, active
**Issue Year:** 2001
**Issue Price:** $525
**2003 Retail Price:** $550

Gres

**Ref. No.:** 1279
**Name:** Facing the Wind
**Height:** 13.75
**Status:** Open issue, retired
**Issue Year:** 1974
**Issue Price:** $250
**Last Year:** 2001
**Last Retail Price:** $830

**Ref. No.:** 2009
**Name:** Boy With Goat
**Height:** 13.75
**Status:** Open edition, retired
**Issue Year:** 1970
**Issue Price:** $100
**Last Year:** 1981
**Last Retail Price:** $390

**Ref. No.:** 2009.3
**Name:** Boy With Goat, White
**Height:** 13.75
**Status:** Open edition, retired
**Issue Year:** 1970
**Issue Price:** $92.50
**Last Year:** 1975
**Last Retail Price:** $110

**Ref. No.:** 2075
**Name:** Nuns
**Height:** 13.75
**Status:** Open issue, retired
**Issue Year:** 1977
**Issue Price:** $90
**Last Year:** 2000
**Last Retail Price:** $250

**Ref. No.:** 2078
**Name:** Lola
**Height:** 13.75
**Status:** Open edition, retired
**Issue Year:** 1978
**Issue Price:** $250
**Last Year:** 1981
**Last Retail Price:** $350
**High Auction Price:** $900
**Low Auction Price:** $500

**Ref. No.:** 2129
**Name:** Waiting for Sailor
**Height:** 13.75
**Status:** Open issue, retired
**Issue Year:** 1983
**Issue Price:** $325
**Last Year:** 1985
**Last Retail Price:** $325
**High Auction Price:** $700
**Low Auction Price:** $600

**Ref. No.:** 2024
**Name:** Little Girl
**Height:** 14
**Status:** Open edition, retired
**Issue Year:** 1971
**Issue Price:** $120
**Last Year:** 1985
**Last Retail Price:** $285
**Auction Price:** $400

**Ref. No.:** 2046
**Name:** Girl's Head
**Height:** 14
**Status:** Open edition, retired
**Issue Year:** 1971
**Issue Price:** $105
**Last Year:** 1975
**Last Retail Price:** $200
**High Auction Price:** $625
**Low Auction Price:** $600

**Ref. No.:** 2149
**Name:** Young Madonna
**Height:** 14
**Status:** Open edition, retired
**Issue Year:** 1985
**Issue Price:** $400
**Last Year:** 1988
**Last Retail Price:** $475

**Ref. No.:** 2323
**Name:** Water Girl
**Height:** 14
**Status:** Open edition, active
**Issue Year:** 1995
**Issue Price:** $245
**2003 Retail Price:** $250

**Ref. No.:** 2326
**Name:** Physician
**Height:** 14
**Status:** Open issue, retired
**Issue Year:** 1995
**Issue Price:** $350
**Last Year:** 1997
**Last Retail Price:** $350

**Ref. No.:** 2367
**Name:** Pensive Harlequin
**Height:** 14
**Status:** Open issue, retired
**Issue Year:** 1997
**Issue Price:** $560
**Last Year:** 1999
**Last Retail Price:** $560

*Gres*

**Ref. No.:** 2370
**Name:** Intermission
**Height:** 14
**Status:** Open issue, active
**Issue Year:** 1997
**Issue Price:** $655
**2003 Retail Price:** $775

**Ref. No.:** 2375
**Name:** Emperor
**Height:** 14
**Status:** Open issue, retired
**Issue Year:** 1998
**Issue Price:** $695
**Last Year:** 2000
**Last Retail Price:** $695

**Ref. No.:** 2394
**Name:** Island Breeze
**Height:** 14
**Status:** Open issue, retired
**Issue Year:** 1999
**Issue Price:** $550
**Last Year:** 2001
**Last Retail Price:** $550

**Ref. No.:** 2425
**Name:** Cozy Kitties
**Height:** 14
**Status:** Open issue, active
**Issue Year:** 2001
**Issue Price:** $325
**2003 Retail Price:** $350
**Comment:** To be retired as of
December 31, 2003

**Ref. No.:** 2085
**Name:** Rosita
**Height:** 14.25
**Status:** Open issue, retired
**Issue Year:** 1978
**Issue Price:** $175
**Last Year:** 1983
**Last Retail Price:** $222.5
**Auction Price:** $375

**Ref. No.:** 2293
**Name:** Joyful Event
**Height:** 14.25
**Status:** Open issue, active
**Issue Year:** 1994
**Issue Price:** $880
**2003 Retail Price:** $895

**Ref. No.:** 2300
**Name:** Emperor
**Height:** 14.25
**Status:** Open issue, retired
**Issue Year:** 1995
**Issue Price:** Unknown
**Last Year:** 1999
**Last Retail Price:** $765

**Ref. No.:** 3525
**Name:** Classic Water Carrier
**Height:** 14.25
**Status:** Open edition, active
**Issue Year:** 1981
**Issue Price:** $360
**2003 Retail Price:** $750

**Ref. No.:** 2026
**Name:** Oriental Woman
**Height:** 14.5
**Status:** Open issue, retired
**Issue Year:** 1971
**Issue Price:** $45
**Last Year:** 1975
**Last Retail Price:** $75

**Ref. No.:** 2081
**Name:** Fisherwoman
**Height:** 14.5
**Status:** Open issue, retired
**Issue Year:** 1978
**Issue Price:** $550
**Last Year:** 1985
**Last Retail Price:** $710
**Auction Price:** $1400

**Ref. No.:** 2231
**Name:** Afternoon Verse
**Height:** 14.5
**Status:** Open edition, retired
**Issue Year:** 1992
**Issue Price:** $580
**Last Year:** 2001
**Last Retail Price:** $595

**Ref. No.:** 2241
**Name:** Winged Harmony
**Height:** 14.5
**Status:** Open issue, retired
**Issue Year:** 1993
**Issue Price:** $300
**Last Year:** 1995
**Last Retail Price:** $310

*Gres*

**Ref. No.:** 2309
**Name:** Windblown Girl
**Height:** 14.5
**Status:** Open edition, retired
**Issue Year:** 1995
**Issue Price:** $320
**Last Year:** 1998
**Last Retail Price:** $320

**Ref. No.:** 2409
**Name:** Loving Mother
**Height:** 14.5
**Status:** Open issue, active
**Issue Year:** 2000
**Issue Price:** $1090
**2003 Retail Price:** $1150

**Ref. No.:** 2412
**Name:** Thoughts Of Peace
**Height:** 14.5
**Status:** Open issue, retired
**Issue Year:** 2000
**Issue Price:** $1000
**Last Year:** 2002
**Last Retail Price:** $1100

**Ref. No.:** 2416
**Name:** In Mother's Arms
**Height:** 14.5
**Status:** Open issue, retired
**Issue Year:** 2000
**Issue Price:** $990
**Last Year:** 2002
**Last Retail Price:** $990

**Ref. No.:** 5155
**Name:** Monks at Prayer
**Height:** 14.5
**Status:** Open issue, retired
**Issue Year:** 1982
**Issue Price:** $130
**Last Year:** 2002
**Last Retail Price:** $300

**Ref. No.:** 2247
**Name:** Just Us
**Height:** 14.75
**Status:** Open issue, retired
**Issue Year:** 1993
**Issue Price:** $650
**Last Year:** 1995
**Last Retail Price:** $650

**Ref. No.:** 2296
**Name:** Life's Small Wonders
**Height:** 14.75
**Status:** Open issue, active
**Issue Year:** 1995
**Issue Price:** $370
**2003 Retail Price:** $375

**Ref. No.:** 2297
**Name:** Elephants
**Height:** 14.75
**Status:** Open issue, retired
**Issue Year:** 1995
**Issue Price:** $875
**Last Year:** 2001
**Last Retail Price:** $875

**Ref. No.:** 2343
**Name:** Care and Tenderness
**Height:** 14.75
**Status:** Open issue, retired
**Issue Year:** 1996
**Issue Price:** $860
**Last Year:** 1999
**Last Retail Price:** $860

**Ref. No.:** 2430
**Name:** Little Hairdresser
**Height:** 14.75
**Status:** Open issue, active
**Issue Year:** 2001
**Issue Price:** $650
**2003 Retail Price:** $675
**Comment:** To be retired as of
December 31, 2003

**Ref. No.:** 2033
**Name:** Decorative Rooster
**Height:** 15
**Status:** Open edition, retired
**Issue Year:** 1971
**Issue Price:** $55
**Last Year:** 1973
**Last Retail Price:** $70

**Ref. No.:** 2082
**Name:** Nuns Singing
**Height:** 15
**Status:** Open edition, retired
**Issue Year:** 1978
**Issue Price:** $800
**Last Year:** 1981
**Last Retail Price:** $1000

*Gres*

**Ref. No.:** 2119
**Name:** Dressing Up
**Height:** 15
**Status:** Open issue, retired
**Issue Year:** 1980
**Issue Price:** $700
**Last Year:** 1985
**Last Retail Price:** $700
**High Auction Price:** $675
**Low Auction Price:** $600

**Ref. No.:** 2131
**Name:** Mother and Son
**Height:** 15
**Status:** Open issue, retired
**Issue Year:** 1983
**Issue Price:** $850
**Last Year:** 1997
**Last Retail Price:** $1620

**Ref. No.:** 2355
**Name:** Gabriela
**Height:** 15
**Status:** Open issue, active
**Issue Year:** 1997
**Issue Price:** $740
**2003 Retail Price:** $750

**Ref. No.:** 2357
**Name:** In Search of Water
**Height:** 15
**Status:** Open issue, active
**Issue Year:** 1997
**Issue Price:** $410
**2003 Retail Price:** $450

**Ref. No.:** 2379
**Name:** Arctic Explorer
**Height:** 15
**Status:** Open issue, retired
**Issue Year:** 1998
**Issue Price:** $550
**Last Year:** 2000
**Last Retail Price:** $580

**Ref. No.:** 3509
**Name:** Letters to Dulcinea
**Height:** 15
**Status:** Numbered series, retired
**Issue Year:** 1978
**Issue Price:** $1000
**Last Year:** 1997
**Last Retail Price:** $2175

**Ref. No.:** 3521
**Name:** Mother Love
**Height:** 15
**Status:** Open edition, retired
**Issue Year:** 1980
**Issue Price:** $1000
**Last Year:** 1990
**Last Retail Price:** $1150
**High Auction Price:** $1200
**Low Auction Price:** $800

**Ref. No.:** 2407
**Name:** Memories Of Tuscany
**Height:** 15.25
**Status:** Open issue, retired
**Issue Year:** 2000
**Issue Price:** $995
**Last Year:** 2002
**Last Retail Price:** $995

**Ref. No.:** 2452
**Name:** Loving Steps
**Height:** 15.25
**Status:** Open issue, active
**Issue Year:** 2002
**Issue Price:** $525
**2003 Retail Price:** $525

**Ref. No.:** 2062
**Name:** Day Dream
**Height:** 15.5
**Status:** Open issue, retired
**Issue Year:** 1977
**Issue Price:** $400
**Last Year:** 1985
**Last Retail Price:** $600
**Auction Price:** $1300

**Ref. No.:** 2074
**Name:** Water Carrier
**Height:** 15.5
**Status:** Open issue, retired
**Issue Year:** 1977
**Issue Price:** $500
**Last Year:** 1985
**Last Retail Price:** $745
**Auction Price:** $900

**Ref. No.:** 2142
**Name:** Sea Harvest
**Height:** 15.5
**Status:** Open issue, retired
**Issue Year:** 1984
**Issue Price:** $535
**Last Year:** 1990
**Last Retail Price:** $775
**High Auction Price:** $700
**Low Auction Price:** $600

*Gres*

**Ref. No.:** 2252
**Name:** Waiting for Father
**Height:** 15.5
**Status:** Open issue, retired
**Issue Year:** 1993
**Issue Price:** $690
**Last Year:** 1999
**Last Retail Price:** $660

**Ref. No.:** 2013
**Name:** Girl with Little Dog
**Height:** 15.75
**Status:** Open edition, retired
**Issue Year:** 1970
**Issue Price:** $300
**Last Year:** 1975
**Last Retail Price:** $300

**Ref. No.:** 2038
**Name:** Eskimo Boy and Girl
**Height:** 15.75
**Status:** Open issue, retired
**Issue Year:** 1971
**Issue Price:** $70
**Last Year:** 1999
**Last Retail Price:** $595

**Ref. No.:** 2112
**Name:** Charity
**Height:** 15.75
**Status:** Open issue, retired
**Issue Year:** 1978
**Issue Price:** $360
**Last Year:** 1981
**Last Retail Price:** $465

**Ref. No.:** 2138
**Name:** Friar Juniper
**Height:** 15.75
**Status:** Open issue, retired
**Issue Year:** 1984
**Issue Price:** $160
**Last Year:** 1993
**Last Retail Price:** $275

**Ref. No.:** 2339
**Name:** The Sultan
**Height:** 15.75
**Status:** Open issue, retired
**Issue Year:** 1996
**Issue Price:** $480
**Last Year:** 2002
**Last Retail Price:** $480

**Ref. No.:** 2017
**Name:** Gardener Girl
**Height:** 16
**Status:** Open edition, retired
**Issue Year:** 1970
**Issue Price:** $120
**Last Year:** 1981
**Last Retail Price:** $275
**Auction Price:** $700

**Ref. No.:** 2090
**Name:** Saint Francis
**Height:** 16
**Status:** Open issue, retired
**Issue Year:** 1978
**Issue Price:** $565
**Last Year:** 1981
**Last Retail Price:** $725

**Ref. No.:** 2224
**Name:** Cherish
**Height:** 16
**Status:** Open issue, active
**Issue Year:** 1992
**Issue Price:** $1750
**2003 Retail Price:** $1850

**Ref. No.:** 2315
**Name:** On the Green
**Height:** 16
**Status:** Open issue, retired
**Issue Year:** 1995
**Issue Price:** $575
**Last Year:** 2000
**Last Retail Price:** $575

**Ref. No.:** 2365
**Name:** Holy Mother
**Height:** 16
**Status:** Open issue, active
**Issue Year:** 1997
**Issue Price:** $230
**2003 Retail Price:** $250

**Ref. No.:** 2439
**Name:** Waters of the Oasis
**Height:** 16
**Status:** Open issue, active
**Issue Year:** 2002
**Issue Price:** $560
**2003 Retail Price:** $575

*Gres*

**Ref. No.:** 4952
**Name:** Meditation
**Height:** 16
**Status:** Open edition, retired
**Issue Year:** 1976
**Issue Price:** $200
**Last Year:** 1979
**Last Retail Price:** $220
**High Auction Price:** $925
**Low Auction Price:** $500

**Ref. No.:** 2034
**Name:** St. Elizabeth of Hungary
**Height:** 16.5
**Status:** Open issue, retired
**Issue Year:** 1971
**Issue Price:** $40
**Last Year:** 1973
**Last Retail Price:** $50

**Ref. No.:** 2084
**Name:** Don Quixote Dreaming
**Height:** 16.5
**Status:** Open issue, retired
**Issue Year:** 1978
**Issue Price:** $550
**Last Year:** 1985
**Last Retail Price:** $780
**Auction Price:** $2100

**Ref. No.:** 2110
**Name:** Elephant
**Height:** 16.75
**Status:** Open edition, retired
**Issue Year:** 1978
**Issue Price:** $750
**Last Year:** 1983
**Last Retail Price:** $975

**Ref. No.:** 2437
**Name:** Reflections of Beauty
**Height:** 16.75
**Status:** Open issue, active
**Issue Year:** 2002
**Issue Price:** $1335
**2003 Retail Price:** $1395

**Ref. No.:** 2040
**Name:** Fawn Head
**Height:** 17
**Status:** Open edition, retired
**Issue Year:** 1971
**Issue Price:** $70
**Last Year:** 1985
**Last Retail Price:** $242.50
**High Auction Price:** $600
**Low Auction Price:** $475

**Ref. No.:** 2069
**Name:** Thai Dancer
**Height:** 17
**Status:** Open edition, retired
**Issue Year:** 1977
**Issue Price:** $300
**Last Year:** 1999
**Last Retail Price:** $760

**Ref. No.:** 2294
**Name:** Jesus and Joseph
**Height:** 17
**Status:** Open issue, retired
**Issue Year:** 1995
**Issue Price:** $550
**Last Year:** 1999
**Last Retail Price:** $550

**Ref. No.:** 2366
**Name:** Bread of Life
**Height:** 17
**Status:** Open issue, active
**Issue Year:** 1997
**Issue Price:** $230
**2003 Retail Price:** $250

**Ref. No.:** 2387
**Name:** Karina
**Height:** 17
**Status:** Open issue, active
**Issue Year:** 1998
**Issue Price:** $390
**2003 Retail Price:** $425

**Ref. No.:** 2005
**Name:** Shepherdess Sleeping
**Height:** 17.25
**Status:** Open edition, retired
**Issue Year:** 1970
**Issue Price:** $100
**Last Year:** 1981
**Last Retail Price:** $570
**High Auction Price:** $750
**Low Auction Price:** $675

**Ref. No.:** 2005.3
**Name:** Shepherdess Sleeping
**Height:** 17.25
**Status:** Open edition, retired
**Issue Year:** 1970
**Issue Price:** $92.50
**Last Year:** 1975
**Last Retail Price:** $160
**Auction Price:** $600

*Gres*

**Ref. No.:** 2080
**Name:** Woman
**Height:** 17.25
**Status:** Open issue, retired
**Issue Year:** 1978
**Issue Price:** $625
**Last Year:** 1985
**Last Retail Price:** $850
**High Auction Price:** $750
**Low Auction Price:** $625

**Ref. No.:** 2107
**Name:** Woman with Mandolin
**Height:** 17.25
**Status:** Open edition, retired
**Issue Year:** 1978
**Issue Price:** $800
**Last Year:** 1981
**Last Retail Price:** $1000

**Ref. No.:** 2150
**Name:** A Tribute to Peace
**Height:** 17.25
**Status:** Open issue, active
**Issue Year:** 1985
**Issue Price:** $470
**2003 Retail Price:** $1000

**Ref. No.:** 2337
**Name:** Madonna of Montserrat
**Height:** 17.25
**Status:** Open issue, active
**Issue Year:** 1996
**Issue Price:** $1000
**2003 Retail Price:** $1000
**Comment:** To be retired or sold
    out as of December 31, 2003

**Ref. No.:** 2396
**Name:** From The Spring
**Height:** 17.25
**Status:** Open issue, active
**Issue Year:** 1999
**Issue Price:** $475
**2003 Retail Price:** $495

**Ref. No.:** 2424
**Name:** Dance of Joy
**Height:** 17.25
**Status:** Open issue, active
**Issue Year:** 2001
**Issue Price:** $725
**2003 Retail Price:** $775

**Ref. No.:** 2229
**Name:** Seasonal Gifts
**Height:** 17.5
**Status:** Open edition, active
**Issue Year:** 1992
**Issue Price:** $450
**2003 Retail Price:** $475

**Ref. No.:** 2448
**Name:** Blessed Event
**Height:** 17.5
**Status:** Open issue, active
**Issue Year:** 2002
**Issue Price:** $875
**2003 Retail Price:** $875

**Ref. No.:** 2133
**Name:** Autumn Shepherdess
**Height:** 17.75
**Status:** Open edition, retired
**Issue Year:** 1983
**Issue Price:** $285
**Last Year:** 1985
**Last Retail Price:** $285

**Ref. No.:** 2004
**Name:** Torero
**Height:** 18
**Status:** Open edition, retired
**Issue Year:** 1970
**Issue Price:** $100
**Last Year:** 1975
**Last Retail Price:** $100
**Auction Price:** $800

**Ref. No.:** 2004.3
**Name:** Torero
**Height:** 18
**Status:** Open edition, retired
**Issue Year:** 1970
**Issue Price:** $92.50
**Last Year:** 1975
**Last Retail Price:** $160

**Ref. No.:** 2027
**Name:** Camel
**Height:** 18
**Status:** Open edition, retired
**Issue Year:** 1971
**Issue Price:** $135
**Last Year:** 1975
**Last Retail Price:** $210

*Gres*

**Ref. No.:** 2035
**Name:** Virgin of the Orange
**Height:** 18
**Status:** Open issue, retired
**Issue Year:** 1971
**Issue Price:** $85
**Last Year:** 1973
**Last Retail Price:** $105

**Ref. No.:** 2044
**Name:** Horse Head
**Height:** 18
**Status:** Open edition, retired
**Issue Year:** 1971
**Issue Price:** $115
**Last Year:** 1975
**Last Retail Price:** $185

**Ref. No.:** 2132
**Name:** Spring Shepherdess
**Height:** 18
**Status:** Open edition, retired
**Issue Year:** 1983
**Issue Price:** $450
**Last Year:** 1985
**Last Retail Price:** $450

**Ref. No.:** 2362
**Name:** Braving the Storm
**Height:** 18
**Status:** Open issue, retired
**Issue Year:** 1997
**Issue Price:** $470
**Last Year:** 1999
**Last Retail Price:** $470

**Ref. No.:** 2363
**Name:** Pampered Puppy
**Height:** 18
**Status:** Open issue, retired
**Issue Year:** 1997
**Issue Price:** $345
**Last Year:** 2000
**Last Retail Price:** $375

**Ref. No.:** 2364
**Name:** Melodies
**Height:** 18
**Status:** Open issue, active
**Issue Year:** 1997
**Issue Price:** $590
**2003 Retail Price:** $675

**Ref. No.:** 2433
**Name:** Music From My Heart
**Height:** 18
**Status:** Open issue, active
**Issue Year:** 2001
**Issue Price:** $595
**2003 Retail Price:** $650

**Ref. No.:** 2023
**Name:** Girl to the Fountain
**Height:** 18.5
**Status:** Open issue, retired
**Issue Year:** 1971
**Issue Price:** $35
**Last Year:** 1979
**Last Retail Price:** $90
**Auction Price:** $375

**Ref. No.:** 2429
**Name:** Gentle Embrace
**Height:** 18.75
**Status:** Open issue, active
**Issue Year:** 2001
**Issue Price:** $440
**2003 Retail Price:** $495

**Ref. No.:** 2359
**Name:** First Crush
**Height:** 19
**Status:** Open issue, active
**Issue Year:** 1997
**Issue Price:** $945
**2003 Retail Price:** $995

**Ref. No.:** 2374
**Name:** Spring Inspiration
**Height:** 19
**Status:** Open issue, active
**Issue Year:** 1998
**Issue Price:** $635
**2003 Retail Price:** $750

**Ref. No.:** 2121
**Name:** Harpooner
**Height:** 19.25
**Status:** Open issue, retired
**Issue Year:** 1980
**Issue Price:** $820
**Last Year:** 1988
**Last Retail Price:** $950
**High Auction Price:** $1400
**Low Auction Price:** $850

Gres

**Ref. No.:** 2395
**Name:** Serenity
**Height:** 19.25
**Status:** Open issue, active
**Issue Year:** 1999
**Issue Price:** $1450
**2003 Retail Price:** $1475

**Ref. No.:** 2403
**Name:** Pacific Beauty
**Height:** 19.25
**Status:** Open issue, retired
**Issue Year:** 1999
**Issue Price:** $850
**Last Year:** 2001
**Last Retail Price:** $850

**Ref. No.:** 2406
**Name:** Dawn
**Height:** 19.5
**Status:** Open issue, active
**Issue Year:** 1999
**Issue Price:** $550
**2003 Retail Price:** $575

**Ref. No.:** 2065
**Name:** Chinese Farmer with Staff
**Height:** 19.75
**Status:** Open issue, retired
**Issue Year:** 1977
**Issue Price:** $340
**Last Year:** 1985
**Last Retail Price:** $465
**Auction Price:** $2375

**Ref. No.:** 2058
**Name:** Thai Couple
**Height:** 20
**Status:** Open issue, active
**Issue Year:** 1974
**Issue Price:** $650
**2003 Retail Price:** $1950

**Ref. No.:** 2393
**Name:** A Girl in Love
**Height:** 20
**Status:** Open issue, active
**Issue Year:** 1998
**Issue Price:** $465
**2003 Retail Price:** $550

**Ref. No.:** 3554
**Name:** Stormy Sea
**Height:** 20
**Status:** Open issue, active
**Issue Year:** 1982
**Issue Price:** $675
**2003 Retail Price:** $1695

**Ref. No.:** 1327
**Name:** Playing Cards
**Height:** 20.5
**Status:** Numbered series, active
**Issue Year:** 1976
**Issue Price:** $3800
**2003 Retail Price:** $6600

**Ref. No.:** 2139
**Name:** Aztec Indian
**Height:** 20.5
**Status:** Open issue, retired
**Issue Year:** 1984
**Issue Price:** $552.50
**Last Year:** 1988
**Last Retail Price:** $630
**Auction Price:** $600

**Ref. No.:** 2443
**Name:** Loving Words
**Height:** 20.5
**Status:** Open issue, active
**Issue Year:** 2002
**Issue Price:** $2050
**2003 Retail Price:** $2050

**Ref. No.:** 2068
**Name:** Chinese Farmer
**Height:** 20.75
**Status:** Open issue, retired
**Issue Year:** 1977
**Issue Price:** $340
**Last Year:** 1985
**Last Retail Price:** $465
**High Auction Price:** $1100
**Low Auction Price:** $750

**Ref. No.:** 2083
**Name:** Carmen
**Height:** 20.75
**Status:** Open issue, retired
**Issue Year:** 1978
**Issue Price:** $275
**Last Year:** 1981
**Last Retail Price:** $400
**High Auction Price:** $750
**Low Auction Price:** $650

*Gres*

**Ref. No.:** 2136
**Name:** The King
**Height:** 20.75
**Status:** Open issue, retired
**Issue Year:** 1984
**Issue Price:** $570
**Last Year:** 1988
**Last Retail Price:** $650
**Auction Price:** $450

**Ref. No.:** 2390
**Name:** Joelia
**Height:** 20.75
**Status:** Open issue, active
**Issue Year:** 1999
**Issue Price:** $1300
**2003 Retail Price:** $1400

**Ref. No.:** 2402
**Name:** Africa
**Height:** 20.75
**Status:** Open issue, active
**Issue Year:** 1999
**Issue Price:** $700
**2003 Retail Price:** $750

**Ref. No.:** 2022
**Name:** Woman from Altamira
**Height:** 21.25
**Status:** Open issue, retired
**Issue Year:** 1971
**Issue Price:** $40
**Last Year:** 1979
**Last Retail Price:** $105

**Ref. No.:** 2039
**Name:** Aida
**Height:** 21.5
**Status:** Open issue, retired
**Issue Year:** 1971
**Issue Price:** $65
**Last Year:** 1979
**Last Retail Price:** $165

**Ref. No.:** 2070
**Name:** Coiffure
**Height:** 21.5
**Status:** Open issue, active
**Issue Year:** 1977
**Issue Price:** $530
**2003 Retail Price:** $1525

**Ref. No.:** 2055
**Name:** Harlequin
**Height:** 22
**Status:** Open edition, retired
**Issue Year:** 1974
**Issue Price:** $350
**Last Year:** 1978
**Last Retail Price:** $440

**Ref. No.:** 2073
**Name:** Graceful Duo
**Height:** 22
**Status:** Open issue, retired
**Issue Year:** 1977
**Issue Price:** $775
**Last Year:** 1994
**Last Retail Price:** $1650

**Ref. No.:** 2341
**Name:** Oriental Fantasy with
    Brooch
**Height:** 22
**Status:** Open issue, retired
**Issue Year:** 1996
**Issue Price:** $1350
**Last Year:** 2000
**Last Retail Price:** $1350

**Ref. No.:** 2135
**Name:** Mystical Joseph
**Height:** 22.75
**Status:** Open issue, retired
**Issue Year:** 1984
**Issue Price:** $427.50
**Last Year:** 1988
**Last Retail Price:** $500
**High Auction Price:** $700
**Low Auction Price:** $400

**Ref. No.:** 2340
**Name:** Oriental Fantasy with Bow
**Height:** 23
**Status:** Open issue, retired
**Issue Year:** 1996
**Issue Price:** $1350
**Last Year:** 2000
**Last Retail Price:** $1350

**Ref. No.:** 2369
**Name:** Early Awakening
**Height:** 23
**Status:** Open issue, active
**Issue Year:** 1998
**Issue Price:** $595
**2003 Retail Price:** $725

*Gres*

**Ref. No.:** 2384
**Name:** What about me?
**Height:** 23
**Status:** Open issue, retired
**Issue Year:** 1998
**Issue Price:** $790
**Last Year:** 2000
**Last Retail Price:** $925

**Ref. No.:** 2072
**Name:** Woman and Child
**Height:** 23.25
**Status:** Open edition, retired
**Issue Year:** 1977
**Issue Price:** $1325
**Last Year:** 1981
**Last Retail Price:** $1850
**Auction Price:** $1800

**Ref. No.:** 2137
**Name:** Fairy Ballerina
**Height:** 23.5
**Status:** Open issue, retired
**Issue Year:** 1984
**Issue Price:** $500
**Last Year:** 1988
**Last Retail Price:** $575

**Ref. No.:** 2400
**Name:** Waiting At The Beach
**Height:** 23.5
**Status:** Open issue, retired
**Issue Year:** 1999
**Issue Price:** $900
**Last Year:** 2000
**Last Retail Price:** $900

**Ref. No.:** 2123
**Name:** Dancer
**Height:** 23.75
**Status:** Open issue, retired
**Issue Year:** 1980
**Issue Price:** $790
**Last Year:** 1985
**Last Retail Price:** $790
**Auction Price:** $1500

**Ref. No.:** 2126
**Name:** Mother Feeding Baby
**Height:** 23.75
**Status:** Open issue, retired
**Issue Year:** 1981
**Issue Price:** $2900
**Last Year:** 1985
**Last Retail Price:** $1300

**Ref. No.:** 2386
**Name:** Low Tide
**Height:** 25
**Status:** Open issue, retired
**Issue Year:** 1998
**Issue Price:** $560
**Last Year:** 2000
**Last Retail Price:** $675

**Ref. No.:** 2143
**Name:** Aztec Dancer
**Height:** 25.5
**Status:** Open issue, retired
**Issue Year:** 1984
**Issue Price:** $462.50
**Last Year:** 1988
**Last Retail Price:** $525
**Auction Price:** $550

**Ref. No.:** 2071
**Name:** Madonna With Dove
**Height:** 26.75
**Status:** Open issue, retired
**Issue Year:** 1977
**Issue Price:** $925
**Last Year:** 1983
**Last Retail Price:** $1330
**Auction Price:** $900

*Gres*

**Ref. No.:** 2372
**Name:** It's Magic!
**Height:** 27
**Status:** Open issue, retired
**Issue Year:** 1998
**Issue Price:** $1045
**Last Year:** 2000
**Last Retail Price:** $1100

**Ref. No.:** 2059
**Name:** Musketeer
**Height:** 27.25
**Status:** Open issue, retired
**Issue Year:** 1974
**Issue Price:** $900
**Last Year:** 1981
**Last Retail Price:** $1840
**Auction Price:** $2200

**Ref. No.:** 2053
**Name:** Motherhood
**Height:** 30
**Status:** Open issue, retired
**Issue Year:** 1974
**Issue Price:** $375
**Last Year:** 1985
**Last Retail Price:** $825
**High Auction Price:** $1050
**Low Auction Price:** $750

**Ref. No.:** 2342
**Name:** Returning From the Well
**Height:** 31.75
**Status:** Open issue, active
**Issue Year:** 1996
**Issue Price:** $1800
**Last Year:** 2000
**Last Retail Price:** $1800

**Ref. No.:** 2015
**Name:** Knowledge
**Height:** 35
**Status:** Open issue, retired
**Issue Year:** 1970
**Issue Price:** $325
**Last Year:** 1985
**Last Retail Price:** $1240

# *Goyescas*

**Ref. No.:** 1744
**Name:** My Only Friend
**Height:** 7
**Status:** Limited edition, sold out
**Edition Size:** 200
**Issue Year:** 1990
**Issue Price:** $1474
**Last Year:** 1991
**Last Retail Price:** $1475
**High Auction Price:** $2050
**Low Auction Price:** $1700

**Ref. No.:** 1747
**Name:** Nesting Doves
**Height:** 7
**Status:** Limited edition, sold out
**Edition Size:** 300
**Issue Year:** 1991
**Issue Price:** Unknown
**Last Year:** 1994
**Last Retail Price:** $875
**Auction Price:** $725

**Ref. No.:** 1696
**Name:** Little Boy
**Height:** 7.75
**Status:** Open edition, retired
**Issue Year:** 1988
**Issue Price:** $525
**Last Year:** 1991
**Last Retail Price:** $480

**Ref. No.:** 1745
**Name:** Dawn
**Height:** 9
**Status:** Limited edition, sold out
**Edition Size:** 200
**Issue Year:** 1991
**Issue Price:** Unknown
**Last Year:** 1992
**Last Retail Price:** $1260
**High Auction Price:** $2400
**Low Auction Price:** $1300

**Ref. No.:** 1697
**Name:** Country Guide
**Height:** 10
**Status:** Open edition, retired
**Issue Year:** 1988
**Issue Price:** $725
**Last Year:** 1991
**Last Retail Price:** $640

**Ref. No.:** 1703
**Name:** Harlequin with
    Cornered Hat
**Height:** 10
**Status:** Open edition, retired
**Issue Year:** 1988
**Issue Price:** $595
**Last Year:** 1991
**Last Retail Price:** $535

**Ref. No.:** 1729
**Name:** Mayoress
**Height:** 10
**Status:** Open edition, retired
**Issue Year:** 1989
**Issue Price:** $600
**Last Year:** 1991
**Last Retail Price:** $650

**Ref. No.:** 1702
**Name:** Harlequin with Hat
**Height:** 10.25
**Status:** Open edition, retired
**Issue Year:** 1988
**Issue Price:** $765
**Last Year:** 1991
**Last Retail Price:** $695

**Ref. No.:** 1708
**Name:** Boy at the Fair
**Height:** 11
**Status:** Open edition, retired
**Issue Year:** 1988
**Issue Price:** $550
**Last Year:** 1993
**Last Retail Price:** $685

**Ref. No.:** 1708.3
**Name:** Boy at Fair (Bronze)
**Height:** 11
**Status:** Open edition, retired
**Issue Year:** 1988
**Issue Price:** $650
**Last Year:** 1991
**Last Retail Price:** $850

**Ref. No.:** 1728
**Name:** Mayor
**Height:** 11
**Status:** Open edition, retired
**Issue Year:** 1981
**Issue Price:** $1100
**Last Year:** 1991
**Last Retail Price:** $700

**Ref. No.:** 1751
**Name:** Maggie
**Height:** 11
**Status:** Limited edition, sold out
**Edition Size:** 300
**Issue Year:** 1991
**Issue Price:** Unknown
**Last Year:** 1994
**Last Retail Price:** $990

*Goyescas*

**Ref. No.:** 1753
**Name:** The Student
**Height:** 11
**Status:** Limited edition, sold out
**Edition Size:** 300
**Issue Year:** 1991
**Issue Price:** Unknown
**Last Year:** 1998
**Last Retail Price:** $1425

**Ref. No.:** 1752
**Name:** Apple Seller
**Height:** 11.75
**Status:** Limited edition, sold out
**Edition Size:** 300
**Issue Year:** 1991
**Issue Price:** Unknown
**Last Year:** 1993
**Last Retail Price:** $990
**High Auction Price:** $1150
**Low Auction Price:** $600

**Ref. No.:** 1774
**Name:** A Treasured Moment
**Height:** 11.75
**Status:** Limited edition, sold out
**Edition Size:** 350
**Issue Year:** 1993
**Issue Price:** $950
**Last Year:** 1996
**Last Retail Price:** $1060

**Ref. No.:** 1714
**Name:** Nanny
**Height:** 12.25
**Status:** Open edition, retired
**Issue Year:** 1988
**Issue Price:** $575
**Last Year:** 1993
**Last Retail Price:** $700
**Auction Price:** $700

**Ref. No.:** 1750
**Name:** Circus Show
**Height:** 12.25
**Status:** Limited edition, sold out
**Edition Size:** 300
**Issue Year:** 1991
**Last Year:** 1994
**Last Retail Price:** $1525
**Auction Price:** $1600

**Ref. No.:** 1700
**Name:** Cellist
**Height:** 13
**Status:** Open edition, retired
**Issue Year:** 1988
**Issue Price:** $950
**Last Year:** 1993
**Last Retail Price:** $1050

**Ref. No.:** 1724
**Name:** Belle Epoque
**Height:** 13
**Status:** Open edition, retired
**Issue Year:** 1989
**Issue Price:** $700
**Last Year:** 1993
**Last Retail Price:** $775
**Auction Price:** $600

**Ref. No.:** 1769
**Name:** Fruitful Harvest
**Height:** 13
**Status:** Limited edition, sold out
**Edition Size:** 350
**Issue Year:** 1993
**Issue Price:** $1300
**Last Year:** 1996
**Last Retail Price:** $1300

**Ref. No.:** 1763
**Name:** Trusting Friend
**Height:** 13.25
**Status:** Limited edition, sold out
**Edition Size:** 350
**Issue Year:** 1993
**Issue Price:** $1200
**Last Year:** 1996
**Last Retail Price:** $1200

**Ref. No.:** 1772
**Name:** Back to Back
**Height:** 13.5
**Status:** Limited edition, sold out
**Edition Size:** 350
**Issue Year:** 1993
**Issue Price:** $1450
**Last Year:** 2000
**Last Retail Price:** $1700

**Ref. No.:** 1730
**Name:** Nativity
**Height:** 13.75
**Status:** Open issue, sold out
**Issue Year:** 1990
**Issue Price:** Unknown
**Last Year:** 1996
**Last Retail Price:** $1325

**Ref. No.:** 1709
**Name:** Exodus
**Height:** 13.75
**Status:** Open edition, retired
**Issue Year:** 1988
**Issue Price:** $785
**Last Year:** 1993
**Last Retail Price:** $865

**Ref. No.:** 1718
**Name:** Dress Rehearsal
**Height:** 13.75
**Status:** Open edition, retired
**Issue Year:** 1988
**Issue Price:** $1150
**Last Year:** 1993
**Last Retail Price:** $1200

**Ref. No.:** 1701
**Name:** Saxophone Player
**Height:** 14
**Status:** Open edition, retired
**Issue Year:** 1988
**Issue Price:** $835
**Last Year:** 1993
**Last Retail Price:** $1100

**Ref. No.:** 1719
**Name:** Back From The Fair
**Height:** 14.25
**Status:** Open edition, retired
**Issue Year:** 1989
**Issue Price:** $1650
**Last Year:** 1993
**Last Retail Price:** $1785

**Ref. No.:** 1748
**Name:** Comforting News
**Height:** 14.25
**Status:** Limited edition, sold out
**Edition Size:** 300
**Issue Year:** 1991
**Issue Price:** Unknown
**Last Year:** 1996
**Last Retail Price:** $1345

**Ref. No.:** 1746
**Name:** Champion
**Height:** 14.5
**Status:** Limited edition, sold out
**Edition Size:** 300
**Issue Year:** 1991
**Issue Price:** Unknown
**Last Year:** 1994
**Last Retail Price:** $1950

**Ref. No.:** 1749
**Name:** Baggy Pants
**Height:** 14.5
**Status:** Limited edition, sold out
**Edition Size:** 300
**Issue Year:** 1991
**Issue Price:** Unknown
**Last Year:** 1994
**Last Retail Price:** $1650

**Ref. No.:** 1710
**Name:** School Boy
**Height:** 15
**Status:** Open edition, retired
**Issue Year:** 1988
**Issue Price:** $750
**Last Year:** 1993
**Last Retail Price:** $865

**Ref. No.:** 1711
**Name:** School Girl
**Height:** 15
**Status:** Open edition, retired
**Issue Year:** 1988
**Issue Price:** $680
**Last Year:** 1993
**Last Retail Price:** $775

**Ref. No.:** 1743
**Name:** The Prophet
**Height:** 15
**Status:** Limited edition, sold out
**Edition Size:** 300
**Issue Year:** 1991
**Issue Price:** Unknown
**Last Year:** 1996
**Last Retail Price:** $950

**Ref. No.:** 1754
**Name:** Tree Climbers
**Height:** 15.5
**Status:** Limited edition, sold out
**Edition Size:** 300
**Issue Year:** 1991
**Issue Price:** Unknown
**Last Year:** 1994
**Last Retail Price:** $1650

**Ref. No.:** 1723
**Name:** Hopeful Group
**Height:** 15.75
**Status:** Limited edition, sold out
**Edition Size:** 1000
**Issue Year:** 1989
**Issue Price:** $1825
**Last Year:** 1993
**Last Retail Price:** $1950

**Ref. No.:** 3700
**Name:** The Journey
**Height:** 16
**Status:** Limited edition, sold out
**Edition Size:** 500
**Issue Year:** 1997
**Issue Price:** $700
**Last Year:** 2000
**Last Retail Price:** $700

*Goyescas*

**Ref. No.:** 1716
**Name:** Harlequin with Puppy
**Height:** 16
**Status:** Open edition, retired
**Issue Year:** 1988
**Issue Price:** $825
**Last Year:** 1993
**Last Retail Price:** $940

**Ref. No.:** 1722
**Name:** Group Discussion
**Height:** 16
**Status:** Open edition, retired
**Issue Year:** 1989
**Issue Price:** $1500
**Last Year:** 1993
**Last Retail Price:** $1550

**Ref. No.:** 1725
**Name:** Young Lady with Parasol
**Height:** 16
**Status:** Open edition, retired
**Issue Year:** 1989
**Issue Price:** $950
**Last Year:** 1993
**Last Retail Price:** $975

**Ref. No.:** 1727
**Name:** Pose
**Height:** 16
**Status:** Open edition, retired
**Issue Year:** 1989
**Issue Price:** $725
**Last Year:** 1993
**Last Retail Price:** $875

**Ref. No.:** 1770
**Name:** Gypsy Dancers
**Height:** 16.25
**Status:** Limited edition, sold out
**Edition Size:** 250
**Issue Year:** 1993
**Issue Price:** $2250
**Last Year:** 1995
**Last Retail Price:** $2500

**Ref. No.:** 1764
**Name:** He's My Brother
**Height:** 16.75
**Status:** Limited edition, sold out
**Issue Year:** 1993
**Issue Price:** $1500
**Last Year:** 1993
**Last Retail Price:** $1500

**Ref. No.:** 1726
**Name:** Young Lady with Fan
**Height:** 17
**Status:** Open edition, retired
**Issue Year:** 1989
**Issue Price:** $750
**Last Year:** 1993
**Last Retail Price:** $975
**Auction Price:** $800

**Ref. No.:** 1715
**Name:** On Our Way Home
**Height:** 17.25
**Status:** Open edition, retired
**Issue Year:** 1988
**Issue Price:** $1900
**Last Year:** 1993
**Last Retail Price:** $2100

**Ref. No.:** 1717
**Name:** Harlequin with Dove
**Height:** 17.25
**Status:** Open edition, retired
**Issue Year:** 1988
**Issue Price:** $900
**Last Year:** 1993
**Last Retail Price:** $940

**Ref. No.:** 3701
**Name:** In Concert
**Height:** 18
**Status:** Limited edition, sold out
**Edition Size:** 350
**Issue Year:** 1997
**Issue Price:** $1050
**Last Year:** 2000
**Last Retail Price:** $1050

**Ref. No.:** 3703
**Name:** Imagination
**Height:** 18
**Status:** Limited edition, sold out
**Edition Size:** 500
**Issue Year:** 1997
**Issue Price:** $750
**Last Year:** 2000
**Last Retail Price:** $750

**Ref. No.:** 1773
**Name:** Mischievous Musician
**Height:** 18.75
**Status:** Limited edition, sold out
**Edition Size:** 350
**Issue Year:** 1993
**Issue Price:** $975
**Last Year:** 1996
**Last Retail Price:** $1050

Goyescas

**Ref. No.:** 3702
**Name:** Pensive Journey
**Height:** 19
**Status:** Limited edition, sold out
**Edition Size:** 500
**Issue Year:** 1997
**Issue Price:** $700
**Last Year:** 2000
**Last Retail Price:** $700

**Ref. No.:** 1768
**Name:** Traveller's Respite
**Height:** 19.75
**Status:** Limited edition, sold out
**Edition Size:** 250
**Issue Year:** 1993
**Issue Price:** $1825
**2003 Retail Price:** $1960

**Ref. No.:** 1766
**Name:** Ties That Bind
**Height:** 22
**Status:** Limited edition, sold out
**Edition Size:** 250
**Issue Year:** 1993
**Issue Price:** $1700
**Last Year:** 1993
**Last Retail Price:** $1700

**Ref. No.:** 1767
**Name:** Motherly Love
**Height:** 22
**Status:** Limited edition, sold out
**Edition Size:** 250
**Issue Year:** 1993
**Issue Price:** $1330
**Last Year:** 1993
**Last Retail Price:** $1330

**Ref. No.:** 1765
**Name:** Course of Adventure
**Height:** 22.5
**Status:** Limited edition, sold out
**Edition Size:** 250
**Issue Year:** 1993
**Issue Price:** $1625
**Last Year:** 1997
**Last Retail Price:** $1625

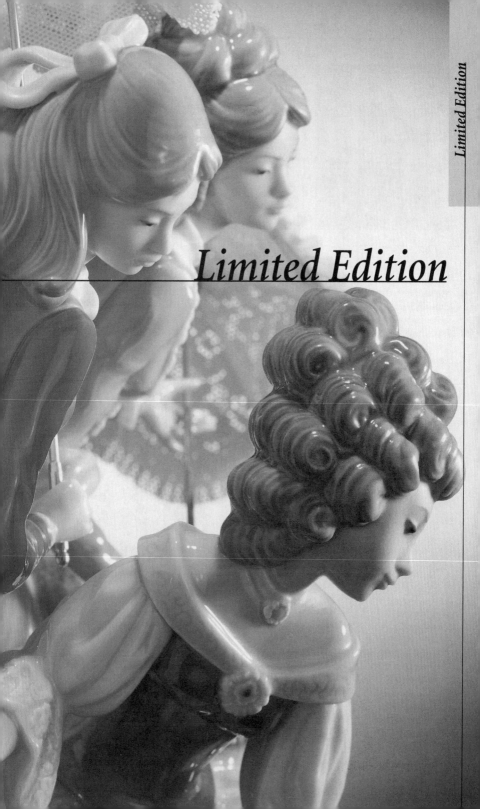

*Limited Edition*

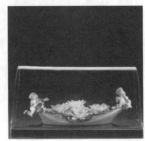

**Ref. No.:** 1837
**Name:** Bridal Bouquet
**Height:** 3.5
**Status:** Limited edition, sold out
**Edition Size:** 2000
**Issue Year:** 1999
**Issue Price:** $875
**Last Year:** 2001
**Last Retail Price:** $875

**Ref. No.:** 1796
**Name:** Floral Enchantment
**Height:** 5.5
**Status:** Limited edition, sold out
**Edition Size:** 300
**Issue Year:** 1994
**Last Year:** 1999
**Last Retail Price:** $3080

**Ref. No.:** 1819
**Name:** Words of Love
**Height:** 6
**Status:** Limited edition, sold out
**Issue Year:** 1997
**Issue Price:** $475
**Edition Size:** 2000
**Last Year:** 2000
**Last Retail Price:** $475

**Ref. No.:** 5915
**Name:** Young Mozart
**Height:** 6.75
**Status:** Limited edition, sold out
**Edition Size:** 2500
**Issue Year:** 1992
**Issue Price:** $500
**Last Year:** 1992
**Last Retail Price:** $500
**High Auction Price:** $2100
**Low Auction Price:** $1000

**Ref. No.:** 5343
**Name:** Love Boat
**Height:** 7.75
**Status:** Limited edition, sold out
**Edition Size:** 3000
**Issue Year:** 1985
**Issue Price:** $775
**Last Year:** 1996
**Last Retail Price:** $1350

**Ref. No.:** 5884
**Name:** Motoring In Style
**Height:** 7.75
**Status:** Limited edition, sold out
**Edition Size:** 1500
**Issue Year:** 1992
**Issue Price:** $3700
**Last Year:** 1997
**Last Retail Price:** $3850

**Ref. No.:** 7508
**Name:** Three Wise Monkeys
**Height:** 7.75
**Status:** Limited edition, sold out
**Edition Size:** 150
**Issue Year:** 1991
**Last Year:** 1991
**Last Retail Price:** Not sold in
    the United States

**Ref. No.:** 1841
**Name:** Prelude In White
**Height:** 8
**Status:** Limited edition, retired
**Edition Size:** 300
**Issue Year:** 1999
**Issue Price:** $650
**Last Year:** 2002
**Last Retail Price:** $650

**Ref. No.:** 1846
**Name:** Butterfly Fantasy
**Height:** 8
**Status:** Limited edition, sold out
**Edition Size:** 2000
**Issue Year:** 1999
**Issue Price:** $725
**Last Year:** 2002
**Last Retail Price:** $725

**Ref. No.:** 6614
**Name:** Ovation
**Height:** 8
**Status:** Limited edition, active
**Edition Size:** 3000
**Issue Year:** 1999
**Issue Price:** $525
**2003 Retail Price:** $550

**Ref. No.:** 1487
**Name:** Fantasia
**Height:** 8.5
**Status:** Limited edition, sold out
**Edition Size:** 5000
**Issue Year:** 1986
**Issue Price:** $1500
**Last Year:** 2002
**Last Retail Price:** $2700

**Ref. No.:** 1845
**Name:** Bumblebee Fantasy
**Height:** 8.67
**Status:** Limited edition, sold out
**Edition Size:** 2000
**Issue Year:** 1999
**Issue Price:** $725
**Last Year:** 2002
**Last Retail Price:** $725

**Ref. No.:** 1739
**Name:** Heavenly Swing
**Height:** 8.75
**Status:** Limited edition, sold out
**Edition Size:** 1000
**Issue Year:** 1991
**Issue Price:** $1900
**Last Year:** 2001
**Last Retail Price:** $2050

**Ref. No.:** 1842
**Name:** Harmony In Pink
**Height:** 8.75
**Status:** Limited edition, sold out
**Edition Size:** 300
**Issue Year:** 1999
**Issue Price:** $650
**Last Year:** 2002
**Last Retail Price:** $650

**Ref. No.:** 1843
**Name:** Serenade In White
**Height:** 8.75
**Status:** Limited edition, active
**Edition Size:** 300
**Issue Year:** 1999
**Issue Price:** $650
**2003 Retail Price:** $650

**Ref. No.:** 3574
**Name:** Test of Strength
**Height:** 8.75
**Status:** Limited edition, active
**Edition Size:** 1000
**Issue Year:** 1995
**Issue Price:** $950
**2003 Retail Price:** $950
**Comment:** Gres Limited Edition.
To be retired or sold out as of
December 31, 2003

**Ref. No.:** 1742
**Name:** Onward!
**Height:** 9
**Status:** Limited edition, sold out
**Edition Size:** 1000
**Issue Year:** 1991
**Issue Price:** $2500
**Last Year:** 1993
**Last Retail Price:** $2700
**Auction Price:** $2450

**Ref. No.:** 5718
**Name:** A Ride in the Park
**Height:** 9
**Status:** Limited edition, sold out
**Edition Size:** 1000
**Issue Year:** 1990
**Issue Price:** $3200
**Last Year:** 1993
**Last Retail Price:** $3895

**Ref. No.:** 5847
**Name:** The Voyage of Columbus
**Height:** 9
**Status:** Limited edition, sold out
**Edition Size:** 7500
**Issue Year:** 1992
**Issue Price:** $1450
**Last Year:** 1993
**Last Retail Price:** $1450
**High Auction Price:** $1600
**Low Auction Price:** $1100

**Ref. No.:** 1877
**Name:** Floral Serenade
**Height:** 9.5
**Status:** Limited edition, active
**Edition Size:** 1500
**Issue Year:** 2002
**2003 Retail Price:** $1395

**Ref. No.:** 6886
**Name:** A Timeless Moment
**Height:** 9.5
**Status:** Limited edition, active
**Edition Size:** 1500
**Issue Year:** 2002
**Issue Price:** $450
**2003 Retail Price:** $450
**Comment:** The Bathers
    Collection

**Ref. No.:** 6888
**Name:** Soothing Reflections
**Height:** 9.5
**Status:** Limited edition, active
**Edition Size:** 1500
**Issue Year:** 2002
**Issue Price:** $450
**2003 Retail Price:** $450
**Comment:** The Bathers
    Collection

**Ref. No.:** 1243
**Name:** The Forest
**Height:** 9.75
**Status:** Limited edition, sold out
**Edition Size:** 500
**Issue Year:** 1973
**Issue Price:** $625
**Last Year:** 1976
**Last Retail Price:** $1500

**Ref. No.:** 1290
**Name:** Partridge
**Height:** 9.75
**Status:** Limited edition, sold out
**Edition Size:** 800
**Issue Year:** 1974
**Issue Price:** $700
**Last Year:** 1976
**Last Retail Price:** $925

**Ref. No.:** 1731
**Name:** Valencian Cruise
**Height:** 9.75
**Status:** Limited edition, sold out
**Edition Size:** 1000
**Issue Year:** 1991
**Issue Price:** $2700
**Last Year:** 1998
**Last Retail Price:** $2950

**Ref. No.:** 1788
**Name:** Floral Figure
**Height:** 9.75
**Status:** Limited edition, sold out
**Edition Size:** 300
**Issue Year:** 1994
**Issue Price:** $2198
**Last Year:** 2000
**Last Retail Price:** $2200

**Ref. No.:** 1815
**Name:** Young Beethoven
**Height:** 10
**Status:** Limited edition, active
**Issue Year:** 1997
**Edition Size:** 2500
**2003 Retail Price:** $875

**Ref. No.:** 5423
**Name:** Carnival Time
**Height:** 10
**Status:** Limited edition, sold out
**Edition Size:** 1000
**Issue Year:** 1987
**Issue Price:** $2400
**Last Year:** 1993
**Last Retail Price:** $3900

**Ref. No.:** 1597
**Name:** Southern Tea
**Height:** 10.25
**Status:** Limited edition, sold out
**Edition Size:** 1000
**Issue Year:** 1989
**Issue Price:** $1775
**Last Year:** 1995
**Last Retail Price:** $2300

**Ref. No.:** 1732
**Name:** Venice Vows
**Height:** 10.25
**Status:** Limited edition, sold out
**Edition Size:** 1500
**Issue Year:** 1991
**Issue Price:** $3755
**Last Year:** 1998
**Last Retail Price:** $4100

**Ref. No.:** 1779
**Name:** High Speed
**Height:** 10.5
**Status:** Limited edition, sold out
**Edition Size:** 1500
**Issue Year:** 1994
**Issue Price:** $3830
**Last Year:** 1997
**Last Retail Price:** $3830

**Ref. No.:** 1866
**Name:** River of Dreams
**Height:** 10.5
**Status:** Limited edition, active
**Edition Size:** 2500
**Issue Year:** 2001
**Issue Price:** $1900
**2003 Retail Price:** $2250

**Ref. No.:** 2250
**Name:** Autumn Glow
**Height:** 10.75
**Status:** Limited edition, sold out
**Edition Size:** 1500
**Issue Year:** 1993
**Issue Price:** $775
**Last Year:** 1997
**Last Retail Price:** $750

**Ref. No.:** 5800
**Name:** Youth
**Height:** 10.75
**Status:** Limited edition, sold out
**Edition Size:** 500
**Issue Year:** 1991
**Issue Price:** $650
**Last Year:** 1993
**Last Retail Price:** $725

**Ref. No.:** 1472
**Name:** Valencian Couple
on Horse
**Height:** 11
**Status:** Limited edition, sold out
**Edition Size:** 3000
**Issue Year:** 1985
**Issue Price:** $885
**Last Year:** 2001
**Last Retail Price:** $1550

**Ref. No.:** 1493
**Name:** At the Stroke of Twelve
**Height:** 11
**Status:** Limited edition, sold out
**Edition Size:** 1500
**Issue Year:** 1986
**Issue Price:** $4250
**Last Year:** 1992
**Last Retail Price:** $7500
**High Auction Price:** $6500
**Low Auction Price:** $6250

**Ref. No.:** 1755
**Name:** Princess and Unicorn
**Height:** 11
**Status:** Limited edition, sold out
**Edition Size:** 1500
**Issue Year:** 1991
**Issue Price:** $1750
**Last Year:** 1993
**Last Retail Price:** $1950
**High Auction Price:** $1900
**Low Auction Price:** $1400

**Ref. No.:** 3578
**Name:** A Soft Refrain
**Height:** 11
**Status:** Limited edition, active
**Edition Size:** 1000
**Issue Year:** 1998
**Issue Price:** $1300
**2003 Retail Price:** $1495
**Comment:** Gres Limited Edition

**Ref. No.:** 5366
**Name:** Rey de Copas
**Height:** 11
**Status:** Limited edition, sold out
**Edition Size:** 2000
**Issue Year:** 1986
**Issue Price:** $325
**Last Year:** 1993
**Last Retail Price:** $600

**Ref. No.:** 5367
**Name:** Rey de Oros
**Height:** 11
**Status:** Limited edition, sold out
**Edition Size:** 2000
**Issue Year:** 1986
**Issue Price:** $325
**Last Year:** 1993
**Last Retail Price:** $600

**Ref. No.:** 5368
**Name:** Rey de Espadas
**Height:** 11
**Status:** Limited edition, sold out
**Edition Size:** 2000
**Issue Year:** 1986
**Issue Price:** $325
**Last Year:** 1993
**Last Retail Price:** $600

**Ref. No.:** 5369
**Name:** Rey de Bastos
**Height:** 11
**Status:** Limited edition, sold out
**Edition Size:** 2000
**Issue Year:** 1986
**Issue Price:** $325
**Last Year:** 1993
**Last Retail Price:** $600

**Ref. No.:** 1801
**Name:** Young Bach
**Height:** 11.25
**Status:** Limited edition, sold out
**Edition Size:** 2500
**Issue Year:** 1994
**Issue Price:** $850
**Last Year:** 1995
**Last Retail Price:** $850

**Ref. No.:** 1784
**Name:** Flower Wagon
**Height:** 11.5
**Status:** Limited edition, active
**Edition Size:** 3000
**Issue Year:** 1994
**Issue Price:** $3290
**2003 Retail Price:** $3290

**Ref. No.:** 1797
**Name:** Enchanted Outing
**Height:** 11.5
**Status:** Limited edition, active
**Edition Size:** 3000
**Issue Year:** 1995
**Issue Price:** $3950
**2003 Retail Price:** $3950

**Ref. No.:** 1854
**Name:** Spring's New Arrivals
**Height:** 11.5
**Status:** Limited edition, active
**Edition Size:** 1000
**Issue Year:** 2000
**2003 Retail Price:** $1100

**Ref. No.:** 1491
**Name:** Oriental Music
**Height:** 11.75
**Status:** Limited edition, sold out
**Edition Size:** 5000
**Issue Year:** 1986
**Issue Price:** $1350
**Last Year:** 2002
**Last Retail Price:** $2445

**Ref. No.:** 1580
**Name:** Return to La Mancha
**Height:** 11.75
**Status:** Limited edition, sold out
**Edition Size:** 500
**Issue Year:** 1988
**Issue Price:** $6400
**Last Year:** 2001
**Last Retail Price:** $8350

**Ref. No.:** 1762
**Name:** Paella
**Height:** 11.75
**Status:** Limited edition, active
**Edition Size:** 500
**Issue Year:** 1993
**Issue Price:** $10000
**2003 Retail Price:** $10000

**Ref. No.:** 5541
**Name:** Pious
**Height:** 11.75
**Status:** Limited edition, sold out
**Edition Size:** 1000
**Issue Year:** 1989
**Issue Price:** $1075
**Last Year:** 1991
**Last Retail Price:** $1200

**Ref. No.:** 1281
**Name:** Judge
**Height:** 12.25
**Status:** Limited edition, sold out
**Edition Size:** 1200
**Issue Year:** 1974
**Issue Price:** $325
**Last Year:** 1978
**Last Retail Price:** $500
**High Auction Price:** $1400
**Low Auction Price:** $1000

**Ref. No.:** 1384
**Name:** Henry VIII
**Height:** 12.25
**Status:** Limited edition, sold out
**Edition Size:** 1200
**Issue Year:** 1978
**Issue Price:** $650
**Last Year:** 1993
**Last Retail Price:** $995
**High Auction Price:** $1250
**Low Auction Price:** $950

**Ref. No.:** 2063
**Name:** Violin Player
**Height:** 12.25
**Status:** Limited edition, sold out
**Edition Size:** 1200
**Issue Year:** 1977
**Issue Price:** $500
**Last Year:** 1988
**Last Retail Price:** $1200
**High Auction Price:** $1300
**Low Auction Price:** $1100

**Ref. No.:** 2249
**Name:** Holiday Glow
**Height:** 12.25
**Status:** Limited edition, sold out
**Edition Size:** 1500
**Issue Year:** 1993
**Issue Price:** $775
**Last Year:** 1997
**Last Retail Price:** $750

**Ref. No.:** 3011.1
**Name:** Don Quixote
**Height:** 12.25
**Status:** Limited edition, sold out
**Edition Size:** 750
**Issue Year:** 1986
**Issue Price:** $975
**Last Year:** 1988
**Last Retail Price:** $1125

**Ref. No.:** 3011.2
**Name:** Don Quixote
**Height:** 12.25
**Status:** Limited edition, sold out
**Edition Size:** 750
**Issue Year:** 1986
**Issue Price:** $975
**Last Year:** 1988
**Last Retail Price:** $1125

**Ref. No.:** 3011.3
**Name:** Don Quixote
**Height:** 12.25
**Status:** Limited edition, sold out
**Edition Size:** 750
**Issue Year:** 1986
**Issue Price:** $975
**Last Year:** 1988
**Last Retail Price:** $1125

**Ref. No.:** 3011.6
**Name:** Don Quixote
**Height:** 12.25
**Status:** Limited edition, sold out
**Edition Size:** 750
**Issue Year:** 1986
**Issue Price:** $975
**Last Year:** 1988
**Last Retail Price:** $1125

**Ref. No.:** 3567
**Name:** Trapper
**Height:** 12.25
**Status:** Limited edition, sold out
**Edition Size:** 3000
**Issue Year:** 1994
**Issue Price:** $950
**Last Year:** 1998
**Last Retail Price:** $950

**Ref. No.:** 5602
**Name:** Freedom
**Height:** 12.25
**Status:** Limited edition, sold out
**Edition Size:** 1500
**Issue Year:** 1989
**Issue Price:** $875
**Last Year:** 1990
**Last Retail Price:** $950
**High Auction Price:** $1250
**Low Auction Price:** $800

**Ref. No.:** 5937
**Name:** Infant of Cebu
**Height:** 12.25
**Status:** Limited edition, sold out
**Edition Size:** 1500
**Issue Year:** 1993
**Issue Price:** Unknown
**Last Year:** 1998
**Last Retail Price:** $1309

**Ref. No.:** 1605
**Name:** Kitakami Cruise
**Height:** 12.5
**Status:** Limited edition, sold out
**Edition Size:** 500
**Issue Year:** 1989
**Issue Price:** $6350
**Last Year:** 1993
**Last Retail Price:** $7350

**Ref. No.:** 1771
**Name:** Country Doctor
**Height:** 12.5
**Status:** Limited edition, sold out
**Edition Size:** 250
**Issue Year:** 1993
**Issue Price:** Unknown
**Last Year:** 1998
**Last Retail Price:** $1700

**Ref. No.:** 1863
**Name:** A Heavenly Christmas
**Height:** 12.5
**Status:** Limited edition, sold out
**Edition Size:** 2500
**Issue Year:** 2000
**Last Year:** 2002
**Last Retail Price:** $850

**Ref. No.:** 3582
**Name:** My Special Garden
**Height:** 12.5
**Status:** Limited edition, active
**Edition Size:** 1000
**Issue Year:** 2000
**2003 Retail Price:** $1995
**Comment:** Gres Limited Edition

**Ref. No.:** 5342
**Name:** Pack of Hunting Dogs
**Height:** 12.5
**Status:** Limited edition, sold out
**Edition Size:** 3000
**Issue Year:** 1985
**Issue Price:** $1575
**Last Year:** 1995
**Last Retail Price:** $1650
**High Auction Price:** $2000
**Low Auction Price:** $1100

**Ref. No.:** 1810
**Name:** Easter Fantasy
**Height:** 12.75
**Status:** Limited edition, sold out
**Edition Size:** 1000
**Issue Year:** 1996
**Issue Price:** $3500
**Last Year:** 2002
**Last Retail Price:** $3500

**Ref. No.:** 5849
**Name:** Sorrowful Mother
**Height:** 12.75
**Status:** Limited edition, sold out
**Edition Size:** 1500
**Issue Year:** 1992
**Issue Price:** $1750
**Last Year:** 1999
**Last Retail Price:** $1850

**Ref. No.:** 5952
**Name:** Where to, Sir?
**Height:** 12.75
**Status:** Limited edition, sold out
**Edition Size:** 1500
**Issue Year:** 1993
**Issue Price:** $5250
**Last Year:** 1998
**Last Retail Price:** $5250

**Ref. No.:** 1145
**Name:** Othello and Desdemona
**Height:** 13
**Status:** Limited edition, sold out
**Edition Size:** 750
**Issue Year:** 1971
**Issue Price:** $275
**Last Year:** 1973
**Last Retail Price:** $350
**High Auction Price:** $3000
**Low Auction Price:** $2500

**Ref. No.:** 1146
**Name:** Antique Auto
**Height:** 13
**Status:** Limited edition, sold out
**Edition Size:** 750
**Issue Year:** 1971
**Issue Price:** $1000
**Last Year:** 1975
**Last Retail Price:** $1750
**High Auction Price:** $10500
**Low Auction Price:** $7000

**Ref. No.:** 1240
**Name:** Turtle Doves
**Height:** 13
**Status:** Limited edition, sold out
**Edition Size:** 750
**Issue Year:** 1973
**Issue Price:** $250
**Last Year:** 1976
**Last Retail Price:** $675

**Ref. No.:** 1338
**Name:** Shakespeare
**Height:** 13
**Status:** Limited edition, sold out
**Edition Size:** 1200
**Issue Year:** 1977
**Issue Price:** $550
**Last Year:** 1985
**Last Retail Price:** $685
**High Auction Price:** $1850
**Low Auction Price:** $1050

**Ref. No.:** 1459
**Name:** Napoleon Planning the
    Battle
**Height:** 13
**Status:** Limited edition, sold out
**Edition Size:** 1500
**Issue Year:** 1985
**Issue Price:** $825
**Last Year:** 1995
**Last Retail Price:** $1450

**Ref. No.:** 1523
**Name:** A Happy Encounter
**Height:** 13
**Status:** Limited edition, sold out
**Edition Size:** 1500
**Issue Year:** 1987
**Issue Price:** $2900
**Last Year:** 2001
**Last Retail Price:** $4900

**Ref. No.:** 1609
**Name:** Circus Parade
**Height:** 13
**Status:** Limited edition, sold out
**Edition Size:** 1000
**Issue Year:** 1989
**Issue Price:** $5200
**Last Year:** 1998
**Last Retail Price:** $6550

**Ref. No.:** 1821
**Name:** Prince of the Sea
**Height:** 13
**Status:** Limited edition, active
**Issue Year:** 1997
**Edition Size:** 2500
**Last Year:** 1998
**Last Retail Price:** $575

**Ref. No.:** 1822
**Name:** Beneath the Waves
**Height:** 13
**Status:** Limited edition, sold out
**Issue Year:** 1997
**Edition Size:** 2500
**Last Year:** 1999
**Last Retail Price:** $575

**Ref. No.:** 3024
**Name:** Discoveries
**Height:** 13
**Status:** Limited edition, sold out
**Edition Size:** 100
**Issue Year:** 1990
**Issue Price:** $1500
**Last Year:** 1994
**Last Retail Price:** $1750

**Ref. No.:** 6453
**Name:** Romantic Gesture
**Height:** 13
**Status:** Limited edition, sold out
**Edition Size:** 2000
**Issue Year:** 1998
**Issue Price:** $990
**Last Year:** 2001
**Last Retail Price:** $1050

**Ref. No.:** 6478
**Name:** The Pelicans
**Height:** 13
**Status:** Limited edition, sold out
**Edition Size:** 1000
**Issue Year:** 1998
**Issue Price:** $990
**Last Year:** 2000
**Last Retail Price:** $1200

**Ref. No.:** 6520
**Name:** Fourth Of July
**Height:** 13
**Status:** Limited edition, active
**Edition Size:** 2000
**Issue Year:** 1998
**Issue Price:** $700
**2003 Retail Price:** $700

**Ref. No.:** 1225
**Name:** Hansom Carriage
**Height:** 13.25
**Status:** Limited edition, sold out
**Edition Size:** 750
**Issue Year:** 1972
**Issue Price:** $1450
**Last Year:** 1975
**Last Retail Price:** $1750
**High Auction Price:** $10000
**Low Auction Price:** $4000

**Ref. No.:** 1331
**Name:** My Baby
**Height:** 13.25
**Status:** Limited edition, sold out
**Edition Size:** 1000
**Issue Year:** 1976
**Issue Price:** $275
**Last Year:** 1981
**Last Retail Price:** $850
**High Auction Price:** $1000
**Low Auction Price:** $850

**Ref. No.:** 1462
**Name:** Flock of Birds
**Height:** 13.25
**Status:** Limited edition, active
**Edition Size:** 1500
**Issue Year:** 1985
**Issue Price:** $1060
**2003 Retail Price:** $1750

**Ref. No.:** 1496
**Name:** Hawaiian Festival
**Height:** 13.25
**Status:** Limited edition, sold out
**Edition Size:** 4000
**Issue Year:** 1986
**Issue Price:** $1850
**Last Year:** 1996
**Last Retail Price:** $3200

**Ref. No.:** 1867
**Name:** Flowers of Peace
**Height:** 13.25
**Status:** Limited edition, active
**Edition Size:** 4000
**Issue Year:** 2001
**Issue Price:** $650
**2003 Retail Price:** $725
**Comment:** Premiere for Privilege
members in 2001

**Ref. No.:** 3023
**Name:** After the Bath
**Height:** 13.25
**Status:** Limited edition, sold out
**Edition Size:** 300
**Issue Year:** 1990
**Issue Price:** $350
**Last Year:** 1991
**Last Retail Price:** $415
**High Auction Price:** $1000
**Low Auction Price:** $850

**Ref. No.:** 3566
**Name:** Indian Chief
**Height:** 13.25
**Status:** Limited edition, sold out
**Edition Size:** 3000
**Issue Year:** 1994
**Issue Price:** $1095
**Last Year:** 1998
**Last Retail Price:** $1095

**Ref. No.:** 3568
**Name:** American Cowboy
**Height:** 13.25
**Status:** Limited edition, sold out
**Edition Size:** 3000
**Issue Year:** 1994
**Issue Price:** $950
**Last Year:** 1998
**Last Retail Price:** $950

**Ref. No.:** 5338
**Name:** Napoleon Bonaparte
**Height:** 13.25
**Status:** Limited edition, sold out
**Edition Size:** 5000
**Issue Year:** 1985
**Issue Price:** $265
**Last Year:** 1994
**Last Retail Price:** $495
**High Auction Price:** $650
**Low Auction Price:** $500

**Ref. No.:** 5339
**Name:** Beethoven
**Height:** 13.25
**Status:** Limited edition, sold out
**Edition Size:** 3000
**Issue Year:** 1985
**Issue Price:** $760
**Last Year:** 1993
**Last Retail Price:** $1300
**Auction Price:** $1100

**Ref. No.:** 5341
**Name:** I've Found Thee, Dulcinea
**Height:** 13.25
**Status:** Limited edition, sold out
**Edition Size:** 750
**Issue Year:** 1985
**Issue Price:** $1460
**Last Year:** 1991
**Last Retail Price:** $2000
**High Auction Price:** $3500
**Low Auction Price:** $2750

**Ref. No.:** 6035
**Name:** The Hand of Justice
**Height:** 13.25
**Status:** Limited edition, sold out
**Edition Size:** 1000
**Issue Year:** 1993
**Issue Price:** $1250
**Last Year:** 1997
**Last Retail Price:** $1250

**Ref. No.:** 6887
**Name:** Lost in Thought
**Height:** 13.25
**Status:** Limited edition, active
**Edition Size:** 1500
**Issue Year:** 2002
**Issue Price:** $550
**2003 Retail Price:** $550
**Comment:** The Bathers
Collection

**Ref. No.:** 1756
**Name:** Outing in Sevilla
**Height:** 13.5
**Status:** Limited edition, active
**Edition Size:** 500
**Issue Year:** 1991
**Issue Price:** $23000
**2003 Retail Price:** $24500

**Ref. No.:** 1806
**Name:** A Family of Love
**Height:** 13.5
**Status:** Limited edition, active
**Edition Size:** 2500
**Issue Year:** 1995
**Issue Price:** $1750
**2003 Retail Price:** $1995

**Ref. No.:** 1870
**Name:** Gondola of Love
**Height:** 13.5
**Status:** Limited edition, active
**Edition Size:** 3000
**Issue Year:** 2002
**2003 Retail Price:** $4250

**Ref. No.:** 1802
**Name:** Love and Marriage
**Height:** 13.75
**Status:** Limited edition, sold out
**Edition Size:** 1500
**Issue Year:** 1995
**Issue Price:** $2650
**Last Year:** 2000
**Last Retail Price:** $2650

**Ref. No.:** 1223
**Name:** Group of Eagle Owls
**Height:** 14
**Status:** Limited edition, sold out
**Edition Size:** 750
**Issue Year:** 1972
**Issue Price:** $225
**Last Year:** 1983
**Last Retail Price:** $1150
**High Auction Price:** $1250
**Low Auction Price:** $1000

**Ref. No.:** 1492
**Name:** Three Sisters
**Height:** 14
**Status:** Limited edition, active
**Edition Size:** 3000
**Issue Year:** 1986
**Issue Price:** $1850
**2003 Retail Price:** $3250

**Ref. No.:** 1813
**Name:** Christmas Journey
**Height:** 14
**Status:** Limited edition, sold out
**Issue Year:** 1997
**Edition Size:** 1000
**Last Year:** 1999
**Last Retail Price:** $1295

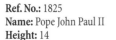

**Ref. No.:** 1825
**Name:** Pope John Paul II
**Height:** 14
**Status:** Limited edition, active
**Edition Size:** 2500
**Issue Year:** 1998
**Issue Price:** $600
**2003 Retail Price:** $675

**Ref. No.:** 1862
**Name:** Love's First Light
**Height:** 14
**Status:** Limited edition, active
**Edition Size:** 1500
**Issue Year:** 2000
**2003 Retail Price:** $2250

**Ref. No.:** 6449
**Name:** Goddess of Youth
**Height:** 14
**Status:** Limited edition, sold out
**Edition Size:** 2500
**Issue Year:** 1998
**Issue Price:** $1150
**Last Year:** 2001
**Last Retail Price:** $1500

**Ref. No.:** 6885
**Name:** Hopes and Dreams
**Height:** 14
**Status:** Limited edition, sold out
**Edition Size:** 1000
**Issue Year:** 2002
**Issue Price:** $650
**Last Year:** 2003
**Last Retail Price:** $650

**Ref. No.:** 3008.1
**Name:** Quixote and Sancho
**Height:** 14.25
**Status:** Limited edition, sold out
**Edition Size:** 400
**Issue Year:** 1986
**Issue Price:** $1375
**Last Year:** 1988
**Last Retail Price:** $1575

**Ref. No.:** 3008.2
**Name:** Quixote and Sancho
**Height:** 14.25
**Status:** Limited edition, sold out
**Edition Size:** 400
**Issue Year:** 1986
**Issue Price:** $1375
**Last Year:** 1988
**Last Retail Price:** $1575

**Ref. No.:** 3008.3
**Name:** Quixote and Sancho
**Height:** 14.25
**Status:** Limited edition, sold out
**Edition Size:** 400
**Issue Year:** 1986
**Issue Price:** $1375
**Last Year:** 1988
**Last Retail Price:** $1575

**Ref. No.:** 3008.6
**Name:** Quixote and Sancho
**Height:** 14.25
**Status:** Limited edition, sold out
**Edition Size:** 400
**Issue Year:** 1986
**Issue Price:** $1375
**Last Year:** 1988
**Last Retail Price:** $1575

**Ref. No.:** 3570
**Name:** Ethereal Music
**Height:** 14.25
**Status:** Limited edition, active
**Edition Size:** 1000
**Issue Year:** 1994
**Issue Price:** $2450
**2003 Retail Price:** $2500

**Ref. No.:** 1433
**Name:** Venetian Serenade
**Height:** 14.5
**Status:** Limited edition, sold out
**Edition Size:** 750
**Issue Year:** 1983
**Issue Price:** $2600
**Last Year:** 1990
**Last Retail Price:** $3750
**High Auction Price:** $3900
**Low Auction Price:** $3750

**Ref. No.:** 1490
**Name:** Floral Offering
**Height:** 14.5
**Status:** Limited edition, active
**Edition Size:** 3000
**Issue Year:** 1986
**Issue Price:** $2500
**2003 Retail Price:** $4450

**Ref. No.:** 1510
**Name:** A Sunday Drive
**Height:** 14.5
**Status:** Limited edition, sold out
**Edition Size:** 1000
**Issue Year:** 1987
**Issue Price:** $3400
**Last Year:** 1999
**Last Retail Price:** $5250

**Ref. No.:** 1848
**Name:** Celestial Journey
**Height:** 14.5
**Status:** Limited edition, active
**Edition Size:** 1500
**Issue Year:** 1999
**Issue Price:** $3900
**2003 Retail Price:** $3900

**Ref. No.:** 6677
**Name:** Tranquility
**Height:** 14.5
**Status:** Limited edition, active
**Edition Size:** 2000
**Issue Year:** 2000
**2003 Retail Price:** $1395

**Ref. No.:** 3572
**Name:** Proud Warrior
**Height:** 14.75
**Status:** Limited edition, sold out
**Edition Size:** 3000
**Issue Year:** 1995
**Issue Price:** $995
**Last Year:** 1998
**Last Retail Price:** $995

**Ref. No.:** 5942
**Name:** The Blessing
**Height:** 14.75
**Status:** Limited edition, sold out
**Edition Size:** 2000
**Issue Year:** 1993
**Issue Price:** $1345
**Last Year:** 2001
**Last Retail Price:** $1345

**Ref. No.:** 1883
**Name:** A Message of Joy
**Height:** 14.75
**Status:** Limited edition, active
**Edition Size:** 3000
**Issue Year:** 2002
**Issue Price:** $1175
**2003 Retail Price:** $1175

**Ref. No.:** 1194
**Name:** Sea Birds
**Height:** 15
**Status:** Limited edition, sold out
**Edition Size:** 500
**Issue Year:** 1972
**Issue Price:** $300
**Last Year:** 1975
**Last Retail Price:** $750

**Ref. No.:** 1269
**Name:** Man of La Mancha
**Height:** 15
**Status:** Limited edition, sold out
**Edition Size:** 1500
**Issue Year:** 1974
**Issue Price:** $700
**Last Year:** 1977
**Last Retail Price:** $1100
**Auction Price:** $4000

**Ref. No.:** 1317
**Name:** Ducks at the Pond
**Height:** 15
**Status:** Limited edition, sold out
**Edition Size:** 1200
**Issue Year:** 1974
**Issue Price:** $4250
**Last Year:** 1984
**Last Retail Price:** $6100

**Ref. No.:** 1329
**Name:** Comforting Baby
**Height:** 15
**Status:** Limited edition, sold out
**Edition Size:** 750
**Issue Year:** 1976
**Issue Price:** $350
**Last Year:** 1978
**Last Retail Price:** $750
**Auction Price:** $1050

**Ref. No.:** 1458
**Name:** Camelot
**Height:** 15
**Status:** Limited edition, sold out
**Edition Size:** 3000
**Issue Year:** 1985
**Issue Price:** $950
**Last Year:** 1994
**Last Retail Price:** $1650
**High Auction Price:** $1900
**Low Auction Price:** $1500

**Ref. No.:** 2061
**Name:** Saint Theresa
**Height:** 15
**Status:** Limited edition, sold out
**Edition Size:** 1200
**Issue Year:** 1977
**Issue Price:** $387.50
**Last Year:** 1987
**Last Retail Price:** $900
**Auction Price:** $900

**Ref. No.:** 3009.1
**Name:** Owl
**Height:** 15
**Status:** Limited edition, sold out
**Edition Size:** 400
**Issue Year:** 1986
**Issue Price:** $1375
**Last Year:** 1988
**Last Retail Price:** $1575

**Ref. No.:** 3009.6
**Name:** Owl
**Height:** 15
**Status:** Limited edition, sold out
**Edition Size:** 400
**Issue Year:** 1986
**Issue Price:** $1375
**Last Year:** 1988
**Last Retail Price:** $1575

**Ref. No.:** 3009.7
**Name:** Owl
**Height:** 15
**Status:** Limited edition, sold out
**Edition Size:** 400
**Issue Year:** 1986
**Issue Price:** $1375
**Last Year:** 1988
**Last Retail Price:** $1575

**Ref. No.:** 3009.8
**Name:** Owl
**Height:** 15
**Status:** Limited edition, sold out
**Edition Size:** 400
**Issue Year:** 1986
**Issue Price:** $1375
**Last Year:** 1988
**Last Retail Price:** $1575

**Ref. No.:** 3009.9
**Name:** Owl
**Height:** 15
**Status:** Limited edition, sold out
**Edition Size:** 400
**Issue Year:** 1986
**Issue Price:** $1375
**Last Year:** 1988
**Last Retail Price:** $1575

**Ref. No.:** 5362
**Name:** Fox Hunt
**Height:** 15
**Status:** Limited edition, active
**Edition Size:** 1000
**Issue Year:** 1986
**Issue Price:** $5200
**2003 Retail Price:** $8750

**Ref. No.:** 1776
**Name:** Conquered by Love
**Height:** 15.25
**Status:** Limited edition, active
**Edition Size:** 2500
**Issue Year:** 1994
**Issue Price:** $2950
**2003 Retail Price:** $3000
**Comment:** To be retired or sold
out as of December 31, 2003

**Ref. No.:** 1804
**Name:** Violin Sonata
**Height:** 15.25
**Status:** Limited edition, sold out
**Edition Size:** 3000
**Issue Year:** 1995
**Issue Price:** $815
**Last Year:** 1999
**Last Retail Price:** $815

**Ref. No.:** 1834
**Name:** A Day With Mom
**Height:** 15.25
**Status:** Limited edition, sold out
**Edition Size:** 1000
**Issue Year:** 1999
**Issue Price:** $3450
**Last Year:** 2002
**Last Retail Price:** $3600

**Ref. No.:** 1840
**Name:** Promises Of Love
**Height:** 15.25
**Status:** Limited edition, active
**Edition Size:** 1000
**Issue Year:** 1999
**Issue Price:** $1500
**2003 Retail Price:** $1500

**Ref. No.:** 6803
**Name:** Waiting for a Rainbow
**Height:** 15.25
**Status:** Limited edition, active
**Edition Size:** 2000
**Issue Year:** 2001
**Issue Price:** $975
**2003 Retail Price:** $1050
**Comment:** Premiere for Privilege
  members in 2001

**Ref. No.:** 1457
**Name:** Festival in Valencia
**Height:** 15.5
**Status:** Limited edition, sold out
**Edition Size:** 3000
**Issue Year:** 1985
**Issue Price:** $1400
**Last Year:** 1994
**Last Retail Price:** $2350

**Ref. No.:** 1798
**Name:** Far Away Thoughts
**Height:** 15.5
**Status:** Limited edition, sold out
**Edition Size:** 1500
**Issue Year:** 1995
**Issue Price:** $3600
**Last Year:** 1997
**Last Retail Price:** $3910

**Ref. No.:** 1856
**Name:** Summer In Saint Tropez
**Height:** 15.5
**Status:** Limited edition, sold out
**Edition Size:** 1500
**Issue Year:** 2000
**Last Year:** 2002
**Last Retail Price:** $1300

**Ref. No.:** 5340
**Name:** Thoroughbred Horse
**Height:** 15.5
**Status:** Limited edition, sold out
**Edition Size:** 1000
**Issue Year:** 1985
**Issue Price:** $590
**Last Year:** 1993
**Last Retail Price:** $1050

**Ref. No.:** 1196
**Name:** Turkey Group
**Height:** 15.75
**Status:** Limited edition, sold out
**Edition Size:** 350
**Issue Year:** 1972
**Issue Price:** $325
**Last Year:** 1982
**Last Retail Price:** $2350

**Ref. No.:** 1465
**Name:** Classic Spring
**Height:** 15.75
**Status:** Limited edition, sold out
**Edition Size:** 1500
**Issue Year:** 1985
**Issue Price:** $620
**Last Year:** 1995
**Last Retail Price:** $890
**High Auction Price:** $1650
**Low Auction Price:** $1100

**Ref. No.:** 1466
**Name:** Classic Fall
**Height:** 15.75
**Status:** Limited edition, sold out
**Edition Size:** 1500
**Issue Year:** 1985
**Issue Price:** $620
**Last Year:** 1995
**Last Retail Price:** $975
**High Auction Price:** $1000
**Low Auction Price:** $800

**Ref. No.:** 1738
**Name:** Liberty Eagle
**Height:** 15.75
**Status:** Limited edition, sold out
**Edition Size:** 1500
**Issue Year:** 1991
**Issue Price:** $1000
**Last Year:** 1999
**Last Retail Price:** $1100

**Ref. No.:** 1805
**Name:** Portrait of a Family
**Height:** 15.75
**Status:** Limited edition, active
**Edition Size:** 2500
**Issue Year:** 1995
**2003 Retail Price:** $1995

**Ref. No.:** 1838
**Name:** The Awakening Of Spring
**Height:** 15.75
**Status:** Limited edition, sold out
**Edition Size:** 500
**Issue Year:** 1999
**Issue Price:** $1500
**Last Year:** 2000
**Last Retail Price:** $1500

**Ref. No.:** 2064
**Name:** Flying Partridges
**Height:** 15.75
**Status:** Limited edition, sold out
**Edition Size:** 1500
**Issue Year:** 1977
**Issue Price:** $1750
**Last Year:** 1987
**Last Retail Price:** $3900

**Ref. No.:** 3519
**Name:** Turtle Dove Nest
**Height:** 15.75
**Status:** Limited edition, sold out
**Edition Size:** 1200
**Issue Year:** 1980
**Issue Price:** $3600
**Last Year:** 1994
**Last Retail Price:** $6050

**Ref. No.:** 3564
**Name:** Gentle Moment
**Height:** 15.75
**Status:** Limited edition, sold out
**Edition Size:** 1000
**Issue Year:** 1994
**Issue Price:** $1835
**Last Year:** 2002
**Last Retail Price:** $1850

**Ref. No.:** 3565
**Name:** At Peace
**Height:** 15.75
**Status:** Limited edition, sold out
**Edition Size:** 1000
**Issue Year:** 1994
**Issue Price:** $1650
**Last Year:** 2001
**Last Retail Price:** $1750

**Ref. No.:** 1814
**Name:** Call of the Sea
**Height:** 16
**Status:** Limited edition, active
**Issue Year:** 1997
**Edition Size:** 500
**2003 Retail Price:** $4250

**Ref. No.:** 1835
**Name:** Creativity
**Height:** 16
**Status:** Limited edition, sold out
**Edition Size:** 2000
**Issue Year:** 2001
**Issue Price:** $850
**Last Year:** 2002
**Last Retail Price:** $950

**Ref. No.:** 1873
**Name:** A Child's Love
**Height:** 16
**Status:** Limited edition, active
**Edition Size:** 1000
**Issue Year:** 2002
**2003 Retail Price:** $1750

**Ref. No.:** 3010.1
**Name:** Isabel La Catolica
**Height:** 16
**Status:** Limited edition, sold out
**Edition Size:** 350
**Issue Year:** 1986
**Issue Price:** $1375
**Last Year:** 1988
**Last Retail Price:** $1575

**Ref. No.:** 3010.2
**Name:** Isabel La Catolica
**Height:** 16
**Status:** Limited edition, sold out
**Edition Size:** 350
**Issue Year:** 1986
**Issue Price:** $1375
**Last Year:** 1988
**Last Retail Price:** $1575

**Ref. No.:** 3010.6
**Name:** Isabel La Catolica
**Height:** 16
**Status:** Limited edition, sold out
**Edition Size:** 350
**Issue Year:** 1986
**Issue Price:** $1375
**Last Year:** 1988
**Last Retail Price:** $1575

**Ref. No.:** 3010.7
**Name:** Isabel La Catolica
**Height:** 16
**Status:** Limited edition, sold out
**Edition Size:** 350
**Issue Year:** 1986
**Issue Price:** $1375
**Last Year:** 1988
**Last Retail Price:** $1575

**Ref. No.:** 3560
**Name:** The Reader
**Height:** 16
**Status:** Limited edition, sold out
**Edition Size:** 200
**Issue Year:** 1992
**Issue Price:** $2650
**Last Year:** 2000
**Last Retail Price:** $2815

**Ref. No.:** 1393
**Name:** First Date
**Height:** 16.25
**Status:** Limited edition, active
**Edition Size:** 1500
**Issue Year:** 1982
**Issue Price:** $3800
**2003 Retail Price:** $5900

**Ref. No.:** 6168
**Name:** The Apollo Landing
**Height:** 16.25
**Status:** Limited edition, sold out
**Issue Year:** 1994
**Issue Price:** $450
**Last Year:** 1995
**Last Retail Price:** $450

**Ref. No.:** 1144
**Name:** Hamlet
**Height:** 16.5
**Status:** Limited edition, sold out
**Edition Size:** 750
**Issue Year:** 1971
**Issue Price:** $125
**Last Year:** 1973
**Last Retail Price:** $350
**Auction Price:** $2500

**Ref. No.:** 1432
**Name:** Columbus
**Height:** 16.5
**Status:** Limited edition, sold out
**Edition Size:** 1200
**Issue Year:** 1982
**Issue Price:** $535
**Last Year:** 1988
**Last Retail Price:** $725
**High Auction Price:** $1800
**Low Auction Price:** $1150

**Ref. No.:** 1741
**Name:** Columbus Reflecting
**Height:** 16.5
**Status:** Limited edition, sold out
**Edition Size:** 1000
**Issue Year:** 1991
**Issue Price:** $1850
**Last Year:** 1994
**Last Retail Price:** $1995
**Auction Price:** $1700

**Ref. No.:** 1839
**Name:** Poetry
**Height:** 16.5
**Status:** Limited edition, sold out
**Edition Size:** 2000
**Issue Year:** 2000
**Last Year:** 2002
**Last Retail Price:** $995

**Ref. No.:** 1847
**Name:** Floral Harmony
**Height:** 16.5
**Status:** Limited edition, sold out
**Edition Size:** 150
**Issue Year:** 1999
**Issue Price:** $3150
**Last Year:** 2002
**Last Retail Price:** $3150

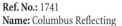

**Ref. No.:** 1875
**Name:** Underwater Fantasy
**Height:** 16.5
**Status:** Limited edition, active
**Edition Size:** 1500
**Issue Year:** 2002
**2003 Retail Price:** $1725

**Ref. No.:** 1878
**Name:** Lord Ganesha
**Height:** 16.5
**Status:** Limited edition, sold out
**Edition Size:** 2000
**Issue Year:** 2002
**Issue Price:** $1490
**Last Year:** 2002
**Last Retail Price:** $1490

**Ref. No.:** 3562
**Name:** Indian Brave
**Height:** 16.5
**Status:** Limited edition, sold out
**Edition Size:** 1500
**Issue Year:** 1994
**Issue Price:** $2250
**Last Year:** 1998
**Last Retail Price:** $2250

**Ref. No.:** 5413
**Name:** Inspiration
**Height:** 16.5
**Status:** Limited edition, sold out
**Edition Size:** 500
**Issue Year:** 1987
**Issue Price:** $1200
**Last Year:** 1993
**Last Retail Price:** $2100

**Ref. No.:** 5864
**Name:** Maternal Joy with base
**Height:** 16.5
**Status:** Limited edition, sold out
**Edition Size:** 1500
**Issue Year:** 1992
**Issue Price:** $1600
**Last Year:** 1997
**Last Retail Price:** $1700

**Ref. No.:** 5890
**Name:** The Way of the Cross
**Height:** 16.5
**Status:** Limited edition, sold out
**Edition Size:** 2000
**Issue Year:** 1992
**Issue Price:** $975
**Last Year:** 1998
**Last Retail Price:** $1050

**Ref. No.:** 5951
**Name:** Our Lady of Rocio
**Height:** 16.5
**Status:** Limited edition, active
**Edition Size:** 2000
**Issue Year:** 1993
**Issue Price:** $3500
**2003 Retail Price:** $3500

**Ref. No.:** 6889
**Name:** Inner Beauty
**Height:** 16.5
**Status:** Limited edition, active
**Edition Size:** 1500
**Issue Year:** 2002
**Issue Price:** $575
**2003 Retail Price:** $575
**Comment:** The Bathers
  Collection

**Ref. No.:** 1375
**Name:** Car In Trouble
**Height:** 16.75
**Status:** Limited edition, sold out
**Edition Size:** 1500
**Issue Year:** 1978
**Issue Price:** $3000
**Last Year:** 1987
**Last Retail Price:** $4100
**High Auction Price:** $8500
**Low Auction Price:** $5500

**Ref. No.:** 1777
**Name:** Farewell of the Samurai
**Height:** 16.75
**Status:** Limited edition, active
**Edition Size:** 2500
**Issue Year:** 1994
**Issue Price:** $3950
**2003 Retail Price:** $3950

**Ref. No.:** 5911
**Name:** Presenting Credentials
**Height:** 16.75
**Status:** Limited edition, sold out
**Edition Size:** 1500
**Issue Year:** 1992
**Issue Price:** $19500
**Last Year:** 1999
**Last Retail Price:** $20500

**Ref. No.:** 1352
**Name:** Flight of the Gazelles
**Height:** 17
**Status:** Limited edition, sold out
**Edition Size:** 1500
**Issue Year:** 1978
**Issue Price:** $1225
**Last Year:** 1984
**Last Retail Price:** $2450

**Ref. No.:** 1757
**Name:** Hawaiian Ceremony
**Height:** 17
**Status:** Limited edition, sold out
**Edition Size:** 1000
**Issue Year:** 1992
**Issue Price:** $9800
**Last Year:** 2002
**Last Retail Price:** $10250

**Ref. No.:** 1808
**Name:** Virgin of the Pillar
**Height:** 17
**Status:** Limited edition, sold out
**Edition Size:** 3000
**Issue Year:** 1995
**Issue Price:** $650
**Last Year:** 1998
**Last Retail Price:** $650

**Ref. No.:** 3006.1
**Name:** Don Quixote
**Height:** 17
**Status:** Limited edition, sold out
**Edition Size:** 200
**Issue Year:** 1986
**Issue Price:** $1375
**Last Year:** 1988
**Last Retail Price:** $1575

**Ref. No.:** 3006.2
**Name:** Don Quixote
**Height:** 17
**Status:** Limited edition, sold out
**Edition Size:** 200
**Issue Year:** 1986
**Issue Price:** $1375
**Last Year:** 1988
**Last Retail Price:** $1575

**Ref. No.:** 3006.3
**Name:** Don Quixote
**Height:** 17
**Status:** Limited edition, sold out
**Edition Size:** 200
**Issue Year:** 1986
**Issue Price:** $1375
**Last Year:** 1988
**Last Retail Price:** $1575

**Ref. No.:** 3006.4
**Name:** Don Quixote
**Height:** 17
**Status:** Limited edition, sold out
**Edition Size:** 200
**Issue Year:** 1986
**Issue Price:** $1375
**Last Year:** 1988
**Last Retail Price:** $1575

**Ref. No.:** 3504
**Name:** Rescue
**Height:** 17
**Status:** Limited edition, sold out
**Edition Size:** 1500
**Issue Year:** 1978
**Issue Price:** $2900
**Last Year:** 1987
**Last Retail Price:** $4050
**High Auction Price:** $5000
**Low Auction Price:** $3250

**Ref. No.:** 3563
**Name:** St. James the Apostle
**Height:** 17
**Status:** Limited edition, sold out
**Edition Size:** 1000
**Issue Year:** 1994
**Issue Price:** $950
**Last Year:** 1996
**Last Retail Price:** $960

**Ref. No.:** 6513
**Name:** Melody
**Height:** 17
**Status:** Limited edition, sold out
**Edition Size:** 2000
**Issue Year:** 1998
**Issue Price:** $870
**Last Year:** 2002
**Last Retail Price:** $950

**Ref. No.:** 1807
**Name:** A Dream of Peace
**Height:** 17.25
**Status:** Limited edition, sold out
**Edition Size:** 2000
**Issue Year:** 1995
**Issue Price:** $1160
**Last Year:** 1997
**Last Retail Price:** $1160

**Ref. No.:** 3007
**Name:** Miguel de Cervantes
**Height:** 17.25
**Status:** Limited edition, sold out
**Edition Size:** 200
**Issue Year:** 1986
**Issue Price:** Unknown
**Last Year:** 1988
**Last Retail Price:** $1575

**Ref. No.:** 3007.1
**Name:** Miguel de Cervantes
**Height:** 17.25
**Status:** Limited edition, sold out
**Edition Size:** 200
**Issue Year:** 1986
**Issue Price:** $1375
**Last Year:** 1988
**Last Retail Price:** $1575

**Ref. No.:** 3007.2
**Name:** Miguel de Cervantes
**Height:** 17.25
**Status:** Limited edition, sold out
**Edition Size:** 200
**Issue Year:** 1986
**Issue Price:** $1350
**Last Year:** 1988
**Last Retail Price:** $1575

**Ref. No.:** 3007.6
**Name:** Miguel de Cervantes
**Height:** 17.25
**Status:** Limited edition, sold out
**Edition Size:** 200
**Issue Year:** 1986
**Issue Price:** $1375
**Last Year:** 1988
**Last Retail Price:** $1575

**Ref. No.:** 3571
**Name:** At the Helm
**Height:** 17.25
**Status:** Limited edition, sold out
**Edition Size:** 3500
**Issue Year:** 1994
**Issue Price:** $1495
**Last Year:** 1998
**Last Retail Price:** $1495

**Ref. No.:** 1485
**Name:** 18th Century Coach
**Height:** 17.5
**Status:** Limited edition, active
**Edition Size:** 500
**Issue Year:** 1985
**Issue Price:** $14000
**2003 Retail Price:** $31000

**Ref. No.:** 1876
**Name:** Spring of Love
**Height:** 17.5
**Status:** Limited edition, active
**Edition Size:** 2000
**Issue Year:** 2002
**Issue Price:** $1375
**2003 Retail Price:** $1375

**Ref. No.:** 1879
**Name:** Bridge of Dreams
**Height:** 17.5
**Status:** Limited edition, active
**Edition Size:** 1500
**Issue Year:** 2002
**Issue Price:** $3550
**2003 Retail Price:** $3595

**Ref. No.:** 3580
**Name:** Intermezzo
**Height:** 17.5
**Status:** Limited edition, sold out
**Edition Size:** 1000
**Issue Year:** 1999
**Issue Price:** $1300
**Last Year:** 2001
**Last Retail Price:** $1330

**Ref. No.:** 1238
**Name:** Hunting Scene
**Height:** 17.75
**Status:** Limited edition, sold out
**Edition Size:** 800
**Issue Year:** 1973
**Issue Price:** $400
**Last Year:** 1976
**Last Retail Price:** $850

**Ref. No.:** 1275
**Name:** Queen Elizabeth II
**Height:** 17.75
**Status:** Limited edition, sold out
**Edition Size:** 250
**Issue Year:** 1974
**Issue Price:** $3650
**Last Year:** 1984
**Last Retail Price:** $3650
**Auction Price:** $5000

**Ref. No.:** 1308
**Name:** The Hunt
**Height:** 17.75
**Status:** Limited edition, sold out
**Edition Size:** 750
**Issue Year:** 1974
**Issue Price:** $3750
**Last Year:** 1984
**Last Retail Price:** $6300
**Auction Price:** $6750

**Ref. No.:** 3501
**Name:** Elk
**Height:** 17.75
**Status:** Limited edition, sold out
**Edition Size:** 500
**Issue Year:** 1982
**Issue Price:** $950
**Last Year:** 1987
**Last Retail Price:** $1050

**Ref. No.:** 3520
**Name:** Turtle Dove Group
**Height:** 17.75
**Status:** Limited edition, sold out
**Edition Size:** 750
**Issue Year:** 1980
**Issue Price:** $6800
**Last Year:** 1998
**Last Retail Price:** $11900

**Ref. No.:** 1778
**Name:** Pegasus
**Height:** 18
**Status:** Limited edition, active
**Edition Size:** 1500
**Issue Year:** 1994
**Issue Price:** $1950
**2003 Retail Price:** $1950

**Ref. No.:** 1864
**Name:** The Birth of Venus
**Height:** 18
**Status:** Limited edition, active
**Edition Size:** 1000
**Issue Year:** 2001
**Issue Price:** $3200
**2003 Retail Price:** $3595

**Ref. No.:** 2051
**Name:** Passionate Dance
**Height:** 18
**Status:** Limited edition, sold out
**Edition Size:** 500
**Issue Year:** 1973
**Issue Price:** $375
**Last Year:** 1975
**Last Retail Price:** $475

**Ref. No.:** 2426
**Name:** Scent of a Flower
**Height:** 18
**Status:** Limited edition, active
**Edition Size:** 1000
**Issue Year:** 2001
**Issue Price:** $1100
**2003 Retail Price:** $1200
**Comment:** Gres Limited Edition

**Ref. No.:** 3573
**Name:** Golgotha
**Height:** 18
**Status:** Limited edition, sold out
**Edition Size:** 1000
**Issue Year:** 1995
**Issue Price:** $1650
**Last Year:** 2000
**Last Retail Price:** $1650

**Ref. No.:** 3585
**Name:** The Gift of Life (dark)
**Height:** 18
**Status:** Limited edition, active
**Edition Size:** 1000
**Issue Year:** 2002
**Issue Price:** $1375
**2003 Retail Price:** $1395

**Ref. No.:** 3586
**Name:** The Gift of Life (white)
**Height:** 18
**Status:** Limited edition, active
**Edition Size:** 1000
**Issue Year:** 2002
**Issue Price:** $1375
**2003 Retail Price:** $1395

**Ref. No.:** 5098
**Name:** A Successful Hunt/Big
   Game
**Height:** 18
**Status:** Limited edition, sold out
**Edition Size:** 1000
**Issue Year:** 1980
**Issue Price:** $5200
**Last Year:** 1993
**Last Retail Price:** $8150

**Ref. No.:** 6385
**Name:** Royal Slumber
**Height:** 18
**Status:** Limited edition, sold out
**Edition Size:** 750
**Issue Year:** 1997
**Issue Price:** $1390
**Last Year:** 2000
**Last Retail Price:** $1425

**Ref. No.:** 1783
**Name:** Circus Fanfare with base
**Height:** 18.25
**Status:** Limited edition, sold out
**Edition Size:** 1500
**Issue Year:** 1994
**Issue Price:** $14240
**Last Year:** 1997
**Last Retail Price:** $14240

**Ref. No.:** 1780
**Name:** Indian Princess
**Height:** 18.5
**Status:** Limited edition, sold out
**Edition Size:** 3000
**Issue Year:** 1994
**Issue Price:** $1630
**Last Year:** 2001
**Last Retail Price:** $1630

**Ref. No.:** 1844
**Name:** Dance Of The Nymphs
**Height:** 18.5
**Status:** Limited edition, active
**Edition Size:** 1000
**Issue Year:** 1999
**Issue Price:** $1450
**2003 Retail Price:** $1450

**Ref. No.:** 2442
**Name:** Flowers from Tahiti
**Height:** 18.5
**Status:** Limited edition, active
**Edition Size:** 1000
**Issue Year:** 2002
**2003 Retail Price:** $2295
**Comment:** Gres Limited Edition

**Ref. No.:** 6033
**Name:** Graceful Moment
**Height:** 18.5
**Status:** Limited edition, active
**Edition Size:** 3000
**Issue Year:** 1993
**Issue Price:** $1475
**2003 Retail Price:** $1475

**Ref. No.:** 5863
**Name:** Justice Eagle
**Height:** 18.75
**Status:** Limited edition, active
**Edition Size:** 1500
**Issue Year:** 1992
**Issue Price:** $1700
**2003 Retail Price:** $1875

**Ref. No.:** 1318
**Name:** Don Quixote and
Sancho Panza
**Height:** 19
**Status:** Limited edition, sold out
**Edition Size:** 1000
**Issue Year:** 1976
**Issue Price:** $1200
**Last Year:** 1983
**Last Retail Price:** $3100
**High Auction Price:** $5000
**Low Auction Price:** $3250

**Ref. No.:** 1823
**Name:** Loving Couple
**Height:** 19
**Status:** Limited edition, sold out
**Issue Year:** 1997
**Issue Price:** $600
**Edition Size:** 1000
**Last Year:** 2000
**Last Retail Price:** $700

**Ref. No.:** 1850
**Name:** Fairy Of The Butterflies
**Height:** 19
**Status:** Limited edition, sold out
**Edition Size:** 1500
**Issue Year:** 1999
**Issue Price:** $2150
**Last Year:** 2000
**Last Retail Price:** $2150

**Ref. No.:** 7575
**Name:** George Washington
**Height:** 19
**Status:** Limited edition, active
**Edition Size:** 2000
**Issue Year:** 1997
**Issue Price:** $1390
**2003 Retail Price:** $1390

**Ref. No.:** 1775
**Name:** Oriental Garden
**Height:** 19.25
**Status:** Limited edition, active
**Edition Size:** 750
**Issue Year:** 1993
**Issue Price:** $22500
**2003 Retail Price:** $22500

**Ref. No.:** 1849
**Name:** The Annunciation
**Height:** 19.25
**Status:** Limited edition, sold out
**Edition Size:** 1000
**Issue Year:** 1999
**Issue Price:** $1550
**Last Year:** 2001
**Last Retail Price:** $1550

**Ref. No.:** 1853
**Name:** Eros
**Height:** 19.25
**Status:** Limited edition, sold out
**Edition Size:** 1000
**Issue Year:** 2000
**Last Year:** 2002
**Last Retail Price:** $1350

**Ref. No.:** 1868
**Name:** A Quiet Conversation
**Height:** 19.25
**Status:** Limited edition, active
**Edition Size:** 1500
**Issue Year:** 2001
**Issue Price:** $1995
**2003 Retail Price:** $2250

**Ref. No.:** 2176
**Name:** Christopher Columbus
**Height:** 19.25
**Status:** Limited edition, sold out
**Edition Size:** 1000
**Issue Year:** 1987
**Issue Price:** $950
**Last Year:** 1994
**Last Retail Price:** $1350

**Ref. No.:** 2188
**Name:** Invincible
**Height:** 19.25
**Status:** Limited edition, retired
**Edition Size:** 300
**Issue Year:** 1990
**Issue Price:** $1100
**Last Year:** 2001
**Last Retail Price:** $1250

**Ref. No.:** 2255
**Name:** Humble Grace
**Height:** 19.25
**Status:** Limited edition, active
**Edition Size:** 2000
**Issue Year:** 1993
**Issue Price:** $2150
**2003 Retail Price:** $2150

**Ref. No.:** 1836
**Name:** Dance
**Height:** 19.5
**Status:** Limited edition, sold out
**Edition Size:** 2000
**Issue Year:** 1999
**Issue Price:** $1200
**Last Year:** 2002
**Last Retail Price:** $1200

**Ref. No.:** 1615
**Name:** Jesus the Rock
**Height:** 19.75
**Status:** Limited edition, sold out
**Edition Size:** 1000
**Issue Year:** 1989
**Issue Price:** $1175
**Last Year:** 1994
**Last Retail Price:** $1550

**Ref. No.:** 1520
**Name:** Listen to Don Quixote
**Height:** 20
**Status:** Limited edition, sold out
**Edition Size:** 750
**Issue Year:** 1987
**Issue Price:** $1800
**Last Year:** 1994
**Last Retail Price:** $2900

**Ref. No.:** 1579
**Name:** Blessed Lady
**Height:** 20
**Status:** Limited edition, sold out
**Edition Size:** 1000
**Issue Year:** 1988
**Issue Price:** $1150
**Last Year:** 1991
**Last Retail Price:** $1500

**Ref. No.:** 1799
**Name:** Immaculate Virgin
**Height:** 20
**Status:** Limited edition, active
**Edition Size:** 2000
**Issue Year:** 1995
**Issue Price:** $2250
**2003 Retail Price:** $2250

**Ref. No.:** 1826
**Name:** On The Balcony
**Height:** 20
**Status:** Limited edition, sold out
**Edition Size:** 1000
**Issue Year:** 1998
**Issue Price:** $3000
**Last Year:** 2002
**Last Retail Price:** $3200

**Ref. No.:** 3561
**Name:** Trail Boss
**Height:** 20
**Status:** Limited edition, sold out
**Edition Size:** 1500
**Issue Year:** 1994
**Issue Price:** $2495
**Last Year:** 1998
**Last Retail Price:** $2595

**Ref. No.:** 3569
**Name:** A Moment's Pause
**Height:** 20
**Status:** Limited edition, active
**Edition Size:** 3500
**Issue Year:** 1994
**Issue Price:** $1635
**Issue Price:** $1620
**2003 Retail Price:** $1650

**Ref. No.:** 7563
**Name:** Statue of Liberty
**Height:** 20
**Status:** Limited edition, active
**Edition Size:** 2000
**Issue Year:** 1996
**Issue Price:** $1620
**2003 Retail Price:** $1620

**Ref. No.:** 1740
**Name:** Columbus, Two Routes
**Height:** 20.5
**Status:** Limited edition, sold out
**Edition Size:** 1000
**Issue Year:** 1991
**Issue Price:** $1500
**Last Year:** 1995
**Last Retail Price:** $1650

**Ref. No.:** 1865
**Name:** Gazebo in Bloom
**Height:** 20.5
**Status:** Limited edition, active
**Edition Size:** 2000
**Issue Year:** 2001
**Issue Price:** $3500
**2003 Retail Price:** $3950

**Ref. No.:** 1858
**Name:** In The Emperor's Forest
**Height:** 20.75
**Status:** Limited edition, active
**Edition Size:** 1000
**Issue Year:** 2000
**2003 Retail Price:** $5450

**Ref. No.:** 3555
**Name:** Desert People
**Height:** 20.75
**Status:** Limited edition, sold out
**Edition Size:** 750
**Issue Year:** 1982
**Issue Price:** $1680
**Last Year:** 1986
**Last Retail Price:** $3100
**High Auction Price:** $3000
**Low Auction Price:** $2400

**Ref. No.:** 3556
**Name:** Road to Mandalay
**Height:** 20.75
**Status:** Limited edition, sold out
**Edition Size:** 750
**Issue Year:** 1982
**Issue Price:** $1390
**Last Year:** 1989
**Last Retail Price:** $1950
**Auction Price:** $2500

**Ref. No.:** 1809
**Name:** Noah
**Height:** 21
**Status:** Limited edition, sold out
**Edition Size:** 1200
**Issue Year:** 1996
**Issue Price:** $1720
**Last Year:** 1998
**Last Retail Price:** $1720

**Ref. No.:** 1330
**Name:** Country Lady
**Height:** 21.25
**Status:** Limited edition, sold out
**Issue Year:** 1976
**Issue Price:** $900
**Last Year:** 1983
**Last Retail Price:** $1565
**Auction Price:** $1700

**Ref. No.:** 1811
**Name:** Moses and the
  Ten Commandments
**Height:** 21.25
**Status:** Limited edition, sold out
**Edition Size:** 1200
**Issue Year:** 1996
**Issue Price:** $1860
**Last Year:** 2002
**Last Retail Price:** $1950

**Ref. No.:** 1860
**Name:** Free As The Wind
**Height:** 21.25
**Status:** Limited edition, active
**Edition Size:** 1500
**Issue Year:** 2000
**2003 Retail Price:** $2995

**Ref. No.:** 7554
**Name:** Abraham Lincoln
**Height:** 21.25
**Status:** Limited edition, active
**Edition Size:** 2500
**Issue Year:** 1995
**Issue Price:** $2190
**2003 Retail Price:** $2195

**Ref. No.:** 1486
**Name:** The New World
**Height:** 21.5
**Status:** Limited edition, sold out
**Edition Size:** 4000
**Issue Year:** 1986
**Issue Price:** $700
**Last Year:** 1996
**Last Retail Price:** $1350

**Ref. No.:** 3557
**Name:** Jesus in Tiberius
**Height:** 21.5
**Status:** Limited edition, active
**Edition Size:** 1200
**Issue Year:** 1984
**Issue Price:** $2600
**2003 Retail Price:** $5550

**Ref. No.:** 2248
**Name:** Days of Yore
**Height:** 21.25
**Status:** Limited edition, sold out
**Edition Size:** 1000
**Issue Year:** 1993
**Issue Price:** $2050
**Last Year:** 1998
**Last Retail Price:** $2050

**Ref. No.:** 3584
**Name:** The Lovers of Verona
**Height:** 21.25
**Status:** Limited edition, active
**Edition Size:** 500
**Issue Year:** 2002
**Issue Price:** $2350
**2003 Retail Price:** $2350

**Ref. No.:** 1851
**Name:** Celestial Ascent
**Height:** 21.5
**Status:** Limited edition, sold out
**Edition Size:** 1500
**Issue Year:** 2000
**Last Year:** 2001
**Last Retail Price:** $1300

**Ref. No.:** 2016
**Name:** Girl With Guitar
**Height:** 21.5
**Status:** Limited edition, sold out
**Edition Size:** 750
**Issue Year:** 1970
**Issue Price:** $325
**Last Year:** 1982
**Last Retail Price:** $1265

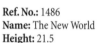

**Ref. No.:** 1377
**Name:** Fearful Flight
**Height:** 22
**Status:** Limited edition, active
**Edition Size:** 750
**Issue Year:** 1978
**Issue Price:** $7000
**2003 Retail Price:** $21000

**Ref. No.:** 1758
**Name:** Circus Time
**Height:** 22
**Status:** Limited edition, active
**Edition Size:** 2500
**Issue Year:** 1992
**Issue Price:** $9200
**2003 Retail Price:** $9650

**Ref. No.:** 1874
**Name:** Waiting in the Willow
**Height:** 22
**Status:** Limited edition, active
**Edition Size:** 1000
**Issue Year:** 2002
**2003 Retail Price:** $1425

**Ref. No.:** 2043
**Name:** Madonna Seated
**Height:** 22
**Status:** Limited edition, sold out
**Edition Size:** 300
**Issue Year:** 1971
**Issue Price:** $400
**Last Year:** 1974
**Last Retail Price:** $450

**Ref. No.:** 3576
**Name:** Playing the Blues
**Height:** 22.25
**Status:** Limited edition, active
**Edition Size:** 1000
**Issue Year:** 1996
**Issue Price:** $2160
**2003 Retail Price:** $2160

**Ref. No.:** 1392
**Name:** Venus and Cupid
**Height:** 22.75
**Status:** Limited edition, sold out
**Edition Size:** 750
**Issue Year:** 1981
**Issue Price:** $1100
**Last Year:** 1988
**Last Retail Price:** $1300
**High Auction Price:** $2500
**Low Auction Price:** $1000

**Ref. No.:** 1578
**Name:** Garden Party
**Height:** 22.75
**Status:** Limited edition, sold out
**Edition Size:** 500
**Issue Year:** 1988
**Issue Price:** $5500
**Last Year:** 1999
**Last Retail Price:** $7250

**Ref. No.:** 2021
**Name:** Young Oriental Man
**Height:** 22.75
**Status:** Limited edition, sold out
**Edition Size:** 500
**Issue Year:** 1971
**Issue Price:** $500
**Last Year:** 1983
**Last Retail Price:** $1100
**Auction Price:** $1850

**Ref. No.:** 3575
**Name:** Samurai
**Height:** 22.75
**Status:** Limited edition, active
**Edition Size:** 1500
**Issue Year:** 1996
**Issue Price:** $1725
**2003 Retail Price:** $1725

**Ref. No.:** 1816
**Name:** Venetian Carnival
**Height:** 23
**Status:** Limited edition, active
**Issue Year:** 1997
**Edition Size:** 1000
**2003 Retail Price:** $3600

**Ref. No.:** 3577
**Name:** Man of the Sea
**Height:** 23
**Status:** Limited edition, sold out
**Edition Size:** 1000
**Issue Year:** 1997
**Issue Price:** $1850
**Last Year:** 2003
**Last Retail Price:** $1850
**Comment:** Gres Limited Edition

**Ref. No.:** 3018
**Name:** Cellist
**Height:** 23.25
**Status:** Limited edition, sold out
**Edition Size:** 300
**Issue Year:** 1988
**Issue Price:** $650
**Last Year:** 1993
**Last Retail Price:** $830

**Ref. No.:** 1881
**Name:** Sighs of Love
**Height:** 23.5
**Status:** Limited edition, active
**Edition Size:** 1500
**Issue Year:** 2002
**Issue Price:** $1750
**2003 Retail Price:** $1750

**Ref. No.:** 2049
**Name:** Country Woman
**Height:** 23.5
**Status:** Limited edition, sold out
**Edition Size:** 750
**Issue Year:** 1973
**Issue Price:** $200
**Last Year:** 1977
**Last Retail Price:** $650

**Ref. No.:** 3553
**Name:** Fire Bird
**Height:** 23.5
**Status:** Limited edition, sold out
**Edition Size:** 1500
**Issue Year:** 1982
**Issue Price:** $800
**Last Year:** 1994
**Last Retail Price:** $1350

**Ref. No.:** 5386
**Name:** Pastoral Scene
**Height:** 23.5
**Status:** Limited edition, sold out
**Edition Size:** 750
**Issue Year:** 1986
**Issue Price:** $1100
**Last Year:** 1995
**Last Retail Price:** $2290
**Auction Price:** $1000

**Ref. No.:** 1202
**Name:** Peace
**Height:** 24
**Status:** Limited edition, sold out
**Edition Size:** 150
**Issue Year:** 1972
**Issue Price:** $550
**Last Year:** 1973
**Last Retail Price:** $550

**Ref. No.:** 1608
**Name:** Mounted Warriors
**Height:** 24
**Status:** Limited edition, active
**Edition Size:** 500
**Issue Year:** 1989
**Issue Price:** $2850
**2003 Retail Price:** $3450

**Ref. No.:** 1759
**Name:** Tea In the Garden
**Height:** 24
**Status:** Limited edition, active
**Edition Size:** 2000
**Issue Year:** 1992
**Issue Price:** $9500
**2003 Retail Price:** $9750

**Ref. No.:** 1785
**Name:** Cinderella's Arrival
**Height:** 24
**Status:** Limited edition, active
**Edition Size:** 1500
**Issue Year:** 1994
**Issue Price:** $25950
**2003 Retail Price:** $26500

**Ref. No.:** 1803
**Name:** Vision of Peace
**Height:** 24.5
**Status:** Limited edition, sold out
**Edition Size:** 1500
**Issue Year:** 1995
**Issue Price:** $1895
**Last Year:** 2003
**Last Retail Price:** $1895

**Ref. No.:** 3552
**Name:** Blue God
**Height:** 24.75
**Status:** Limited edition, sold out
**Edition Size:** 1500
**Issue Year:** 1982
**Issue Price:** $900
**Last Year:** 1994
**Last Retail Price:** $1575

**Ref. No.:** 1812
**Name:** La Menina
**Height:** 25
**Status:** Limited edition, active
**Edition Size:** 1000
**Issue Year:** 1996
**Issue Price:** $3850
**2003 Retail Price:** $3850

**Ref. No.:** 1189
**Name:** Eagles
**Height:** 25.25
**Status:** Limited edition, sold out
**Edition Size:** 750
**Issue Year:** 1972
**Issue Price:** $450
**Last Year:** 1978
**Last Retail Price:** $1475
**Auction Price:** $3000

**Ref. No.:** 1871
**Name:** The Kiss
**Height:** 25.25
**Status:** Limited edition, active
**Edition Size:** 1000
**Issue Year:** 2002
**Issue Price:** $4250
**2003 Retail Price:** $4250
**Comment:** Klimt Collection

**Ref. No.:** 1817
**Name:** The Burial of Christ
**Height:** 26
**Status:** Limited edition, sold out
**Edition Size:** 1250
**Issue Year:** 1997
**Issue Price:** $5300
**Last Year:** 2002
**Last Retail Price:** $6950

**Ref. No.:** 1818
**Name:** Spring Courtship
**Height:** 26
**Status:** Limited edition, sold out
**Issue Year:** 1997
**Edition Size:** 1500
**Last Year:** 2000
**Last Retail Price:** $2400

**Ref. No.:** 2030
**Name:** Oriental Horse
**Height:** 26
**Status:** Limited edition, sold out
**Edition Size:** 350
**Issue Year:** 1971
**Issue Price:** $1100
**Last Year:** 1983
**Last Retail Price:** $2025

**Ref. No.:** 3522
**Name:** Philippine Folklore
**Height:** 26.25
**Status:** Limited edition, sold out
**Edition Size:** 1500
**Issue Year:** 1981
**Issue Price:** $1450
**Last Year:** 1995
**Last Retail Price:** $2400

**Ref. No.:** 1852
**Name:** Lozania
**Height:** 26.5
**Status:** Limited edition, sold out
**Edition Size:** 1500
**Issue Year:** 2000
**Last Year:** 2002
**Last Retail Price:** $1900

**Ref. No.:** 1800
**Name:** To the Rim
**Height:** 27
**Status:** Limited edition, sold out
**Edition Size:** 1500
**Issue Year:** 1995
**Issue Price:** $2475
**Last Year:** 2001
**Last Retail Price:** $2475

**Ref. No.:** 3001
**Name:** Monks
**Height:** 27.25
**Status:** Limited edition, sold out
**Edition Size:** 300
**Issue Year:** 1982
**Issue Price:** $1675
**Last Year:** 1993
**Last Retail Price:** $2550

**Ref. No.:** 2018
**Name:** Madonna With Child
**Height:** 28.75
**Status:** Limited edition, sold out
**Edition Size:** 300
**Issue Year:** 1970
**Issue Price:** $450
**Last Year:** 1974
**Last Retail Price:** $450

**Ref. No.:** 2029
**Name:** Eve at the Tree
**Height:** 28.75
**Status:** Limited edition, sold out
**Edition Size:** 600
**Issue Year:** 1971
**Issue Price:** $450
**Last Year:** 1976
**Last Retail Price:** $600
**Auction Price:** $2000

**Ref. No.:** 2245
**Name:** Inspired Voyage
**Height:** 28.75
**Status:** Limited edition, sold out
**Edition Size:** 1000
**Issue Year:** 1993
**Issue Price:** $4800
**Last Year:** 1998
**Last Retail Price:** $4800

**Ref. No.:** 2028
**Name:** The Three Graces
**Height:** 29.5
**Status:** Limited edition, sold out
**Edition Size:** 500
**Issue Year:** 1971
**Issue Price:** $950
**Last Year:** 1976
**Last Retail Price:** $1100

**Ref. No.:** 3523
**Name:** Eagles Nest
**Height:** 30.25
**Status:** Limited edition, sold out
**Edition Size:** 300
**Issue Year:** 1981
**Issue Price:** $6900
**Last Year:** 1994
**Last Retail Price:** $11500

**Ref. No.:** 1872
**Name:** Cadence
**Height:** 34.5
**Status:** Limited edition, active
**Edition Size:** 1000
**Issue Year:** 2002
**Issue Price:** $2900
**2003 Retail Price:** $2900
**Comment:** Klimt Collection

**Ref. No.:** 3515
**Name:** Saint Michael
**Height:** 37.5
**Status:** Limited edition, sold out
**Edition Size:** 1500
**Issue Year:** 1978
**Last Year:** 1998
**Last Retail Price:** $4900

**Ref. No.:** 2031
**Name:** Lyric Muse
**Height:** 45.5
**Status:** Limited edition, sold out
**Edition Size:** 400
**Issue Year:** 1971
**Issue Price:** $750
**Last Year:** 1973
**Last Retail Price:** $1325
**Auction Price:** $1900

**Ref. No.:** 2032
**Name:** Tahitiana
**Height:** 46
**Status:** Limited edition, sold out
**Edition Size:** 200
**Issue Year:** 1971
**Issue Price:** $295
**Last Year:** 1974
**Last Retail Price:** $425

# Index by Reference Number

*Index*

*Index*

*Index*

*Index*

*Index*

*Index*

*Index*

*Index*

*Index*

*Index*

## Index by Retirement Year

*Index*

*Index*

*Index*

*Index*

*Index*

*Index*